Rorschach Science

Rorschach

SCIENCE · Readings

in Theory & Method

Edited by MICHAEL HIRT

THE FREE PRESS OF GLENCOE

PREFACE

THIS BOOK offers a collection of papers on problems directly related to the development of a rationale for the application of the Rorschach test under conditions that will maximize its validity. Its major objectives are (1) to encourage a more critical evaluation of the Rorschach and its various clinical uses, and (2) to orient the advanced student toward the more fundamental problems of behavior measurement by means of techniques such as the Rorschach. It is not intended to teach methods of either administration or interpretation but rather to help clarify the nature of the pitfalls in the present problems of Rorschach examination.

These objectives require little justification. Although many psychologists have become increasingly aware of the need to modify existing Rorschach theory and practice, there does not appear to have been a systematic effort in this direction. The need for the development of Rorschach principles that are firmly rooted in test and measurement theory is being increasingly recognized.

It is hoped that this book will fill a gap in available textbooks. At the present time no book adequately treats the Rorschach apart from relatively specific clinical applications. The stimulus for preparation of this volume was the recognition of the need for such a textbook while I was a graduate student learning about the Rorschach and a practicing clinician trying to utilize it.

A few words of explanation as to the criteria of selecting the articles included in this volume are in order. The basic consideration was that an article not be limited to a narrow clinical use. I sought articles which attempted to evaluate the Rorschach as a measuring instrument, not as a predictor of specific clinical behavior. For those selections that are directly based on experimental data, the major criterion was the adequacy of their methodology.

I should like to acknowledge the kindness of the various authors, editors, and publishers who gave permission to reproduce their work. Special thanks are due to Drs. Richard A. Cook, James Layman, Bernard L. Mooney, and J. M. Sadnavitch for their encouragement and critical evaluation during the preparation of this book. My first teachers in the Rorschach, Drs. Don W. Dysinger and Marshall R. Jones, were particularly instrumental in imbuing me with the questioning attitude underlying this book. Finally, I wish to express my gratitude to my wife, who bore graciously my various reactions to the numerous frustrations and irritations accompanying the preparation of any manuscript.

MICHAEL HIRT

CONTENTS

III

Scoring

IV

Validity

V

Reliability

VI

Current Status

VII

Summary

I

Introduction

Michael Hirt

MEASUREMENT AND

THE RORSCHACH

PROBLEMS OF PREDICTION

PSYCHOLOGISTS, PARTICULARLY those working in the clinical areas, have been increasingly concerned with the prediction of behavior. To this purpose a large number of papers have been devoted (3, 9, 10, 11, 12, 13), and one of the central issues that has evolved deals with the problems of actuarial or statistical versus individual or clinical approaches to prediction. We will examine this problem as it relates not only to the Rorschach but also to a general concept of measurement theory and practice. It seems apparent that the use and extent of reliance upon various psychological measures is a by-product of how this problem is perceived and resolved by the individual social scientist; it also greatly influences the framework of the research that is carried on.

Probability appears to be of central importance in making predictions. If predictions are made on the basis of past events, wherein the conditions and frequencies under which an event has or has not occurred have been recorded, we are using a frequency concept of probability. Or predictions may be made that are based, not upon past enumerations of an event's specific occurrence or nonoccurrence, but rather on the basis of logical manipulations of factors considered relevant and our understanding of their relationships to the event being studied; this may be considered a logical concept of probability. To illustrate these two concepts of probability, one may consider the problem of predicting the success or desirability of psychotherapy for a given patient. If it is known, for example, from past data, that patients with certain scores on given psychological tests have shown improvement through psychotherapy in eighty-three out of a hundred cases, one can use a frequency concept of probability in recommending psychotherapy for patients with such scores on psychological tests. When, on the other hand, we have a patient who we feel will not be able to tolerate stress, is of very limited intelligence, and the like, we might predict his chances for improvement through psychotherapy as "very poor" if we believe factors such as stress tolerance and intelligence to be related to the outcome of psychotherapy. This, then, would be a probability statement ("very poor") based upon logical relationships of factors.

There appear to be inherent limitations to both approaches. Individual behavior, which usually does not provide data on previous conditions and frequencies of occurrence, does not lend itself very readily to mathematical procedures of probability. Conversely, logical procedures of probability do not involve repetition of an event and therefore do not lend themselves to experimental verification, since verification cannot take place without repeated measurement.

Proponents of logical procedures of probability have argued that statistical prediction tends to distort because it leads to overgeneralization from limited data or to excessive narrowing of the application of specific data (2). They object to quantification because it must eventually be converted into linguistic forms and must be related and limited to the original context, which is attained through words and not numbers. To this purpose Lewin stated, ". . . the importance of a case, and its validity as proof, cannot be evaluated by the frequency of its occurrence . . ." (5, pp. 41–42).

Viewed in another light, it seems apparent that when a single case becomes a member of a class, we have, in essence, events that lend themselves to verification through a statistical approach to probability. That this is essential is attested to by the fact that clinical data not subjected to a statistical probability analysis do not improve the accuracy of prediction made from that data. The prediction can be verified and made more accurate only by ordering the event to a class and then enumerating the number of successes.

Although it is our contention that the specific approach to predicting behavior is quite significant in determining whether one relies on a statistical or clinical orientation, this is an artifact of the sophistication of the individual researcher and the available techniques rather than any inherent difference in the assessment of behavior. To examine this position further, a brief discussion of some of the major differences between so-called objective and projective tests should be useful.

In an objective test, the item pool is so selected and determined as to limit to a very specific context the responses available to the subject. The examiner begins with a circumscribed and limited universe and determines whether the subject does or does not belong to this universe—and possibly the "extent" to which he belongs. Furthermore, because of the predetermined scoring system, the meaning of each item is fixed by the examiner rather than the subject. An implicit assumption, of course, is that the subject, the examiner, and the test constructor all have the same meaning for each item. The ambiguity value of the test item is, or should be, rigidly controlled and kept to a minimum.

Projective tests do not start with a well-defined universe of behavior and must rely on items whose meaning is determined by the subject. It is exactly this value that is sought and evaluated. Although projective tests are conventionally considered as unstructured, this is not altogether accurate. To begin, a wholly unstructured stimulus and/or situation, would not, almost by definition, be capable of eliciting any response whatever. Futhermore, when considering a test situation, we are dealing with the ambiguity (structure) of both the test situation as well as the stimulus. To describe a Rorschach examination as unstructured appears inaccurate, for the instructions given the subject and the expectations communicated to him are quite explicit. He is, for example, to respond verbally to the ink blots, there are numerous responses possible (and therefore expected), and he is encouraged to be spontaneous rather than selective.

A second distinction between objective and projective tests, which is almost a corollary to the previously mentioned one, is that the stimulus value of the material presented is intended to be limited in objective tests. The lack of ambiguity of test items and instructions are examples of the examiner's efforts to limit and control the number of cues confronting the subject. Again the stimulus value of each item has been predetermined as much as possible and is perceived as an extension of a defined universe. In projective tests the opposite effect is sought—namely, by providing a minimum of cues to the subject, to force him to seek his own experiences and perceptions for cues to utilize in responding. But it is misleading to think of the stimulus as completely ambiguous, thereby permitting the subject an infinite choice of responses. Although the choice is considerably greater than in an objective test, the limitations of choice are attested to by our ability to categorize responses with considerable consistency.

A third major distinction between projective and objective tests is that the latter, by virtue of specific, predetermined objectives, have empirically determined units of measurement. It then becomes the function of the test to describe the individual not as an individual, but rather in terms of his approximation to the typical performance of culturally determined tasks for which an arbitrary, but internally consistent, empirical rating scheme has been devised.

It appears that the major limitation in the use of objective tests is their very limited application to a well-defined universe of behavior. They are therefore unable to evaluate the individual in terms other than the ordering of his behavior on the continuum of behavior predetermined by the selection and description of a particular universe. Paradoxically, it is this very limitation that made it possible for objective tests to achieve the degree of respect and usefulness that they now enjoy in many settings. By employing a basically reductionist approach to behavior, it has been possible to develop tests that survive scrutiny for validity and predictive ability. Projective tests are so labeled not only because of the greater ambiguity of their stimulus value, but also because they do not, and possibly cannot, proceed from a well-defined universe of behavior. They consequently are so devised as to maximize both their stimulus value and the variability of responses possible. It then becomes our task to order the obtained responses into the appropriate behavioral universe.

The general principle distinguishing these two approaches is found in the distinction between sign and sample tests (1). The majority of tests within psychology have been developed to sample an arbitrarily defined universe of behavior. The universe is the criterion by which we evaluate the test; the validity of the test is determined by the extent to which performance on the test is similar to the performance of the larger area of similar behavior from which the samples have been drawn. In this situation the criterion is regarded as the independent variable and the only question is: How well does the test correspond to the criterion by which it is to be judged?

A test may also be viewed as a sign, and one is then confronted with deciding to which universe the sign points. In this approach, we begin with observable behavior and try to understand it by discovering the broader context to which the signs belong.

The situation in these two types of test construction and test interpretation appears particularly relevant to the Rorschach technique where the crucial problem appears to be defining the particular universe to which the signs point rather than selecting a sample from a predetermined universe. A further source of confusion directly relevant to the Rorschach is that, although the test is based upon signs that then have to be identified with a universe of behavior, when the Rorschach is scored, the theoretical position is changed to that of a sample test, with the assumption that we have a well-defined universe of behavior of which certain scoring categories are samples.

CHARACTERISTICS OF
GOOD MEASURING INSTRUMENTS

The adequacy of any instrument of evaluation must be determined in terms of the purpose for which it has been constructed. Regardless of purpose, however, there are characteristics of measuring instruments that are desirable and applicable to all measurement situations. These characteristics then become the criteria with which to evaluate any given instrument. A good measuring instrument should, above all else, provide measures which are free of error. The types of error possible are described as compensating and biased ones (15). Compensating errors arise because an infinite number of measurements is not available. It is therefore possible to have errors that result from subject fluctuations at the various times measurements are obtained, errors made by a single rater or judge, and errors from various samples of behavior or test items. These types of errors have a tendency to cancel each other out when an infinite number of measurements is made by an infinite number of judges or when an instrument consists of an infinite number of items. Obviously, then, we are dealing with reliability errors.

Biased errors do not cancel out with repeated measurements. They are a consequence of the failure to reduce any given factor to a level of homogeneous characteristics or the failure to weigh these characteristics proportionally to their contribution to the general factor being measured. Whenever a measuring instrument does not measure the variable for which it is intended or does not contain an adequate cross section of items, biased errors are likely to result.

A good measuring instrument should be adaptable to the range of the variable studied. It is equally important that the units of measurement throughout the range being measured be equal. Although psychological measures usually do not achieve this objective, it is important to understand score differences at any point of the measuring instrument and to be able to determine whether, for example, differences at the lower end of a scale have the same meaning as equivalent differences at the upper end.

A further characteristic of a good measuring instrument is that it yields absolute scores. This means that the zero point of the instrument is equivalent to the zero point of the factor being measured. Although the relative importance of this characteristic is often exaggerated, failure to satisfy this characteristic limits the usefulness of the instrument in inferring the location of the point of "no amount" of the factor being measured and also makes it impossible to interpret ratios between scores.

Some of the remaining characteristics of a good measuring instrument, which, although more "mechanical" in nature, are nevertheless essential, are: the instrument should be administratively feasible to construct and use; it should be available in duplicate forms which are equivalent; it should be able to measure changes at a level sufficiently sensitive for the factor being studied; and it should have adequate normative data. Although there are many aspects of normative data that are necessary and important, the comparability of the group being studied to the standardization group, as well as the size and adequacy of the latter group, are of prime consideration.

In summary, the adequacy of a measuring instrument may be evaluated in terms of the following types of errors:

A. Compensating errors resulting from:
   1. Failure to obtain an infinite number of measurements.
   2. Failure to obtain an infinite number of judges in scoring responses.
   3. Failure to include an infinite number of test items.

B. Biased errors resulting from:
   1. Failure to reduce the trait to homogeneous characteristics.
   2. Failure to weight scores on items in proportion to their importance.
   3. Failure to obtain an adequate cross section of items.
   4. Subject dishonesty or incompetence.

VALIDITY AND RELIABILITY

We shall define validity as the degree to which both compensating and biased errors are absent, while reliability we have described as the degree to which compensating errors alone are absent. A point to bear in mind is that these two concepts cannot be measured directly. Since they are based upon the absence of errors, it is assumed that true scores can be obtained; this is a necessary assumption, but not a true one. Were it otherwise, it would not be necessary to speak in terms of probability values. However, it is possible to determine estimates of both reliability and validity—to a considerable extent by the specific techniques employed in making our estimate. It is to this purpose that we shall now turn our attention.

Predictive validity refers to an instrument's ability to predict accurately behavior that is to be measured in the future. The usual technique for obtaining an estimate of this type of validity is correlation of test results with a subsequent criterion measure; the extreme importance of obtaining an adequate criterion is apparent. The unreliability of the criterion as well as that of the measuring instrument will affect the latter's predictive effectiveness.

Concurrent validity is very similar to predictive validity, the major difference being that the criterion measure is obtained concurrently with the test performance. It is possible to have a high degree of concurrent validity but little predictive validity. This is true because of the nature of problems and criterion measures to which the two types of validity are applied. Estimates of both types of validity, by virtue of usually being expressed in the form of a correlation coefficient, fluctuate as a function of the homogeneity of the group with respect to the variable being studied. Homogeneous groups yield lower correlation coefficients than do more heterogeneous groups.

Construct validity differs from the other types of validity in that no definitive criterion measure is available. The emphasis is upon the theory that underlies the instrument. We first make predictions from the theory and then gather data with which to evaluate the predictions and, indirectly, the theory. The paucity of adequate criterion measures in clinical work has made construct validation of particular significance to psychologists working in this area.

Content validity refers to the adequacy with which the instrument samples content about which inferences are to be made. Although quantitative evidence is usually not readily available, the adequacy with which the instrument samples the population of behavior it is trying to measure can usually be taken as an appropriate indication of the instrument's content validity.

The above described types of validity are those which appear in the *Technical Recommendations* of the A.P.A. (14). They have been criticized on the basis that they are, with the exception of construct validity, excessively criterion-oriented and too specific in purpose (6). Gulliksen (4) summarized this position in stating that "The validity of a test is the correlation of the test with some criterion" and that any given test has many different validities, determined by the various uses of the test. Lord (8) is also a proponent of this position and rejects an over-all concept of validity, considering validity a specific quality. Loevinger (7) argued against such concepts of validity. She recognized only construct validity as scientifically useful. The construct she speaks of is equivalent to a statistic, serving as the best estimate of a parameter, or, in the case of construct validity, a trait. A measure of construct validity then becomes the estimate of behavior on the basis of test performance, taking into adequate consideration the inadequacy of predicting a single external criterion. The meaning of this notion of construct validity is difficult to establish for projective tests. Considering projective test scores as intervening variables and single-item responses as an original datum, the difficulty becomes apparent if one considers structural validity as relationships among data and not intervening variables.

Reliability, as previously explained, may be defined in terms of the degree to which an instrument is free of compensating errors. These errors may occur because of fluctuations from repeated administrations of a test to a given group; the extent of these fluctuations or coefficients of stability is the estimate of reliability. One of the major considerations necessary in interpreting such a coefficient is that the obtained reliability, as a result of restricting the fluctuations of sampling test items, will tend to be an overestimate of the true reliability. Furthermore, the necessary assumption that repeated measurements will not be affected by virtue of the repetition is a tenuous one, which probably cannot be supported empirically.

A correlation between scores from two equivalent forms yields a coefficient of equivalence. Here again it is necessary to keep in mind that the obtained coefficient would have been lower had the compensating errors due to sampling test items been allowed to fluctuate as though truly different test items were provided. However, if the two forms are truly equivalent, the items will have been matched for difficulty and will increase the obtained measure of reliability. It has also been pointed out (6, 7) that since equivalent forms have, by definition, equal means, standard deviations, and mutual intercorrelations, their equivalency and reliability is estimated by the same set of correlations. The circularity of such a definition is apparent when we realize that the correlation or reliability we seek to estimate is used in defining two tests as equivalent.

The coefficient of internal consistency is the relationship based on the internal analysis of the instrument, usually dividing the test into two subtests, one composed of the odd items and the other of the even ones. The measure of reliability obtained from this method represents reliabilities for only half the test. It is then necessary to apply an appropriate formula (the Spearman-Brown formula) to predict the expected reliability of a test twice the length of either the odd or the even half-test.

The magnitude of the above described measures of reliability, like the size of all coefficients of correlation, is a function of the range of the characteristic being measured. If the instrument is applied to a group less homogeneous than the one for which it was devised and on whom it was standardized, the obtained measure of reliability will be considerably reduced. To interpret properly a measure of reliability obtained by any of these methods, it is necessary to consider the assumptions that (a) test items selected are sampled from an infinite population of possible items, (b) all types of compensating errors are free to fluctuate in each form of the test, and (c) errors existing between either alternate forms, or odd and even items, are compensating and biased errors between forms of the subtest are entirely absent.

Clinical Applications of the Rorschach

Since its introduction in 1921, the Rorschach has attained remarkable application and stature, enjoying now a firm position in the repertoire of techniques employed in the understanding and prediction of human behavior. As is often the case, clinical needs have taken precedence over experimental evaluation, and what began as a matter of expediency (use of this technique before it had been adequately assessed) has now become accepted practice. Indeed, the long history of the Rorschach's clinical use is an implicit deterrent for its further evaluation, for the recently trained clinician, better trained as a researcher and more disposed in attitude toward such an approach, is faced with the task of challenging years of use and accumulated "insight through experience."

Those familiar with the Rorschach literature are undoubtedly aware of some of the more frequent shortcomings of the research in the area. Samples that are woefully inadequate in size are used; samples are used to obtain data that have been applied to subjects from apparently different populations; statistical techniques are employed with considerable disregard for their theoretical and mathematical assumptions; constructs are postulated in such a manner that the transition from the theoretical position to the Rorschach data is tenuous, making subsequent generalizations unlikely to be supported by cross-validational studies. However, in spite of its limitations, the use of the Rorschach is gaining in frequency, and the judgments made on the basis of it appear, by and large, to be more respected and, at times, sophisticated. Unfortunately, they still remain unverified, most of the support coming from the clinical judgment of "experts."

Some investigators have sought internal validity for the Rorschach through attempts at finding psychometric groups corresponding to psychiatric ones, testing for criterion discriminations, evaluating the extent of judge's agreement, and inquiring into the basic assumptions underlying the Rorschach and its uses. Many of these assumptions are not explicitly stated in the literature and can only be inferred from traditional practices and interpretations.

External validation has also been sought in many ways, from testing Rorschach factors related to other tests, both of a projective as well as non-

projective nature, to seeking Rorschach factors related to behavioral manifestations of anxiety, suggestibility, impulsiveness, or diagnosis and prognosis. Comparisons have been made with such techniques as the Levy
movement cards, Minnesota Multiphasic Personality Inventory, Bender-
Gestalt, and Behn-Rorschach. The Rorschach has been tested for relationship with stress and emotional control, specific determinants such as color
and social acceptance, and combinations of determinants with various personality traits.

A search of the recent literature indicated that, with the possible exceptions of child studies, relatively little effort is being devoted to developing
adequate normative data for the Rorschach. Most of the studies in this area
deal with special groups of subjects, such as preschool children or retarded
adults, and/or with special problems, such as color, experience balance, and
temporal development. The suggestion that Rorschach norms should describe adequately the samples upon which they are based, explicitly state
whether the norms are based on a psychiatrically or statistically normal
group, and be presented in terms of scoring categories has been almost totally
ignored. Bearing in mind the methodological problems and shortcomings of
much of the Rorschach literature, certain conclusions regarding scoring
categories seem justifiable. The studies on color do not seem to support the
general theory pertaining to the use of color by a subject. Contradictory
results have been obtained in studies dealing with the depressant effects of
color on reaction time. Lack of color in the usually colored cards was not
found to depress the consistency of responses to the cards. Color shock has
been present to a great extent in samples of normal subjects.

In the area of movement, extensor M responses have been said to reflect
assertive personality types and to be found more frequently among male
than female subjects. Those studies seeking to measure intelligence by
means of the movement response have found an average correlation of approximately .40 between M responses and outside criteria of intelligence.
The safest, and probably most accurate appraisal of studies in this area
would indicate the absence of any one-to-one relationship between movement subcategories and behavioral variables.

In the studies concerning space, the findings are nebulous and generally
not in support of the usually accepted theory of space percepts. Correlations
between space responses and external criteria of oppositional tendencies
range from approximately .25 to .45. Studies on shading have not dealt with
the theoretical rationale for the scoring of shading.

The area of popular responses is characterized by considerably more
theorizing than experimental verification. The raw-number method appears

to be equally valid as the percentage of popular responses in determining the adequacy level of a protocol.

Organizational factors do not appear to be related to the use of generalization on structured tasks, with correlation coefficients averaging approximately .35. Computing weighted Z scores does not appear to provide any advantage over noting undifferentiated Z responses.

The over-all effect of studies dealing with determinants is one of caution. This is also true of the efficacy of the Rorschach in differentiating psychiatric groups from each other and/or normal groups. Regarding schizophrenia, for example, there is no single set of scoring categories that consistently differentiates this group from others. Signs such as confabulation, contamination, high variability of form quality, and greater frequency of original responses are often associated with schizophrenics. Such signs as rare details, use of color, quality of form, and position responses, although also often associated with schizophrenics, are also found frequently with other psychiatric groups.

The major impressions regarding clinical use of the Rorschach are the following:

1. Used individually, it does not permit us to make very definitive statements about an individual. Even when used in conjunction with other clinical tests, Rorschach data do not yield unequivocal results, since meaningful interpretations depend more extensively on the examiner's skill and experience than upon the data itself.

2. It is based upon theory and assumptions not sufficiently evaluated. The apparent disregard for this truism appears to have resulted in a very considerable amount of very poor research which has been carried on with the apparent assumption of a well-evaluated and sufficiently validated theory behind it.

Outline of the Book

In the preceding pages the reader should have been oriented toward the selections that will follow. It will be readily apparent that the Rorschach is not being examined within a specific theoretical or conceptual framework of personality. Indeed, it is our contention that to do so would be premature and severely limiting in the attempt to understand the perceptual processes that take place in the course of a Rorschach examination.

The book is divided into the following areas:

Introduction: My article has two major purposes. First, it attempts to make explicit some of the relationships that exist between the field of tests and measurement and the process of personality measurement, emphasizing such basic distinctions as statistical and clinical approaches to the prediction of behavior. Second, it summarizes very briefly the results of Rorschach research that has considered clinical problems.

Mooney concerns himself with the relationships that exist between the field of perception and the assessment of personality. He considers some of the basic relationships that are postulated between the two fields and makes it possible for the reader to make inferences about the areas needing research.

The Projective Method: The article by Frank may well be considered the fundamental exposition of the process of projection and its importance in assessing test results and behavior. Although our understanding of these phenomena has expanded considerably since the writing of this article, the foundation it provided appears to have withstood the critical evaluation of many years of research and thought.

The article by Sargent presents a comprehensive and relatively detailed treatment of numerous projective techniques. For each technique discussed she presents a summary of the theoretical background and appropriate experimental data. In addition, she provides the reader with an extensive bibliography, divided according to the specific projective methods to which it applies. This article is intended to give the reader a historical perspective of the need and subsequent development of the Rorschach.

The article by Lord supports with experimental data the importance of such factors as set and the subject's perception of the test situation upon the protocols obtained. Although numerous studies have dealt with this problem, this article appears to be particularly useful because of its excellent methodological approach.

Scoring: Whether or not one should score a Rorschach protocol remains an unresolved question, with solutions ranging from clinicians who offer a categorical "no" to those who adhere to the most elaborate and detailed scoring schemes. The first study by Wittenborn fails to support the frequently made assumption of the behavioral similarity of responses falling within a given Rorschach scoring category. Furthermore, the assumption of psychologically significant differences between responses assigned into different scoring categories is also not supported. The second article by Wittenborn offers evidence for the need to re-evaluate the use of certain major scoring categories and the emphasis often attached to some of them. Wittenborn's third article, in addition to yielding experimental data upon the meaning and interrelationships of the major Rorschach scoring categories, also discusses some possible approaches to the validation of the Rorschach. Of more practical significance are the results obtained by Knopf, which indicate the futility of utilizing Rorschach summary scores in differentiating psychiatric groups.

Validity: This concept remains as a crucial issue in the use of the Rorschach for purposes other than research. The paper by Schneider outlines some of the methodological and theoretical considerations that might be used in making the Rorschach a more valid measure. Specifically, he views the problem as one of "relating Rorschach variables to independent measures of component personality measures."

The article by Palmer presents two methods for Rorschach validation. He concludes that neither of these is completely adequate for the task, but, used in conjunction with a design suggested by Cronbach, they may make it possible to obtain a satisfactory method for the validation of projective techniques.

Cronbach, reviewing much of the Rorschach literature that has sought statistical evaluation of Rorschach theory, concludes that methodological errors have led to errors of omission in establishing significant relationships between test and behavior variables.

Reliability: The relative paucity of research in this important area is difficult to understand. The study by Hertz, although of considerable vintage, still remains as one of the better sources of verification for the reliability of the Rorschach. The problem of scorer reliability appears to have been even more overlooked. Dana's study, although basically compatible with the assumption that it is possible to have scorer reliability with the Rorschach, yields data indicating that individualized scoring systems and ambiguous scoring categories tend to reduce scorer reliability considerably. The last study in this section provides experimental data to support the cautions recommended in considering a single Rorschach examination as an adequate or stable personality description.

Current Status: In this section an attempt is made to estimate the position of the Rorschach in the field of psychology. The article by Thurstone appears to be an indictment of the Rorschach on the basis of its wide applications without sufficient recourse to experimental evidence to justify such use. Zubin is more specific in his over-all evaluation, concluding that the Rorschach is an interview whose content is of potential usefulness in evaluating behavior. However, the presently employed techniques for analyzing this content are inadequate.

The article by Cronbach and Meehl appears to be particularly relevant to the development of valid procedures in the use of the Rorschach. It offers an extensive discussion of construct validity, which appears uniquely appropriate to the Rorschach.

Summary: The article by Hertz reviews a considerable number of studies concerned with the Rorschach. Her evaluation of these is somewhat more optimistic than that of others who have considered the same body of literature. Although she recognizes the need for more research data, replication of important results obtained through seemingly adequate research designs, and more appropriate statistical techniques, she feels that many important Rorschach hypotheses have been verified and the "test works," failing only when "subjected to piece-meal and rigid statistical manipulations."

REFERENCES

1. ANASTASI, A. *Psychological testing*. New York: Macmillan, 1954.

2. BROWER, D. The problem of quantification in psychological science. *Psychol. Rev.*, 1949, *56*, 325–333.

3. COTTRELL, L. S. The case study method in prediction. *Sociometry*, 1941, *4*, 358–370.

4. GULLIKSEN, H. *Theory of mental tests*. New York: Wiley, 1950.

5. LEWIN, K. *A dynamic theory of personality*. New York: McGraw-Hill, 1935.

6. LOEVINGER, J. Objective tests as instruments of psychological theory. *Psychological Reports, Monograph Supplement* 9, 1957.

7. LOEVINGER, J. The attenuation paradox in test theory. *Psychol. Bull.*, 1954, *51*, 493–504.

8. LORD, F. M. Some perspectives on "The alternation paradox in test theory." *Psychol. Bull.*, 1955, *52*, 505–510.

9. LUNBERG, B. A. Case studies vs. statistical methods—an issue based on misunderstanding. *Sociometry*, 1941, *4*, 379–383.

10. MEEHL, P. *Statistical vs. clinical prediction*. Minneapolis: University of Minnesota Press, 1954.

11. QUEEN, S. A. Social prediction-development and problems. *Sociometry*, 1941, *4*, 371–373.

12. SARBIN, T. R. The logic of prediction in psychology *Psychol. Rev.*, 1944, *51*, 210–228.

13. STOUFFER, S. A. Notes on the case study and the unique cases. *Sociometry*, 1941, *4*, 319–357.

14. Technical recommendations for psychological tests and diagnostic techniques. *Psychol. Bull. Suppl.*, 1954, *5*, No. 2, Part 2, 1–38.

15. WERT, J. E., NEIDT, C. O. AND AHMANN, J. S. *Statistical methods in educational and psychological research*. New York: Appleton-Century-Crofts, 1954.

Bernard Mooney

PERSONALITY ASSESSMENT

AND PERCEPTION

T HE PROVING grounds for testing out the innumerable hypotheses regarding personality assessment and perception have typically been identified with the theory and uses of the projective technique. Judging simply from the voluminous body of research that has grown up around the Rorschach test, it has become the prime vehicle for assaying the verifiability of the many proposed functional linkages between perceptual processes and personality structure.

In the clinical setting, the projective techniques are generally employed to provide a dynamic view of the individual—that is, to afford a hierarchical ranking of the individual's needs (intensity) as well as, perhaps, indications of the objects and events by which these needs are initiated and terminated (direction). Again, in the clinical setting this dynamic view, so obtained, is employed as a data pool that, when integrated, supplies information about the subject not available by other testing techniques.

Undaunted by faint memories of negative research findings regarding the uses of projective techniques, the practicing clinician forges ahead, collecting score upon score of Rorschach protocols. With such data at hand, he will go on to formulate answers to: "Will this patient attempt suicide?" or "Will this person decompensate under present pressures?" Interestingly enough, in the many controversies over the uses of projective techniques, the practicing clinician has been the proverbial straw man, abused as though he and he alone were entirely responsible for the development of these tests. At the least, he is accused of perpetuating their existence. The clinician is not an opinionated, ill-informed individual who turns his back on the facts of the case. Rather, his continued use of such techniques reflects an awareness of an incontrovertible, though perhaps nonverifiable, fact that "These tests can tell me much about the individual's personality."

If the clinician were to make explicit the premises underlying the utilization of the Rorschach test and express them as a syllogism, it would assume a form such as: The Rorschach test is a perceptual task; personality traits are known to determine, in part, perceptual processes; therefore, from a consideration of the operation of perceptual processes as revealed in the Rorschach, the clinician can obtain useful information about an individual's personality structure.

Perhaps there may be objections to the choice of terms employed— "traits," "personality structure," and so on—as hypothetical constructs with much surplus meaning. The syllogism is not proposed as a prime example of the hypothetico-deductive method; it is simply an attempt to represent the implicit understanding most clinicians share in their acceptance of the Rorschach test as a useful assessment technique. Furthermore, the approaches to Rorschach research appear to share, in varying degrees, this outlook toward the test in regarding it as a tool for uncovering new facts about personality dynamics and behavior.

This paper will be devoted to a critical scrutiny of the elements that make up this rationale, with the hope that some insight may be gained into the problems that arise in attempting to establish the Rorschach projective techniques as empirically sound assessment procedures.

In the present paper the Rorschach test will be referred to as an "assessment technique," as distinguished from a "psychometric technique," following the distinction introduced by Cronbach (1960). The psychometric technique insists upon the reduction of test behavior to quantified score units that are combined statistically in predicting a specific criterion. On the other hand, assessment procedures emphasize reliance upon the logical evaluation of test observations combined in a quasi-artistic manner by the clinician. Conceived in this fashion, the problem of assessment techniques does not lie entirely in the unique characteristics of the tests employed (what data are employed), but rather includes the procedures utilized in the clinical application of assessment techniques (how the data are employed). It is not simply a matter of developing and perfecting the tests themselves but necessarily involves the integrative process of the clinician—that is, the area of clinical judgment. It will be the purpose of this article first to consider the import of the premises outlined above in regard to the Rorschach itself, and second, to suggest how these considerations are related to the activity of the clinician.

The major premise indicates that the Rorschach is a perceptual task. For purposes of the present discussion, "perception" will be defined simply as the behavioral process which falls between dependence upon stimuli (sensation) and independence of stimuli (conceptualization or thinking) whereby the individual represents reality to himself. The range of behavior patterns that are included under the label "perception" are not considered to cluster around some point midway between pure sensation and cognitive activity, but rather to extend to both extremes of this imaginary continuum.

Perceptual behavior involves the characteristics of the perceiver as well as the characteristics of the stimuli, so that dependence upon or independence of the stimuli can be influenced in terms of the condition of the perceiver. Now, while one may insist, along with Rorschach (1942, 1951), that the response to the ink blots is a perceptual process, it is evident that the test situation is markedly different from classical perceptual tasks, such as the Gestalt Phiphenomenon or figural aftereffect. It is the distinguishing characteristic of the projective technique that the value of external stimulus cues is markedly reduced so that, ostensibly, the subject is forced to rely predominantly upon the promptings of his own internal cues. According to the projective hypothesis, these internal cues consist basically of the individual's personal needs, drives, and motives. It is further assumed that it is these internal cues that, in some measure, determine perception in the real life situation. More important, it is assumed that these internal cues may be utilized in explaining or predicting the subject's overt behavior, that the organism responds to the external environment according to his perception of it.

In the projective test situation, then, the ambiguity of the stimuli as well as that of the set-determining instructions foster reliance upon cognitive processes. In the classicial perceptual task, however, the entire stimulus complex demands reliance upon sensory processes.

Another way of stating the distinction is that, in the classical perceptual task, the subject is required to make some act of discrimination; that is, his attention is focused upon the sensory elements in the perceptual process. In the Rorschach, however, the subject is required to minimize the sensory elements of the perceptual process and to emphasize, rather, the imaginal or associative elements; he is encouraged to depart from the concrete characteristics of the blot. Were this not so, the subjects' responses could hardly be other than "ink blots," or "smears," or "blotches of paint." To what extent, then, do the facts of perception described in the classical experiment apply to Rorschach behavior? It is not sufficient to indicate merely that they apply with some modifications.

Consider for a moment the typical perceptual variables employed in an analysis of test performance, i.e., the Rorschach scoring categories. These were originally developed by Rorschach himself, who offered no clear rationale for their creation other than their apparent utility in distinguishing among the test records of the various diagnostic groups; they have been little altered down to the present. One becomes involved in a circular validation process unless the existence of such variables can be demonstrated in tasks other than the Rorschach itself. At present, there is no clear-cut linkage between perceptual task variables and the Rorschach categories. In fact, it appears that an empirical basis for the distinctness of the categories is lacking (Murstein, 1960).

Accepting for the moment that scoring categories such as F, W, and M may be related to perceptual variables in some fashion, how is one to relate these to the established principles of perception? If one accepts the standard interpretation of the W response as indicative of organizational activity, then he might predict that W responses would seldom occur on blots that lack the elements of proximity, similarity, and the like, conducive to the perceived cohesiveness of parts. Or, if one accepts Orlansky's findings (1942) that angulated figures lend themselves readily to Phi-phenomena (are readily perceived in motion), he might predict that movement responses would be elicited more readily on blots exhibiting angularity.

Another example might be the phenomenon of atmospheric perspective. Since blurred, indistinct objects are perceived as more distant than clearly outlined ones, blots exhibiting both vague and clear outlines might be predicted to give rise to vista responses. Further, since no blot represents only one of these stimulus features, predictions might be formulated regarding the hierarchy of influence of these factors in determining responses. It is precisely this type of research, attentive to the stimulus value of the blots, that appears most important.

The above are simply indications that it is possible to relate the known facts of perception to performance upon the Rorschach. As is evident, Rorschach himself derived the response categories apart from a consideration of the stimulus value of the blots and of the perceptual factors involved. The importance of filling this void is apparent when one realizes that apart from the test itself these scoring categories have no meaning. With the empirical validation of such relationships between scoring categories and perceptual principles, the voluminous body of Rorschach research may more easily be incorporated into psychological theory. This appears to be the most basic step in a profitable approach to the utilization of the Rorschach. Without such empirical underpinnings, the entire structure of projective tests of this type remains unstable indeed.

On the level of the integrative activity of the clinician, he is forced to classify the subject's responses according to the quasi-perceptual scoring categories. The subject who has not been directed to concentrate upon the specific determinants of his response is usually not capable of delivering the precise introspective report which the clinician desires. While the clinician ostensibly analyzes the subject's perceptual processes into their components, identification of this or that determinant depends largely on the vagaries of the subject's word choice. At this point, one might also pose the question about the extent to which the clinician's personal perception of the blot may contaminate the selection of scoring determinants in the typical response. In other words, may not the clinician learn to assume that in a given population, most animal responses to Card II are large-detail, form-determined responses? In the absence of clear verbalization to the contrary, any animal responses may readily, though perhaps illegitimately, be scored as DF. Finally, the meaning of the scoring categories may be further contaminated by the fairly common practice of assuming that, in the absence of a specific reference to other determinants, a response may be considered to be form-determined.

In summary, the major problem involved at the level of clinician activity in the utilization of scoring categories arises from the fact that such categories depend directly upon the clinician's interpretation of the verbal report of an untrained introspectionist. The ambiguity inherent in such cues fosters the reliance by the clinician upon internal cues such as previous experience with the test.

Regarding the minor premise of the syllogism—that personality traits determine, in part, the perceptual process—there can be little discussion. The precise meaning of this premise in terms of the Rorschach test, however, is another matter entirely. The statement would generally be taken to include all the stock-in-trade hypotheses that the practicing clinician accepts along with the test itself. Interestingly, these hypotheses have changed little since their original presentation by Rorschach. They include: C responses are indicative of emotional instability; and the better the form visualization (F plus %), the better the emotional control. Rorschach derived these hypotheses from the predominance of the various response categories among his psychiatric and normal normative groups. For example, the subjects who gave the most C responses were the "epileptics, manics . . . or notoriously hot headed normals. From this it was concluded that C answers have a 'symptom value' . . . the tendency to impulsive emotional discharge" (p. 33, 1942, 1951). This is the tenor of the derivation of the Rorschach hypotheses.

Needless to say, continuing attempts to prove or disprove these hypotheses do not appear to be the most profitable approach to the use of this test.

Perhaps a more important consideration is the applicability of the stated relationship between personality traits and perception. Many of the studies that established the fact that personal needs, attitudes, and the like influence perception utilized tasks that occupied a position on the continuum between sensation and cognition, lying closer to dependence upon the stimuli; that is, either the stimuli employed were nonambiguous or the subjects were given a definite task to perform which oriented them directly to stimulus characteristics. On the Rorschach test, however, the subject is faced with relatively ambiguous stimuli and, certainly, with an ill-defined task that is generally assumed to be a "test of imagination" (8, p. 61). If this is true, can one legitimately accept the notion that needs and so on influence both types of perceptual activity in the same manner? Does it not appear reasonable to believe that needs influence the behavior of a stimulus-oriented subject differently from the behavior of the subject with an interpretative set?

Again, at the level of clinical judgment, problems are multiplied because of the lack of clarity in the meaning of perceptual processes as applied to Rorschach performance. In reality, the clinician's pool consists of verbalizations that describe the percept achieved rather than the process whereby it is achieved. Thus, while important contributions have been made toward an understanding of the relationship between abnormalities of the sensory processes in perception and constellations of the personality traits (Granger, 1960), the applicability of such research to a task like the Rorschach constitutes a rather knotty problem. To understand, for example, that the severely anxious subject may be less sensitive to the nuances of color when he is forced actively to discriminate colors is not to suggest that the subject who fails to verbalize color when describing his percept is severely anxious. Again, the uncontrolled nature of the response to the Rorschach task is quite at variance with the performance of a subject in a straightforward discriminatory task.

The final premise to be considered is that of the relationship between the Rorschach task and personality structure. The point of departure is the acceptance of a theory of dynamic interrelationships among quantifiable factors that determine overt behavior. These factors generally demonstrate the properties of hypothetical constructs rather than of intervening variables. In practical terms, the intervening variable is created by the facts; it is called into being to "name" an empirically verified relationship between antecedent and consequent conditions. The hypothetical construct, on the other hand, is created within a logical, theoretical framework and may have no existence apart from the theory that called it into being.

In theory construction, of course, the hypothetical construct represents the early attempts to uncover the laws relating the data investigated. At this stage, the constructs possess marked heuristic value in pointing the way toward meaningful experimentation. In time, with the accumulated discovery of a body of lawful relationships, they may be confirmed as intervening variables. At the present stage of development in personality theory, most of the explanatory concepts remain at the level of hypothetical constructs. The use of such constructs reduces the efficiency of the predictive process, because the construct is not tightly bound to the consequents or overt behavior; nor is it specifically linked to the antecedents or test measures of the antecedents.

Thus, at the level of the clinician's attempts to predict behavior, the ambiguity of the personality constructs that he selects will markedly reduce his over-all predictive efficiency. In addition, his reliance upon the use of logically derived scoring categories automatically results in the loss of the highly valued "personal information" about the subject that the projective technique is constructed to yield.

It is proposed that this unique, personal information about the subject rests in the percept achieved—that is, in the content of the subject's verbalizations. While much lip service has been paid to the importance of content analysis, there has been a singular absence of controlled studies focusing upon the more cognitive aspects of perception in the projective techniques. That the content of the response is, at times, a more appropriate source of cues for predicting to a criterion than any system of logical categories is an implicit postulate underlying the cognitive activity of the clinician. The illustration of this fact cited by Hammond (1955) in the context of Rorschach protocols is indeed impressive. Given the task of estimating measured intelligence on the basis of scoring categories alone as opposed to the use of verbatim responses, the correlation between clinician estimates and measured intelligence rose from .47 to .64. As a matter of fact, the estimates by clinically inexperienced college sophomores based on verbatim responses correlated .58 with measured intelligence. It is not contended that a study of this type supports the validity of content analysis, since one may ask, "What is it really in the verbatim response that serves as a cue?" In addition, the study points out the fact that errors in prediction by clinicians arose partially from their erroneous weighting of scoring categories. This last point importantly relates to the objections raised by Holt (1958) in regard to the controversy over clinical judgment vs. statistical methodology. More will be said of these points later.

If the projective techniques are to be considered seriously as measures of perceptual processes, then an analysis of a technique that omits the area of meaning is incomplete. The use of logically derived score categories (as in the Rorschach) often increases the error variance in prediction in several aspects. Though the categories may be logically meaningful, the criteria for inclusion within a category may depend largely upon the value judgments or perceptions of the clinician himself. Hence, such systems prove statistically unreliable. Furthermore, granted a nonambiguous scoring system, the extent to which the categories represent empirically meaningful dimensions in the perceptual process is vitally related to the validity of clinical inferences regarding personality structure. Finally, predictions of behavioral criteria from such categories are mediated by their relationship to the personality constructs. The comments made earlier concerning the function of such hypothetical constructs are applicable here.

But why consider the dimension of meaning in projective testing? First, it is clear that any definition of "perception" necessarily involves, in some fashion, the integration of stimuli into meaningful configurations—that is, "perception" is the process through which one arrives at meaning. It would appear that "meaning" is an appropriate focus in any attempt to relate perception and personality. It is this realization that has stimulated research such as that by Elizur (1949) in rating content according to the degree of anxiety and hostility exhibited. Zubin (11) has concluded that content analysis generates accurate descriptions of personality dynamics. In addition, he (1955) has also demonstrated the utility of a scoring system based upon content analysis in that raters, utilizing the system, evidence a high degree of agreement. However, such approaches still remain one step removed from the area of subject meaning. With scales of the type devised by Zubin, the context of meaning is derived from the experimenter's frame of reference. This frame of reference may or may not be in accord with that of the individual responding. Such attempts to quantify the dimension of meaning are vulnerable to the same objections raised against present systems of categorizing responses.

In the present article, the logically derived scoring systems employed have been subjected to scrutiny, and their tenuous relationship to dimensions of perception has been considered. However, the most important problem in regard to these assessment techniques—that of the stimulus value of the ambiguous stimuli composing the various projective techniques—has not yet been treated. In the context of the logically derived scoring systems in present use, it has been important to consider how the various component elements of the stimulus are related to response tendencies. While research involving these stimulus elements has yielded vital information about the effects of stimulus properties upon subject reactions, it has not touched upon the basic question of the perceptual meaning of the stimuli and their relationship to content. The former type of research is quite atomistic and at times seems in direct contradiction to the holistic principles underlying the personality-assessment techniques. The latter type of research has been lacking, though the techniques for attacking the problem of meaning do exist. The attempts that have been made with the Rorschach—for example, Zax and Laiselle (1960)—have not received the attention due them, perhaps because the results have been interpreted as either supporting or disproving the stock-in-trade clinical hypotheses about the meaning of the blots.

While the problems of the projective tests as methods of personality assessment are many and serious, they do not justify a negative attitude toward the techniques themselves. The function of personality assessment through perceptual processes is not theoretically unsound nor experimentally impossible. What is required, however, is a careful consideration of the problems associated with personality constructs, the definition of the perceptual process, and the methods of quantifying test performance. Basic to all of these points is the matter of stimulus value or the perceptual meaning of the projective stimuli. Without some empirical measures of the meaning dimension, the clinician is faced with an equation consisting of two unknowns, the task and the subject. It is precisely the second member of the equation which the clinician purports to define.

As was suggested earlier, there appears to be overlap between the problems of personality assessment by means of the projective techniques and the contribution of the clinician's judgment to assessment. It is important to understand clearly the unique problems introduced into assessment procedures by the clinician's reliance upon the more cognitive aspects of his own perceptual activity. There is perhaps no better way in which to summarize these possible sources of error than by referring the reader to Holt's (1958) description of predictive process. In his analysis, the problem areas in personality assessment and prediction of behavior through perceptual processes are clearly delineated.

In paraphrase of Holt's analysis, the first two steps require an understanding of the behavior to be predicted and, conjointly, the isolation of the intervening variables related to the criterion behavior. In the present context, these steps demand basic research resembling job analysis, discovering rather than assuming the environmental and organismic variables which interact in determining behavioral outcomes. While the behaviors that the clinician is asked to predict often represent "divergent phenomena" (Cronbach, 1960) and are not amenable to the predictive process, the vast majority of his clinical decisions involve behaviors that represent "convergent phenomena" and that can be subjected to analysis.

In regard to the isolation of relevant intervening variables, the research task is more formidable. As was indicated earlier, the conceptual frameworks within which assessment techniques are interpreted are derived from the various personality theories replete with hypothetical constructs rather than intervening variables. This does not, however, render the research task impossible, though it does caution against unwarranted claims for relative superiority among such constructs. Their functions are basically heuristic, supplying suggestions for fruitful areas of investigation that may or may not eventuate in the development of personality constructs of the intervening variable type.

The third step involves the development of adequate measures of the important variables. In the context of personality assessment through perception, it is proposed that the dimension of meaning be a focus for research. Experimental studies have pointed up the utility of content or meaning analysis, though until recently no systematic procedures for the study of meaning have been utilized. Without some normative data regarding stimulus meaning, the clinician is faced with the dilemma of attempting to explain one unknown (the subject) by means of another (the stimulus).

The final steps in the predictive process are relating the measures to the intervening variables and actually combining the data to yield predictions. These steps constitute the test of the entire process. The results obtained at these levels serve as the standards for evaluating the practical validity of the entire experimental schema.

While Holt's analysis originally applied to the problem of statistical vs. clinical procedures, it also refers pointedly to the problem of projective techniques in personality assessment. The essential focus of his analysis, as well as of the present analysis, is the reasonable demand for the reduction of intuitive linkages between test results and overt behavior (reduction of the clinician's reliance on his own personal internal cues), and the search for lawful functional relationships firmly rooted in sound experimental techniques.

REFERENCES

1. CRONBACH, LEE J. *Essentials of psychological testing.* (2nd ed.) New York: Harper & Brothers, 1960.
2. ELIZUR, A. Content analysis of the Rorschach with regard to anxiety and hostility. *Rorschach Res. Exch.*, 1949, *13*, 247–284.

3. GRANGER, G. W. Abnormalities of sensory perception in Eysenck, H. (ed.) *Handbook of abnormal psychology*. New York: Basic Books, 1961.

4. HAMMOND, K. Probabilistic functionalism and the clinical method. *Psychol. Rev.*, 1955, *62*, 255–262.

5. HOLT, ROBERT. Clinical and statistical prediction: a reformulation and some new data. *J. Abnorm. Soc. Psychol.*, 1958, *56*, 1–12.

6. MURSTEIN, B. I. Factor analyses of the Rorschach. *J. Consult. Psychol.*, 1960, *24*, 262–275.

7. ORLANSKY, JESSE. The effect of similarity and difference in form on apparent visual movement. *Arch. Ps. N. Y.*, 1940, no. 246.

8. RORSCHACH, HERMANN. *Psychodiagnostics*. New York: Grune & Stratton, 1951.

9. ZAX, M. AND LOISELLE, R. H. Stimulus value of Rorschach Inkblots as measured by the semantic differential. *J. Clin. Psychol.*, 1960, *16*, 160–163.

10. ZUBIN, J. Failures of the Rorschach technique. *J. Proj. Tech.*, 1954, *18*, 303–315.

11. ZUBIN, J., ERON, L. D. AND SULTAN, F. A. Psychometric evaluation of the Rorschach experiment. *Amer. J. Orthopsychiat.*, 1956, *26*, 773–782.

II

The Projective Method

Lawrence K. Frank

PROJECTIVE METHODS

FOR THE STUDY OF

PERSONALITY

A N INITIAL difficulty in the study of personality is the lack of any clear-cut, adequate conception of what is to be studied. The recent volumes by Allport and by Stagner, and the monograph by Burks and Jones,[1] may be cited as indicators of the confusion in this field, where, as they show, there are so many conflicting ideas and concepts, each used to justify a wide variety of methods, none of which are wholly adequate.

A situation of this kind evokes different responses from each person according to his professional predilections and allegiances. Obviously pronouncements will be resisted, if not derided, while polemics and apologetics will only increase the confusion. The question may be raised whether any light upon this situation can be obtained by examining the *process* of personality development for leads to more fruitful conceptions and more satisfactory methods and procedures.

Reprinted from *J. Psychol.*, 1939, *8*, 389–413, by permission of The Journal Press.
1. *Cf.* Allport, G. W. *Personality: A Psychological Interpretation.* New York: Holt, 1937. *Cf.* Stagner, R. *Psychology of Personality.* New York: McGraw-Hill, 1937. *Cf.* Burks, Barbara S., & Jones, Mary C. Personality development in childhood: A Survey of problems, methods and experimental findings. *Monog. Soc. Res. Child Devel.*, 1936, *1*, 1–205.

A

Specifically, it is suggested that we reflect upon the emergence of personality as an outcome of the interaction of cultural agents and the individual child. In the space here available only a brief summary statement is permissible of the major aspects of this process in which we may distinguish an individual organism, with an organic inheritance, slowly growing, developing, and maturing under the tutelage of parents and teachers intent upon patterning him to the culturally prescribed and socially sanctioned modes of action, speech, and belief.

As elsewhere stated,[2] the child is not passive clay but a reacting organism with feelings, as are the parents, nurses, and teachers who are rearing him. He therefore receives training in the prescribed cultural and social norms of action, speech, and belief, according to their personal bias and feelings, and he accepts this training with varying degrees of observance, always idiomatically and with feelings toward these instructors. What we can observe then is the dual process of *socialization,* involving sufficient conformity in outer conduct to permit participation in the common social world, and of *individuation,* involving the progressive establishment of a private world of highly idiosyncratic meanings, significances, and feelings that are more real and compelling than the cultural and physical world.

The foregoing does not imply any subjective duality or other traditional dichotomy; it is an attempt at a simple statement of the well-known and generally accepted view that in all events we may observe both similarities or uniformities and also individual deviations. We may concentrate upon the larger uniformities and ignore the individual components that are participating, as we do in measuring the temperature, pressure, and other properties of a gas or we may look beyond the aggregate uniformities to the individual, discrete molecules and atoms and electrons which, as we now are realizing, are highly erratic, unpredictable, and far from that uniformity of behavior described statistically. Thus, we may observe a similar antithesis between the group uniformities of economic, political, and social affairs and the peculiar personal conduct of each of the citizens who collectively exhibit those uniformities and conformities.

Culture provides the socially sanctioned patterns of action, speech, and belief that make group life what we observe, but each individual in that group is a personality who observes those social requirements and uses those

2. *Cf.* Frank, L. K. Fundamental needs of the child. *Men. Hyg.,* 1938, *22,* 353–379. *Cf.* Frank, L. K. Cultural coercion and individual distortion. *Psychiatry,* 1939, *2,* 11–27.

patterns idiomatically, with a peculiar personal inflection, accent, emphasis, and intention.[3] Strictly speaking, there are only these individuals, deviating from and distorting the culture; but with our traditional preoccupation with uniformities we have preferred to emphasize the uniformity of statistical aggregates of all activities as the real, and to treat the individual deviation as a sort of unavoidable but embarrassing failure of nature to live up to our expectations. These deviations must be recognized, but only as minor blemishes on and impediments to the scientific truths we seek!

Those ideas flourished in all scientific work up to about 1900 or 1905 when X-rays, quantum physics, relativity, and other new insights were developed that made these earlier ideas obsolete, except in a number of disciplines which still cling to the nineteenth century. Thus it is scientifically respectable, in some circles, to recognize that uniformity is a statistical group concept that overlays an exceedingly disorderly, discontinuous array of individual, discrete events that just won't obey the scientists' laws! It is also respectable to speak of organization and processes "within the atom," although it is recognized that no direct measurements or even observations can be made within the atom; inferences being drawn from activities and energy transformations that are observable and frequently measurable.

For purposes of discussion it is convenient to see individuals (*a*) as organisms existing in the common public world of nature, (*b*) as members of their group, carrying on their life careers, in the social world of culturally prescribed patterns and practices, but living, (*c*) as personalities in these *private worlds* which they have developed under the impact of experience. It is important to recognize these three aspects of human behavior and living because of their implications for scientific study.

As organisms reacting to the environmental impacts, overtly and physiologically, human activity presents a problem of observation and measurement similar to that of all other organisms and events. The human body moves or falls through geographical space, captures, stores, and releases energy, and so on. As members of the group, individuals exhibit certain patterns of action, speech, and belief that may be aggregated into larger categories of uniformity or cultural and group norms; at least we find certain pronounced, often all-inclusive modes in their observed activities in which they tend to conform to social and cultural prescriptions.

When we examine the personality process or *private worlds* of individuals we face a somewhat peculiar problem, because we are seeking not the cultural and social norms of the uniformities of organic activity, but rather

3. *Cf.* Benedict, Ruth. *Patterns of Culture.* Boston: Houghton Mifflin, 1934. *Cf.* Mead, Margaret. *Sex and Temperament.* New York: Morrow, 1935. *Cf.* Bateson, G. *Naven.* Cambridge: Cambridge Univ. Press, 1936.

the revelation of just that peculiar, individual way of organizing experience and of feeling which personality implies.

In this context we may emphasize then that personality is approachable as a *process* or operation of an individual who organizes experience and reacts affectively to situations. This process is dynamic in the sense that the individual personality imposes upon the common public world of events (what we call nature), his meanings and significances, his organization and patterns, and he invests the situations thus structured with an affective meaning to which he responds idiomatically. This dynamic organizing process will of necessity express the cultural training he has experienced so that until he withdraws from social life, as in the psychoses, he will utilize the group-sanctioned patterns of action, speech, and belief, but as he individually has learned to use them and as he feels toward the situations and people to whom he reacts.

If it were not liable to gross misunderstanding, the personality process might be regarded as a sort of rubber stamp which the individual imposes upon every situation by which he gives it the configuration that he, as an individual, requires; in so doing he necessarily ignores or subordinates many aspects of the situation that for him are irrelevant and meaningless and selectively reacts to those aspects that are personally significant. In other words, the personality process may be viewed as a highly individualized practice of the general operation of all organisms that selectively respond to a figure on a ground,[4] by reacting to the configurations in an environmental context that is relevant to their life careers.

It is interesting to see how the students of personality have attempted to meet the problem of individuality with methods and procedures designed for study of uniformities and norms that ignore or subordinate individuality, treating it as a troublesome deviation which derogates from the real, the superior, and only important central tendency, mode, average, etc. This is not the occasion to review these methods and the writer is not competent to assess them critically, but it is appropriate to point out some aspects of the present methodological difficulty we face in the accepted quantitative procedures.

Since individuals, as indicated earlier, learn to conform to the socially sanctioned patterns of action, speech, and belief (with individual bias and flavor of their own), it is possible to establish the social norms appropriate for *groups* of like chronological age, sex, and so on and to construct standardized tests and to calculate statistically their validity, i.e., do they measure or rate what they are expected to measure or rate for each group; and their

4. *Cf.* Frank, L. K. The problem of learning. *Psychol. Rev.*, 1926, *33*, 329–351.

reliability, i.e., how well or reliably do they measure or rate the performance of the groups?[5]

While standardized tests are generally considered to be measurers of individual differences, it would be more appropriate to say that they are ratings of the degree of likeness to cultural norms exhibited by individuals who are expected, as members of this society, to conform to those group patterns. In other words, the standardized test does not tell very much about the individual, *as an individual,* but rather how nearly he approximates to a normal performance of culturally prescribed tasks for which a more or less arbitrary, but internally consistent, scheme of quantitative ratings is utilized.[6] By the use of an all-over total figure for an individual, it becomes possible to assign numerical evaluations to individuals in various categories of achievement, skill, conformity, and so forth, such as accelerated, average, or retarded mentally; manual or verbal proficiency, etc. Having assigned him to a rank order in a group or class according to the standardized test, the individual is disposed of and adequately explained.[7] The history of the use of standardized tests shows how they are used to place individuals in various classifications that are convenient for administration, for remedial work and therapy, or for segregation for purposes of social control, with little or no concern about understanding the individual so classified or placed, or discovering his characteristics *as an individual.*

It would seem fair to say, therefore, that standardized tests offer procedures for rating individuals in terms of their socialization and how nearly they approximate to the acceptance and use of the culturally prescribed patterns of belief, action, and speech for which statistical norms can be calculated from actual observations of performance of *groups* of individuals, according to age, sex, etc.

In order to apply these and more recently developed quantitative methods to the study of personality it has been necessary to adopt a conception of the personality as an aggregation of discrete, measurable traits, factors, or other separable entities which are present in the individual in differing quantity and organized according to individual patterns. But since the personality is more than overt activity, some way of getting at the underlying personality is necessary. The need for quantitative data has led to the

5. *Cf.* Frank, L. K. Comments on the proposed standardization of the Rorschach method. *Rorschach Res. Exch.,* 1939, *3.*

6. *Cf.* Kent, Grace H. Use and abuse of mental tests in clinical diagnosis. *Psychol. Rec.,* 1938, *2,* 391–400.

7. *Cf.* Lewin, K. *A Dynamic Theory of Personality.* New York: McGraw-Hill, 1935. (Especially Chapter I on Aristotelian and Galilean modes of thought, and the class theory of investigation.)

use of the culturally standardized, socially sanctioned norms of speech and belief and attitudes in and through which the individual has been asked to express his personality, as in questionnaires, inventories, rating scales, etc.

If time allowed, it would be desirable to examine more fully the implications of this procedure which attempts to reveal the individuality of the person by using the social stereotypes of language and motives that necessarily subordinate individuality to social conformity, emphasizing likeness and uniformity of group patterns. This point becomes more significant when we recall that almost identical actions and speech may be used in extraordinarily different senses by each individual using them; while conversely, the widest diversity of action and speech may have almost identical sense and significance for different individuals exhibiting them. Moreover the conventional traits and motives and objectives derived from traditional concepts of human nature and conduct, carry meanings often alien to the investigator using them as data. Words are generalized symbols, are usually obscuring of, when not actually misleading about, the individual idiomatic personality using them.[8]

It should be further noted that many procedures for study of personality rely upon the subject's self-diagnosis and revelation of his *private world* of personal meanings and feelings which the social situation compels the individual to conceal, even if, as is unusual, he had any clear understanding of himself. When we ask an individual to tell what he believes or feels or to indicate in which categories he belongs, this social pressure to conform to the group norms operates to bias what he will say and presses him to fit himself into the categories of the inventory or questionnaire offered for self-diagnosis.[9] Moreover, as Henry A. Murray has observed, the most important things about an individual are what he cannot or will not say. The law has long recognized testimony as unreliable, to be accepted only after many checks and tests as formulated in the law of evidence.

At this point there may be a feeling of dismay, if not resentment, because the discussion has led to a seeming impasse, with no road open to study the personality by the accepted methods and procedures of present-day quantitative psychology. Moreover, the insistence upon the unique, idiomatic character of the personality appears to remove it from the area of scientific study conceived as a search for generalizations, uniformities, invariant relationships, etc. It is proposed, therefore, to discuss a few recent developments in scientific concepts and methods and the new problems they have raised in order to indicate a way out of this apparent impasse.

8. *Cf.* Willoughby, R. P., & Morse, Mary E. Spontaneous reactions to a personality inventory. *Amer. J. Orthopsychiat.*, 1936, *6*, 562–575.

9. *Cf.* Vigotsky, L. S. Thought and speech. *Psychiatry*, 1939, *2*, 29–54.

B

It is appropriate to recall that the uniformity and laws of nature are statistical findings of the probable events and relationships that occur among an aggregate of events, the individuals of which are highly disorderly and unpredictable. Theoretical physics has adjusted itself to the conception of a universe that has statistical regularity and order, and individual disorder, in which the laws of aggregates are not observable in the activity of the individual making up these aggregates. Thus quantum physics and statistical mechanics and many other similar contrasts are accepted without anxiety about scientific respectability. The discrete individual event can be and is regarded as an individual to whom direct methods and measurements have only a limited applicability. We can therefore acknowledge an interest in the individual as a scientific problem and find some sanction for such an interest.

Another recent development is the concept of the *field* in physics and its use in biology. The field concept is significant here because it offers a way of conceiving this situation of an individual part and of the whole, which our older concepts have so confused and obscured.[10] Instead of a whole that dominates the parts, which have to be organized by some mysterious process into a whole, we begin to think of an aggregate of individuals which constitute, by their interaction, a field that operates to pattern these individuals. Parts are not separate, discrete, independent entities that get organized by the whole, nor is the whole a superior kind of entity with feudal power over its parts, e.g., a number of iron filings brought close to a magnet will arrange themselves in a pattern wherein each bit of iron is related to the other bits and the magnet and these relations constitute the whole; remove some bits and the pattern shifts as it does if we add more filings, or bits of another metal. Likewise, in a gas, the gas may be viewed as a field in which individual molecules, atoms, and electrons are patterned by the total interactions of all those parts into the group activity we call a gas. Ecology studies this interaction of various organizations in the circumscribed life zone or field which they constitute.[11]

This field concept is highly important because it leads to the general notion that any "entity" we single out for observation is particpating in a field; any observation we make must be ordered to the field in which it is

10. *Cf.* Burr, H. S., & Northrop, F. S. C. An electro-dynamic theory of life. *Quart. Rev. Biol.,* 1935, *10,* 322–333.
11. *Cf.* du Nouy, P. L. *Biological Time.* New York: Macmillan, 1937. (Other part-whole fields are a candle flame, a fountain jet, a stream of water, etc.)

made or as we say, every observation or measurement is relative to the frame of reference or field in which it occurs.

There are many other far-reaching shifts in concepts and methods that should be discussed here, but the foregoing will suffice to indicate that the study of an individual personality may be conceived as an approach to a somewhat disorderly and erratic activity, occurring in the field we call culture (i.e., the aggregate interaction of individuals whose behavior is patterned by participation in the aggregate). Moreover, the observations we make on the individual personality must be ordered to the field of that individual and his life space. We must also regard the individual himself as an aggregate of activities which pattern his parts and functions.

Here we must pause to point out that the older practice of creating entities out of data has created many problems that are unreal and irrelevant and so are insoluble. In by-gone years it was customary to treat data of temperature, light, magnetic activity, radiation, chemical activity, and so on as separate entities, independent of each other. But the more recent view is to see in these data evidences of energy transformations which are transmitted in different magnitudes, sequences, etc., and so appear as heat, light, magnetism, etc. This has relevance to the study of personality since it warns us against the practice of observing an individual's actions and then reifying these data into entities called traits (or some other discrete term), which we must then find some way of organizing into the living total personality who appears in experience as a unified organism.

With this background of larger, more general shifts in scientific procedures, let us examine some more specific developments that are relevant to our topic.

Within recent years new procedures have been developed for discovering not only the elements or parts composing the whole, but also the way those parts are arranged and organized in the whole, without disintegrating or destroying the whole. The X-rays are used, not merely for photographs or to show on a fluorescent screen what is otherwise invisible within an organism or any object, but also for diffraction analysis, in which the X-rays are patterned by the internal organization of any substance to show its molecular and atomic structure. Spectrographic analysis reveals the chemical components qualitatively, and now quantitatively, and in what compounds, by the way light is distributed along a continuous band of coarse and fine spectral lines, each of which reveals a different element or isotope. The mass spectroscope offers another exceedingly delicate method for determining the composition of any substance that gives off radiations whereby the electrons or their rate of travel can be measured and the composition of the substance inferred.

X-rays, however, are only one of the newer methods whereby any complex may be made to reveal its components and its organization, often quantitatively, when approached by an appropriate procedure. Recently, it has been found that the chemical composition of various substances, especially proteins, can be ascertained by the reflection of a beam of light upon a thin monomolecular film of the protein substance spread on a film of oil on water over a metallic surface. Again, it has been found that metallic ores and coal may be analyzed, i.e., be made to reveal their chemical composition and other properties by the "angle of wetability," the angle of reflection, or the color of the light reflected from a liquid film that adheres to the surface of the unknown material.

Polarized light has also become an instrument for revealing the chemical composition of substances without resort to the usual methods of disintegration or chemical analysis. Electrical currents may also be passed through substances, gaseous, liquid, or solid, and used to discover what they contain and in what form. Indeed, it is not unwarranted to say that these indirect methods that permit discovery of the composition and organization of substances, complexes, and organisms, seem likely to become the method of choice over the older destructive analytical procedures, because these methods do not destroy or disturb the substance or living organism being studied.

In this connection reference should also be made to the development of biological assays, whereby a living organism, plant or animal, is used for assaying the composition of various substances and compounds and determining their potency, such as vitamins, hormones, viruses, drugs, radiation, light, magnetism, and electrical currents (including electrophoresis for separating, without injury or change, the different subvarieties of any group of cells, chemical substances, etc.). In these procedures the response of the living organism is utilized as an indicator, if not an actual measurement, of that about which data are sought, as well as the state, condition, maturation, etc., of the organism being tested. It is appropriate to note also that physicists are using such devices as the Wilson cloud chamber and the Geiger counter to obtain data on the *individual* electrical particle, which reveals its presence and energy by the path traced in water vapor, or by activation of the counter, although never itself observable or directly measurable.

These methodological procedures are being refined and extended because they offer possibilities for ascertaining what is either unknowable by other means or is undeterminable because the older analytic methods destroyed part or all of that which was to be studied. They are being accepted as valid and credible, primarily because they are more congruous with the search for undivided totalities and functioning organisms and are more productive of the data on organization on which present-day research problems are focused. They are also expressive of the recent concepts of whole-and-parts and their interrelations, which no longer invoke the notion of parts as discrete entities upon which an organization is imposed by a superior whole, but rather employ the concept of the field. Finally, they offer possibilities for studying the specific, differentiated individuality of organized structures and particulate events which are ignored or obscured by the older quantitative determinations of aggregates.

Since the threshold task in any scientific endeavor is to establish the meanings and significances of the data obtained by any method of observation and measurement, it should be noted that these indirect methods for revealing the composition and organization of substances and structures rely upon experimental and genetic procedures to establish reliability and validity, not statistical procedures. That is to say, these newer procedures establish the meaning of any datum by employing the procedure upon a substance or structure of known composition, often made to order, so that it is possible to affirm that the resulting bending, patterning, arrangement of light, radiation, and so on, are reliable and valid indicators of the substance or structure when found in an unknown composition. These methods for establishing reliability and validity are therefore genetic in the sense of observing or tracing the origin and development of what is to be tested so that its presence or operation may be historically established: they are also dependent upon the concurrent use of other procedures which will yield consistent data on the same composition which therefore are validated by such internal consistency and congruity of findings.

Psychology developed the statistical procedures for establishing reliability and validity because the only data available were the single observations or measurements taken at one time on each subject. Since no other data were available on the prior history and development of the subjects, reliability had to be determined by statistical manipulation of these test data themselves; also, since no other data were available on the subject's other functions and activities only statistical validity could be established. It would appear that these tests of reliability and validity devised to meet the difficulty presented by absence of other data now act as barriers to the use of any other procedures for personality study in which reliability and validity for each subject is tested through these other nonstatistical methods.

Methods of *temporal validation* offer great promise because they permit testing of the validity of data for a *specific subject* over a period of time, and the method of congruity among data obtained by different procedures from the same subject offer large possibilities for testing the reliability of any data for a *specific subject.*[12] It is appropriate to recall here that the accepted methods for testing reliability and validity of tests, inventories, etc., offer indices only for the *group,* not for any individual subject in that *group.*

We may therefore view the problem of personality in terms of these more recent ideas and conceptions and consider the application of these indirect procedures for revealing the composition and organization of substances and energy complexes.

As indicated earlier the personality may be viewed as a dynamic process of organizing experience, of "structuralizing the life space" (Lewin) according to the unique individual's *private world.* This conception may be made precise and operational by seeing the individual and his changing environment as a series of fields which arise through the interaction of the individual personality with his selective awareness, patterned responses, and idiomatic feelings, with the environmental situations of objects, events, and other persons. A field organization or configuration arises out of this interaction wherein, as suggested, the personality distorts the situation, so far as it is amenable, into the configurations of its *private world,* but has to adjust to the situation in so far as it resists such distortion and imposes its necessities upon the personality. What we have called personality and fumblingly have tried to formulate as the total responses of the whole individual and similar additive conceptions becomes more understandable and approachable for investigation when conceived as the living process in this field created by the individual and the environing situation.

The objective world of objects, organisms, and events likewise may be seen as fields of interacting object-situations, upon which cultural patterns operate in the conduct of human beings who, by very reason of behaving in these learned patterns, create the cultural fields of interacting human conduct. What is highly important to note is that every observation made must be ordered—given its quantitative and qualitative interpretation—to the field in which it occurs, so that the idea of pure objectivity becomes meaningless and sterile if it implies data not biased, influenced, relative to the field in which observed. Likewise the conception of a stimulus that may be described and measured apart from the field and the organism in that field is untenable.[13] The "same" stimulus will differ in every field, and for every field and for every organism which selectively creates its own stimuli in

12. *Cf.* Bateson, G. *Naven.* Cambridge: Cambridge Univ. Press, 1936, in which appears a discussion of diachronic and synchronic procedures.

13. *Cf.* Vigotsky, L. S. Thought and speech. *Psychiatry,* 1939, 2, 29–54. "The investigator who uses such methods may be compared to a man, who, in order to explain why water extinguishes fire, analyzes the water into oxygen and hydrogen and is surprised to find that oxygen helps the process of burning and hydrogen itself burns. This method of analyzing a whole into elements is not a true analysis which can be used to solve concrete problems" (p. 29).

each situation. Indeed, this dynamic conception of the personality as a process implies that there are no stimuli to conduct (as distinct from physical and physiological impacts) except in so far as the individual personality selectively constitutes them and responds to them in its idiosyncratic patterns. In other words the stimuli are functions of the field created by the individual interacting with the situation.

Thus the movement in various areas of scientific work is toward recognition of the field concept and the devising of methods that will record not merely data but the fields in which those data have been observed and find their significance. Those who are appalled by the seeming anarchy thus threatening scientific work may be reminded that the present-day standards of scientific work and of methods are part of a development that will inevitably make today's ideas and procedures obsolete. It is well to recall how proud (justly so) chemistry was to achieve quantitative determinations of the composition of substances and now, how crude those early quantitative methods and findings now appear, when they now are seeking to find out not merely what and how much, but the spatial arrangement of the constituents as in stereochemistry where the same atoms in the same quantity produce different substances according to their spatial arrangement. It is likewise worth recalling, that about 1900, young physicists could find no problems except the more precise measurement of the pressure, temperature, etc., of a gas and were content with such crude quantitative findings. Furthermore, biologists today are accepting as commonplace that the same nutritive components, amino-acids, carbohydrates, fats, minerals, and vitamins are selectively digested, assimilated, and metabolized in different ways by each species and by each individual. Moreover, it is conceded that the proteins of each species are different as are those of each individual with the possibility of an almost unlimited number of different protein molecules, in which the same basic elements are organized into unique spatial-temporal configurations appropriate to the organic field of the individual organism.[14]

C

Coming directly to the topic of projective methods for personality study,[15] we may say that the dynamic conception of personality as a process

14. The concepts of individuality and of individuation are being used by biologists because they find themselves confronted with individual organic activities and idiomatic processes. *Cf.* Blumenthal, H. T. Effects of organismal differentials on the distribution of leukocytes in the circulating blood. *Arch. Path.*, 1939, 27, 510–545. *Cf.* Coghill, G. E. Individuation versus integration in the development of behavior. *J. Gen. Psychol.*, 1930, 3, 431–435. *Cf.* Coghill, G. E. Integration and motivation of behavior as problems of growth. *J. Genet. Psychol.*, 1936, 48, 3–19.

15. References to the projective techniques discussed in this section appear in the references at the end of the chapter.

of organizing experience and structuralizing life space in a field, leads to the problem of how we can reveal the way an individual personality organizes experience, in order to disclose or at least gain insight into that individual's *private world* of meanings, significances, patterns, and feelings.

Such a problem is similar to those discussed earlier where indirect methods are used to elicit the pattern of internal organization and of composition without disintegrating or distorting the subject, which is made to bend, deflect, distort, organize, or otherwise pattern part or all of the field in which it is placed—e.g., light and X-rays. In similar fashion we may approach the personality and induce the individual to reveal his way of organizing experience by giving him a field (objects, materials, experiences) with relatively little structure and cultural patterning so that the personality can project upon that plastic field his way of seeing life, his meanings, significances, patterns, and especially his feelings. Thus we elicit a projection of the individual personality's *private world* because he has to organize the field, interpret the material and react affectively to it. More specifically, a projection method for study of personality involves the presentation of a stimulus-situation designed or chosen because it will mean to the subject, not what the experimenter has arbitrarily decided it should mean (as in most psychological experiments using standardized stimuli in order to be "objective"), but rather whatever it must mean to the personality who gives it, or imposes upon it, his private, idiosyncratic meaning and organization. The subject then will respond to *his* meaning of the presented stimulus-situation by some form of action and feeling that is expressive of his personality. Such responses may be *constitutive* as when the subject imposes a structure or form or configuration (Gestalt) upon an amorphous, plastic, unstructured substance such as clay, finger paints, or upon partially structured and semi-organized fields like the Rorschach cards; or they may be *interpretive* as when the subject tells what a stimulus-situation, like a picture, means to him; or they may be *cathartic* as when the subject discharges affect or feeling upon the stimulus-situation and finds an emotional release that is revealing of his affective reactions toward life situations represented by the stimulus-situation, as when he plays with clay or toys. Other expressions may be *constructive* organizations wherein the subject builds in accordance with the materials offered but reveals in the pattern of his building some of the organizing conceptions of his life at that period, as in block-building.

The important and determining process is the subject's personality which operates upon the stimulus-situation as if it had a wholly private significance for him alone or an entirely plastic character which made it yield to the subject's control. This indicates that, as suggested earlier, a personality is the way an individual organizes and patterns life situations and effectively responds to them, "structuralizes his life space," so that by projective methods we are evoking the very process of personality as it has developed to that moment.[16] Since the way an individual organizes and patterns life situations, imposes his *private world* of meanings and affectively reacts upon the environing world of situations and other persons and strives to maintain his personal version against the coercion or obstruction of others, it is evident that personality is a persistent way of living and feeling that, despite change of tools, implements, and organic growth and maturation will appear continuously and true to pattern.

When we scrutinize the actual procedures that may be called projective methods we find a wide variety of techniques and materials being employed for the same general purpose, to obtain from the subject, "what he cannot or will not say," frequently because he does not know himself and is not aware what he is revealing about himself through his projections.

In the following statement no attempt has been made to provide a complete review of all the projective methods now being used, since such a canvass would be beyond the present writer's competence and intention. Only a few illustrations of projective methods are offered to show their variety and their scope, in the hope of enlisting further interest in and creating a better understanding of, their characteristics and advantages.[17]

The Rorschach ink blots, to which the subject responds by saying what he "sees" in each of a number of different blots, are perhaps the most widely known of these procedures. They have been utilized in Europe and in the United States, frequently in connection with psychiatric clinics and hospitals, for revealing the personality configurations and have been found of increasing value. Insofar as life histories and psychiatric and psychoanalytic studies of the subjects who have had the Rorschach diagnosis are available, the ink blot interpretations are being increasingly validated by these clinical findings. Such comparative findings are of the greatest importance because they mutually reinforce each other and reveal the consistency or any conflicts in the different interpretations and diagnosis of a personality.

Another similar procedure is the *Cloud Picture* method, developed by Wilhelm Stern, to evoke projections from a subject upon more amorphous grounds, with advantages, he believed, over the Rorschach blots. The more amorphous or unstructured the ground, the greater the sensitivity of the procedure which however loses in precision as in most instruments. Hence

16. *Cf.* Dunbar, H. F. *Emotions and Bodily Changes.* New York: Columbia Univ. Press, 1938. (2nd ed.) An individual may express his feelings, otherwise blocked, in illness or physiological dysfunctions.
17. *Cf.* Horowitz, Ruth, & Murphy, Lois B. Projective methods in the psychological study of children. *J. Exper. Educ.*, 1938, 7, 133–140, for further discussion of different procedures and their use.

the Rorschach may be less sensitive than *Cloud Pictures* or clay but more precise and definite. Both the ink blots and the *Cloud Pictures* offer a ground upon which the subject must impose or project whatever configural patterns he "sees" therein, because he can see only what he personally looks for or "perceives" in that ground. The separate details of the responses, however, are significant only in the context of the total response to each blot and are meaningful only for each subject. This does not imply an absence of recurrent forms and meanings from one subject to another but rather that the same letters of the conventionalized alphabet may recur in many different words and the same words may be utilized in a great variety of sentences to convey an extraordinary diversity of statements, which must be understood within the context in which they occur and with reference to the particular speaker who is using them on that occasion.[18]

Play techniques are being increasingly employed for clinical diagnosis and for investigation of the personality development of children. As materials almost any kind of toy or plaything or plain wooden building blocks may be presented to the subject for free play or for performance of some designated action, such as building a house, sorting into groups, setting the stage for a play or otherwise organizing the play materials into some configuration which expresses for the subject an affectively significant pattern. In children, it must be remembered there are fewer disguises and defenses available to hide behind and there is less sophisticated awareness of how much is being revealed in play. The investigator does not set a task and rate the performance in terms of skill or other scale of achievement, since the intention is to elicit the subject's way of "organizing his life space" in whatever manner he finds appropriate. Hence every performance is significant, apart from the excellence of the play construction or activity, and is to be interpreted, rather than rated, for its revelation of how the subject sees and feels his life situations that are portrayed in the play constructions and sequences. The question of how to decide whether a particular activity is or is not meaningful is to be decided, not by its frequency or so-called objective criteria, but by the total play configuration of that particular subject who, it is assumed, performs that particular action or uses that specific construction, as an expression of his way of seeing and feeling and reacting to life, i.e., of his personality. But the degree of relevance is to be found in the context, in what precedes and what follows and in the intensity of feelings expressed. If these criteria appear tenuous and subjective and lacking in credibility, then objections may be made to the use of various methods for

18. *Cf.* Since each personality must use socially prescribed cultural patterns for his conduct and communications he will exhibit many recurrent uniformities but these are significant only for revealing the patterns or organizations or configurations which the personality uses to structuralize his life space.

discovering the composition and structure of an unknown substance through which light, electric current, or radiations are passed, to give patterned arrangements or a spectrum photograph in which the position, number, intensity of lines and the coarse and fine structure indicate what the unknown substance is composed of, how organized internally, and so on. Personality studies by projective methods have not, of course, been as extensively studied nor have the patterns used by subjects been so well explored. The important point is that the way is open to the development of something similar to spectroscopic and diffraction methods for investigation of personality.

If the foregoing appears far-fetched it may be recalled that the lines on the spectroscopic plate were established, not by statistical procedures, but by experimental procedures through which a known chemically tested substance was spectroscopically tested so that its identifying line could be precisely located and thereafter confidently named. In much the same fashion it is being established that a child who is known to be undergoing an affective experience will express that feeling in a play configuration that can be so recognized. Thus, children who have lost a beloved parent or nurse, who have been made anxious by toilet training, are insecure and hostile because of sibling rivalry, etc., will exhibit those feelings in their play configurations. Experimentally produced personality disturbances can be established and their severity investigated by subsequent play forms and expressions. Moreover, the insights derived from play configurations yield interpretations that are not only therapeutically effective but often predictive of what a child will show in the near future.

Not only play toys and objects are utilized but also various plastic amorphous materials such as modeling clay, flour and water, mud and similar substances of a consistency that permits the subject to handle freely and manipulate into various objects. In these play situations the subject often finds a catharsis, expressing affects that might otherwise be repressed or disguised, or symbolically releasing resentments and hostility that have been long overlaid by conventionally good conduct. Dolls, capable of being dismembered, can be used to evoke repressed hostility and aggression against parents and siblings. Dramatic stage play with toy figures and settings have also provided occasions in which a subject not only revealed his personality difficulties but also worked out many of his emotional problems. Clay figures are modeled by child patients in which they express many of their acute anxieties and distortions. Reference should be made to eidetic imagery, which, as Walther Jaensch in his constitutional studies has shown, indicates one aspect of the subject's way of expressing what enters into his personality make-up or way of organizing his life space.

Artistic media offer another series of rich opportunities for projective methods in studying personality. Finger-painting has given many insights into child personality make-up and perplexities. Painting has been found very fruitful for study of personality make-up and emotional disturbances. Other clinical uses of painting have been reported that indicate the way paintings and drawings supplement the clinician's interviews and evoke responses that are exceedingly revealing, often more so than the verbal responses. Puppet shows elicit responses from child patients that are both diagnostic and therapeutic because the intensity of the dramatic experience arouses the child to a vehement expression of his feelings toward authority and toward parents and of his repressed desires to hurt others. Roles have been assigned to individuals who are then asked to act out those roles impromptu, thereby revealing how tangled and repressed his or her feelings are and how release of pent-up emotion leads to insight into one's personality difficulties. Dramatic teachers are finding clues to personality in the way individuals portray the characters assigned them in a play. Music offers similar and often more potent possibilities for expression of affects that are revealing of the personality. It is interesting to note that as psychotherapy proceeds to free the patient, his art expressions, painting, modeling, music, and dramatic rendition become freer and more integrated.

As the foregoing indicates, the individual rarely has any understanding of himself or awareness of what his activities signify. In the Thematic Perception methods this unawareness offers an opportunity to elicit highly significant projections from subjects who are asked to write or tell stories about a series of pictures showing individuals with whom they can identify themselves and others of immediate personal concern. Likewise the subjects project many aspects of their personality in the completion of stories and of sentences, in making up analogies, sorting out and grouping objects, such as toys, and similar procedures in which the subject reveals "what he cannot or will not say."

Expressive movements, especially handwriting, offer another approach to the understanding of the personality who reveals so much of his characteristic way of viewing life in his habitual gestures and motor patterns, facial expressions, posture and gait. These leads to the study of personality have been rejected by many psychologists because they do not meet psychometric requirements for validity and reliability, but they are being employed in association with clinical and other studies of personality where they are finding increasing validation in the consistency of results for the same subject when independently assayed by each of these procedures. In this group of methods should be included observations on tics of all kinds and dancing as indications of tension, anxiety or other partially repressed feelings.

If we will face the problem of personality, in its full complexity, as an active dynamic process to be studied as a *process* rather than as entity or aggregate of traits, factors, or as a static organization, then these projective methods offer many advantages for obtaining data on the process of organizing experience which is peculiar to each personality and has a life career. Moreover, the projective methods offer possibilities for utilizing the available insights into personality which the prevailing quantitative procedures seem deliberately to reject.

Here again it may be re-emphasized that the study of personality is not a task of measuring separate variables on a large group of individuals at one moment in their lives and then seeking, by statistical methods, to measure correlations, nor is it a problem of teasing out and establishing the quantitative value of several factors.[19] Rather the task calls for the application of a multiplicity of methods and procedures which will reveal the many facets of the personality and show how the individual "structuralizes his life space" or organizes experience to meet his personal needs in various media. If it appears that the subject projects similar *patterns* or *configurations* upon widely different materials and reveals in his life history the sequence of experiences that make those projections psychologically meaningful for his personality, then the procedures may be judged sufficiently valid to warrant further experimentation and refinement. In undertaking such explorations the experimenter and clinicians may find reassurance and support in the realization that they are utilizing concepts and methods that are receiving increasing recognition and approval in scientific work that is today proving most fruitful.

19. *Cf.* Jersild, A. T., & Fite, Mary D. The influence of nursery school experience on children's social adjustments. *Child Devel. Monog.*, No. 25, 1939. See especially page 102.

REFERENCES

1. ABEL, THEODORA M. Free designs of limited scope as a personality index. *Charac. & Person.*, 1938, 7, 50–62.

2. ACKERMAN, N. W., with the technical assistance of VIRGINIA REHKOPF. Constructive and destructive tendencies in children. *Amer. J. Orthopsychiat.*, 1937, 7, 301–319.

3. ALLPORT, G. W., & VERNON, P. E. *Studies in Expressive Movement.* New York: Macmillan, 1933. P. 269.

4. ANDERSON, H. H. Domination and integration in the social behavior of young children in an experimental play situation. *Genet. Psychol. Monog.*, 1937, 19, 343–408.

5. BARKER, R. G. The effect of frustration upon cognitive ability. *Charac. & Person.*, 1938, 7, 145–150.

6. BARKER, R. G., DEMBO, T., & LEWIN, K. Experiments in frustration and regression studies in topological and vector psychology. *Iowa Child Wel. Res. St. Monog.*, 1939.

7. BECK, S. J. Autism in Rorschach scoring: A feeling comment. *Charac. & Person.* (News and Notes), 1936, 5, 83–85.

8. ———. Psychological processes in Rorschach findings. *J. Abn. & Soc. Psychol.*, 1937, 31, 482–488.

9. ———. Introduction to the Rorschach method. *Amer. Orthopsychiat. Assoc. Monog.*, No. 1, 1937.

10. ———. Personality structure in schizophrenia. *Nerv. & Ment. Dis. Monog.*, 1938, No. 63, p. 88.

11. BENDER, LAURETTA, & WOLTMANN, A. The use of puppet shows as a psychotherapeutic method for behavior problems in children. *Amer. J. Orthopsychiat.*, 1936, 6, 341–354.

12. BENDER, LAURETTA, KEISER, S., & SCHILDER, P. Studies in aggressiveness. *Genet. Psychol. Monog.*, 1936, 18, 357–564.

13. BENDER, LAURETTA, & SCHILDER, P. Form as a principle in the play of children. *J. Genet. Psychol.*, 1936, 49, 254–261.

14. BENDER, LAURETTA, & WOLTMANN, A. Puppetry as a psychotherapeutic measure with problem children. *Monthly Bull., N.Y. State Assoc. Occup. Therap.*, 1937, 7, 1–7.

15. BENDER, LAURETTA. Art and therapy in the mental disturbances of children. *J. Nerv. & Ment. Dis.*, 1937, 86, 229–238.

16. ———. Group activities on a children's ward as methods of psychotherapy. *Amer. J. Psychiat.*, 1937, 93, 1151–1173.

17. BENDER, LAURETTA, & WOLTMANN, A. The use of plastic material as a psychiatric approach to emotional problems in children. *Amer. J. Orthopsychiat.*, 1937, 7, 283–300.

18. BENDER, LAURETTA. A visual motor gestalt test and its clinical use. *Amer. Orthopsychiat. Assoc. Monog.*, 1938, No. 3, p. 176.

19. BOOTH, G. C. Personality and chronic arthritis. *J. Nerv. & Ment. Dis.*, 1937, 85, 637–662.

20. ———. The use of graphology in medicine. *J. Nerv. & Ment. Dis.*, 1937, 86, 674–679.

21. ———. Objective techniques in personality testing. *Arch. Neur. & Psychiat.*, 1939.

22. CAMERON, N. Individual and social factors in the development of graphic symbolization. *J. of Psychol.*, 1938, 5, 165–183.

23. ———. Functional immaturity in the symbolization of scientifically trained adults. *J. of Psychol.*, 1938, 6, 161–175.

24. ———. Reasoning, regression, and communication in schizophrenics. *Psychol. Monog.*, 1938, 50, 1–34.

25. ———. Deterioration and regression in schizophrenic thinking. *J. Abn. &
Soc. Psychol.,* 1939, *34,* 265–270.

26. CONN, J. H. A psychiatric study of car sickness in children. *Amer. J. Orthopsychiat.,* 1938, *8,* 130–141.

27. CURRAN, F. F. The drama as a therapeutic measure in adolescents. *Amer. J.
Orthopsychiat.,* 1939, *9,* 215–231.

28. DESPERT, J. L., & POTTER, H. W. The story, a form of directed phantasy. *Psychiat.
Quart.,* 1936, *10,* 619–638.

29. ERIKSON, E. H. Configurations in play: Clinical notes. *Psychoanal. Quart.,* 1937,
6, 139–214.

30. FITE, MARY D. Aggressive behavior in young children and children's attitudes
toward aggression. *Genet. Psychol. Monog.,* 1939.

31. GERARD, MARGARET W. Case for discussion at the 1938 symposium. *Amer. J.
Orthopsychiat.,* 1938, *8,* 1–8.

32. GITELSON, M. (Chairman), *et al.* Section on "play therapy," 1938. *Amer. J.
Orthopsychiat.,* 1938, *8,* 499–524.

33. GITELSON, M. Clinical experience with play therapy. *Amer. J. Orthopsychiat.,*
1938, *8,* 466–478.

34. GRIFFITHS, R. *Imagination in Young Children.* London: Kegan Paul, 1936.

35. HANFMANN, EUGENIA. Social structure of a group of kindergarten children.
Amer. J. Orthopsychiat., 1935, *5,* 407–410.

36. HANFMANN, EUGENIA, & KASANIN, J. A method for the study of concept formation. *J. of Psychol.,* 1937 *3,* 521–540.

37. ———. Disturbances in concept formation in schizophrenia. *Arch. Neur. &
Psychiat.,* 1938, *40,* 1276–1282.

38. HANFMANN, EUGENIA. Analysis of the thinking disorder in a case of schizophrenia. *Arch. Neur. & Psychiat.,* 1939, *41,* 568–579.

39. HERTZ, MARGUERITE R. The method of administration of the Rorschach ink blot
test. *Child Devel.,* 1936, *7,* 237–254.

40. HERTZ, MARGUERITE R., & RUBENSTEIN, B. B. A comparison of three "blind" Rorschach analyses. *Amer. J. Orthopsychiat.,* 1939, *9,* 295–314.

41. HOLMER, P. The use of the play situation as an aid to diagnosis. *American J.
Orthopsychiat.,* 1937, *7,* 523–531.

42. HOROWITZ, RUTH E., & MURPHY, LOIS B. Projective methods in the psychological
study of children. *J. Exper. Educ.,* 1938, *7,* 133–140.

43. HOROWITZ, RUTH E. Racial aspects of self-identification in nursery school children.
J. of Psychol., 1939, *7,* 91–99.

44. HUNTER, MARY. The practical value of the Rorschach test in a psychological
clinic. *Amer. J. Orthopsychiat.,* 1939, *9,* 287–294.

45. JAENSCH, E. R. *Eidetic Imagery and Typological Methods of Investigation.* New
York: Harcourt, Brace, 1930.

46. KASANIN, J., & HANFMANN, EUGENIA. An experimental study of concept formation in schizophrenia: I. Quantitative analysis of the results. *Amer. J.
Psychiat.,* 1938, *95,* 35–48.

47. KELLEY, D. M., & KLOPFER, B. Application of the Rorschach method to research in schizophrenia. *Rorschach Res. Exch.,* 1939, *3,* 55–66.

48. KLOPFER, B. *Rorschach Research Exchange.* September, 1936, to date.

49. KLÜVER, H. The Eidetic Child, in *Handbook of Child Psychology.* Worcester: Clark Univ. Press, 1931.

50. LEVY, D. M. Use of play technique as experimental procedure. *Amer. J. Orthopsychiat.,* 1933, *3,* 266–277.

51. ———. Hostility patterns in sibling rivalry experiments. *Amer. J. Orthopsychiat.,* 1936, *6,* 183–257.

52. ———. "Release therapy" in young children. *Psychiatry,* 1938, *1,* 387–390.

53. LEVY, J. The use of art techniques in treatment of children's behavior problems. *Proc. Amer. Assoc. Ment. Def.,* 1934, *58,* 258–260.

54. ———. The active use of phantasy in treatment of children's behavior problems. (Unpublished paper presented at a meeting of the American Psychiatric Association.)

55. LEWIN, K. Environmental forces. *Handbook of Child Psychology.* Worchester: Clark Univ. Press, 1933.

56. ———. *A Dynamic Theory of Personality.* New York: McGraw-Hill, 1935. Pp. 286.

57. ———. *Principles of Topological Psychology.* New York: McGraw-Hill, 1936. Pp. 231.

58. ———. Psychoanalysis and topological psychology. *Bull. Menninger Clin.,* 1937, *1,* 202–211.

59. LISS, E. Play techniques in child analysis. *Amer. J. Orthopsychiat.,* 1936, *6,* 17–22.

60. ———. The graphic arts. *Amer. J. Orthopsychiat.,* 1938, *8,* 95–99.

61. LOWENFELD, V. *The Nature of Creative Activity.* London: Kegan Paul, 1938.

62. MASSERMAN, J. H., & BALKEN, EVA R. The clinical application of phantasy studies. *J. of Psychol.,* 1938, *6,* 81–88.

63. MORENO, J. L. Who shall survive? *Nerv. & Ment. Dis. Monog.,* 1934, No. 58.

64. MORENO, J. L., & JENNINGS, H. Spontaneity training, a method of personality development. *Sociomet. Rev.,* 1936.

65. MORENO, J. L. Psychodramatic shock therapy—A sociometric approach to the problem of mental disorders. *Sociometry,* 1939, *2,* 1–30.

66. ———. Creativity and cultural conserves—with special reference to musical expression. *Sociometry,* 1939, *2,* 1–36.

67. MORGAN, CHRISTINE D., & MURRAY, H. A. Method for investigating fantasies—the thematic apperception test. *Arch. Neur. & Psychiat.,* 1935, *34,* 289–306.

68. MURPHY, LOIS B. *Social Behavior and Child Personality. An Exploratory Study of Some Roots of Sympathy.* New York: Columbia Univ. Press, 1937. P. 325.

69. MURRAY, H. A., *et al.* Papers in *J. Soc. Psychol.,* 1933, *4; J. Abn. & Soc. Psychol.,* 1934, *28; J. of Psychol.,* 1937, *3,* 27–42.

70. MURRAY, H. A. Techniques for a systematic investigation of fantasy. *J. of Psychol.,* 1937, *3,* 115–143.

71. MURRAY, H. A., *et al. Explorations in Personality.* New York: Oxford Univ. Press, 1938.

72. NEWMAN, S., & MATHER, VERA G. Analysis of spoken language of patients with affective disorders. *Amer. J. Psychiat.,* 1938, *94,* 913–942.

73. NEWMAN, S. Personal symbolism in language patterns. *Psychiatry,* 1939, *2,* 177–184.

74. PIOTROWSKI, Z. The methodological aspects of the Rorschach personality method. *Kwart. Psychol.,* at Poznan, 1937, *9,* 29.

75. ———. The *M, FM,* and *m* responses as indicators of changes in personality. *Rorschach Res. Exch.,* 1937, *1,* 148–156.

76. PLANT, J. S. Personality and the culture pattern. *J. Soc. Philos.,* 1938, *3,* 126–142.

77. PORTER, E. L. H. Factors in the fluctuation of fifteen ambiguous phenomena. *Psychol. Rec.,* 1937, *2,* 231–253.

78. ROSENZWEIG, S. & SHAKOW, D. Play technique in schizophrenia and other psychoses: I. Rationale; II. An experimental study of schizophrenic constructions with play materials. *Amer. J. Orthopsychiat.,* 1937, *7,* 32–35, 36–47.

79. SAPIR, E. The emergence of the concept of personality in a study of culture. *J. Soc. Psychol.,* 1934, *5,* 408–415.

80. SENDER, SADIE, & KLOPFER, B. Application of the Rorschach test to child behavior problems as facilitated by a refinement of the scoring method. *Rorschach Res. Exch.,* 1936. Issue No. 1, 1–17.

81. SHAW, R. F. *Finger Painting.* Boston: Little Brown, 1934. P. 232.

82. STEIN-LEWINSON, THEA. An introduction to the graphology of Ludwig Klages. *Charac. & Person.,* 1933, *6,* 163–177.

83. TROUP, EVELYN. A comparative study by means of the Rorschach method of personality development in twenty pairs of identical twins. *Genet. Psychol. Monog.,* 1938, *20,* 465–556.

84. VAUGHN, J., & KRUG, OTHILDA. The analytic character of the Rorschach ink blot test. *Amer. J. Orthopsychiat.,* 1938, *8,* 220–229.

85. WERNER, H. William Stern's personalistics and psychology of personality. *Charac. & Person.,* 1938, *7,* 109–125.

Helen Sargent

PROJECTIVE METHODS

Their Origins, Theory, and Application

in Personality Research

PROJECTIVE METHODS were in use prior to 1939, but were not designated as such until after that date which marks the introduction of the term in an article by L. K. Frank (5). Since then, the concept has been specifically employed in an increasing number of titles in the *Psychological Abstracts,* and has become common usage in the literature of personality research. A lively experimental attack utilizing the projective approach has grown up in child psychology, psychopathology, and personality.

Fairly representative of definitions usually offered is the following:

> A projective method for the study of personality involves the presentation of a stimulus situation designed or chosen because it will mean to the subject not what the experimenter has arbitrarily decided it should mean (as in most psychological experiments using standardized stimuli in order to be "objective") but rather whatever it must mean to the personality who gives it, or imposes upon it, his private, idiosyncratic meaning and organization (5, p. 403).

Reprinted from *Psychol. Bull.,* 1945, *42,* 257–293 by permission of the American Psychological Association and the estate of the author.

These methods which Frank described, and for which he furnished a rationale as well as a name, are in no sense a new discovery, although their current popularity is in part derived from a research atmosphere peculiarly suited to their rapid growth in the past five years. The very wording of the above definition implies a controversy: it presents projective techniques not only as an addition to our present stock of instruments; it also implies that they are set up in opposition to something. In order to understand either their promise, or the obstacles which stand in the way of their unqualified welcome in scientific circles, it will be necessary to examine their historical roots as well as the contemporary theoretical climate in which they flourish; to survey the problems to which they have been applied and the results obtained; and to study certain methodological difficulties which beset them. Furthermore, it will be necessary to hold a patient hearing of somewhat repetitive controversial views.

Background

The developing family of projective methods might be regarded as the legitimate children of two parents: a brilliant and daring mother, psychiatry, and an equally intelligent but more conservative father, academic psychology. The five-year-old offspring partake of the characteristics of both forebears; they have a promising future, but have not yet overcome insecurity engendered by the fact that each parent is inclined to berate them for faults presumably inherited from the other.

Putting metaphor aside, we may discern in the context which surrounds projective techniques, three major theoretical trends which have contributed to a general point of view, and four lines of research more or less closely related to projective experimentation. The most important theoretical influences include psychoanalysis, *global* theory, and certain developments in twentieth-century general science. Relevant research includes studies in imagination and phantasy, the word-association method, investigations of language, and the development of methods for the use and interpretation of *personal documents*.

THEORETICAL CLIMATE

1. Psychoanalysis. The term *projection* was first used by Freud to describe one of the unconscious minor *mechanisms* of conflict solution (230). The ego, unable to accept in itself certain thoughts, wishes, or characteristics, attributes these to environmental objects or to persons (222, p. 75). Sears, quoting a somewhat elaborate definition by Healy, Bronner and Bowers, which expresses a similar connotation, prefers to withdraw the term from its *metapsychological setting* and to define it as follows:

A wish, attitude, or habit-hierarchy which is not compatible with other attitudes or habits of an individual may be attributed by that individual to other persons rather than to himself, providing he lacks insight into the fact that he himself possesses the trait in question. This process of attribution is unconscious, i.e., the subject does not give any verbal evidence that he knows his perception is false (19, p. 561).

Sears has also called attention to a distinction between the above use of the term projection as applied to the basic paranoid mechanism, and its usage with reference to projective techniques. He states that "in the latter case the implication is that the motivational and organizational properties of a personality influence the perceptual and judgmental processes" (262, p. 121). Important as it is to differentiate these two connotations, there appears to be reason rather than confusion in the dual application of the word. The alleged defensive reactions of the ego are subject to observation in the selective effect upon perception, and in diverse expressive responses; conversely the motivations which are assumed to be operative are subject to explanation in terms of ego defense. It may be said that the noun *projection* describes one type of defense, and that the adjective *projective* applies more broadly to the observable effects of this and other psychic processes, and to the methods used to elicit and study them.

That the mechanism of projection is one of the most readily understood and accepted of any in the Freudian scheme is demonstrated by its easy translation into the idiom of a child, or of a schizophrenic. Feigenbaum reports that a little girl to whom a paranoid acquaintance had been described as "hating people" replied promptly: "I know why he hates them! It's like when Mother wants to go to the toilet, she asks me if I have to" (4, p. 305). A schizophrenic, one of Balken's subjects, remarked: "If I refuse to recognize it, it is not for me" (144, p. 249). The fields of art and literature also provide an almost unexplored territory for the study of projection as a psychological phenomenon. In fiction and in poetry it is possible to trace not only the projections of the writer, but to discover subtle techniques used by authors (and by musicians and artists as well) to provide a medium in which others may project and enjoy release. Dean Addison Hibbard of Northwestern University has for a number of years assigned items from the personal columns in English newspapers to students as a starting point for compositions, and reports that he has regularly noted the inclusion of personally significant material.

The debt of projective theory is not confined to the term, nor to the description of mechanism. It was Freud who first made systematic inquiry into hidden motivations and into the genetic determinants of mental life, and it is exactly these that the projective methods seek to uncover. The psychoanalytic methods for interpreting behavior, both verbal and motor, in terms of their symbolic rather than their obvious meaning; Freud's emphasis upon the unconscious; and the distinctions he drew between latent and manifest dream content, have had a profound influence upon the significance attached to projective productions. White, writing of Freud's method of dream interpretation, describes the dream as "a natural projective method capable of revealing much valuable information if only the signs can be directly read" (23, p. 218). Play techniques, although used by analysts only as secondary tools, had their origin in orthodox child psychoanalysis (75, 82, 99). Play methods today are variously used and interpreted, but many analysts still claim them as their own special prerogative (79).

In our times, the indebtedness to psychoanalysis is becoming somewhat more even. Psychiatrists, including analysts and psychoanalytically oriented psychologists, are going beyond the traditional techniques of free association and dream interpretation, and are turning with increasing interest to the illuminating and time-saving data which the projective methods appear able to provide (155, 156).

2. *"Global" theory.* The period in which projective methods have developed is pervaded by revolt against what has been termed the *atomistic* tradition of the early experimental psychology, especially behaviorism, represented in the personality field today by investigations concerned with trait lists, rating scales, psychographs and other *objective* methods. Tests such as the Bernreuter and other personality inventories purporting to measure such traits as introversion-extraversion, dominance-submission, neuroticism and the like, imply what Allport has called *omnibus* or *sumtotal* definitions of personality (210, p. 43).

Atomistic research is alleged to begin with the attempt to analyze psychological phenomena into elements. Opposed to this viewpoint is one which has been variously termed *global, holistic, organismic,* or *field theoretical.* Lewin's topological concepts (249), Allport's version of William Stern's *personalistic psychology* (210), Murray's adaptation of organismic theory (14), and the dynamic approach recently advocated by Maslow (253), differ somewhat in conceptualization, but unite in stressing the importance of totality and wholeness. Murray, whose theory of personality leans heavily upon the organismic biological viewpoint, quotes the following from E. S. Russell:

> The organism is from the beginning a whole, from which the parts are derived by self-differentiation. The whole and its parts are mutually related; the whole being as essential to an understanding of the parts as the parts are to an understanding of the whole (14, pp. 38–39).

Murray and Maslow have both emphasized a rather fundamental division among psychologists, not only in the holistic-analytic controversy, but over the entire range of theory construction. Maslow, who describes his view as "holistic rather than atomistic, functional rather than taxonomic, dynamic rather than static, dynamic rather than causal, purposive rather than simple mechanical," points out that writers who "think dynamically" are also inclined to think "holistically rather than atomistically, purposively rather than mechanically, and so on" (253, p. 520).

The emphasis which Maslow places upon the word *dynamic* demands a brief digression at this point, since the word has been widely and often indiscriminately used, and hence has been subject to criticism. The term is, apparently, as essential in the vocabulary of the psychologist who regards interactions between parts of a system as more important than the parts themselves, and who needs to describe the process of complex change *per se,* rather than a succession of static frames run together in a moving picture. To the *dynamic* psychologist, the *moving* picture cannot be described in terms of the sum of cross-sectional views. The accusation of vagueness is, perhaps, inevitable since the term refers to phenomena which themselves lack precision. Fairly representative of current usage is the following definition:

> Since psychology deals only with motion—processes occurring in time—none of its proper formulations can be static. They all must be dynamic in the larger meaning of this term. Within recent years, *dynamic* has come to be used in a special sense: to designate a psychology which accepts as prevailingly fundamental the goal directed (adaptive) character of behavior, and attempts to discover and formulate the internal as well as the external factors which determine it (14, p. 36).

Murray, like Maslow, attempts to brand psychological sheep and goats by setting the *peripheralists* off against the *centralists*. Peripheralists, he states, are attracted to observable things and quantities; they prefer to confine themselves to measurable facts. For them the data of psychology are environmental objects and physiologically responding organisms: bodily movements, verbal successions, physiological changes.

If the peripheralists ever do indulge in speculation about what goes on within the brain, they usually fall back upon the conceptual scheme which has been found efficient in dealing with simpler partial functions. . . . Men of this stamp who study people usually come out with a list of common action patterns and expressive movements, though occasionally they go further and include social traits and interests (14, p. 7).

The centralists, on the contrary, are attracted to subjective facts, such as feelings, desires, and intentions. Their terminology is subjectively derived and "they do not hesitate to use such terms as wishes, emotions, and ideas" (14, pp. 8 ff.). They are conceptualists rather than positivists.

It may be that we encounter here an example of what Seashore has called the *all-or-none fallacy* in the acceptance or rejection of a given viewpoint (263, p. 605). On the other hand, these differences reflect an age-old conflict between empiricism and rationalism, positivism and phenomenology, which has been felt in the physical sciences as well as in psychology. Whether or not this is a pseudo-issue or a real one, the hope for early reconciliation is not bright, as long as the *globalist* yawns in boredom over the statistics of the *specifist,* and the latter sneers at the constructs of the former. We should, perhaps, cultivate tolerance toward the extremists in both camps and recognize the stimulus value of controversy. We can also admit the truth of Murray's comment that "personology is still in diapers, enjoying random movements" (14, p. 6), and hope that as the infant matures his activity will become better channelized.

The special relevance of the global, conceptual approach to projective methods is clarified by an example which Maslow has used, stressing the point that his attack is not upon science itself but upon *one* possible view of science, which he calls the *reductive effort,* i.e., the attempt to analyze psychological phenomena into fundamental variables without taking account of unity and interaction.

If we take an example, such as blushing or trembling or stammering, it is easy to see that we may study this behavior in two different ways. On the one hand we may study it as if it were an isolated, discrete phenomenon, self-contained and understandable in itself. On the other, we may study it as one expression of the whole organism, attempting to understand it in its richness of inter-relationships with the organism and with other expressions of the organism. This distinction can be made clearer if we make the analogy with the two possible ways of studying an organ like the stomach. (1) It can be cut out of the cadaver and laid on the dissecting table, or (2) it can be studied *in situ* in the living functioning organism (253, p. 516).

Projective methods, it is claimed, are one means by which aspects of personality may be studied without distortion. Harrison suggests that "the global approach at least respects the complexity of personality problems and seeks some elementary understanding before bursting into figures" (154, p. 50).

Before leaving the discussion of holistic viewpoints, brief notice should be taken of the fact that, at least in psychology, this approach had its inception in *Gestalt* theory, which began with Wertheimer's well-known studies in perception about 1910. Aside from its indirect theoretical influence, the *Gestalt* experiments in the patterning of perceptual experience have a more direct bearing on projective techniques. If personality is defined as "a dynamic process of organizing experience" (5), the manner in which a person perceives is quite as important as how he behaves or what he says. This has led to great interest in the selective response of individuals to ink blots or nonsense sounds, and in the formal structures imposed upon expressive mediums. Tests such as the Rorschach (102–142), Murray's Thematic Apperception Test (TAT, 143–173), or Shakow's Tautophone (174–178), depend on selective attention and perceptual organization; hence the determinants of response can be studied as well as the response itself. Concern with these determinants and with the way in which they are patterned by subjects is reflected in the formal scoring categories of the Rorschach, in certain approaches to TAT analysis (145, 160, 173), in Benders' analysis of form qualities in children's games and drawings (29, 64), in Kerr's and Wertham's analyses of form elements in the Lowenfeld mosaic test (193, 204), and in Erikson's use of spatial variables in describing the play of children (72, 73, 74). It should be emphasized that, although the formal approach to scoring is no more exclusively dependent upon specific *Gestalt* doctrine than content analysis is upon orthodox Freudian dogma, a close relationship exists.

3. Support from general science. L. K. Frank, approaching the problems of personality from the standpoint of a student of psychology as one among other sciences, finds much to support the newer concepts in personality research and the methods based upon them. His important article, quoted at the beginning of this review, ought to be read in its entirety for its abundant illustration from fields in which the busy psychological specialist has little time to become oriented.

With reference to the controversy discussed in the preceding section, Frank shows that the older sciences, including physics, have been forced to develop new approaches demanded by a changing view of the space-time universe, but have been able to digest revisions of theory with less heartburn than psychology has experienced.

> Theoretical physics has adjusted itself to the conception of a universe that has statistical regularity and order, and individual disorder, in which the laws of aggregates are not observable in the activity of the individual making up these aggregates. Thus, quantum physics and statistical mechanics and many other similar contrasts are accepted without anxiety about scientific respectability. The discrete individual event can be and is regarded as an individual to whom direct methods and measurements have only a limited applicability. We can therefore acknowledge an interest in the individual as a scientific problem and find some sanction for such an interest (5, p. 395).

Frank compares our factor analyzing and trait isolating techniques to the analytic-destructive methods in nineteenth-century physics, which required the breakdown of the substance studied, and hence failed to reveal their true nature. For example, physical phenomena such as temperature and light, which were once studied in isolation, are now seen as transformations of energy variously manifested. In the indirect approaches to personality through a study of its projection in *neutral situations* or *unstructured fields,* Frank finds a parallel to the use of electric current or polarized light in determining the composition of substances through their effect upon these media. It is just such methods as these that have led modern physics to the discussion of processes *within the atom* and to an interest in the behavior of individual electric particles which are themselves not directly observable. Similarly, he holds that personality, which is not observable in essence, can be understood as an organizing process through its projection on the screen of a meaningless ink blot or a formless chunk of clay. If these criteria appear subjective and incredible, Frank points out that certain methods in physics are also open to criticism.

Personality studies by projective methods have not, of course, been as extensively used, nor have the patterns used by subjects been so well explored. The important point is that the way is open to the development of something similar to spectroscopic and diffraction methods (5, p. 406).

Better known in general psychology, and more influential outside the field of personality, is the physicist Bridgman, whose introduction of the "operational definition" has had a far-reaching influence on psychological thought (see Kantor's discussion, 244). For Bridgman, a concept must be defined in terms of the operations by which it was derived; for example, dimensions are defined in terms of meter sticks and time by clock readings (220). Frank's definition of personality as process, "a way of living and feeling," or "a manner of organizing and patterning the life situation" leads to an operational definition of personality as that which an individual does in situations described as projective.

If it appears that the subject projects similar patterns or configurations upon widely different materials and reveals in his life history the sequence of experiences which make those projections psychologically meaningful for his personality, then the procedures may be judged sufficiently valid to warrant further experimentation and refinement. In undertaking such exploration, the experimenter and clinician may find reassurance in the realization that they are utilizing concepts and methods that are receiving recognition and approval in scientific work that is today proving most fruitful (5, p. 409).

HISTORY OF RELATED RESEARCH

1. Studies in imagination and phantasy. In 1930, when the writer happened to undertake a paper on the subject of phantasy, very little experimental work had been done from the individual point of view. Empirical material was available in psychoanalytic case studies, but emphasis was placed upon the description of typical, *universal* phantasies, such as the *Oedipus phantasy* (247), the *phantasy of illegitimacy* (248), *phantasies of rebirth* (252), and a number of others (228, 230, 237, 259). Much space was devoted to the symbolism of phantasy and its relation to dreams and myths (230, 252), but although it was recognized that the personal meaning of day-dreams is less disguised than in dream content, and that the subject is more loath to disclose them (247), interest in techniques for eliciting such material had not developed. L. P. Clark, apparently, must be credited with the first attempt to stimulate phantasy, using it as an approach to narcissistic patients incapable of transfer (224).

The psychological literature, although it reflected the growing emphasis upon affective and conflict-solving aspects of imagination, was concerned with phantasy chiefly as one manifestation of thought; as a psychological process rather than as a key to individual mental life. Varendonck had produced an extended analysis of daydreams, based on an introspective examination of his own foreconscious activity (269), and a systematic developmental study of daydreaming had been published by Green (234). Lehrman had written several articles on the compensatory nature of normal and neurotic phantasy (247, 248); imaginary playmates had been studied as the projection of young children's needs and wishes (237); and Conklin, in one of the earliest attempts to test psychoanalytic theory by a psychological technique, had conducted a questionnaire study of the *foster child phantasy* as recalled by college students (225). Although the Rorschach test was nine years old, already in use in Europe, and arousing the interest of a small group of American workers, there were few references to it in the English literature.

If the individual approach had been neglected, an experimental attack on imagination as a mental function had not. Galton, among his many interests, began investigations of imagery in 1883 (231). Binet and Simon used ink blots in early tests (217), and this use was extended by American experimentalists including Whipple, Dearborn, and G. S. Hall. (See review of early work in Krugman, 128.) Although these studies were largely concerned with cognitive rather than emotional aspects of phantasy, they form one branch of the ancestry of present projective methods because of the materials and techniques suggested. The most recent experimental approach to developmental aspects of imagination and its relationship to cognitive thinking was published by M. D. Vernon in 1940 (260).

The earliest direct forebears of the best known and most widely used of modern projective methods (Rorschach and Thematic apperception) were Britain's investigation in 1907 of imagination by means of compositions written in response to pictures (221), and the use of ink blots by Bartlett, another English researcher, in 1916 (214). The latter, in his use of the blots, went beyond mere investigation of imagination, and speculated on differences in intelligence, background, vocational interests, and the like. Content was analyzed, and in many ways the handling of the materials bears striking similarity to the method which Rorschach later developed.

Hermann Rorschach, Swiss psychiatrist, first published his *Psychodiagnostik* in German in 1922 (135). As noted above, Rorschach was not the first to use ink blots, but he was the first to develop a workable method (a *shorthand* as Beck has called it) for handling the complex individual response pattern. Rorschach himself died shortly after the publication of his famous work, but a tremendous amount of research has followed. The test is widely used in clinical diagnosis (103, 104, 108, 124), has been introduced in the armed services for research and diagnostic purposes (112, 113), and has been applied to a variety of problems, including psychopathology (104, 124, 133), developmental psychology (122, 126, 127) and recently to vocational guidance (134), not to mention innumerable other problems of personality research. (For comprehensive reviews and bibliographies, see references 116 and 128.)

Historical milestones in the progress of Rorschach research in this country have been the publication in 1924 of the Rorschach-Oberholzer monograph in the *Journal of Nervous and Mental Diseases* (136); Vernon's article in 1933 which called attention to the success of the test in Europe (138); the publication of Beck's *Introduction to the Rorschach Method* (103) in 1937 (the first systematic guide to administration, scoring, and interpretation); and the founding of the Rorschach Institute in 1939, with Klopfer as its guiding spirit and the *Rorschach Research Exchange* (established in 1936) as its medium of communication. In 1942, two books appeared almost simultaneously, one by Klopfer and Kelly (125), and a somewhat overpopularized presentation by Bochner and Halpern (108). At the time of this writing a new book by Beck is in press (106). There is probably no topic in psychology concerning which pro and con feeling runs higher, but despite the rash enthusiasm of converts and the blind opposition of skeptics, it has grown in use and reputation. White refers to the Rorschach as "a good example of that happy combination of genius and hard work which the study of personality so sorely needs" (23, p. 227).

Another important family of projective tests made its appearance in the American literature in 1935 with the publication of Morgan and Murray's paper on a method for investigating phantasy (157). Here the basic technique of the Thematic Apperception Test (TAT) was first described. The test consists of pictures which the subject is asked to use as illustrations for plots of his own creation. Certain investigators, Harrison among them (152), still prefer this earlier series of pictures to later modifications introduced in the set now provided by the Harvard Psychological Clinic (158).

Historically, as well as from the point of view of standardization, these two methods (the ink blot and the picture-story) are the aristocrats of a growing clan. Others will be mentioned later; at present we are concerned with beginnings and major trends. Among these was a five-year investigation of children's phantasy published by Griffith in England in 1935 (235). This study, which utilized imagery tests, ink blots, dreams and drawings of fifty normal children, led to the conclusion that phantasy is one of the ways in which children deal with their problems, and hence should be viewed not merely as withdrawal from reality but as an aspect of adjustment. This finding is important both for diagnosis and for therapy.

2. *Studies in word association.* It is a well known historical fact that interest in "the association of ideas in the mind" considerably antedates the beginnings of experimental psychology. The preoccupation of philosophers with this topic gave to the British Associationist school its name. The history of the movement leads from the speculations of John Locke down through the conditioning experiments of the modern behaviorists. Galton's work in 1879, Wundt's in 1880, and the introduction of association experiments into American laboratories by Cattell, Munsterberg, and Jastrow before 1890, marked the beginning of scientific interest in associational activity (226).

As in the studies of imagination, interest from the individual standpoint developed first in psychiatry, followed a parallel court, and finally gained enough momentum for recognition by psychology in general. It was not until the publication of Jung's first studies in word association in 1904, followed by the extensive experiments of Kent and Rosanoff in 1910 that the significance of association tests for personality study became impressive. Moreover, in the statements of early users of the method, we find concern with a problem which we have already seen as central in modern personality study: that is, the search for techniques which not only add to our knowledge of what Titchener called the "generalized, normal, adult, human mind," but also serve as an approach to the whole, unique personality. Bleuler, in his chapter in Eder's translation of *Studies in Word Association,* writes:

In the activity of association there is mirrored the whole psychical essence of the past and of the present with all their experiences and desires. It thus becomes an index of all the phychical processes which we have but to decipher in order to understand the complete man (218, p. 4).

Eder points out in his own introduction to Jung's *Studies* that the departure we owe to Jung is the application of the association method to unconscious mental processes, and the theory of unconscious complexes (243). Thus it represents the first effort to study the deeper strata of personality by an experimental technique. Again stressing the importance of studying psychic functions in context, Jung writes:

We must bear in mind that the association experiment cannot deal with a separated psychic function, for any psychic occurrence is never a thing in itself but is always the resultant of the entire psychological past (242, p. 225).

The work of Kent and Rosanoff which led to the compilation of frequency tables for the evaluation of common and unusual responses to word lists, and their efforts in the direction of standardizing both technique and interpretation (245, 260) were followed by numerous other studies by Hull and Lugoff (238), Woodrow and Lowell (274), and Woodworth and Wells (273), to cite only a few. An excellent bibliography of this material is furnished in H. R. Crossland's monograph published in 1929 (226). Of special interest in conjunction with projective methods is the fact that similar problems of standardization were encountered. Wells and Woodworth point out that standardization cannot easily be accomplished. They conclude, however, that such difficulties do not detract from the significance of association techniques.

Few procedures in experimental psychology have so richly rewarded their investigators with the possibilities of practical application as the association method. . . . Within the past seven years it has achieved and bids fair to hold indefinitely its place in the foremost rank among the methods of individual psychology (273, p. 73).

Although the method has been supplemented to some extent by more flexible techniques for tapping affective thought and phantasy, this estimate does not appear extreme even today.

3. *Studies in language.* Although the recent revival of interest in language analysis has a history of its own and is not strictly a branch of projective research, the two topics have several points in common. The first of these is an interest in the formal qualities of expression.

Language traditionally has been known as the "vehicle of thought" with the thought attracting far more attention than the vehicle. But there are those who object to the traditional distribution of attention on the ground that the vehicle as well as the freight should be given systematic scrutiny (261, p. 181).

Piaget's extensive investigations of children's language usage (257, 258) as an approach to the ontogenetic evolution of thought and socialization, have stimulated a great deal of interest in this area. Although his emphasis is upon establishing universal generalizations appropriate with reference to the progressive developmental stages of social and moral consciousness, rather than the clinical study of individuals, Piaget's recognition of the manner in which language forms (such as egocentric expressions and causal statements) may reflect the *inner* or emotional level of the speaker, bears a significant relationship to the theory underlying projective experimentation.

Southard, the psychiatrist, made an earlier application of formal language analysis to personality structure, pointing out a similarity between the use of the four grammatical moods (imperative, indicative, subjunctive, and optative) and the traditional temperaments: choleric, phlegmatic, melancholic, and sanguine (265). Grings has recently used grammatical classifications in analyzing responses to *Tautaphone* records (174), and Balken and Masserman have suggested others which have been applied in studying the TAT protocols of neurotic patients (145). Among the categories utilized, these authors revived Busemann's verb-adjective ratio and offered further evidence that high quotients are associated with anxiety and instability (144, 145). Johnson (239, 240) and Boder (261) have also used this and other formal counts in studies of written materials.

Research in language undertaken from this viewpoint is compatible with Frank's conception of personality structure. If a personality does, as he assumes, organize experience in terms of its "own private idiosyncratic world of meanings," it is logical to extend this assumption to include an individual's choice of language for self-expression as one aspect of personality. If this line of research is to prove truly productive, results are likely to come, as Sanford suggests, from a search for psychologically meaningful categories, in place of strict adherence to traditional grammatical modes of analysis (261, p. 831).

The recent interest in semantics is another expression of the conviction that no manifestation of personality is meaningless or outside the legitimate field of investigation (255, 272). Although the semanticists appear to insist on a peculiar reversal of what would seem the more acceptable conclusion, in assuming that bad semantic practices produce rather than result from maladjustment, their work has focused attention on possible relations between speech and personality (241,246). Since many of the projective methods elicit a verbal response expressed in a subject's own idiom, analysis of language forms has direct bearing on these problems.

4. The use of "personal documents." Gordon Allport has long been interested in what he terms *idiographic* as opposed to *nomothetic* research. The former is simply another name for research concerned with the single case, and the latter is used to describe normative science which seeks to establish uniformities. In the personal document Allport sees the ideal datum for the intensive study of individuals. His recent monograph (209) traces historically the use of such materials; discusses the possibility of quantitative treatment from the idiographic point of view; points to various studies which offer methods for judging reliability and validity, and cites a number of examples showing their usefulness. Since Allport's definition is applicable to any projective protocol, it is pertinent here:

The personal document may be defined as any self-revealing record that intentionally or unintentionally yields information regarding the structure, dynamics and functioning of the author's mental life (209, p. xii).

In defending the use of such data (which until recently have been considered worthless for scientific purposes because of their subjective nature) Allport discusses Clifford Beers's classic *A Mind That Found Itself* (216) and comments:

From the point of view of controls few documents are worse, yet from a pragmatic point of view we are warned that scientific safeguards will not in themselves save a poor document from the dust pile nor prevent a good one from contributing to the course of scientific progress (209, p. 11).

We are probably justified in the following inquiry: Suppose we study carefully Beers's document. Suppose, also, that this source of information is supplemented by other data which enable us to know the writer so well that we might predict his subsequent acts, and might even conceivably express relationships within his personality in numerical terms, as Baldwin did in a single case study using intra-individual statistics (212). What have we added to the science of personality? What does our knowledge of Beers contribute to our knowledge of others?

Allport would reply that this question is raised from the nomothetic point of view and is the result of thinking only in terms of generalization and comparison. His emphasis is expressly not upon the study of an individual case as a basis for generalization but, rather, as a legitimate scientific end in itself. Although Frank has rallied support from other disciplines for single case research and Lewin has argued its scientific respectability (249), on the basis of Allport's presentation it seems desirable to go beyond the rationalization "They do it, why can't I?" which imitators of physical science are prone to use in support of borrowed methods. Allport does not explicitly state the following answer, but it runs throughout his monograph by implication. It is necessary to assume that the final justification for the study of particular individuals lies neither in what we learn about personality *in general,* nor in what we learn about Beers, or any other unique individual. It is, rather, what we learn about *how* to know Beers that provides an approach to other case studies, thus leading in the direction of valid prediction. The predictions for which validity is sought are not predictions for other individuals on the basis of one, but for one individual based on sample observations designed to illuminate the dynamics of his own personality.

Although Frank and others grant that investigations based on such a philosophy are in the exploratory stage, preoccupation with the problem of controlling observation technique in such a way that the behavior studied is not distorted nor its unifying principles obscured distinguishes the newer approach. The special questions which arise in relation to control of experimental conditions are discussed later under *Techniques* and in the section on *Methodology*. It is sufficient to note here that single-case research, the use of personal documents, and the projective techniques all share in common the objective of discovering sound and reliable, and at the same time more penetrating and comprehensive methods for the study of personality.

Applications

There are several ways in which projective methods may be classified. They may be grouped according to:

1. the nature of the materials used for projection,
2. the functional use which the subject makes of the materials,
3. the techniques of presentation used by the experimenter, and
4. the purposes which govern the various applications.

The diversity of the methods themselves, and the variety of ends served can best be illustrated by considering the techniques under each of the above headings.

Materials. Ink blots, as we have seen, are the oldest and from many points of view the most versatile of the materials used. In the first place, they have a definite structure which makes it possible to classify responses in terms of specific determinants, an advantage which is lacking in more vague mediums, such as Stern's cloud pictures (202). At the same time, they are less meaningful in terms of personal experience than pictures, which may have rather definite associations. An additional advantage of the blots is that they elicit a response in which factors can be scored both for content and for the characteristics of its formal pattern.

Pictures, such as the TAT set (158), are about equal in popularity, and although they are subject to the limitations discussed above, they often provide a more readily intelligible sample of thought content for interpretation. Amen developed a series of pictures for use with children which included silhouettes and movable figures (143). Symonds has set up criteria for the selection of pictures suitable for use with adolescents (170). In the Szondi test, pictures are presented in pairs, the subject being asked to choose the one preferred or disliked (2, 200). Horowicz has made use of a similar technique with children (189, 190, 191).

Other materials include stories which the subject is asked to retell or complete (159, 183, 186, 187). Art media, such as clay modeling, finger painting, and drawing have been extensively used (25–47). Materials such as blocks

(57, 58) and mosaic patterns (193, 204) have also proved effective. Dramatic play, ranging from the puppet shows used by Bender, Woltmann, and others in group treatment (48, 52, 53, 56) to the psychodrama introduced by Moreno and his coworkers (49, 50, 54, 55) has been utilized. A unique device introduced by Skinner and adapted by Shakow, Grings, and Trussell, is the so-called *Tautaphone* or verbal summator (174–178). This instrument produces low vowel sounds which resemble speech. Subjects are asked to tell what the voice is saying, thus projecting their own preoccupations and meanings into an auditory medium. Pickford made use of nonsense syllables as projective materials (198) and Mira turned the simple motor task of drawing lines into a *myokinetic* technique for studying various aspects of personality (196). A recent attempt has been made by Sargent (201) to incorporate projective principles in a "paper and pencil" personality test for group use.

Functional uses. Frank (5) distinguishes:

1. *constitutive* methods, in which the subject imposes structure upon unstructured or partially structured materials;

2. *interpretive* methods, in which the subject is led to express or describe what a stimulus situation means to him;

3. *cathartic* methods used for the discharge of affect; and

4. *constructive* methods which call upon subjects to organize and arrange materials according to their own conceptions.

There is, of course, considerable overlap in this classification. Constitutive methods are exemplified by the various plastic media. The one criterion is that the material should be amorphous and easily adaptable for subjective expression. The interpretive-methods category is illustrated by ink blots and pictures. The attribution of meaning is not, however, confined to such stimuli. Whether the subject molds his own object or responds to one ready made, subjective interpretations direct or symbolic, verbalized or implied, are usually evident. Likewise, discharge of affect is thought to be present to some extent in all of the experimental situations. It is generally assumed that the subject sees in an ink blot what he *must* see in order to solve unconscious conflicts; in his story themes he voices his dilemmas and arrives at emotionally satisfying outcomes.

Ordinarily, the cathartic function is most evident in techniques which are suited to the release of aggressive impulses, as in certain play techniques. Despert's experiment involving the use of a knife (182) is an interesting attempt to provide both for the expression of aggression and for its eventual reorganization into more socialized activity: Children were allowed to use a knife to scrape cardboard into shreds (destruction); next they were given water with which to mix the materials into a plastic (gratification of the supposed impulse to *mess*); and finally they were encouraged to use this product for the construction of masks for use in play.

Finally, under constructive methods we may list blocks, mosaics, and building materials, as well as such highly specific objects as dolls, household articles, and *world toys* (181, 194) from which the subject constructs his *microcosm* (a term used by Erikson [74] to describe the miniature life scene depicted in the play model). Wertham has developed differential diagnostic criteria for the mosaic test, which he advocates as simpler and less time consuming than the Rorschach. Patterns are derived which in many respects parallel the Rorschach findings for various personality syndromes found in psychoses, neuroses, and organic conditions.

Techniques. Classification by techniques may be made both on the basis of differences in experimental control and in approach to interpretation. Control is introduced first according to the nature of the chosen stimulus. Degree of structure varies on a continuum from unstructured clay to definitely representative toys. Here a paradox is introduced. The more structured the material, the more limited is the subject's range of response. Hence, *subject* controls vary inversely with control over the essential *neutrality* of the situation itself, thus defeating the very purpose of control, which is to provide a standard by which response variations may be judged. As structure is increased, meaning also increases and there is less opportunity for personally significant differences from subject to subject to appear. Moreover, when differences do appear, the impossibility of estimating effects of experiential background furnishes an uncertain ground for comparison. The same is true when special techniques of presentation, such as paired comparisons, set questions and the like are introduced, since there is no way of equating their stimulus value for different individuals.

This has been called the *stimulus fallacy* by L. L. Thurstone. Frank, in his introduction to the Lerner-Murphy monograph (7), cites an early paper of Thurstone's in which he expresses the view that a subject creates his own stimulus to which he then responds in characteristic manner, hence a stimulus situation, no matter how well *controlled* does not always mean what the tester intends (268).

In projective experiments the fallacy is turned to account and the variegated qualities of a stimulus not only cease to be a disadvantage, but become of crucial importance. For example, when a subject sees sexual symbolism in an ink blot which others view as a landscape or as an animal form, or when Bender's children spontaneously produce such material in drawings (28), it is more logical to regard these productions as individually significant than the attitudes elicited by Levy's controlled and highly suggestive procedure. The latter presents the child with dolls and clay, the child is encouraged to make breasts for the mother, and the baby is put to nurse. This method is highly successful in drawing out sexual attitudes as well as hostility, but how much of this effect should be attributed to the technique, and how much to the child is a debatable question (83).

The range of procedural variations is illustrated by contrast between the standardized methods of Levy (83, 84), Ackerman (57, 58), the somewhat more flexible techniques of Conn (66, 67, 68), and Solomon (95, 96), and the almost complete freedom of action maintained in some free play situations (74).

Interpretive systems for handling responses range from the empirical analyses of Harrison (152, 153) to conceptualization based on psychoanalysis or the Murray press-need system (14). Interpretations also vary in the relative emphasis on form and content. In Bender and Woltmann's reports of group responses to puppet shows (48, 56) and Despert's analysis of play situations (69, 70, 71, 182), symbolic interpretations of content are emphasized. In the mosaic test (193, 204) form is paramount. In Homburger Erikson's studies, content is interpreted from the psychoanalytic viewpoint but spatial variables are also introduced and interpreted in terms of configuration (72–74). Of the two most extensively used tests, the Rorschach and the TAT, the former relatively stresses form and the latter relatively emphasizes content. These two, however, fall somewhere near the middle range in the use of both scoring approaches.

Purposes. An examination of projective methods with regard to the ends they serve shows three major purposes for which they are commonly used. These may be subsumed under the topics of diagnosis, therapy, and experiment.

1. Diagnosis. As already indicated, projective methods developed first in the clinical setting as devices for tapping phantasies, sampling conscious and unconscious thought, and revealing the characteristics of individual perceptual organization. As a psychiatrist, Rorschach's primary aim was to provide a method which would help to illuminate dynamic factors in mental disease and serve as an aid to differential diagnosis. Recent reports on the clinical use of the test, and the demonstrations of fairly stable response patterns for various pathognomic conditions, have gone far toward the realization of that aim (103, 105, 125). The more recent TAT is also demonstrating similar potentialities (151, 160, 161).

In child analysis the special diagnostic value of play, which has been described as the child's language, a medium of expression which precedes facility in verbal communication, was first recognized by Melanie Klein. Anna Freud has also been a pioneer in the use of play techniques, but she has evolved an approach which is far more conservative than Klein's. Freud (75) uses play primarily to gain rapport and insight, reserving *deep* analysis for later stages of therapy; Klein, however, regaled her fascinated young patients with symbol interpretation from the beginning of the first contact (82). Following these leads, play situations were used extensively by others as an adjunct to both diagnosis and therapy (57–100). Sargent (93) has reported an observation of a *normal* child which tends to confirm observations and interpretations of play made under clinical conditions. As a diagnostic method play has been used more informally than formally, but certain controlled techniques are being developed (67, 84) and other possibilities, such as the adaptation of play methods as a *readiness* test for preschool children, have been explored (97). Mayer and Mayer (87), Rosenzweig and Shakow (91), and Murray (14) have adapted certain play methods for use with adults.

2. *Therapy*. It was soon discovered that expressive methods, especially play, art techniques, and drama, frequently served a double purpose. Insight into pathogenic factors and adjustment mechanisms was obtained, while at the same time the release which the projective situation both stimulated and permitted, appeared therapeutic in its effect. The literature is replete with case material indicating that play therapy can bring about reorganization and reintegration of attitudes (65, 81, 85, 98). Some workers attribute the benefit to the release and desensitization provided by play itself (83, 84, 88); others believe that improvement comes indirectly as the result of relationship with the therapist which the latter uses in treatment (59, 65, 75, 79); still others hold that insights developed in play and verbalized by the child are essential for therapy to take place (66, 67). Some form of interpretation, support or suggestion from the therapist, directly or indirectly given to the child, is considered necessary by Cameron (65), Liss (85), Solomon (95, 96), and others but all except Klein (82) recommend extreme caution in its use.

Whatever the explanatory theory, experimenters with projective techniques are in substantial agreement that emotional growth and symptom remission can and often do result, even when the methods are used primarily for diagnostic purposes. Experience has demonstrated, in fact, that a rigid distinction between diagnostic and therapeutic contacts is unjustified and perhaps dangerous (97). In the course of therapy, information is gained which leads to greater precision in diagnosis; whereas even in the short diagnostic session the subject undergoes an experience which can be traumatic, or therapeutic, or neither, depending upon the emotional state of the patient, and the handling of the relationship with the clinician. Even in a relatively stereotyped situation, such as an intelligence test, favorable or unfavorable changes may be initiated, as in the case of a child seen at the Psychological Clinic at Northwestern University who, following an intelligence test, announced to his mother that the examiner had "taught him to concentrate." In the projective situation such changes can be quite radical, depending upon how effective that situation is in releasing impulses, and upon the manner in which the resulting anxiety is handled. These facts have caused many writers to urge that only trained persons should use projective methods, and that experienced psychologists should handle them with caution (78, 79). Certainly the practice of interpreting the results of projective tests to subjects and, for that matter, the irresponsible passing out of test scores of any kind, cannot be too severely condemned.

3. Experiment. Extensive use of projective methods for research purposes has been made in the Harvard Psychological Clinic under the direction of H. A. Murray. An ambitious personality study of fifty-one paid subjects (most of them Harvard students) utilized projective tests such as the Rorschach, Murray's own TAT, and certain tests devised specifically for this investigation. Among the special tests were *imaginal productivity* tests (including story completion, *similes,* and *Beta* ink blots), *dramatic productions,* and *musical reveries.* The battery also included a variety of non-projective tests including measures of hypnotizability, level of aspiration, reactions to frustration, and the like. Conspicuously absent were the usual inventories and ratings. Commenting on the omission, Murray launches another attack:

> We included some of the procedures commonly employed in academic studies; intelligence tests and a variety of questionnaires, but these contributed little to our understanding. American personologists base their conclusions on a much larger number of subjects than we studied, and in this respect their findings are more representative than ours. What they usually study, however, are the physical attributes of movement, manifest traits and superficial attitudes, facts which subjects are entirely conscious of and quite willing to admit. Thus their researches do not penetrate below the level of what is evident to the ordinary layman. . . . The original data, then, are of uncertain value, and no amount of factor analysis can make them more reliable (14, p. 33).

At Sarah Lawrence College, Lerner and Murphy and a group of collaborators have conducted a four-year study of nursery-school children in which projective techniques have played a leading role. Their equipment included *miniature life toys, sensory toys,* and plastic materials such as dough and cold cream. Group play formed a part of the experiment, and several ingenious *active play techniques* were introduced (7).

Both the Murray and the Lerner-Murphy experiments were exploratory in nature; designed to gather a variety of information "which would somehow illuminate personality development." Lerner and Murphy state that they have "accepted the general focus of working toward a small collection of intensive case studies" (7, p. viii). Their announced aim is to gather cross-sectional data at a later time when the intensive studies have given direction to the search.

In other experiments, projective data have been used to throw light on many different psychological problems. Horowicz used paired pictures in developmental studies of race prejudice (190), self-identification (189), and social conformity (191). Aggression in children has been the subject of several studies, utilizing various techniques; Baruch used a free-play technique with young children (61); Fite has made use of rather specific questions and comments to stimulate aggression in her subjects (185); and destructive behavior has been investigated by Ackerman in an ingenious experimental set-up using blocks. In the latter study, the child upon entering the room was confronted with two rows of toy structures, one torn down ready for building, the other set up to invite demolition, thus offering an opportunity to study the contrasting behaviors of different children (57, 58).

Frustration studies have utilized projective techniques as auxiliary tests (162, 167). Bellak investigated the projection of aggressive feelings in TAT stories told after the first five plots offered by a subject had been severely criticized (148). Sarason has applied the TAT in experiments with feeble-minded girls (166), and Slutz discussed its value for developmental studies (169). Investigations of attitudes using projective devices have been carried out by Tuddenheim (203), Dubin (184), and Proshansky (199). Tuddenheim used a *reputation test* as a measure of projected attitudes; Dubin predicted the answers to attitude tests on war, government and labor on the basis of play constructions built by undergraduates on the subject "the world as I see it." Proshansky's experiment involved comparisons between replies to a labor attitude scale and interpretations of pictures which had been previously judged ambiguous as to "outcome for labor." Adaptations of other techniques have been turned to projective use, as in Buhler's study of neurotic and normal performance on the 1916 Stanford Binet *ball and field* test (180), and in Marquidt's use of eight simple oral questions based on an idea suggested by Binet (195). All of these studies present some degree of positive results in the direction expected according to the hypothesis of projection.

Experimental Results

Projective methods are not yet ready to fill a bulky section on *experimental results* if by that title is meant a list of findings in crucial experiments. The preceding section gives a cursory view of the problems to which they have been applied, and indicates the general trend of results. Although a great deal of incidental information has been contributed to personality study, psychopathology, and special problems, it seems important at this state of development to examine results which support theories on which the techniques are based, and the findings of experiments designed to test the efficacy of the methods, rather than to classify miscellaneous outcomes of innumerable investigations covering a wide range of psychological phenomena, from psychiatric problems to social attitudes. As long as projective methods remain in the exploratory period, research interest should be focussed on questions of method itself. In the final section of this survey, methodological problems will be discussed. At present it is necessary to examine a few outstanding researches which bear on underlying assumptions and predictive value.

Two experiments, one by Sears and one by Murray, are worth noting because of their attempt to demonstrate experimentally the basic mechanism of projection. Sears used a rating scale technique in which a group of fraternity men were asked to rate themselves and others on the possession of certain traits. On the assumption that some individuals would use projection to protect themselves from the acknowledgment of undesirable traits in their own personalities, Sears further assumed that the largest amount of projection would occur in those who lacked insight. A subject's average rating by others was used as the estimate of his *true* score in a trait; his average score in attribution of the trait to other individuals was taken as the measure of projection, and agreement between self and others' ratings provided the criterion of insight. Results were in the expected direction: those who were more *stingy* than average, and who lacked insight into that fact, rated others higher in stinginess, on the average, than did those who were equally stingy but recognized this characteristic. Each trait in Freud's *anal erotic* syndrome (stinginess, obstinacy, disorderliness) was given more extreme ratings by the insightless group. Sears concludes:

Without belaboring the question of whether lack of insight was a result of repression in a Freudian sense, or whether it was a conscious or unconscious process, it can be said that the effects of projection have appeared in this situation in a way that was predictable from the present redefinition of that process (19, p. 576).

Another fundamental experiment has been conducted by Murray, who has studied the effects of fear upon response to pictures (13). Two series of 15 photographs were administered to five 11-year-old children at a house party. The photographs were clipped from *Time* and the subjects were asked to rate the maliciousness of the pictured persons on a nine-point scale. Each series was administered twice, once after *a normal pleasure experience,* and once after a game of *murder.* Series A was given first under the pleasure condition preceding the *scare* game, both series were administered after the game, and series B was repeated the following morning after the effects of fear had presumably subsided. (The reality of the fear situation was further supported by the fact that one of the children actually hallucinated a burglar early the following morning!) The results show a marked increase in the *badness* scores assigned to the photographs seen under the fear condition.

A number of studies claim some degree of predictive success for projective methods, but only two will be described in detail, one of which uses the TAT, the other a modified version of the Rorschach method.

Harrison, impressed with the fruitfulness of the TAT in clinical practice, undertook in conjunction with a qualitative study by Rotter (163), a "quantified and controlled validity study" (152, 153) on the assumption that:

Evidence for the congruence and unity of the personality would be clearly demonstrated if it were shown that an individual cannot relate what at face value are impersonal stories without revealing so much about himself that a thumbnail personality sketch including characteristic traits, biographical facts, attitudes, intelligence level, personal problems and conflicts, could with varying degrees of accuracy be written from story analysis (152, p. 123).

The test was given to 40 patients at the Worcester State Hospital about whom nothing was known to the experimenter. Personality sketches were written, and the items included were subsequently checked by an assistant against the hospital records. The index of validity used was the ratio of right guesses to right-plus-wrong, which yielded a quotient expressible as a per cent. Two controls were used. First, the themes of 15 patients were randomly matched with histories, using the same technique of checking. This furnished an empirical criterion of chance expectancy. As a second control, ten case histories were matched with ten artificial or *guessed* write-ups. Harrison obtained a validity index of 82.5 per cent correct inferences by means of his experimental technique, which was significantly higher than the indices obtained by either control method. The correlations between guessed and actual I.Q.'s was .78 with an average deviation of 9.5 points. Although diagnostic labels are themselves subject to error, guesses as to disease classification were 75 per cent correct. This figure is all the more impressive, in view of possible sources of error in the diagnosis itself as well as in the TAT interpretation.

Harrison further separated biographical from personality and intellectual items since, as the writer points out, differential validity, if it markedly favored biographical information, would detract from the practical potentialities of the method, proving the test more efficient in uncovering information easily obtainable by other means.

The comparison showed no significant difference between the two types of data, and a somewhat higher validity was found for etiological items (guesses as to motivation and causes of difficulty) than for the other item groups. In a supplementary experiment one further caution was introduced. This time the analysis was done *blind;* that is, another examiner administered the test in order to eliminate cues from direct contact with the subjects. The validity fell from 82 per cent to 74 per cent. This difference is statistically insignificant and without clinical interest, since blind interpretation is a research tool which has no place in practical diagnostic work.

Rorschach validity studies utilizing the blind-interpretation technique (115, 133) as well as degree of correspondence with other criteria such as psychiatric diagnoses (107) have been promising, but because they are based on small numbers of cases and have not always been rigorously controlled, the results are interesting rather than definitive. Ruth Munroe's experiment at Sarah Lawrence College is not subject to these criticisms. Munroe's *Inspection Technique* (130, 131, 132) and Harrower Erickson's method for group presentation (113, 114) are beginning to make possible wide-scale administration which should overcome some of these objections.

For two consecutive years the individual Rorschach was given to the entire freshman class at Sarah Lawrence, the protocols were scored by the *Inspection Technique* and the results were put aside until spring when a checkup on the predictions could be made. A group of problem students selected by independent criteria such as academic failure, referral to the psychiatrist, and problem behavior observed by teachers, had an average of 7.9 deviations on the check list of problem indicators, with a range of 5.1, whereas a group of 15 selected as unusually well adjusted by teachers, had an average of 2.6 deviations with a range of 1.4. Scarcely any overlapping appears between the groups (130, p. 233). Of 43 students having five checks or less, only one appeared on any list of girls having difficulty of any sort during their freshman year, and this one girl was not, according to Munroe, considered a serious problem either by psychiatrists or teachers. Only one serious problem was altogether missed, "a girl whom two psychiatrists described as delinquent and a nuisance, but probably not deeply neurotic." The author states that errors in classification did occur. Two students who were rated D+ on a scale from A to E, should have been placed in E, the lowest group. In spite of occasional misjudgments of this sort, the test acquitted itself much better than experience has led us to expect the *paper and pencil* tests to do. The Bernreuter, administered to the same subjects in this study, completely missed some of the most seriously maladjusted students (130, 132).

Methodological Problems

The variety and richness of material which the projective methods provide is at once the delight of the clinician and the despair of the experimentalist. The research worker who attempts to use any of these methods is immediately impressed both with their infinite possibilities for interpretation and insight, and the seemingly insurmountable difficulties in the way of scientific treatment of the data. Many able psychologists dismiss them as "vague"; no doubt they are justified in the choice of adjective. Others are challenged by that very vagueness, and the pioneer hope that there may be "gold in them thar hills" behind the fog. All scientific problems are unclear until ways are found to approach them.

Problems of quantification and standardization have been the chief source of controversy, not only between advocates and opponents of the methods, but among the enthusiasts themselves. To standardize or not to standardize, and if so how, is invariably an adequate stimulus for argument. It is generally recognized that the complexity of personality can no more be expressed by a psychograph of traits than it can be represented by a photograph of the physical profile. Another point on which nearly all can agree is that established mental test procedures cannot be carried over unmodified to the newer techniques.

Usual standardization procedures of mental tests have not been successfully applied to these (projective) methods, as it is the configuration of factors present rather than the independent quantity of each factor that describes the personality. Broad experience of the psychologist rather than statistically reliable norms is the necessary prerequisite for using these procedures (2, p. 76).

The misunderstandings which arise when configuration is overlooked are illustrated in a recent study of the relative efficacy of various personality tests used in a study of delinquent and normal girls (219). This experiment demonstrated that, contrary to expectation, the delinquents showed less of a certain Rorschach factor commonly associated with lack of control and impulsivity, than the normal high school group. As Rorschach workers have frequently explained, factors taken out of context have little meaning, for the reason that it is not the absolute amount of one determinant but its relation to the whole pattern which gives it significance in the individual protocol.

The application of standard methods for estimating reliability and validity further complicates the problem of quantification:

Reliability. In psychometrics, the usual checks on reliability have been the split-half technique, and correlations either between repetitions of the same test, or between alternate forms. None of these methods are wholly satisfactory for projective tests. For example, split-half correlations of Rorschach factors mean little because the ten cards are admittedly uneven in the type and amount of response they produce, and because the technique involves isolating factors from context. Hertz claims reasonably satisfactory results for the split-half method, but does not recommend it (116).

Repetition of projective tests is also somewhat dubious, although it has been claimed that *basic* aspects of the Rorschach pattern are little altered upon retesting (110, 124). Fosberg found that although subjects could produce *good* or *poor* Bernreuter scores at will according to instructions, they were successful only in changing content, rather than fundamental pattern on their Rorschach psychograms (110). Tomkins, however, repeating the TAT daily with a group of subjects found that 20 sessions were required to bring out all the significant themas for one person (172). This finding is enough to indicate that high reliability can hardly be expected upon just one repetition of a test.

The most useful approach to the reliability of qualitative material is by means of comparisons between judges and interpreters. If a group of judges, using predetermined criteria for judgment, agree among themselves in the scoring of a number of protocols, reliability for the yardstick chosen is usually assumed. Stouffer obtained a reliability coefficient of .96 among four judges' estimates of attitudes toward prohibition based on subjects' autobiographies (266). In the application of this method the fact should not be overlooked that the coefficient may measure communality of thinking among the judges, resulting in spurious correspondence of ratings, quite independent of the particular materials to which the judgments are applied.

Validity. The most frequently proposed methods for establishing validity for projective techniques are (1) correspondence with other criteria, (2) internal consistency, and (3) predictive success. These are orthodox procedures which have long been advocated, but in their transfer to projective problems certain modifications are necessary due to the nature of the data which must be compared.

Clinical data have often been chosen as the reference point in validation studies. Many experiments of this sort have been conducted, only a few of which could be included in the bibliography of this paper. (Clinical validation of the Rorschach test is described in references 107, 116, 120, 126, 129, 133, and 137; references 145, 152, 153, 154, and 163 report similar experiments with the TAT.) In handling the material, the correlation technique has seldom been applicable, since it is impossible to reduce a complicated personality interpretation, or a life history, to a single variable for plotting on a chart. As a measure of congruence between data, Vernon's matching technique (271) has been used by Kerr (193), Murray (14), Hertz (115), and many others, with good results. For example, in the Harvard experiment already described, three judges were asked to match ten sets of phantasies with ten biographies. One judge matched five, and two matched all ten correctly (14, p. 390). Likewise, of 20 mosaic patterns done by ten normal and ten neurotic children in Kerr's experiment, 15 correct identifications were made by the investigators. Contingency coefficients for various matchings in this study ranged from .86 to .96 (193).

There are two disadvantages in the matching technique. The first, which is shared by all validation procedures which depend upon correspondence with a criterion, is the difficulty of selecting an adequate standard. The usual procedure is to match a projective protocol with case history material, or other test results, but as Harrison (153) and Macfarlane (8) note, the case history itself may be highly inaccurate. The second objection is the dependence of the matching results upon the skill of judges. The judge who matched five would appear to possess less insight than the judge who matched ten in the experiment mentioned above. A poor judge can lower the matching coefficient while *true* congruence in the materials themselves remains unaltered, but still unknown. Regardless of these drawbacks, if successful matching can be accomplished, some degree of correspondence can safely be assumed and further tested by more refined measures.

The criterion of internal consistency, as originally applied to such personality inventories as the Thurstone and others which followed, has been used to test the agreement of separate items in a battery of questions with the battery as a whole. This method has been criticized on the grounds that validity thus established seldom holds beyond the standardization group. The unity demonstrated is between the given question and the original list of questions and does not constitute proof of coherence and "occurring-togetherness" of the traits themselves (254, p. 794).

In projective techniques, internal consistency applies to agreement found between results of assorted projective tests administered to the same subjects. But what constitutes *agreement?* The quotation from Frank cited above advocates this criterion; Allport lists it as one test for the validity of personal documents (209, p. 171); and Lerner and Murphy defend it as follows:

> We aim for validity through comparison of a child with himself in different units of one and the same play situations in the nursery school and, insofar as possible at home. . . . The investigation of a few children, studied in this detailed fashion, can lead to as great or greater validity than large scale comparisons of so many children on a few ill-understood responses to *standard* stimuli (7. p. viii).

Although it seems reasonable to look for consistency within a person's performance in different situations, it must be recalled that true validity cannot be established through correspondence between measures which are not themselves validated. Even the conclusion that agreement offers evidence to support the theory that different tests measure the same thing (whatever it may be in the particular instance) calls for a warning sounded by Macfarlane. She points out that consistency may be a result of consistency in the experimenters' concepts, rather than between data themselves. (See discussion of this point in connection with reliability in an earlier section of this paper.)

Probably the soundest tests of validity are tests of predictive capacity. In several studies of validity, indices based on prediction have proved to be higher than the reliability of the same ratings. Cartwright and French (223), after reading several years' diary entries, attempted to predict the diarist's answers to certain tests and questionnaires. Results showed more agreement between predicted and actual answers, than between the two judges' predictions. A similar phenomenon occurred when three experts made blind analyses of the Rorschach record of a single subject (115). Both Hertz (116) and Allport (209) explain the paradox as due to the fact that each analyst understood correctly different aspects of the personalities under inspection.

Prediction of actual behavior in concrete situations has not so far been attempted, if the designation *actual behavior* excludes responses to attitude tests (184, 199), prognosis in mental disease (124), or facts expected in the follow-up cases (132, 153), and if *concrete* implies a particular stimulus set-up. The possibility of suicide has been prognosticated from Rorschach records, the presence of hostile feelings and the likelihood of their overt expression has been noted, and numbers of similar motivational directions have been mapped and tested for individuals. It is not, however, possible to predict precise response sequences (Murray's *actones, verbones,* or *motones* [14]), since a diversity of acts may be equivalent for discharging the same drives in different individuals, and identical behavior may vary in motivation from person to person. Furthermore, a quantitative statement as to "how much" of a stimulus is needed to activate a tendency must remain relative rather than absolute.

Standardization. Progress toward the quantitative standardization of projective methods has been blocked not merely by the difficulties discussed above, but by a genuine distrust of the psychostatistical approach on the part of many. Allport illustrates the ludicrous results of what he terms "empiricism gone wild" by an example from one factor-analyzed inventory which assigns a score of plus six on *loyalty to the gang* for the response *green* to the word *grass* (210, p. 329). Frank points out that statistical tests of reliability and validity were originally devised to meet these problems in the absence of supplementary data (5, p. 400). Now that the latter are available, routine procedures should not be made a fetish to stand in the way of more effective, non-statistical techniques. Moreover, it has been claimed that *psychostatistical manipulations* and rigidly objective procedures are less applicable when carried over from the investigation of cognitive functions, such as intelligence, to the more affective aspects of total personality (154). *Paper and pencil* tests have come in for much unfavorable comment. Krugman describes them as having had "high reliability but practically no validity when the criterion of validity was not an artificially constructed one but agreement with other clinical data" (128, p. 100). Harrison describes the same measures as possessing strict objectivity and high reliability, but as "lacking in the one requirement of a good test and that unfortunately rather an essential one, validity" (154, p. 49).

As an alternative, many investigators hold to the belief that, instead of being content with relatively invalid, objective tests, the more difficult and important task of validating subjective methods should be attempted. Harrison states this aim and adds:

In the end it may turn out to be an easier task to objectify a plastic, subjective method which is based on sound principles, than to validate an objective test standardized along lines of test construction which have time and again proved unsuccessful (152, p. 122).

Munroe sounds the same note in discussing the possible standardization of her *inspection technique* for the Rorschach. That this would be possible is quite evident from her results, but Munroe sees the real issue as whether or not it would be desirable.

Such standardization by its very nature ignores the individual. . . . None of our present personality scales, including the Rorschach, if it were standardized in this manner, rest upon anything more than an empirical approximation. All our theories of personality are at variance with the notion that the summation of a series of items determined by discrete frequency tables could ever be expected to give an accurate dynamic picture of an individual (130, p. 233).

Criticisms and cautions. The opinion quoted so far in this survey has emanated almost entirely from within the frame of reference of projective techniques, rather than from the critical vantage point of a detached observer. What of the other side? What have the much criticized, even belittled adherents to traditional methodology in the personality field to say on the subject? Unfortunately, although there are many who disapprove the trend, projective methods have for the most part been "damned with faint praise" or simply ignored. Critics of the Rorschach, for example, are known to be numerous, but experimental refutations of claims made are practically nonexistent. There is, in the literature, not one comprehensive critical review of projective methods by anyone outside the group of interested researchers. Does this mean that the advocates of newer approaches are attacking insensible straw men, or are they alive but inarticulate? Even the ESP research was for a time honored by highly vocal opposition.

Only two frankly critical articles can be cited. One was read by Balken at the 1941 meeting of the American Psychological Association (1). This paper directed its attack chiefly at the lack of precision in the terminology used, and against what the author regarded as unjustified claims and interpretations, but which she did not specifically illustrate. In further discussion of her paper at a round-table meeting, Balken expressed objections which appeared to be grounded in the belief that psychoanalysis has been insufficiently credited for underlying principles, and that its theories are being irresponsibly extended without sufficient knowledge of its basic implications.

Macfarlane (8) discusses the problems of standardization, reliability and validity, and adds two important cautions. The first relates to sampling. Clinicians, she warns, are "conspicuously subject to faulty over-generalization" and should be required to tabulate their own sample experience as a check against extending theories beyond the groups familiar to the investigator. She speaks of the *mushroom growth* of the methods, objects to their use by persons of sundry qualification or lack of it, and pleads that the inexperienced should be barred from this area of research, lest promising leads be bungled. Furthermore, she emphasizes the important and often neglected fact that all validation must rest upon the concepts and hypotheses underlying the research. Since there are as yet no universally accepted terms which do justice to *the richness and diversity* of personality, she suggests that an *articulated conceptualization* is basic.

It should become a part of the scientific mores in this pioneering, unstructured stage, that the first step in projective research should be an explicit statement of concepts used, and an orientation with respect to theoretical biases. Further, such a statement should appear on page one of any article instead of leaving it to the inference of the reader (8, p. 406).

Although projective methods can be and frequently are used for nomothetic as well as idiographic purposes, they are peculiarly well suited to the former; hence the controversy which rages about the single case study is an important related issue. John E. Anderson objects that the single case in physics in which the weight of factors is known in advance and controlled in order to design a crucial experiment is not comparable to the single case in psychology in which there is no knowledge of the weight of factors and little or no possibility of control. This criticism, although pertinent in its emphasis upon the absence of crucial experimentation in the psychology of personality, appears to arise from a difference in fundamental premise. If we regard personality as an aggregate of parts, their action and interaction are obviously too complex for control. No matter how standardized the external situation, we cannot control the momentary inner state of the individual due to influences beyond our jurisdiction. If, on the other hand, we join the organismic personologists in regarding personality as a unified whole, then the person and not the part becomes the unit for study. This unit may be thought of as a construct, no more and no less directly observable than an atom. From this viewpoint it is feasible to control the immediate external conditions of experiment, and to study the composition of our *substance* (that elusive *inner state* or those *processes within* which baffle other procedures) through its effect upon something else, as in the physical experiments Frank describes. Exponents of the totalistic approach claim more logic and greater rigor in such method, than in attempts to set up elaborate control of conditions surrounding some arbitrary partial aspect of personality (such as a trait or an attitude) which is rendered distorted and meaningless by removal from the intrapersonal context.

Certain further disadvantages of projective methods have been noted by interested workers within the field. Some of the techniques, such as the *Tautaphone,* are considered better suited to research than to clinical diagnosis because they are awkward, time consuming, and add little information which could not be more efficiently obtained by a psychiatric interview (174). Harrison holds that, except for the Rorschach and the TAT, which have been *partially validated,* most of the methods are *terra incognita* with validity and true value still to be demonstrated. "Others appear best suited for qualitative and interpretive work, and by their nature offer little opportunity for compromise with objective procedures" (154, p. 52).

Evaluation

A review of the literature on projective methods shows first that they have a long and respectable lineage, with ties of kinship extending beyond the boundaries of psychology itself. Whether the offspring will grow into ne'er-do-well dreamers, fulfilling the prophecies of conservative relatives, or will develop their originality in a maturity of scientific respectability, is a matter for the future to decide.

The theoretical issues will probably never be settled in an *either-or* fashion, since they represent philosophies of science which, in one shape or another, are as old as science itself. Psychology does well to be jealous of its painstaking empirical techniques, in spite of scoffers who hold that "the more exact methods generally yield the least information" (14, p. 547). On the other hand, if complex molar behavior and its hidden springs of action are not to be ignored, an open-minded attitude toward theory revision and toward innovations in method seems necessary. The admission of *explanatory theory,* combined with attempts to verify its constructs by experimentation, has been offered as one solution.

Bavink, the philosopher, has distinguished two types of theory: *elaborative* theory which contains practically no hypothetical elements since the fundamental assumptions are themselves data of experience; and *explanatory* theory in which "the unification of facts is only reached on the basis of a speculative assumption which is described as the hypothesis on which the theory is based," as in the atomic theory (215, p. 168).

Certain immediate issues seem more pseudo than real. Does standardization, for example, actually involve forsaking such important aspects as context and interrelationships among variables? If so, perhaps it is reasonable to ask that it be postponed or even abandoned. Certainly normative data, interindividual comparisons on single traits, and the search for uniformities should not be pursued exclusively at the expense of intensive individual studies of both the horizontal and vertical type. Interest in the methodology of personal documents and intensive projects such as the Harvard and Sarah Lawrence studies help to correct overemphasis. But does the value of the new approach rule out the need for normative research as well? It would seem that the latter could at least provide orienting data which, properly used and interpreted, could furnish the clinician and student of personality with a stronger framework for his studies in interrelationship.

A fact which is often overlooked both by those who scorn statistics and those who reify them is that numbers do not bestow precision but are, rather, a convenient way to express it when it exists. Quantitative method might profitably be applied more extensively to the properties of the projective tests themselves. For example, as Harrison suggests (154), it would be valuable to have frequency tables similar to those for the Kent Rosanoff word-association test, showing the relative frequency of certain common phantasies produced by each of the TAT pictures. If we think of these numerical results as adding to the precision of the instrument itself, instead of reading into the figures oversimplified generalizations about people, no atomistic conception of personality is implied. The clinician would not need to alter either his theory or his interpretation of certain Rorschach syndromes if he also knew more about the frequency of the component determinants, both singly and in constellations. Such knowledge would, on the contrary, serve both as an added support and as a check on his conclusions.

Beck (103), Hertz (117) and others have developed tables showing the most commonly perceived forms on the Rorschach test. Zubin (139–141) has suggested a radical revision of Rorschach scoring to provide for more exact quantification. Common or *normal* details selected; forms frequently seen in the blots; as well as response determinants such as color, shading and movement have been intensively studied (106, 117, 118, 121, 124). Nothing comparable has been done for some of the other aspects of scoring, and rigid tests of various ratios used in interpretation have not been carried out. Other projective techniques are still more difficult to quantify and little or nothing has been done to develop workable scoring schemes.

Questions raised in regard to sampling are another issue which ought not to be insoluble. If projective methods are used to provide comparative data, Macfarlane's caution (see above) should be observed. For situations of this kind, the accepted rules of random sampling are sufficient, but it may be that we need supplementary principles to determine the adequacy of sampling in individual studies. An individual, as F. H. Allport has suggested (208), may also be regarded as a *population* of *events* and characteristics. What constitutes an adequate sample from an individual life? The validity of individual diagnosis and prediction might be increased by controls relating to the number of tests to be given, their distribution in time or under varying emotional conditions, the number of different observers needed, and so on. Some of these problems would be difficult to investigate, but with ingenuity should not be impossible to attack. For example, Tomkins' daily repetition of the TAT to determine the new thema limit (172) is one step in the direction of amassing data which might be used as a basis for individual sampling theory.

Recent advances in statistics have been little exploited in the quantitative treatment of results of projective experiments capable of expression in numbers, whether derived from repeated observations on single individuals under systematically varied conditions or from multivariable experiments involving exhaustive treatment of a small number of cases. Many authors are content to report their findings in per cents without statements of significance. Small-sample theory, including the techniques of analysis of variance and covariance have not been used to any extent in projective experimentation, although Brenman and Reichardt (109) have recently made use of Fisher's t-test to show the significance of differences in hypnotizability predicted from Rorschach records.

The advantage of these statistics, originally developed by Fisher in agricultural research and adapted to educational problems by Snedecor (264) and Lindquist (250), lies not in the unfortunate assumption that they offer a means for obtaining *significant* figures from scanty data or carelessly designed experiments. Instead, they avoid generalization beyond the data at hand by supplying a numerical means of expressing relationships found in a sample and of comparing these with results expected by chance in *samples of the same size* (250, p. 54). Moreover, the poorly designed experiment tends to defeat itself, since inadequate control of important variables results in large errors (*Within groups* variances) which reduce significance. Three advantages of the variance methods which seem especially promising as applied to projective experiments are as follows: First, in the exploratory study in which a number of factors must be controlled, these can be handled simultaneously. Second, by the selection of cases to fit prescribed conditions, variables may be controlled without the laborious necessity of holding them constant. Finally, a measure of the amount and significance of variability due to the interaction of one or more variables, or to the effect of uncontrolled variables, is obtainable (232, 233).

For clinical psychology, which may be regarded as the applied branch of the psychology of personality, projective methods furnish one of the most promising hopes for a science of diagnosis and treatment. An experimental study by Davis (227) on the relative weight given to data from tests and from case histories in arriving at clinical judgments found that clinicians are unwilling and unable to rely solely on objective criteria. Many believe that the final synthesis must forever rest upon the clinician's skill, experience, and "intuition," but the fact that these assets must be possessed and used does not relieve us of the responsibility of attempting at every turn to expand such subjective equipment by the development of scientific devices to supplement and check upon our conjectures.

Murray has remarked that psychology has the choice of two alternatives: to study important problems with as yet inadequate instruments, or to study with adequate instruments unimportant problems (15). Whatever their present status, the interest in projective procedures is evidence of an attempt to improve upon inadequate techniques, and evinces a constructive and hopeful preoccupation with method itself. There is a growing recognition that we must not be limited by narrow conceptions of what constitutes *the* scientific method, but instead must be on the watch for new approaches which conform to the broad aims of science, rather than to its dogmas (211). Historically, science arose in response to the need for knowing and dealing with the natural world, or in other words:

> Science aims to give man an understanding, a power of prediction, and a power of control, beyond that which he can achieve through his own unaided common sense (209, p. 148).

If projective methods can be refined and safeguarded in order to serve that end, they deserve interested attention and exhausted research. There appears to be considerable evidence that they may be well worth the expenditure of time and effort involved in thorough exploration.

BIBLIOGRAPHY

Since the term *projective methods* includes a variety of techniques, a number of which represent special interest areas, the bibliography has been organized accordingly. Section I lists articles devoted chiefly to theory, or to discussions and experiments which include an assortment of representative techniques. Section II covers all of the special methods, subdivided alphabetically under the appropriate headings. In Section III will be found books and articles of historical importance, and other works mentioned in the text as having theoretical or incidental bearing on the problems involved. The sections on *Projective Methodology, Thematic Appercep-tion,* and *Miscellaneous Projective Techniques* are believed to be nearly exhaustive at the time of writing. The Rorschach section is selective since a complete list would run to hundreds of titles. The section on *Play techniques* omits a large number of articles concerned with their use in therapy.

SECTION I

Projective Methodology

1. BALKEN, EVA RUTH. Projective techniques for the study of personality. A critique. *Psychol. Bull.,* 1941, 38, 596. (Abstract.)

2. BROWN, J. F. & RAPAPORT, D. The role of the psychologist in the psychiatric clinic. *Bull. Menninger Clin.,* 1941, 5, 75–84.

3. BOOTH, GEORGE C. Objective techniques in personality testing. *Arch. Neurol. Psychiat., Chicago,* 1939, 42, 514–530.

4. FEIGENBAUM, D. On projection. *Psychoanal. Quart.,* 1936, 5, 303–319.

5. FRANK, L. K. Projective methods for the study of personality. *J. Psychol.,* 1939, 8, 389–413. (Also in *Trans. N. Y. Acad. Sci.,* 1939, 1, 129–132.)

6. HOROWICZ, RUTH, & MURPHY, LOIS. Projective methods in the psychological study of children. *J. Exp. Educ.,* 1938, 7, 133–140.

7. LERNER, E., MURPHY, LOIS, STONE, L. J., BEYER, EVELYN, & BROWN, ELINOR. Study-ing child personality. *Monogr. Soc. Res. Child Develpm.,* 1941, 6, No. 4.

8. MACFARLANE, JEAN W. Problems of validation inherent in projective methods. *Amer. J. Orthopsychiat.,* 1942, 12, 405–411.

9. MASLOW, A. H. & MITTELMANN, B. *Principles of abnormal psychology.* Appendix I. Projective methods of examination. Pp. 611–622. New York: Harper, 1941.

10. MOELLENHOFF, F. A projection returns and materializes. *Amer. Imago,* 1942, 3, 3–13.

11. MURPHY, LOIS B. Interiorization of family experiences by normal preschool chil-dren as revealed by some projective methods. *Psychol. League J.,* 1940, 4, 3–5.

12. MURPHY, LOIS B. Patterns of spontaneity and constraint in the use of projective materials by preschool children. *Trans. N.Y. Acad. Sci.,* 1942, 4, 124–138.

13. MURRAY, H. A. Effect of fear on estimates of maliciousness of other person-alities. *In* Tomkins, Silvan S. *Contemporary Psychopathology.* Cambridge: Harvard Univ. Press, 1943. Pp. 545–561.

14. MURRAY, H. A. *Explorations in personality.* New York: Oxford Univ. Press, 1938.

15. MURRAY, H. A. An investigation of fantasies. *In* Abstract of C. L. Hull's informal seminar at Yale University, 1936. (Unpublished.)

16. RAPAPORT, D. Principles underlying projective techniques. *Character & Pers.,* 1942, 10, 213–219.

17. RICHENBERG, W. & CHIDESTER, LEONA. Lack of imagination as a factor in delinquent behavior. *Bull. Menninger Clin.*, 1937, 1, 226–231.

18. ROSENZWEIG, S. Fantasy in personality and its study by test procedures. *J. Abnorm. Soc. Psychol.*, 1942, 37, 40–51.

19. SEARS, R. R. Experimental studies of projection: I. Attribution of traits. *In* Tomkins, Silvan S. *Contemporary Psychopathology*, Cambridge: Harvard Univ. Press, 1943. Pp. 561–571.

20. STRANG, RUTH. Technical instruments of mental hygiene diagnosis and therapy. *Rev. Educ. Res.*, 1940, 10, 450–459.

21. SYMONDS, P. M. & SAMUEL, E. A. Projective methods in the study of personality. *Rev. Educ. Res.*, 1941, 11, 80–93.

22. UPDEGRAFF, RUTH. Recent approaches to the study of the preschool child. I. Indirect and projective methods. *J. Consult. Psychol.*, 1938, 2, 159–161.

23. WHITE, R. W. The interpretation of imaginative productions. *In* Hunt, J. McV. *Personality and the Behavior Disorders. A handbook based on experimental research.* (2 vol.) New York: Ronald Press, 1944. Pp. 214–254.

24. WOLFF, W. Projective methods for personality analysis of expressive behavior in preschool children. *Character & Pers.*, 1942, 10, 309–330.

SECTION II

Art Techniques

25. ABEL, THEODORA M. Free designs of limited scope as a personality index. *Character & Pers.*, 1938, 7, 50–62.

26. ANASTASI, A. & FOLEY, J. P. A survey of the literature on artistic behavior in the abnormal: III. Spontaneous productions. *Psychol. Monogr.*, 1942, 52, No. 237.

27. BARNHART, E. N. Stages in construction of children's drawing as revealed through a recording device. *Psychol. Bull.*, 1940, 37, 581. (Abstract.)

28. BENDER, LAURETTA. Art and therapy in the mental disturbances of children. *J. Nerv. Ment. Dis.*, 1937, 86, 249–263.

29. BENDER, LAURETTA. Gestalt principles in the side-walk drawings and games of children. *J. Genet. Psychol.*, 1932, 41, 192–210

30. BENDER, LAURETTA. The Goodenough test in chronic encephalitis in children. *J. Nerv. Ment. Dis.*, 1940, 91, 277–286.

31. BENDER, LAURETTA & WOLTMANN, A. G. The use of plastic material as a psychiatric approach to emotional problems of children. *Amer. J. Orthopsychiat.*, 1937, 7, 283–300.

32. FLEMING, J. Observations on the use of finger painting in the treatment of adult patients with personality disorders. *Character & Pers.*, 1940, 8, 301–310.

33. HARMS, E. Child art as an aid in the diagnosis of juvenile neuroses. *Amer. J. Orthopsychiat.*, 1941, 11, 191–209.

34. LEVY, J. Use of art techniques in treatment of children's behavior problems. *Proc. Amer. Ass. Stud. Ment. Def.*, 1934, 58, 258–260.

35. LEWIS, N. D. C. Graphic art productions in schizophrenia. *Proc. Ass. Res. Nerv. ment. Dis.*, 1928, 5, 344–368.

36. MCINTOSH, J. R. An inquiry into the use of children's drawings as a means of psychoanalysis. *Brit. J. Educ. Psychol.*, 1939, 9, 102–103. (Abstract.)

37. MCINTOSH, J. R. & PICKFORD, R. W. Some clinical and artistic aspects of a child's drawings. *Brit. J. Med. Psychol.*, 1943, 19, 342–362.

38. MOSSE, E. P. Painting analysis in the treatment of neuroses. *Psychoanal. Rev.*, 1940, 27, 68–82.

39. NAUMBERG, M. Children's art expressions and war. *Nerv. Child*, 1943, 2, 360–373.

40. REITMAN, F. Facial expression in schizophrenic drawing. *J. Ment. Sci.*, 1939, 85, 264–272.

41. SCHMIDLE-WAEHNER, T. Formal criteria for the analysis of children's drawing. *Amer. J. Orthopsychiat.*, 1942, 12, 95–104.

42. SCHUBE, K. & COWELL, G. Art of psychotic persons. *Arch. Neurol. & Psychiat.*, Chicago, 1939, 41, 709–720.

43. SHAW, RUTH F. *Finger painting.* Boston: Little Brown, 1934.

44. SHAW, RUTH F. & LYLE, JEANNETTE. Encouraging fantasy expression in children. *Bull. Menninger Clin.*, 1937 1, 78–86.

45. SPOERL, D. T. Personality and drawing in retarded children. *Character & Pers.*, 1940, 8, 227–239.

46. SPRINGER, N. N. A study of the drawings of maladjusted and adjusted children. *J. Genet. Psychol.*, 1941, 58, 131–138.

47. WILLIAMS, J. N. Interpretation of drawings made by maladjusted children. *Virg. Med. Monogr.*, 1940, 67, 533–538.

Drama and Puppets

48. BENDER, LAURETTA, & WOLTMANN, A. G. The use of puppet shows as a psychotherapeutic method for behavior problems in children. *Amer. J. Orthopsychiat.*, 1936, 6, 341–354.

49. BORDIN, RUTH. The use of psychodrama in an institute for delinquent girls. *Sociometry*, 1940, 3, 80–90.

50. CURRAN, FRANK J. The drama as a therapeutic measure in adolescence. *Amer. J. Orthopsychiat.*, 1939, 9, 215–232.

51. FRANZ, J. G. The place of the psychodrama in research. *Sociometry*, 1940, 3, 49–61.

52. JENKINS, R. L. & BECKH, E. Finger puppets and mask making as a media for work with children. *Amer. J. Orthopsychiat.*, 1942, 12, 294–301.

53. LYLE, J. & HOLLY, S. B. The therapeutic value of puppets. *Bull. Menninger Clin.*, 1941, 5, 223–226.

54. MORENO, J. L. Mental catharisis and the psychodrama. *Sociometry*, 1940, 3, 209–244.

55. MORENO, J. L. Psychodramatic shock therapy. A sociometric approach to the problem of mental disorders. *Sociometry*, 1939, 2, 1–30.

56. WOLTMANN, A. G. The use of puppets in understanding children. *Ment. Hyg., N.Y.*, 1940, 24, 445–458.

Play Techniques

57. ACKERMAN, N. W. Constructive and destructive tendencies in children. *Amer. J. Orthopsychiat.*, 1937, 7, 301–319.

58. ACKERMAN, N. W. Constructive and destructive tendencies in children. An experimental study. *Amer. J. Orthopsychiat.*, 1938, 8, 265–285.

59. ALLEN, F. H. *Psychotherapy with children.* New York: W. W. Norton, 1942.

60. ALLEN, F. H. Therapeutic work with children. *Amer. J. Orthopsychiat.*, 1934, 4, 193–202.

61. BARUCH, DOROTHY W. Aggression during doll play in a preschool. *Amer. J. Orthopsychiat.*, 1941, 11, 252–260.

62. BARUCH, DOROTHY W. Play techniques in pre-school as an aid in guidance. *Psychol. Bull.*, 1939, 36, 570. Abstract.

63. BENDER, LAURETTA & SCHILDER, P. Aggressiveness in children. *Genet. Psychol. Monogr.*, 1936, 18, 410–525.

64. BENDER, LAURETTA & SCHILDER, P. Form as a principle in the play of children. *J. Genet. Psychol.*, 1936, 49, 254–261.

65. CAMERON, W. M. The treatment of children in psychiatric clinics with particular reference to the use of play techniques. *Bull. Menninger Clin.*, 1940, 4, 172–180.

66. CONN, J. H. The child reveals himself through play. *Ment. Hyg., N.Y.*, 1939, 23, 49–69.

67. CONN, J. H. The play interview. A method of studying children's attitudes. *Amer. J. Dis. Child.*, 1939, 58, 1199–1214.

68. CONN, J. H. A psychiatric study of car sickness in children. *Amer. J. Orthopsychiat.*, 1938, 8, 130–141.

69. DESPERT, J. LOUISE. A method for the study of personality reactions in pre-school age children by means of analysis of their play. *J. Psychol.*, 1940, 9, 17–29.

70. DESPERT, J. LOUISE. Technical approaches used in the study of emotional problems in children. Part IV. Collective phantasy. *Psychiat. Quart.*, 1937, 11, 491–506.

71. DESPERT, J. LOUISE. Technical approaches used in the study of emotional problems in children. Part V. The playroom. *Psychiat. Quart.*, 1937, 11, 677–693.

72. ERIKSON, ERIK HOMBURGER. Configurations in play. Clinical notes. *Psychoanal. Quart.*, 1937, 6, 139–214.

73. ERIKSON, ERIK HOMBURGER. Further explorations in play construction. Three spatial variables in relation to sex and anxiety. *Psychol. Bull.*, 1938, 41, 748. (Abstract.)

74. ERIKSON, ERIK HOMBURGER. Studies in the interpretation of play. Clinical observations of play disruption in young children. *Genet. Psychol. Monogr.*, 1940, 22, 557–671.

75. FREUD, ANNA. Introduction to the technique of child analysis. (Authorized trans. supervised by L. P. Clark.) *Nerv. & Ment. Dis. Monogr.*, 1928, No. 48.

76. FRIES, MARGARET E. Play technique in the analysis of young children. *Psychoanal. Rev.*, 1937, 24, 233–245.

77. FRIES, MARGARET E. The value of play for a child development study. *Understand. Child*, 1938, 7, 15–18.

78. GITELSON, M. Clinical experience with play therapy. *Amer. J. Orthopsychiat.*, 1938, 8, 466–478.

79. GITELSON, M., ROSS, H., HOMBURGER, E., ALLEN, F., BLANCHARD, PHYLLIS, LIPPMAN, H. S., GERARD, M. & LOWRY, L. Section on play therapy. *Amer. J. Orthopsychiat.*, 1938, 8, 499–524.

80. HOLMER, P. The use of the play situation as an aid to diagnosis. A case report. *Amer. J. Orthopsychiat.*, 1937, 7, 523–531.

81. KANNER, LEO. Play investigations and play treatment of children's behavior disorders. *J. Pediat.*, 1940, 17, 533–545.

82. KLEIN, MELANIE. The psychoanalysis of children. London: Hogarth Press, 1932.

83. LEVY, D. Studies in sibling rivalry. *Res. Mongr. Amer. Orthopsychiat. Ass.*, 1937, No. 2.

84. LEVY, D. Use of play technique as experimental procedure. *Amer. J. Orthopsychiat.*, 1933, 3, 266–277.

85. LISS, E. Play techniques in child analysis. *Amer. J. Orthopsychiat.*, 1936, 6, 17–22.

86. LOWENFELD, MARGARET. The theory and use of play in the psychotherapy of childhood. *J. Ment. Sci.*, 1938, 4, 1057–1058.

87. MAYER, A. M. & MAYER, E. B. Dynamic concept test. A modified play technique for adults. *Psychiat. Quart.*, 1941, 15, 621–634.

88. NEWELL, H. W. Play therapy in child psychiatry. *Amer. J. Orthopsychiat.*, 1941, 11, 245–252.

89. RICHARDS, S. S. & WOLFF, E. The organization and function of play activities in the set-up of a pediatrics department. *Ment. Hyg., N. Y.*, 1940, 24, 229–235.

90. ROGERSON, C. H. *Play therapy in childhood*. New York: Oxford Univ. Press, 1939.

91. ROSENZWEIG, S. & SHAKOW, D. Play techniques in schizophrenia and other psychoses. I. Rationale. *Amer J. Orthopsychiat.*, 1937, 7, 32–35.

92. ROSENZWEIG, S. & SHAKOW, D. Play techniques in schizophrenia and other psychoses. II. Schizophrenic constructions. *Amer J. Orthopsychiat.*, 1937, 7, 36–47.

93. SARGENT, HELEN D. Spontaneous doll play of a nine-year-old. *J. Consult. Psychol.* 1943, 7, 216–222.

94. SIMPSON, G. Diagnostic play interviews. *Understand. Child*, 1938, 7, 6–10.

95. SOLOMON, J. C. Active play therapy. *Amer. J. Orthopsychiat.*, 1938, 8, 479–498.

96. SOLOMON, J. C. Active play therapy. Further experiences. *Amer. J. Orthopsychiat.*, 1940, 10, 763–781.

97. SYMONDS, P. M. Play technique as a test of readiness. *Understand. Child*, 1940, 9, 8–14.

98. TALLMAN, F. & GOLDENSOHN, L. N. Play techniques. *Amer. J. Orthopsychiat.*, 1941, 11, 551–561.

99. WALDER, R. The psychoanalytic theory of play. *Psychoanal. Quart.*, 1933, 2, 208–224.

100. WEISS-FRANKL, A. B. Diagnostic and remedial play. *Understand. Child*, 1938, 7, 3–5.

Rorschach Method

101. BECK, S. J. Configurational tendencies in Rorschach responses. *Amer. J. Psychol.*, 1933, 45, 433–443.

102. BECK, S. J. Error, symbol and method in the Rorschach test. *J. Abnorm. Soc. Psychol.*, 1942, 37, 83–103.

103. BECK, S. J. Introduction to the Rorschach method. A manual of personality study. *Res. Monogr. Amer. Orthopsychiat. Ass.*, 1937, No. 1.

104. BECK, S. J. Personality structure in schizophrenia. A Rorschach investigation on 81 patients and 64 controls. *Nerv Ment. Dis. Monogr.*, 1938, No. 63.

105. BECK, S. J. The Rorschach test in psychopathology. *J. Consult. Psychol.*, 1943, 7, 103–111.

106. BECK, S. J. *Rorschach's test*. New York: Grune & Stratton, 1944. Vol. I. Elementary principles.

107. BENJAMIN, J. D. & EBAUGH, F. G. The diagnostic validity of the Rorschach test. *Amer. J. Psychiat.*, 1938, 94, 1163–1178.

108. BOCHNER, RUTH & HALPERN, FLORENCE. *Clinical application of the Rorschach test*. New York: Grune & Stratton, 1942.

109. BRENMAN, MARGARET & REICHARD, SUZANNE. Use of the Rorschach test in the prediction of hypnotizability. *Bull. Menninger Clin.*, 1943, 7, 183–188.

110. FOSBERG, I. A. An experimental study of the reliability of the Rorschach psychodiagnostic technique. *Rorschach Res. Exch.*, 1941, 5, 72–84.

111. FRANK, L. K. Foreword to issue on the Rorschach method. *J. Consult. Psychol.*, 1943, 7, 63–66.

112. HARROWER-ERICKSON, MOLLIE R. The contribution of the Rorschach method to war-time psychological problems. *J. Ment. Sci.*, 1940, 86, 1–12.

113. HARROWER-ERICKSON, MOLLIE R. Large scale experimentation with the Rorschach method. *J. Consult. Psychol.*, 1943, 7, 120–127.

114. HARROWER-ERICKSON, MOLLIE R. Modification of the Rorschach method for use as a group test. *Rorschach Res. Exch.*, 1941, 5, 130–144.

115. HERTZ, MARGUERITE R. Comparison of three blind Rorschach analyses. *Amer. J. Orthopsychiat.*, 1939, 9, 295–315.

116. HERTZ, MARGUERITE R. Rorschach twenty years after. *Psychol. Bull.*, 1942, 39, 529–572.

117. HERTZ, MARGUERITE R. Scoring the Rorschach test with specific reference to the normal detail category. *Amer. J. Orthopsychiat.*, 1938, 8, 100–121.

118. HERTZ, MARGUERITE, R. The shading response in the Rorschach inkblot test: a review of its scoring and interpretation. *J. Gen. Psychol.*, 1940, 23, 123–167.

119. HERTZ, MARGUERITE R. The Rorschach method: science or mystery. *J. Consult. Psychol.*, 1943, 7, 67–80.

120. HERTZ, MARGUERITE R. Validity of the Rorschach method. *Amer. J. Orthopsychiat.*, 1941, 11, 512–520.

121. HERTZMANN, M. Recent research on the group Rorschach test. *Rorschach Res. Exch.*, 1943, 7, 1–6.

122. HERTZMANN, M. & MARGULIES, HELEN. Developmental changes in Rorschach test responses. *J. Genet. Psychol.*, 1943, 62, 189–216.

123. KELLEY, D. M. The present state of the Rorschach method as a psychological adjunct. *Rorschach Res. Exch.*, 1940, 4, 30–36.

124. KISKER, G. W. A projective approach to personality patterns during insulin shock and metrazol convulsive therapy. *J. Abnorm. Soc. Psychol.*, 1942, 37, 120–124.

125. KLOPFER, B. & KELLY, D. *The Rorschach technique.* Yonkers on Hudson: World Book, 1942.

126. KRUGMAN, J. E. A clinical validation of the Rorschach with problem children. *Rorschach Res. Exch.*, 1942, 6, 61–70.

127. KRUGMAN, M. The Rorschach in child guidance. *J. Consult. Psychol.*, 1943, 7, 80–88.

128. KRUGMAN, M. Out of the inkwell: the Rorschach method. *Character & Pers.*, 1940, 9, 91–110.

129. MIALE, F. R., CLAPP, H. & KAPLAN, A. H. Clinical validation of a Rorschach interpretation. *Rorschach Res. Exch.*, 1938, 2, 153–163.

130. MUNROE, RUTH. An experiment in large scale testing by a modification of the Rorschach method. *J. Psychol.*, 1942, 13, 229–263.

131. MUNROE, RUTH. The inspection technique. A modification of the Rorschach method of personality diagnosis for large scale application. *Rorschach Res. Exch.*, 1941, 5, 166–190.

132. MUNROE, RUTH. Use of the Rorschach in college counseling. *J. Consult. Psychol.*, 1943, 7, 89–97.

133. PIATROWSKI, Z. Blind analysis of a case of compulsion neurosis. *Rorschach Res. Exch.*, 1937, 2, 89–111.

134. PIATROWSKI, Z. Use of the Rorschach in vocational selection. *J. Consult. Psychol.*, 1943, 7, 97–102.

135. RORSCHACH, H. *Psychodiagnostics: a diagnostic test based on perception.* (Trans. by P. Lemkau & B. Kronenburg.) Bern: Hans Huber, 1942. New York: Grune & Stratton.

136. RORSCHACH, H. & OBERHOLZER, E. The application of the interpretation of form to psychoanalysis. *J. Nerv. Ment. Dis.*, 1924, 60, 225–248; 359–379.

137. VARVEL, W. A. Suggestions toward the experimental validation of the Rorschach test. *Bull. Menninger Clin.*, 1937, 1, 220–226.

138. VERNON, P. E. The Rorschach inkblot test. *Brit. J. Med. Psychol.*, 1933, 13, 89–118; 179–200; 271–291.

139. ZUBIN, J. A. Psychometric approach to the evaluation of the Rorschach test. *Psychiatry*, 1941, 4, 547–566.

140. ZUBIN, J. A. Quantitative approach to measuring regularity of succession in the Rorschach experiment. *Character & Pers.*, 1941, 10, 67–78.

141. ZUBIN, J. A., CHUTE, E. & VERNIAR, E. Psychometric scales for scoring Rorschach test responses. *Character & Pers.*, 1943, 11, 277–301.

142. YOUNG, R. A. & HIGGENBOTHAM, S. A. Behavior checks on the Rorschach method. *Amer. J. Orthopsychiat.*, 1942, 12, 87–95.

Thematic Apperception

143. AMEN, E. W. Individual differences in apperceptive reaction: a study of response of pre-school children to pictures. *Genet. Psychol. Monogr.*, 1941, 23, 319–385.

144. BALKEN, EVA RUTH. A delineation of schizophrenic language and thought in a test of imagination. *J. Psychol.*, 1943, 16, 239–272.

145. BALKEN, EVA RUTH & MASSERMAN, J. H. The language of phantasy. III. The language of phantasies of patients with conversion hysteria, anxiety state and obsessive compulsive neuroses. *In* Tomkins, Silvan S. *Contemporary Psychopathology*. Cambridge: Harvard Univ. Press, 1943, Pp. 244–253.

146. BALKEN, EVA RUTH & VANDERVEER, A. H. The clinical application of the Thematic apperception test to neurotic children. *Psychol. Bull.*, 1940, 37, 517. (Abstract.)

147. BALKEN, EVA RUTH & VANDERVEER, A. H. The clinical application of a test of imagination to neurotic children. *Amer. J. Orthopsychiat.*, 1942, 12, 68–81.

148. BELLAK, L. An experimental investigation of projection. *Psychol. Bull.*, 1942, 39, 489. (Abstract.)

149. BENNETT, GEORGIA. Structural factors related to the substitute value of activities in normal and schizophrenic persons. I. A technique for the investigation of central areas of personality. *Character & Pers.*, 1941, 10, 42–50.

150. BENNETT, GEORGIA. Some factors related to substitute value at the level of fantasy. *Psychol. Bull.*, 1942, 39, 488. (Abstract.)

151. CHRISTENSON, J. A. JR. Clinical application of the Thematic apperception test. *J. Abnorm. Soc. Psychol.*, 1943, 38, 104–107.

152. HARRISON, R. Studies in the use and validity of the Thematic apperception test with mentally disordered patients. II. A quantitative study. *Character & Pers.*, 1940, 9, 122–133.

153. HARRISON, R. Studies in the use and validity of the Thematic apperception test with mentally disordered patients. III. Validation by the method of "blind analysis." *Character & Pers.*, 1940, 9, 134–138.

154. HARRISON, R. The Thematic apperception and Rorschach methods of personality investigation in clinical practice. *J. Psychol.*, 1943, 15, 49–74.

155. MASSERMAN, J. H. & BALKEN, EVA RUTH. The clinical application of phantasy studies. *J. Psychol.*, 1938, 6, 81–88.

156. MASSERMAN, J. H. & BALKEN, EVA RUTH. The psychoanalytic and psychiatric significance of phantasy. *Psychoanal. Rev.*, 1939, 26, 243–279.

157. MORGAN, C. D. & MURRAY, H. A. A method for investigating fantasies: the Thematic apperception test. *Arch. Neurol. Psychiat., Chicago*, 1935, 34, 289–306.

158. MURRAY, H. A. *Manual for the Thematic apperception test.* Cambridge: Harvard Univ. Press, 1943.

159. MURRAY, H. A. Techniques for a systematic investigation of fantasy. *J. Psychol.*, 1937, 3, 115–145.

160. RAPAPORT, D. The clinical application of the Thematic apperception test. *Bull. Menninger Clin.*, 1943, 7, 106–113.

161. RAPAPORT, D. The Thematic apperception test. Qualitative conclusions as to its interpretation. *Psychol. Bull.*, 1942, 39, 592. (Abstract.)

162. RODNICK, E. H. & KLETANOFF, S. G. Projective reactions to induced frustrations as a measure of social adjustment. *Psychol. Bull.*, 1942, 39, 389. (Abstract.)

163. ROTTER, J. R. Studies in the use and validity of the Thematic apperception test with mentally disordered patients. I. Method of analysis and clinical problems. *Character & Pers.*, 1940 9, 18–34.

164. SANFORD, R. N. *Procedure for scoring the Thematic apperception test.* Cambridge: Harvard Psychological Clinic, 1939. (Privately printed.)

165. SANFORD, R. N. Some quantitative results from the analysis of children's stories. *Psychol. Bull.*, 1941, 38, 749. (Abstract.)

166. SARASON, S. B. The use of the Thematic apperception test with mentally deficient children. I. A study of high grade girls. *Amer. J. Ment. Def.*, 1943, 47, 414–421.

167. SARASON, S. B. & ROSENZWEIG, S. An experimental study of the triadic hypothesis: reaction to frustration, ego-defense, and hypnotizability. II. Thematic apperception approach. *Character & Pers.*, 1942, 11, 150–165.

168. SCHWARTZ, L. A. Social situation pictures in the psychiatric interview. *Amer- J. Orthopsychiat.*, 1932, 2, 124–132.

169. SLUTZ, M. The unique contribution of the Thematic apperception test to a developmental study. *Psychol. Bull.*, 1941, 38, 704. (Abstract.)

170. SYMONDS, P. M. Adolescent phantasy. *Psychol. Bull.*, 1941, 38, 596. (Abstract.)

171. SYMONDS, P. M. Criteria for the selection of pictures for the investigation of adolescent phantasies. *J. Abnorm. Soc. Psychol.*, 1939, 34, 271–274.

172. TOMKINS, S. S. Limits of material obtainable in the single case study by daily administration of the Thematic apperception test. *Psychol. Bull.*, 1942, 39, 490. (Abstract.)

173. WYATT, F. Formal aspects of the Thematic apperception test. *Psychol. Bull.*, 1942, 39, 491. (Abstract.)

Verbal Summator

174. GRINGS, W. W. The verbal summator technique and abnormal mental states. *J. Abnorm. Soc. Psychol.*, 1942, 37, 529–545.

175. SHAKOW, D. Schizophrenic and normal profiles of response to an auditory apperceptive test. *Psychol. Bull.*, 1938, 35, 647. (Abstract.)

176. SHAKOW, D. & ROSENZWEIG, S. The use of the Tautaphone (verbal summator) as an auditory apperceptive test for the study of personality. *Character & Pers.*, 1940, 8, 216–226.

177. SKINNER, B. F. The verbal summator and a method for the study of latent speech. *J. Psychol.*, 1936, 2, 71–107.

178. TRUSSEL, M. The diagnostic value of the verbal summator. *J. Psychol.*, 1939, 34, 533–538.

Miscellaneous Projective Techniques

179. BENDER, LAURETTA. A visual motor Gestalt test and its clinical use. *Res. Monogr. Amer. Orthopsychiat. Ass.*, 1938, No. 3.

180. BUHLER, CHARLOTTE. The ball and field test as a help in the diagnosis of emotional difficulties. *Character & Pers.*, 1938, 6, 257–273.

181. BUHLER, CHARLOTTE & KELLEY, G. *The world test.* New York: Psychological Corporation, 1941.

182. DESPERT, J. LOUISE. Technical approaches used in the study and treatment of emotional problems in children. Part II. Using a knife under certain conditions. *Psychiat. Quart.*, 1937, 11, 111–130.

183. DESPERT, J. LOUISE. Technical approaches used in the study and treatment of emotional problems in children. Part I. The story: a form of directed phantasy. *Psychiat. Quart.*, 1936, 10, 619–638.

184. DUBIN, S. S. Verbal attitude scores predicted from responses in a projective technique. *Sociometry*, 1940, 3, 24–48.

185. FITE, MARY D. Aggressive behavior in young children and children's attitudes toward aggression. *Genet. Psychol. Monogr.*, 1940, 22, 151–319.

186. FOULDS, G. The childs response to fictional characters and its relationship to personality traits. *Character & Pers.*, 1942, 10, 289–295.

187. HAGGARD, E. A. A projective technique using comic strip characters. *Character & Pers.*, 1942, 10, 289–295.

188. HAGGARD, E. A. & SARGENT, HELEN. Use of comic strip characters in diagnosis and therapy. *Psychol. Bull.*, 1941, 38, 714. (Abstract.)

189. HOROWICZ, RUTH E. A pictorial method for the study of self-identification in preschool children. *J. Genet. Psychol.*, 1943, 63, 135–148.

190. HOROWICZ, RUTH E. Racial aspects of self-identification in nursery school children. *J. Psychol.*, 1939, 7, 91–101.

191. HOROWICZ, RUTH & HOROWICZ, E. H. Development of social attitudes in children. *Sociometry*, 1938, 1, 301–338.

192. KELLY, G. A. & BISHOP, F. A projective method of personality investigation. *Psychol. Bull.*, 1942, 39, 599. (Abstract.)

193. KERR, MADELINE. The validity of the mosaic test. *Amer. J. Orthopsychiat.*, 1939, 9, 232–236.

194. LOWENFELD, MARGARET. The world pictures of children. A method of recording and studying them. *Brit. J. Med. Psychol.,* 1939, 18, 65–100.

195. MARQUIDT, SYBIL. A technique of inquiry into individual personality. *Psychol. Bull.,* 1941, 38, 598. (Abstract.)

196. MIRA, E. Myokinetic psychodiagnosis: a new technique for exploring the conative trends of personality. *Proc. R. Soc. Med.,* 1940, 33, 9–30.

197. MURPHY, LOIS B. *Social behavior and child personality.* New York: Columbia Univ. Press, 1937.

198. PICKFORD, R. W. Imagination and the nonsense syllable: a clinical approach. *Character & Pers.,* 1938, 7, 19–40.

199. PROSHANSKY, H. M. A projective method for the study of attitudes. *J. Abnorm. & Soc. Psychol.,* 1943, 38, 393–395.

200. RAPAPORT, D. The Szondi test. *Bull. Menninger Clin.,* 1941, 5, 33–39.

201. SARGENT, HELEN. An experimental application of projective principles in a paper and pencil personality test. *Psychol. Monogr.,* 1944, 57, No. 5, 1–57.

202. STERN, W. Cloud pictures: a new method for testing imagination. *Character & Pers.,* 1938, 6, 132–146.

203. TUDDENHEIM, R. The reputation test as a projective technique. *Psychol. Bull.,* 1931, 38, 749. (Abstract.)

204. WERTHAM, F. & GOLDEN, LILI. A differential diagnostic method of interpreting mosaic and colored block designs. *Amer. J. Orthopsychiat.,* 1941, 98, 124–131.

Films

205. FISHER, M. S., STONE, L. J., & BUCHER, J. Balloons: demonstration of a projective technique for the study of aggression and destruction in young children. New York: New York Univ. Film Library, 1941. (650 ft., sound.)

206. FISHER, M. S., STONE, L. J., & BUCHER, J. I. Blocking games. II. Frustration game. New York: New York Univ. Film Library, 1942. (1200 ft., sound.)

207. FISHER, M. S., STONE, L. J., & BUCHER, J. Finger painting: children's use of plastic materials. New York: New York Univ. Film Library, 1941. (790 ft., Kodachrome.)

SECTION III

Supplementary References

208. ALLPORT, F. H. Teleonomic description in the study of personality. *Character & Pers.,* 1937, 5, 202–214.

209. ALLPORT, G. W. Personal documents in psychological science. *Soc. Sci. Res. Coun. Monogr.,* 1942, No. 49.

210. ALLPORT, G. W. *Personality: a psychological interpretation.* New York: Holt, 1937.

211. ALLPORT, G. W. The psychologist's frame of reference. *Psychol. Bull.,* 1940, 37, 1–28.

212. BALDWIN, A. L. The statistical analysis of the structure of a single personality. *Psychol. Bull.*, 1940, 37, 518–519. Abstract. (See also discussion in 209.)

213. BALKEN, EVA RUTH. Psychological researches in schizophrenic language and thought. *J. Psychol.*, 1943, 16, 153–176.

214. BARTLETT, F. C. An experimental study of some problems of perceiving and imagining. *Brit. J. Psychol.*, 1916, 8, 222–266.

215. BENJAMIN, A. C. *An introduction to the philosophy of science.* New York: Macmillan, 1937.

216. BEERS, C. *A mind that found itself.* New York: Longmans, Green, 1908.

217. BINET, A. & SIMON, T. The development of the intelligence in children. *L'Année Psychologique*, 1905, 11, 163–244.

218. BLEULER, E. Upon the significance of association experiments. *In* Jung, C. G., *Studies in Word Association.* (Trans. by M. R. Eder.) New York: Moffat Yard, 1919. Pp. 107.

219. BOYNTON, P. L. & WALSWORTH, B. M. Emotionality test scores for delinquent and non-delinquent girls. *J. Abnorm. Soc. Psychol.*, 1943, 38, 87–93.

220. BRIDMAN, P. W. *The nature of physical theory.* Princeton: Princeton Univ. Press, 1936.

221. BRITTAIN, H. L. A study of imagination. *Ped. Sem.*, 1907, 14, 137–207.

222. BROWN, J. F. *Psychodynamics of abnormal behavior.* New York: McGraw-Hill, 1940.

223. CARTWRIGHT, D. & FRENCH, J. R. R., JR. The reliability of life history studies. *Character & Pers.*, 1939, 8, 110–119.

224. CLARK, L. P. The phantasy method of analyzing narcissistic neuroses. *Med. J. and Rec.*, 1926, 123, 154–158.

225. CONKLIN, E. S. The foster child phantasy. *Amer. J. Psychol.*, 1920, 32, 59–76.

226. CROSSLAND, H. R. The psychological meethod of word-association. *Univ. Oregon Psychol. Ser.*, 1929.

227. DAVIS, F. P., JR. Diagnostic methods in clinical psychology. Unpublished doctoral dissertation. Univ. Texas, 1943.

228. DUFF, I. F. A psychoanalytic study of a fantasy of St. Thérèse de l'enfant Jésus. *Brit. J. Med. Psychol.*, 1926, 5, 345–353.

229. FREUD, ANNA. *The ego and the mechanisms of defense.* (Trans. by C. Baines.) London: Hogarth, 1937.

230. FREUD, S. *General introduction to psychoanalysis.* New York: Boni & Liveright, 1920.

231. GALTON, F. *Inquiries into human faculty and its development.* London: J. M. Dent Co., 1883.

232. GARRETT, H. E. & ZUBIN, J. The analysis of variance in psychological research. *Psychol., Bull.*, 1943, 40, 233–267.

233. GRANT, D. A. On "The analysis of variance in psychological research." *Psychol. Bull.*, 1944, 41, 158–166.

234. GREEN, G. H. *The daydream. A study in development.* London: Univ. London Press, 1923.

235. GRIFFITHS, R. A. *A study of imagination in early childhood, and its function in early development.* London: Kegan Paul, 1935.

236. HALL, G. S. Notes on cloud fancies. *Ped. Sem.,* 1903, 10, 96–100.

237. HARVEY, N. A. Imaginary playmates and other mental phenomena of children. Ypsilanti, Mich.: State Normal College, 1918.

238. HULL, C. L. & LUGOFF, L. S. Complex signs in diagnotsic free association. *J. Exp. Psychol.,* 1921, 4, 111–136.

239. JOHNSON, W. The quantitative study of language behavior. *Psychol. Bull.,* 1931, 38, 528.

240. JOHNSON, W., FAIRBANKS, HELEN, MARY B., & CHOTLOS, J. W. Studies in language behavior. *Psychol. Monogr.,* 1944, 56, No. 2.

241. JOHNSON, W. Language and speech hygiene. Chicago: Institute of General Semantics, 1939.

242. JUNG, C. G. The association method. *Amer. J. Psychol.,* 1910, 21, 219–269.

243. JUNG, C. G. *Studies in word association.* (Trans. by M. D. Eder.) New York: Moffatt Yard & Co., 1919.

244. KANTOR, J. H. Current trends in psychological theory. *Psychol. Bull.,* 1941, 38, 29–61.

245. KENT, GRACE H. & ROSANOFF, A. The study of association in insanity. *Amer. J. Insan.,* 1910, 67, 37–96.

246. KORSYBSKI, A. *Science and sanity.* Lancaster: Science Press, 1933.

247. LEHRMANN, P. R. Phantasy in neurotic behavior. *Med. J. Rec.,* 1927, 126, 342–344.

248. LEHRMANN, P. R. The phantasy of not belonging to one's family. *Arch. Neurol. Psychiat., Chicago,* 1927, 18, 1015–1025.

249. LEWIN, K. *A dynamic theory of personality.* New York: McGraw-Hill, 1935.

250. LINQUIST, E. F. *Statistical analysis in educational research.* New York: Houghton Mifflin, 1940.

251. LLOYD, WILMA. Some aspects of language as significant of personality. *Psychol. Bull.,* 1941, 38, 747. (Abstract.)

252. MACCURDY, J. Phantasy of the mother's body in the Hephaestus myth and a novel by Bulwer-Lytton. *Psychoanal. Rev.,* 1920, 7, 295. (Abstract.)

253. MASLOW, A. H. Dynamics of personality organization. *Psychol. Rev.,* 1943, 50, 514–539, 541–558.

254. MURPHY, G., MURPHY, LOIS, & NEWCOMB, T. *Experimental social psychology.* New York: Harper, 1938. Pp. 279–299.

255. NEWMAN, S. Personal symbolism in language patterns. *Psychiatry,* 1939, 2, 177–183.

256. NEWMAN, S. & MATHER, V. G. Analysis of spoken language of patients with affective disorders. *Amer. J. Psychiat.,* 1938, 94, 913–942.

257. PIAGET, J. *Judgment and reasoning in the child.* New York: Harcourt, Brace, 1928.

258. PIAGET, J. *Language and thought in the child.* New York: Harcourt, Brace, 1932.

259. ROBINSON, E. E. The compensatory function of make-believe play. *Psychol. Rev.*, 1920, 27, 434–438.

260. ROSANOFF, A. J. *The free association test.* (Reprinted from *Manual of Psychiatry.*) New York: Wiley, 1927.

261. SANFORD, F. H. Speech and personality. *Psychol. Bull.*, 1942, 39, 811–845.

262. SEARS, R. R. Survey of objective studies of psychoanalytic concepts. *Soc. Sci. Res. Coun. Monogr.*, 1943, Bull. 51.

263. SEASHORE, R. H. *Fields of Psychology: An experimental approach.* (Chap. 40, Convergent trends in psychological theory.) New York: Holt, 1942.

264. SNEDECOR, G. W. Analysis of variance and covariance of statistically controlled grades. *J. Amer. Statist. Ass.*, 1935, 30, 263–268.

265. SOUTHARD, E. E. On the application of grammatical categories to the analysis of delusions. *Phil. Rev.*, N.Y., 1916, 25, 424–455.

266. STOUFFER, S. A. An experimental comparison of statistical and case history methods of attitude research. (Unpublished.) Chicago Univ. Library, 1930. (See discussion in 209.)

267. SYMONDS, P. M. *Diagnosing personality and conduct.* New York: Century, 1931.

268. THURSTONE, L. L. The stimulus response fallacy. *Psychol. Rev.*, 1922, 30, No. 5.

269. VARENDONCK, J. *The psychology of daydreams.* London: Allen & Unwin, 1921.

270. VERNON, M. D. The relation of cognition and phantasy in children. *Brit. J. Psychol.*, 1940, 31, 1–19.

271. VERNON, P. E. The matching method applied to investigations of personality. *Psychol Bull.*, 1936, 33, 149–177.

272. VIGOTSKY, L. L. Thought and speech. (Trans. by Drs. Helen Kogan, Eugenia Hanfmann, and Jacob Kasanin.) *Psychiatry*, 1939, 8, 29–54.

273. WELLS, F. L. & WOODWORTH, R. S. Association tests. *Psychol Rev. Mongr. Sup.*, 1911, No. 57.

274. WOODROW, H. & LOWELL, F. Children's association frequency tables. *Psychol. Rev. Mongr. Sup.*, 1916, No. 97.

Edith Lord

EXPERIMENTALLY INDUCED

VARIATIONS IN RORSCHACH

PERFORMANCE

I. Introduction

URING THE past decade many new personality tests have been devised, little-used old tests have been revised, popular tests have been polished, refined, and expanded. College catalogues throughout the United States have lengthened lists of courses offered in psychology to include instruction in the administration and interpretation of personality tests in general, of "projective techniques" in particular, and of the Rorschach Ink Blot Test specifically.

Literally hundreds of research reports and observational articles have been published on the Rorschach and its clinical use. The bulk of this literature has been concerned with Rorschach patterns as they relate to psychiatric syndromes, to social or cultural groups, to successful and unsuccessful students, workers, or military groups. The practical or empirical success of the instrument has been widely reported. The operational results

Reprinted from *Psychol. Monogr.*, 1950, *60* (10, Whole No. 316) by permission of the American Psychological Association and the author.

of the Rorschach as a diagnostic instrument have been repeatedly acclaimed.

There is, however, a dearth of laboratory investigation of this important and widely-used clinical tool. In fact, there is even a question as to whether the test actually is a projective technique. Schachtel (31) offers an excellent critique of the projection hypothesis of the Rorschach test, and Bellak (3) states flatly that Rorschach's test is *not* a projective method. More clarification of these philosophical and theoretical areas underlying the Rorschach is definitely indicated.

Too, the paucity of statistical studies of reliability and validity, or of adequate norms, plus the existence of contradictory reports on these crucial points has given rise to a diapason of criticism. This cacophony has been particularly painful to the ears of the conscientious clinical psychologist who daily uses the Rorschach for diagnosis, for recommendations for therapy, for vocational or educational guidance and counseling, etc.

As Hsü (16) points out, there are two popular and disparate attitudes toward the Rorschach held by equally psychologically sophisticated persons. One maintains that the prime importance of the instrument is its revelation in symbolic terms of the personality of the individual, considered as a unique universe; the other stoutly maintains that this test, like all other psychological measuring devices, should meet at least minimum standards of statistical reliability and validity.

Hunt (17) criticizes the overemphasis in clinical psychology on quantitative data rather than qualitative, and bases his hopes for the future progress of clinical testing on an increased attention to qualitative behavior of the person tested rather than on quantitative results of the test.

Qualitatively, does a subject, in fact, satisfy one of the basic assumptions underlying all projective techniques—that his concepts reveal his consistent way of organizing experience, as measured by the ideas and feelings he projects into "meaning-free" or ambiguous stimuli? Is a subject reacting only to the "unstructured" or "semi-structured" ink blots on the Rorschach test, or is he reacting to the total perceptual and social field, which includes the administrator of the test and the affective tone of the administrative situation? If these latter two variables are altered, will the subject's perception of the ink blots vary significantly? Can a subject conceal his way of organizing experience or stimulate a pattern not his own? Can an administrator induce an altered Rorschach pattern by explicit or implicit suggestion?

There have been some very interesting explorations of these last two questions. Fosberg (11) studied attempts to fake Rorschach results, and also (12) examined protocols obtained under varied instructions. He demonstrated that psychologically sophisticated subjects, given a neutral or control Rorschach, could not conceal their basic test patterns on two subsequent tests in which they tried to give the best, then the worst, possible impression.

Schachtel (30) emphasizes the importance of a subject's personal definition of the test situation and its demands. He also strongly presents his personal conviction that the three most common subjective definitions of the Rorschach situation are as authoritarian, competitive, or resistance situations. These definitions, he maintains, influence Rorschach results.

Levine (22, 23) reports a study of a series of protocols produced by the same subject while experiencing different situations hypnotically induced. There were marked changes in the Rorschach records of the various situations, each taking on the coloring considered characteristic of a person experiencing the situation created by hypnotic suggestion.

Luchins (27) studied the influence on Rorschach responses of situational and attitudinal factors. Among his findings was the marked need for the development of methods which would prepare a subject for the Rorschach test. A significant factor in the Rorschach results he analyzed proved to be misunderstandings of directions and subjects' hazy concepts of what was expected of them in the testing situation.

Wilkins and Adams (33) studied results of Rorschachs obtained under hypnosis, under sodium amytal, and in the normal, waking state. They found that both the chemically and psychologically induced abnormal states contributed to increased productivity on the Rorschach among subjects described as "overly cautious" or "fearful."

An interesting variation in the sort of study conducted by Levine is that of Bergman, Graham, and Leavitt (4) who reported the Rorschach records of a hypnotically regressed patient, diagnosed as a conversion hysteric. They found that the protocols varied with the level of hypnotic regression but closely followed the expectancies growing out of other clinical data.

Cofer (9) studying the changes in responses given by a patient with organic involvement while under hyoscine, found that some of the cards are more sensitive than others to situational variations.

A recently published research project of the Army Air Forces (32) included an analysis of the influence of the examiner on the number of responses obtained on Rorschach records. Of 36 t-ratios between the means of nine examiners, 12 were significant at the 1 per cent level of confidence and three at the 5 per cent level. Clearly this one scoring symbol (R) would seem to vary with the examiner.

Keeping this last finding in mind, and hypothesizing a continuum between the findings of Levine and Fosberg, one wonders whether the non-hypnotized subject ever experiences attitudes toward the administrator or mood reactions to the total administrative situation which are adequate to alter the determinants of his Rorschach record significantly.[1] This, in brief, is the problem which led to the development of the present study.

II. *The Problem*

Statement of the problem: This study of the influence of neagtive and positive rapport conditions on Rorschach performance is based on the hypothesis that the perception of ambiguous or "unstructured" stimuli is not influenced by the perceiver's affective reaction toward the total stimulus field, which includes the administrator—the person presenting the "unstructured" stimuli. If an experimental test proves this hypothesis false, implications are legion for the interpretation of test results and for the training of administrators.

Of importance is the possibility that this study—a test of the foregoing hypothesis—may reveal whether or not the administrator is a significant part of the stimulus field during the administration of projective tests.[2] The theory behind projective testing is that the subject structures stimuli presented to him in nonstructured or semi-structured form. If a subject is projecting meanings, ideas, and feelings into ambiguous stimuli uninfluenced by the person presenting the stimuli or by the affective tone of the administrative situation, there should be no significant variation in his structuring of the stimuli if either the administrator or the affective tone of the administration is varied.

The problem of transference arises in all therapies, regardless of type, and the findings of this project might conceivably throw some needed light on the subject of transference elements. If the requirements for positive transference could be determined or the situations in which it flourishes could be measured, the selection and training of therapists could be more clearly defined. It is thought that the present study may hold implications for this related problem.

Outside the realm of clinical psychology, this study may have implications for social psychology. Too, the manner in which interpersonal rela-

1. An explanation of the Rorschach scoring symbols used in this study is given in the Appendix. (See p. 141.)

2. Cognizance is taken here of the fact that one cannot amplify specific findings related to the Rorschach ink blots into generalizations concerning projective techniques as a category; however, it is thought that any light on the variability or stability of one projective technique may, at least, suggest areas of desirable investigation for all other clinical tools falling within the "projective" category.

tionships affect perceptual processes is of great current interest to systematic psychology (14) as well as to the field of clinical psychology. While the present study does not answer the questions here posed, it does provide implications for future research in these areas.

Within the framework of the therapeutic situation, there may be at work individual variables which cause one subject to function more "normally" in a threatening environment, another to function more productively or adequately in an environment of heightened acceptance or permissiveness. In so far as the therapist's personality may structure these mood-situations, the results of this project could be revealing.

Designing an experiment to test whether Rorschach records will vary with experimental variation of administrator and tone of administration, one must ask himself, from a theoretical point of view, what variations might be expected. Remembering the experiments of Levine, one might hypothesize radical shifts in protocols from one administration to another if the administrations were adequately loaded with different affective tones. Remembering the experiments of Fosberg, wherein psychologically sophisticated subjects proved incapable of successfully simulating the Rorschach records of personality types other than their own, one might predict no significant variation in total protocol, regardless of administrator or of type of administration.

Somewhere between these extremes, one may ask what sort of variation might be expected (a) if a group of subjects were given control Rorschach administrations, later were given positively loaded[3] Rorschach administrations, and still later negatively loaded administrations; (b) if a group of subjects were given Rorschachs by three different administrators at intervals of four to six weeks. Following are the hypotheses which seem to follow from the cited relevant studies, and which seem reasonable from the standpoint of personality dynamics and the Rorschach symbols or projective response-categories which are widely believed to be related to these dynamics.

1. There will be a variation in the number of responses elicited by the various administrators, regardless of affective variable or sequence of administration. This hypothesis is based on the A.A.F. study, cited above.

2. There will be no consistent variation in number of responses between the first, second, and third administrations; i.e., no increase or decrease in number of responses with successive administrations. However, the variation in number of responses will be related to a subject's initial performance. If a subject gives thirty or fewer responses on his first test, he will increase the

---

3. The word *loaded* is here used to mean *weighted* or *slanted*. See IV, C for complete exposition of this term as herein employed.

number with subsequent testings; if he gives seventy or more on the first, he will decrease his responses on subsequent testing.[4]

3. Even among "normal" subjects, the alterations attendant upon variations of affective tone of administration will be largely dependent upon individual differences, the more stable personality records showing less change, the more labile records showing more change. It is predicted that approximately a third of the subjects' records will show no differences or only minimal changes regardless of administrator, order of administration, or experimentally varied affective tone of administration; a third will be extremely variable, fluctuating with administration order, administrator, and tone of administration. This stability or lability will be reflected in the constancy or shift of the M : sumC ratio.[5]

4. Regardless of the order of administration or the affective loading, there will be some variation in the records obtained by the three administrators which will be a function of the different personalities of the administrators. Since this factor is an unknown variable, it is not possible to predict the anticipated variations specifically. This hypothesis is a logical outgrowth of the known variation of the number of responses with examiner differences (32). Responses are scored as to location areas and determinants. An increase in responses insures an increase in one or another of these scoring categories. Furthermore, since number of responses has been shown to vary with examiner differences, it is not unreasonable to hypothesize that other scoring categories of the Rorschach may be equally sensitive to administrator differences.

5. Regardless of the administrator or the sequence of administration, there will be variations in the protocols produced under the three different administrative situations: neutral or control, positive affective loading, negative affective loading. Specific variations anticipated are the following:

a. Negatively loaded administration.

1) Greater scattering of response determinants among the signs k, K, Fc, and C', indicating a withdrawal from the painful situation (k or K), a depression of a situational sort (C'), and a sensitive approach to the total stimulus environment (Fc) as a way of handling anxiety provoked by the situation. These signs will tend to increase at the cost of the movement and color responses. Fm will appear with greater frequency as an indicator of tension in the face of a threatening situation.

2) There will be an increase in white-space responses (S) as an indication of negativistic or oppositional tendencies.

3) There will be an increase in F% and in FK + F + Fc/R as a reflection of an

4. Since thirty to seventy responses is usually considered the normal range, this hypothesis is based on an anticipation of the operation of central tendency.

5. The particular choice of thirds in this hypothesis is based on verbal prediction made by Dr. Bruno Klopfer.

increased effort to master the situation through intellectual control or through this control supported by heightened sensitivity and introspection.

b. Positively loaded administration.

1) There will be a greater emotional expression, or emotional relationship with the environment in this more permissive situation; this will be reflected in an increase in sumC.

2) There will be an increase in movement responses, M and FM, indicating a wider play of creativity and a greater freedom of expression of "Id drives."

III. Procedure

An experimental design was constructed which aimed toward controlling as many variables as possible. The basic unit of the study was 36 males between the ages of 19 and 27. They were selected at random from a list of approximately 200 college sophomores enrolled in an introductory course in general psychology. Each subject was given three Rorschachs at four to six weeks' intervals. Each of the three Rorschachs was administered by a different person.

The three administrators, A, B, and C, were females, not different in any grossly apparent way; i.e., no one of the three was outstandingly fat or thin, ugly or beautiful. Administrators A and C were brunettes, B was a reddish-blonde. The age range among the three was twelve years, with B the youngest and C the oldest. Each administrator holds a degree in psychology and has had several years' experience in the use of the Rorschach according to the Klopfer technique.

The Rorschach tests were given in a systematic or rotated order so that twelve subjects received control tests first, twelve second, and twelve third. Twelve received negative tests and twelve received positive tests first. The second and third testing sessions were similarly varied.

No subject was tested twice by the same person. Twelve were tested first by Administrator A, second by B, and third by C. The other administrations were distributed similarly. Each administrator used exactly the same technique for the administration of the Rorschach Test, regardless of the affective loading of the pretest situation and regardless of whether the administration was the first, second, or third for the subject.

The negative and positive situations included two simple card-sorting tests administered prior to the Rorschach test for the purpose of setting the affective tone of the session. Identical directions, terminology, and techniques were used in both the negative and positive pre-tests; however, the tone of the administrations was differently slanted. Specific directions for the administration of the three sessions were followed explicitly and without variation by the three administrators. These directions were as follows:

Neutral. Standard Rorschach procedure will be used. The administrator will be courteous but businesslike in manner. She must attempt to avoid either negative or positive affective loading of the situation. There will be no pre-tests nor any gathering of biographical data.

Negative administration. The administrator will assume the role of a harsh, rejecting, authoritarian figure. She must be deliberately unconcerned about the subject, not look at him while asking questions, preparing tests, or giving directions; never smile, give directions in a voice of dictatorial harshness, make every "Hm!" sound like a sneer.

Positive administration. The administrator will be personally warm, charming, appreciative in manner. She must look at subject with a smile while asking questions, preparing tests, or giving directions in an encouraging tone of voice, making every "Hm!" sound like a compliment for work well done.

The following administration will be used verbatim for *both* negative and positive administrations:

Are you Mr. Blank? Come with me! This room. Sit here.

What is your full name? You have an address? Freshman, Sophomore, Junior? Your birthdate?

Are you familiar with an ordinary deck of playing cards? (Place deck face down, with one black nine on the bottom of the pack.) When I say GO turn the cards, one at a time, and pull out all the black nines and the red tens. Put the black nines here and the red tens here (indicate areas with gestures). Work as fast as you can. Ready? Go! (Answer any questions only by repeating words in the foregoing instructions. Note any cheating, i.e., number of times subject turns two or more cards at a time; also note any errors in carrying out instructions or any requests for repetition of instructions.) Record time.

Hm! Some speed! (Leave nines and tens; shuffle remaining cards; replace, face down, before subject.)

Now, when I say GO, turn the cards, one at a time, and see how many face cards—Jacks, Queens, and Kings—you can pull out before I say STOP. Put the red face cards on the black nines and the black face cards on the red tens. Ready? Go! (Allow thirty seconds.)

STOP! (Count face cards and record number.)

Hm! Not bad!

(The Rorschach Test will follow using the same instructions as for the neutral administration.)

As the experimental design reveals, each subject follows a unique pattern. Consequently, if a subject were lost at any stage of the experiment, a substitute would have to be started from the very beginning. In order to insure completion of the design, the entire pattern was started in duplicate; i.e., seventy-two subjects were given first Rorschachs. Despite this precaution, there were several cases wherein both of the pair were lost, and a third subject (with his parallel substitute) was started through the design.

The principal cause for loss appeared to be the subject's reactions to the negatively administered session. Following this session, the subjects seemed more difficult to contact for testing appointments and frequently broke appointments or failed to appear as scheduled. Thirteen of the original seventy-two subjects were dropped following the negatively administered test because they had failed to keep from three to five appointments for the subsequent test. Two subjects were dropped for the same reason following positively administered sessions. Eight of the thirteen were given negatively loaded tests during the first session, five during the second. The losses, by examiner, were approximately equal, two losing four subjects each, the third losing five after negative administrations. The only reason for dropping these subjects, rather than persisting until an appointment was kept, was the time factor. If a period longer than six weeks elapsed between sessions, the subject was dropped and his parallel substituted in the pattern.

With this evidence in mind, one may speculate that the differences between negative results and positive or neutral results might have been greater if methodology had permitted retention of the negative records of the subjects who apparently rejected the entire project after experiencing the negative administration.

A few subjects were lost for other reasons. Three moved from the community before completing the three sessions; two were ill between sessions and unable to meet the requirement of a maximum time-lapse of six weeks between tests.

In every other case, testing of parallel partners was dropped as soon as the principal subject had completed his pattern and thereby precluded the need for a substitute.

As Rorschach records were accumulated, they were coded and mixed. The 108 records were then scored without reference to subject, name of administrator, type or order of administration. Only main responses and determinants were used in the analyses of the records for two reasons: (1) incorporation of additional responses and determinants would unprofitably over-complicate the study; (2) there are marked differences among exponents of the Rorschach method (e.g., Beck, Buhler, and Klopfer) as to the most desirable use to make of these additional determinants in scoring and in interpretation.

IV. Results of the Experiment

In addition to the loss of subjects following negative administrations, there is other evidence that the negative situation was actually traumatic to the subjects. Although the very simple card-sorting pre-tests were designed merely to set the administrative tone of the administration for the Rorschach, behavior on the pre-tests suggests that in many cases the subjects were reacting differently by the time the pre-tests were introduced. The initial greeting, without a smile or a direct look, plus the manner and tone of voice in which the four personal-data questions were asked, apparently caused the subjects some concern.

A. BEHAVIOR ON PRE-TESTS

Not a single subject on the positively-loaded administrations misunderstood the pre-test directions or made an error in carrying them out. Twelve of the thirty-six subjects made from one to six errors on the negative administrations, with a total of twenty-five errors. Failure to understand directions was counted as an error if the subject requested repetition or clarification. If he demonstrated his confusion through incorrectly carrying out the directions, he was not corrected, but the error was noted.

During the Rorschach administration, the writer recorded every audible sigh or audible laugh. The laughs and sighs elicited by this one administrator give further qualitative evidence that the subjects were, in fact, reacting differently to the different affective loadings of the administrations: Eleven of the thirty-six subjects sighed aloud from one to seven times (total of thirty-two sighs) during the free-association period of the Rorschach, i.e., during the initial presentation of the plates. One subject sighed aloud during the positive, two during the neutral, and eight during the negative administrations. Seven subjects laughed aloud once or twice with a total of nine audible laughs; three laughed during the positive, two during the negative, and two during the neutral administrations. No effort was made to tabulate smiles and merely visible sighs.

One observes that audible sighs occur with greater frequency during a cold or rejecting situation than during a warm, permissive situation or a neutral situation, but that laughing aloud occurs with approximately equal frequency during the three different situations.

B. VARIATION IN NUMBER OF RESPONSES

The hypothesis concerning successive increase or decrease of number of responses as a function of the number given on the initial test held well for two cases which initially gave more than seventy responses but failed to hold consistently for twenty-six cases giving fewer than thirty responses at the outset.

There is an apparent bias in testing response limits exceeded by such an uneven number of subjects as exceeded our limits; i.e., two versus twenty-six. The explanation of this procedure rests in the earlier hypothesis based on erroneous original expectancy as to number of responses. Rorschach literature quite generally states that thirty responses can be considered the minimum expectancy with normal, intelligent, adult subjects, seventy responses the maximum expectancy. The failure of our subjects to conform to this expectancy is discussed later under the subheading, "Number of responses."

C. ERLEBNISTYP

Hermann Rorschach's theory of personality rests on the foundation of what he called *Erlebnistyp,* a word which has been variously translated but which is consistently rendered *Experience Type* in the English translation of Rorschach's original paper. He (29) makes reference to the problem, so labeled, throughout his *Psychodiagnostik,* and insists that an individual's protocol should be interpreted within the framework of his *Erlebnistyp,* that is, his introversive, extratensive, or ambiversive orientation, his "experience-balance" in responding to stimuli from within and/or stimuli from without. Rorschach found that *Erlebnistyp* was reflected in the ratio between movement and color responses (M : sumC).

The scoring symbol M denotes, according to Rorschach, "Form perceptions plus kinaesthetic factors"; (29, p. 25) and he adds that "The more kinaesthesis, the more stable the affectivity" (29, p. 26). "Color responses," he continues, "have proved to be the representative of the affectivity and the rule is, the more color in the test, the greater the emotional instability of the subject" (29, p. 76).

A person with more M than C in his record would be designated the M-type (introversive), described by Rorschach (29, p. 81) as having the following characteristics:

1. Predominance of personalized productivity.
2. Intensive rapport.
3. Stable affect and motility, awkwardness, insufficient adaptability to reality and insufficient extensive rapport.

A subject with more C than M would be designated the C-type, more extratensive than introversive. The general characteristics of this type, Rorschach (29, p. 83) lists as follows:

1. The urge to live in the world outside oneself.
2. Restless motility.
3. Unstable affective reactions.

Klopfer (21) has pointed out the necessity of taking into consideration other factors in the record before venturing more than a simple statement of the subject's "natural inclinations" as reflected in his M : sumC ratio. These additional considerations give information as to whether the individual follows these inclinations or is in a state of conflict over them.

For the purpose of the present study, we may confine ourselves to an analysis of the extent to which lability and stability of the M : sumC ratio exists within the framework of our experimentally varied testing situations.

Rorschach recognized the existence of temporary variations in number of M and C in a subject's record if the mood of the subject shifted between dejection and elation; however, he stated that despite the variation in absolute number, "the proportion between them (M and C) changes little or not at all" (29, p. 94).

In the 108 records produced by our thirty-six subjects, variation in absolute number ranged from 0 to 19 on the M side and from 0 to 13 on the sumC side. The proportion between the M and C was exceedingly shifty; and, in addition, there were numerous actual shifts of weight in the ratio from one side to the other. The number and direction of these variations in Experience Balance are summarized in Table I.

TABLE I

Number and Direction of Shifts in Balance on M: sumC Ratios

Frequency and Direction of Change

Situation	M to C	C to M	A* to M	A to C	M to A	C to A	Stable	Per Cent Stable	Per Cent Unstable
I to II	1	2	0	3	4	1	25	69	31
I to III	5	4	2	3	3	0	19	53	47
II to III	6	6	1	4	1	0	18	50	50
A to B	7	2	1	2	4	2	18	50	50
A to C	8	2	3	2	1	1	19	53	47
B to C	2	4	2	4	0	0	24	67	33
0 to +	2	5	2	1	2	4	20	56	44
+ to −	4	5	3	2	2	0	20	56	44
0 to −	2	7	1	2	1	2	21	58	42
Totals	37	37	15	23	18	10	184	57	43

* The symbol A is used to denote ambi-equality of M and sumC.

From Table I it can be seen that the greatest stability of M: sumC ratio exists between administrations I and II; even here, 31 per cent of the cases shifted from one balance to another; i.e., there was variation *within* approximately a third of the persons tested, as measured by an individual's production of more movement than color responses in one situation, more color than movement responses in another situation. A close second in rank order of stability is that between records obtained by administrators B and C, wherein 67 per cent maintained a constant balance.

The greatest number of shifts in balance occurred equally between Administrations II and III and between Administrators A and B. In both these categories, exactly half the cases maintained a constant balance and half shifted in one direction or another.

In reading Table I, it must be remembered that a shift, from M to C for example, means that the subject actually showed more M than C under the first condition considered and more C than M under the second condition listed.

A first glance at the totals in the columns labeled "Per Cent Stable" and "Per Cent Unstable" might suggest that approximately half the subjects maintained a constant stability throughout the experiment regardless of sequence, administrator, or type of administration. Such a conclusion cannot be drawn from Table I, however, since stability therein is noted within, but not between, the variable situations.

An examination of the data reveals that only fourteen of the thirty-six cases maintained a constant balance on the M: sumC ratio throughout all variations in testing situations. Of these fourteen, ten held a balance weighted on the M side of the ratio, four showed consistent weighting on the sumC side, and none maintained ambi-equality of weighting. One may, therefore, conclude that 39 per cent of the subjects retained a stable Experience Type throughout the experiment, approximately three fourths of whom were introversively oriented, a quarter of whom were extratensively oriented.

These conclusions, then, would support the prediction stated earlier in this study that approximately a third of the subjects would produce stable records. However, on the basis of Rorschach's description of the M-type and C-type personalities, noted earlier in this discussion, one would have suggested that the fourteen subjects with stable records would *all* have been of the M-type. Table I shows us that A-type, M-type, and C-type personalities in one situation can become another personality type in another situation. The additional analysis of the data shows us that both M-type and C-type personalities are capable of maintaining their personality type in the face of varying situations, but that the odds are three to one that the subject who maintains such constancy will be an M-type personality.

D. STATISTICAL TREATMENT OF THE DATA

In order adequately to test the principal hypothesis of this experiment concerning the influence of negative and positive rapport conditions on Rorschach performance, and the numerous collateral hypotheses—the influence of successive administrations and different administrators, and the kind and amount of variation in the numerous scoring categories—one must look to statistical analysis.

To justify the greatest confidence in probabilities obtained from analysis of the data, *t*-ratios were computed for the numerous pairs of series offered by the data.[6] The particular *t*-ratio used was Fisher's formula as described by Lindquist (26, p. 58 ff.) under the title "The Significance of a Difference in the Means of Related Measures":

$$t = \frac{M_0 - M_H}{\dfrac{\text{Sum } d^2}{n(n-1)}}$$

These *t*-ratios (a total of 243) and the interpretations of them are presented in the following pages.

In working the *t*-tests, data were fractionated in the following manner: All tests given during the first session were grouped, regardless of who gave them or of what kind of affective tone marked the administration; this procedure was followed for the second and third administrations as well. All tests given by Administrator A were grouped, regardless of whether they were administered first, second, or third in the series, regardless of whether the tone of administration was positive, negative, or neutral. A similar grouping was made for tests given by Examiners B and C. All tests given during a positively loaded test situation were grouped without respect to who administered them or to the serial number of the situation. Identical groupings were made for tests administered in the negative and the neutral situations.

This combination of heterogeneous data, of course, introduces a special problem in the interpretation of the results of the *t*-tests. If variance is found due to administrations, this variance is operating when testing the differences between administrators and between types of administrations. Where significant variance exists only within one of the three major groups of variables, this problem loses some of its importance. If, however, variance is shown to exist as a function of the repetition of the test, this variance will operate to enlarge the sigma, hence enlarge the denominator, of the *t*-tests

6. Cognizance is taken here of the criticism to which this study is subject as a result of the practice of treating scoring categories as unique parts of a whole without reference to the whole of which they are an integral part. The writer can think of no other method of experimental approach to the investigation of the Rorschach and the personality factors it is judged to measure except by analysis of the separate elements which contribute to the whole. Recognizing the imperfection of the approach, the plea is offered that it remains the best of all possible existing approaches.

between other variables. The influence would produce spuriously low *t*-ratios among the other groups of variables.

This weakness of the *t*-test, which inevitably exists when data are fractionated and combined as in the present study, is not a serious drawback if one bears in mind that *t*-ratios approximating zero (say, under 1.000) throughout one whole set of data strongly indicate no real differences; if one remembers, also, that any significant or very significant *t*-ratio in one of the three groups of variables within a set will contribute to spuriously low *t*-ratios among the other groups, and that, therefore, a marginal *t*-ratio would be significant if the variance due to other factors were partialed out.

One other element of the statistical treatment demands discussion: Computation of *t*-ratios has been made on mean frequencies of scoring categories regardless of whether these scores are expressed as percentages of the total responses or as absolute numbers. While the percentages are not seriously affected by the variation in total number of responses, the absolute numbers are. For example, if the positive administration produces more responses than the negative, there will not necessarily be any alteration in the per cent of whole responses; there will, however, necessarily be an increase on the positive administration in the frequency of certain of the response determinants. On a statistical level, one is eager to discover *which* determinants increase; on an interpretative level, one attempts to explain *why* one determinant increases and another does not, whether the increase is a concomitant of increased responses or not.

If there were a significant difference in number of responses from the first to the second to the third administration, any differences in tabulated scoring symbols would have to be held suspect as an artifact or the frequencies would have to be reduced to ratios. However, no such differences in R were found to exist.

E. STATISTICAL FINDINGS

Number of responses. The greatest constancy in mean number of responses proved to be that between administrations. It is interesting to note here that Rorschach literature is consistent in reporting that the normal number of responses is around thirty with normal ranges reported from fifteen to seventy-five.

Hermann Rorschach: Normal subjects generally give from 15 to 30 responses, rarely less than 15, often more than 30 (29, p. 21).

Klopfer and Kelley: The range of responses found most frequently in all large-scale investigations of adults seems to be between twenty and forty (21, pp. 208–209).

Brussel and Hitch: Normal is around 34. . . . Normal range is from 25 to 75 (6, p. 3).

Bochner and Halpern: The average [number of responses] seems to fall between 20 and 50 (5, p. 71).

Charlotte Buhler gives a minus weighting for 3 for fewer than twenty-five responses (7, p. 11).

As an aside, one wonders if these published means and ranges are not a bit high. Only on the positive administration and under C's administration do our subjects reach or exceed means of thirty responses.

Further in this vein, it should be noted that the previously cited study conducted by the Army Air Forces (32) shows the average number of responses for servicemen undergoing classification testing to be only twenty. Perhaps this particular Army test situation stimulated an inhibition of responses. Perhaps, too, the special population of the present study experienced a speical kind of inhibition of response.

Perhaps, on the other hand, the figure thirty is not the true mean for the population as a whole, is not the appropriate cut-off point for a normal number of responses. Possibly separate norm-groups should be established for various segments of the population.

Although there is an increase in the mean number of responses on both the negatively and positively loaded administrations over the neutral administration, with the positive eliciting more than the negative, the variability within each type of administration is large enough to keep the differences below the critical cut-off point for statistical significance higher than the 10 per cent level of confidence which exists between the positive and the neutral administrations.

There is a very significant difference, however, between the number of responses elicited by Administrators A and C. Whether giving a first, second or third administration, whether being negative, positive, or neutral, Administrator C obtained, on the average, a sufficiently larger number of responses virtually to rule out chance as a cause of the difference (1 per cent level of confidence).

Average time per response. Very significant differences were found in the average response time between the first test and both the second and the third tests. These differences can be explained rather easily in terms of familiarity with the task. On being first confronted with the Rorschach plates, the subjects uniformly spent more time formulating their concepts than they spent on subsequent reassociation with the stimuli. The reduction in response-time is uniform in direction from beginning to end of the series, despite the lack of a significant difference between the second and third administrations.

There is a consistent tendency toward a difference in response times between Administrator C and the other two administrators; in fact, the difference between A and C is significant at the 5 per cent level when rounded to two decimal places. Apparently the subjects, on the average, lingered longer over their responses when giving them to Administrator C.

Crude control. F% is considered to be one of the key determinants in a Rorschach protocol. It is the scoring symbol used to indicate the percentage of responses determined solely by the shape, contour, or outline of the blot. Briefly, it is interpreted as a measure of the control exercised by the subject. Buhler and Lefever (8) designate it as a measure of rational functioning. Excessive F% (50 per cent or above) is considered to be an indication of undue constriction, or an accompaniment of depression or anxiety.

While the means of the various measures of our subjects stay well under the 50 per cent upper limit for normalcy, we may speculate that significant increases in F% mean increased depression, anxiety, or constriction. No such significant increases are found as a function of the number or the type of the administration; however, it is interesting to observe that the lowest mean is found for the positive administration and the highest for the negative.

Again we find significant differences among administrators. A differing at the 1 per cent level with C and at the 5 per cent level with B. There is no difference between B and C.

Refined control and its components. The FK + F + Fc per cent is another measure of control; however, it is distinguished from F% alone by the quality of the control it reflects. Klopfer (21) has called the latter "crude control" and the former "refined control." Separately considered, the determinant FK (vista concept) is usually interpreted as reflecting introspection or insight; Fc (texture concept), as reflecting tact or sensitivity.

Although there is not a critically significant difference in the amount of refined control displayed in the various types of administration, the means show a consistent increase from the lowest mean on the positive administration to the highest mean on the negative administration, paralleling the tendency on F% or crude control.

A significant difference between the first and the third administration suggests several alternative possibilities. The mere repetition of the Rorschach probably brought about a degree of loss of spontaneity in responding to the stimuli. This was replaced successively more frequently by increased refined control of reactions to the stimuli.

While there is practically no difference between Administrators A and B in the average percentage of responses with this combination of determinants, Administrator C differs at the 10 per cent confidence level from A and differs significantly from B.

Further light may be thrown on the factors influencing these differences in the combination-score by inspecting the components that contribute to it. F% has already been analyzed. The raw data show a low frequency of FK and Fc responses. The responses, however, occur with adequate frequency and with sufficient approach to normality of distribution to permit application of the *t*-ratio statistic.

A *t*-ratio for Fc between Administrators B and C was not computed since the difference between means of .05 is so small as to insure a *t*-ratio of approximately zero. Despite the low frequency and small differences in means between A and the other two administrators, the variability was sufficiently small to produce a significant difference between A and C, and a very significant difference between A and B. The latter two administrators consistently elicited more Fc responses than did A. This observation would tend to rule out Fc as a contributing factor to the significant difference between B and C on the FK + F + Fc percentage. Considering, too, the insignificant *t*-ratio between B and C on F%, one might suppose that despite very low frequency and apparent scatter, the FK responses are the greatest single contributing factor to the FK + F + Fc per cent difference between B and C; however, this convenient supposition is not supported by the data, as will be subsequently shown.

It is interesting to note that F% (crude control) was sufficiently higher for A than for B or C to produce significant and very significant differences respectively; whereas, Fc (tact or sensitivity) was sufficiently *lower* for A than for B and C to produce very significant and significant differences respectively. It is not surprising, then, that when these two determinants, F and Fc, are summed with a third determinant FK the differences between A and both B and C disappear but the difference between B and C is exposed.

The scoring category FK is used for concepts incorporating vista, distance, perspective. There are no significant differences in FK on the successive administrations, although the means reflect a consistent decrease in the use of this determinant. Nevertheless, no inferences can be made from such data.

The lack of significant differences among administrators also permits no interpretation, inference, or conclusion. We may only say that our analysis of FK offered no clarification of the questions growing out of the findings for FK +F + Fc per cent. This latter category, then, appears to be a unique whole, not paralleling any one of its three components in its stability or variation under the varied situations.

The affective loading of the administrations had a significant degree of influence on the scoring category FK. Both the negative and the positive administrations show more mean FK than does the control administration.

The difference between the neutral and the positive administrations is significant at the 5 per cent level of confidence.

The symbols K and k. Responses classified as K are interpreted as a sign of "free-floating" anxiety or of insecurity. Douglas (10) found the use of this type of response serving "as conversational material until something further can be found."

K responses remain quite stable through the successive administrations. There is a noticeable difference, however, in the amount of K elicited by the different administrators, B and C differing at the 10 per cent level of confidence.

Like K, responses classified as k are interpreted as reflecting feelings of anxiety, insecurity, or inadequacy; however, the two categories are differentiated by the control factors implicit in a k response, absent in a K response.

The low frequency of the determinant k is reflected in low means for the various measures. Neither the variation of administrator nor the type of administration affected this scoring symbol to a degree worth noticing. There is a consistent, though insignificant, reduction in the appearance of this determinant on the successive tests, each administration eliciting somewhat fewer such responses than the preceding.

The C′ determinant. Our thirty-six subjects produced, on the average, about one and a half achromatic color responses (C′) per record without variation from one administration to the next. There was variation in the C′ responses with type of administration. The increase from an average of one C′ on the control Rorschachs to an average of two on the positively loaded Rorschachs boosts the confidence level between these variables to 10 per cent. Administrator A elicited the lowest frequency of C′ responses, differing from both B and C at the 5 per cent confidence level.

Movement responses. There are no statistically significant differences higher than the 10 per cent level of confidence in the number of Fm, inanimate movement, responses produced under any of the three variations of the testing situation. The constancy in number from one administration to another is so great as to preclude the necessity of computing *t*-ratios.

Mean differences, however, exist as a function of the variation in type of administration, the *t*-ratio between the control and the positive administrations exceeding the 10 per cent level of confidence that a real, not chance, difference exists.

The animal movement responses, FM, vary little or not at all on the successive administrations, and they fail to vary significantly with variation in type of administration. However, there are differences at the 5 per cent level of confidence between Administrators A and C, and at the 1 per cent level between B and C, Administrator C eliciting the larger number of responses in both comparisons.

The frequency of responses classified as M, human movement, varied sufficiently to reach the 5 per cent level of confidence between one pair of variables and the 10 per cent level between four other pairs. Human movement is consistently interpreted as a sign of inner adjustment or equilibrium, a capacity for the absorption of emotional stimuli whether originating from within or without.

An excess of M on the positive administration over the neutral created a difference significant at the 5 per cent level of confidence, and the positive administration shows a difference from the negative at the 10 per cent level.

Administrator C provoked the highest mean frequency of M responses, differing from both A and B at the 10 per cent level of confidence. Further, the mean number of M on the third administration was sufficiently below the number on the second to give a *t*-ratio significant at the 10 per cent level.

Emotionality. The C-type personality was discussed earlier in this paper, and the relationship of sumC to M was defined. Not forgetting the importance of this interrelationship, let us look at the meaning of color responses per se in Rorschach records. Color is considered to be the determinant of emotionality. Lack of color is considered an indication of constriction; excessive use of color is interpreted as emotional lability or overreaction to external emotional stimuli.

The use of color varied little on successive administrations. There was an infinitesimal difference between the subjects' sum of color responses on the neutral and the negative administrations; in fact, no significant differences occurred among any of the types of administration.

The really important differences in the use of color responses occurred with the variation of examiners. Administrator A elicited significantly fewer color responses than C and very significantly fewer than B.

Content categories. Normally, the sum of animal and animal-detail concepts constitutes approximately 50 per cent of the content of Rorschach concepts. Our subjects linger close to this norm. An increase in A% is usually interpreted as evidence of stereotypy of thinking or a repression of intellectual activity; a decrease in A%, contrarily, is widely interpreted as less confinement to the obvious, a broader range of thinking and/or interests.

There are completely unimportant differences in A% on successive administrations of the test. There is no appreciable difference in A% from one examiner to another; although, again, the differences between Administrator A and the other two examiners show a stronger tendency toward significance than does the difference between B and C, that between A and C closely approaching the 10 per cent level of confidence.

The percentage of A% responses on the affectively loaded administrations differs significantly, with the negative administration producing the percentage higher than that on the positive administration. Also, the neutrally conducted tests deviate from the positive with a difference at the 10 per cent level of confidence.

There is agreement among users of the Rorschach that the number of animal responses should and do exceed the number of animal-detail responses in a normal, healthy record. Therefore, it was considered advisable to break down the A% scoring symbol into its component parts in an effort to examine the circumstances under which both animal responses and animal-detail responses may vary or remain stable.

Examination reveals no significant differences in the number of whole animal responses elicited in the various situations. Even the means do not show a difference worth comment. Certainly this analysis of the number of whole animal responses does not help appreciably to clarify the differences obtained in the A%. A look at the means and critical ratios for animal details is indicated; however, one must not overlook the fact that absolute number frequencies introduce different considerations from those under consideration when one is speaking of percentages.

In all measures, the number of A responses exceeds the number of Ad responses, indicating that our subjects on the average maintain the healthier balance regardless of variation in testing situations. With both symbols there are infinitesimal differences in frequencies from one testing situation to the next. Among administrators, C elicits the highest frequency for both A and Ad responses. Among the types of administrations, the control Rorschachs show the lowest mean for both scoring categories.

Differences at the 5 per cent level of confidence exist between Administrator A and both B and C, with A gleaning significantly fewer Ad responses than B or C.

As with other scoring categories, the number of A and Ad responses by themselves are considered to have little meaning. Whereas, an increase in Ad may indicate a tendency toward a critical attitude, this interpretation of excessive Ad in a record is made only if the sum of animal-detail and human-detail responses exceeds the sum of whole animal and whole human responses. This observation calls for an analysis of the number of human and human-detail responses.

Several measurable differences in number of whole human responses exist. The frequencies are exceedingly stable from the first through the third administration. While Administrator C provoked a larger mean number of human responses than did either A or B, only the difference with A is great enough to produce a *t*-ratio significant at the 10 per cent level of confidence.

The means of the types of administration show an increase in human concepts on both the negative and positive administrations over the number on the control administration, with the difference between the neutral and positive rising to the 10 per cent level of confidence.

Again, the frequency of whole versus part concepts of human figures is a more important consideration than the mere number of either.

A comparison of means reveals that the records of our subjects, regardless of variables, maintain a healthy preponderance of H over Hd responses.

Administrator C evoked a greater number of Hd responses than either B or A, and the mean of C's administrations differs significantly from that of A.

Popular responses. The means of the popular responses elicited by the various examiners are identical. There is a slight but steady increase in mean P from the first to the second to the third administration, which may easily be explained in terms of increased familiarity with the material through mere repetition.

The difference between the means of the negative and positive administrations reaches the 10 per cent level of confidence, the permissive situation stimulating the higher number.

Use of ground as figure. Neither repetition of administration nor affective loading of administration produced any difference in the number of white-space, S, responses on the Rorschach records. Neither are Administrators A and B essentially different in the amount of S they provoked on the protocols. Administrator C, however, differed from both A and B in eliciting a higher frequency of white-space responses, and differed from A at the 5 per cent level of confidence.

An earlier discussion of additional responses explained why they were not incorporated into the analysis of results on this study. An exception should be made, however, of the white-space scoring category. Among normal or near-normal subjects, white-space responses occur most frequently concomitant with reaction to inked areas of the plates. Arbitrary scoring methodology requires that, in such mixed concepts, the inked area be scored as the main response location and the white space be scored as an additional response location. Consequently, many clear-cut reactions to white space are buried among the additional responses. Better to understand the actual amount of and variability in the use of white space, it was decided to sum the absolute number of main and additional S responses and analyze the distribution of this total reaction to ground.

The total use of white spaces by our subjects varies significantly with type of administration and among administrators. The smallest amount of total S + (s) was elicited on the neutral or control administrations, the most on the positive administrations. While the actual mean difference between neutral and negative administrations is small, the direction of change is so consistent, the variability within the columns so small, that the difference reaches the 5 per cent level of confidence. The higher mean difference between neutral and positive administrations is accompanied by sufficiently increased variability to hold the difference down to a 10 per cent level of confidence.

Among administrators there exist real differences in the amount of sum-S produced, regardless of number or type of administration. A evoked the least, and C the most, use of white space. The difference is significant at the 5 per cent level of confidence. C also exceeded B in elicitation of total S responses with a difference significant at the 10 per cent level. The most significant difference, however, is between administrators A and B, with a *t*-ratio at the 1 per cent level of confidence.

Percentage of responses to all-color cards. Color, as previously stated, is interpreted as a correlate of emotionality. Since cards VIII, IX, and X on the Rorschach test are composed exclusively of bright-color inks, they are construed to have particular significance in reflecting emotional components of a subject's personality. The normal expectancy of responses on these all-color cards is approximately 40 per cent of the total responses.

Our subjects consistently approximate normal expectancy, with little variation from one administrative situation to another. The largest difference occurs between the neutral and negative administrations, where the *t*-ratio rises to a 10 per cent level of confidence.

Apparently the overrejecting situations brought about a measurable decrease in response to external emotional stimulation, creating a dampening effect on the subjects.

Manner of approach. The number of whole responses in a Rorschach record provides two separate clues for interpretative analysis: (1) a clue as to the percentage of responses which are based on incorporation of the total blot-stimulus in the concept-formation; (2) a clue as to the ratio between whole responses and movement responses, i.e., the W : M ratio.

The first of these clues will be explored later upon the presentation of means and *t*-ratios for W%. The second requires the reintroduction of the means for the scoring symbol M.

There is a steady decrease in the mean number of whole responses with each repetition of the test, the difference between number of W responses on administrations I and III being significant at the 5 per cent level of confidence.

If the W : M ratio much exceeds 2 : 1, the interpretation is usually made that the subject is overextending himself; i.e., he is striving beyond his means of achievement. It is not considered a healthy sign. Let us compare our W : M mean ratios for any evidence of this imbalance.

One ratio that was obtained on the second administration achieves the ideal relationship of 2 : 1. With one exception, all other ratios show heavier W weighting; however, the ratio 3 : 1 is not sufficiently in excess of the ideal to merit interpretation of a significant imbalance. The ratio on the neutral administration of 4 : 1, however, is twice the expectancy ratio. On the basis of Rorschach literature, one would have predicted a 2 : 1 ratio on this control administration, regardless of what other predictions attended the other administrations.

The really crucial interpretative factor related to whole responses is the scoring symbol W%—the percentage of total responses which use all of the inked surface of the cards within the framework of a single concept. "In a normal record," say Brussel and Hitch, "about 25 per cent of whole answers are expected" (6). The Individual Record Blank for scoring Rorschach protocols, developed by Klopfer and Davidson, and in wide use, shows a normal range of W% extending from 20 to 40. Every mean in the present study exceeds not only the figure given as a normal mean but also the figure given as the upper limit in the range of normal expectancy for W%. One might assume that the stated norms are in error; however, it seems less arrogant to consider the possibility that the subjects in the present study deviate from the population as a whole somewhat.

Examination supports the earlier finding of reduction of whole responses as a mere function of repetition of the test. When working with percentages rather than absolute numbers, this reduction in tendency is more dramatically revealed. While the decrease in W% is insignificant from the first to the second administrations, the decrease is significant at the 1 per cent level between the third and both the first and the second administrations. C's protocols show the lowest mean percentage of whole responses and differ at the 5 per cent level of confidence with A's records, which show the highest mean W% among administrators.

While none of the differences in means of varied types of administration are statistically significant, it is interesting to observe that the negative administration shows the highest percentage of whole responses and the positive situation the lowest percentage.

As W% decreases, it is mathematically certain that other location subdivisions will increase. The nature of these increases can be explored only by analyzing the frequencies in the data of large details, small details, and tiny or unusual details as they are employed by the subjects in concept-formations.

One clear-cut difference exists between Administrators A and C. Administrator A elicited the highest percentage of W% responses and the lowest percentage of D% responses; in both scoring categories, A and C differ at the 5 per cent level of confidence.

No other variation in testing situation creates differences of statistical significance. Nevertheless, consistent tendencies are revealed by the means of the various types of administrations. The negative administration provoked the lowest mean D% and the positive administration the highest. The *t*-ratio between them barely misses reaching the 10 per cent level of confidence.

The location-scoring symbol D is used when subjects form a concept using a large, insular part of the blot, frequently perceived as a separate entity by normal subjects. Between 45 per cent and 55 per cent of total responses are expected to be D responses.

Not until the third administration did the subjects show any measurable increase in the use of small usual details in the blots. The production of concepts based on these small areas remained constant from the first to the second test but differed between the second and the third to a degree significant at the 10 per cent level of confidence.

The average intelligent subject is expected to have from 5 per cent to 15 per cent of his responses in the d% category. The third administration, then, most nearly provoked d% responses up to a minimum of expectancy for our intelligent subjects. Decreased d% is not generally interpreted as having any particular significance, and increased d% is ignored unless it exceeds 15 per cent of the total responses.

Although there is a lack of significant differences between the various administrators, Administrator C has the highest mean d% within the administrator group, just missing 10 per cent *t*-values with both A and B.

Dd + S% is a sort of wastebasket category for all responses based on blot areas not defined as W, D, or d. Such responses may include tiny details, inside or edge details, unusual combinations of large or small blot areas, and the use of ground as figure. White-space responses were analyzed earlier by absolute number because of their special qualitative meaning in Rorschach interpretation. Their tabulation in combination with unusual details is a necessary part of the process of recording percentages of responses by location areas alone.

There is complete agreement among Rorschach authorities that absence of Dd + S% is normal. There is, however, some difference of opinion as to how high this percentage may go before the upper limit of normalcy is exceeded. The range of estimates is from 2 per cent to 10 per cent, with the consensus approaching the larger figure. In any event, the records of normal persons rarely exceed 10 per cent in this category. On all variations of the testing situation, the subjects in this study remain under this 10 per cent maximum; however, the ceiling is approached in the means of third administration and of the positively administered tests. None of the differences between means are statistically significant.

While Dd + S per cent in excess of 10 per cent is interpreted as an abnormal sign, even an excess of 5 per cent in the category is, by some authorities, considered to be evidence of a pedantic approach to the test (and, by extension, to the environment and to external stimuli, in general). All nine of our means exceed 5 per cent. The foregoing interpretation is more readily made if the higher percentage of Dd + S responses occurs in conjunction with high W%, a fact which we have already observed to exist with our group.

Summary of t-ratios. This completes the statistical analysis of the data on the numerous Rorschach scoring categories. The somewhat lengthy analysis of means and *t*-ratios by Rorschach scoring categories seemed the most clear-cut way of presenting the data of this study. However, that procedure inevitably produces some confusion as to how many statistically significant *t*-ratios were found and where, how frequently Administrator A or administration + had the highest means and on which types of response. These data are presented in summary form in Tables II to IV.

Table II serves to show the administrative circumstances under which the means of each of the thirty-one Rorschach response categories, herein analyzed, held the highest, middle, or lowest numerical position within its group.

Table III shows the frequency with which each variable, within each of the administrative groups, achieved the highest, middle, and lowest means. It will be noted that the positive administration and Administrator C reveal almost identical frequency patterns. No other pairs show this marked parallel tendency.

As Table IV reveals, there were, at the 1 per cent level of confidence, a total of ten differences, over four times as many significant *t*-ratios as one would expect by random sampling; four of these were a function of repetition of the test, six a function of examiner differences. Administrator A differed very significantly from B on three of the scoring categories and from C on two of the measures. B and C differed only once at this level of significance.

At the 5 per cent level of confidence, one would expect twelve significant differences by random samplings; whereas, we obtained twenty-one additional differences at this level alone. Combined with the ten *t*-values at

TABLE II

Rank Order of Means, According to Type of Response

Type of Response	Administration			Administrator			Type of Administration		
	I	II	III	A	B	C	+	−	0
R	2	1	3	3	2	1	1	2	3
T	1	2	3	3	2	1	1	3	2
F%	3	2	1	1	2	3	3	1	2
FK	1	2	3	2	3	1	1	2	3
K	1	2	3	2	3	1	1	2	3
Fk	1	2	3	2	3	1	1	3	2
#F	3	1	2	1	3	2	2	1	3
FC	1	3	2	3	2	1	1	2	3
CF	1	2	3	3	1.5	1.5	1	3	2
C	1	3	2	1	2	3	1	3	2
FK + F + Fc/R	3	2	1	2	1	3	3	1	2
M	2	1	3	2	3	1	1	2	3
sumC	1	3	2	3	1	2	1	3	2
FM	2	1	3	2	3	1	1	3	2
Fm	2.5	2.5	1	3	2	1	1	2	3
Fc	3	2	1	3	2	1	1	3	2
C'	1	2	3	3	2	1	1	2	3
A%	2	3	1	1	2	3	3	1	2
P	3	2	1	2.5	2.5	1	1	3	2
H	2	1	3	2	3	1	1	2	3
A	2	1	3	2	3	1	1	2	3
Hd	3	1	2	3	2	1	1	2	3
Ad	3	2	1	3	2	1	2	1	3
CR%	2	3	1	3	1	2	2	3	1
W%	1	2	3	1	2	3	3	1	2
#W	1	2	3	3	2	1	1	2	3
D%	3	2	1	3	2	1	1	3	2
d%	2	3	1	3	2	1	2	3	1
Dd + S%	3	2	1	3	2	1	1	2	3
S	1	3	2	3	2	1	1	2	3
S + (S)	1	3	2	3	2	1	1	2	3

the 1 per cent level, our total is thirty-one *t*-ratios equal to or above the value required for confidence at the 5 per cent level. This figure is almost three times chance expectancy. Successive administrations accounted for two of the significant differences, and type of administration for four. The fifteen differences among examiners point up the greater frequency between A and C than between either A and B or C and B. Three of the administrator differences were between A and B, one between B and C, but eleven

TABLE III

Frequency of Mean Position, According to Administrative Variable

Administration	Highest Mean	Middle Mean	Lowest Mean
I	13	8½	9½
II	7	15½	8½
III	11	7	13
A	5	8½	17½
B	3½	19	8½
C	22½	3½	5
+	23	4	4
−	6	14	11
0	2	13	16

existed between A and C. Combining differences at the 1 per cent and 5 per cent levels, A differs six times with B and thirteen times with C, while B and C differ a total of twice.

Differences (5 per cent level) resulting from variation in the emotional tone of the testing situation occurred twice between the neutral and negative administrations, once between the positive and neutral, and once between the positive and negative administrations.

Clearly, the largest number of significant and very significant differences at the 1 per cent and 5 per cent levels were the result of examiner differences; and, within our group of examiners, A was the greatest contributing factor to frequency of differences. The negative and neutral administrations appear with equal frequency (three times each) as contributing factors to significant differences in type of administrations. The positive administration is a factor in two of the four differences.

Table IV summarizes the seventeen *t*-ratios at the 10 per cent level of confidence. This figure brings to forty-eight the total number of *t*-values reaching or exceeding the 10 per cent confidence level, a total exactly twice as large as the twenty-four one would expect by random sampling.

At this level of significance, 10 per cent, the variations with type of administration predominated, with nine differences tending toward significance. Two differences were a function of repetition of the test, and six

TABLE IV

Number of Meaningful *t*-Ratios by Variables

Confidence Level	I II	II III	I III	A B	A C	B C	+−	+0	−0	Cumulative Total
1%	1	0	3	3	2	1	0	0	0	10
5%	0	1	1	3	11	1	1	1	2	31
10%	0	2	0	0	3	3	2	6	1	48

occurred with change of administrators. Administrator C was a party to all of these variations, differing three times with A and three times with B. Of the nine differences occurring with variation in the tone of the administration, the positively loaded situation differed six times with the neutral administration and twice with the negatively loaded situation. The negative and positive administrations showed differences at this level of confidence only twice, the negative and neutral only once. Summarizing, the positive administration was a factor eight times, the neutral seven times, and the negative three times.

Summary of results by scoring categories. A few of the Rorschach scoring categories proved exceedingly stable, showing no variation from test to retest, from examiner to examiner, from positive to negative to neutral administration. These stable categories are the following: Dd + S per cent, Fk, and number of A responses.

The majority of the Rorschach scoring categories showed measurable variability as the testing situation varied. The degree of variation, together with the administrative variable which produced the variation in each shifting category, was as follows:

a. R: There was one difference at the 1 per cent level of confidence between administrators and one difference at the 10 per cent level with variation in types of affective loading of the administrative situation.

b. T: There were two differences at the 1 per cent level in average time per response on the successive administrations and one difference at the 5 per cent level between administrations.

c. M: This scoring symbol proved to be quite variable, with one difference at the 5 per cent level and another at the 10 per cent level as a function of the varied affective loading of the testing situation; two differences occurred at the 10 per cent level with variation in administrators, and one difference at the 10 per cent level grew out of mere repetition of the test.

d. FM: Neither successive administrations nor variation in affect in the testing situation influenced FM. Change of administrators, however, produced one difference at the 1 per cent level, another at the 5 per cent level.

e. Fm: This scoring symbol was resistant to change with repetition of the test or with change of examiners. It varied only with the variation in type of administration, and then only at the 10 per cent level of confidence.

f. K. Administrator differences produced one difference in K at the 10 per cent level of confidence. No other variables in the testing situations measurably influenced this determinant.

g. FK: This response determinant also remained stable through successive tests and despite variation in examiners, but it showed a 5 per cent level of significant difference with variation in affective loading of the testing situation.

h. Fc: Examiner difference again is evident with this determinant, there being both a 1 per cent and a 5 per cent difference among administrators. Neither retesting nor affective loading affected the mean number of Fc produced.

i. C': This scoring symbol varied once at the 5 per cent level with repetition of the test, twice at the 5 per cent level with change in administrators, and once at the 10 per cent level with variation in tone of administration.

j. sumC: The composite score sumC remained stable from one test to the next and despite variation in affective loading of the testing situation; however, the mean scores varied significantly twice with change of administrators, once at the 1 per cent level, once at the 5 per cent level.

k. F%: This factor also resisted change with number and type of administration; however, it, too, varied with the examiner once at the 1 per cent level, again at the 5 per cent level.

l. A%: The difference in the type of administration produced two differences in A%, one at the 5 per cent level, the other at the 10 per cent level. Neither administrators nor successive testing influenced the means significantly.

m. P: The number of popular responses remained somewhat constant throughout the experiment. One difference, at the 10 per cent level, occurred with variation in the affective loading of the testing situation.

n. FK + F + Fc / R: The affective loading of the administration did not influence this composite scoring factor; however, both successive testing and change in administrators brought about one difference each at the 5 per cent level of confidence. Examiner differences accounted for an additional difference at the 10 per cent level.

o. H: The number of human-figure responses varied at the 10 per cent level once with change in administrators and once with variation in the type of administration.

p. Hd: Human-detail responses were unaffected by retesting or by affective loading of the test situation; however, there was one difference at the 5 per cent level with change in administrators.

q. Ad: Animal-detail responses were also impervious to the emotional tone of the administration and to successive testing, but they twice showed a difference at the 5 per cent level with variation in administrators.

r. CR%: The percentage of responses to the all-color cards remained somewhat stable, showing only a single difference at the 10 per cent level of confidence upon variation of the affective loading of the administration.

s. #W: The number of whole responses varied once at the 5 per cent level with successive testing but remained impervious to change with varied administration.

t. W%: W% remained unchanged with variation in emotional loading of the test situation, but showed two differences at the 1 per cent level with retesting and one difference at the 5 per cent level with variation in administrators.

u. D%: This location scoring symbol varied once at the 5 per cent level with change in examiners but otherwise quite unchanged.

v. d%: The percentage of small usual details remained stable except for one difference at the 10 per cent level with successive testing.

w. S: The number of white-space responses did not differ from one examination to the next but varied between examiners once at the 5 per cent level and differed once at the 10 per cent level with alteration of affective loading of the administration.

x. S + (s): The sum of main and additional white-space responses resisted change with successive administrations; however, the variation in affective loading produced one difference at the 5 per cent level. Change of administrators proved to be the most significant variable with one difference at the 1 per cent level, one at the 5 per cent level, and a third at the 10 per cent level of confidence.

F. REVIEW OF RESULTS RELATED TO
ORIGINAL HYPOTHESES

Let us briefly review the specific hypotheses and predictions made at the outset of this experiment and check our results against them.

1. The crucial hypothesis related to the stability of responses to the ink blots regardless of variation in environmental stimuli other than the ink blots; i.e., the person presenting the blots, the implicit attitude of the administrator, or the mere repetition in presentation of the blots. Of the twenty-three Rorschach elements subjected to statistical analysis, only three were relatively unaffected by the extra-test stimuli, by "situational" stimuli. Nineteen of the twenty-three elements entered into differences at least once at the 1 per cent, 5 per cent, or 10 per cent levels of confidence. These nineteen varying factors showed a total of forty-six differences attendant upon some variation in stimuli other than the test stimuli—the ink blots themselves. The hypothesis of stability does not hold.

2. It was predicted at the outset that the number of responses would vary with administrators, regardless of number or affective tone of the administration. The means of responses for the three administrators were, roughly, 24, 27, and 33, the difference between highest and lowest means being significant at the 1 per cent level of confidence. These findings support the prediction.

3. No consistent variation in the number of responses was anticipated from the first to the second to the third administration; and, in fact, there was none. Initial records of over seventy responses were expected to decrease with successive administrations, which they did. However, the prediction that initial records under thirty responses would show successive increase in number of responses was not supported by the data.

4. Stability as a function of individual differences reflected in M : sumC ratio proved, as predicted, to isolate approximately 30 per cent of the cases. Also fulfilled was the prediction that the more stable personality records, those of the M-type individuals, would show more situational stability than the records of the C-type persons. Thirty-nine per cent of the subjects retained a stable Experience Type throughout the experiment, approximately three-fourths of whom were M-type personalities, one-fourth C-type.

5. The hypothesis that there would be some variation in the records obtained by the three administrators, regardless of number or type of adminis-

tration, was more than supported by the data. In fact, examiner differences proved the most pervasive influence in the experiment—perhaps the most dramatic finding of the study.

6. The predicted increase in frequency of k, K, c, and C′ with the negative administrations was in no particular realized. In fact, both Fk and Fc had the lowest mean frequency in the negative testing situation; the other symbols—K, FK, and C′—showed means on the negative administrations which were exceeded by the mean frequencies on the positive administrations. Apparently, as judged by these determinants, our thirty-six subjects found the positively loaded testing situation more challenging or threatening than the negatively loaded. This finding negates the hypothesis under discussion.

7. The hypothesized increase in white-space responses in the negative testing situation was somewhat supported, if one judges negative means against control means. Both main S and main-plus-additional S responses showed a mean increase in the negative administrations over the control administrations. However, the negative means of both measures were exceeded by the means on the positive administrations. Apparently the negative administrations did provoke more oppositional behavior than the control administrations; however, the positive administrations elicited even more of this type of response than either the negative or the neutral administrations, a finding which, in effect, negates the hypothesis of peak negativistic behavior on the negative administration.

8. Both crude and refined control, as measured by F% and FK + F + Fc per cent respectively, were expected to increase in the negative administrations. These predictions were supported by the data.

9. The anticipated increase in emotionality on the positive administration, as measured by sumC, was realized. There was a steady rise in mean sumC from the negative to the neutral to the positive administrations.

10. The increase in movement responses (M and FM) on the positive administrations occurred as predicted. Both scoring categories achieved their highest mean with the positive administration. The lowest mean frequency on FM occurred with the negative administration; on M, with the neutral administration.

V. Discussion of Results

In the foregoing report of all of the significant findings for the experimental variables of this study—administrations, administrators, and types of administrations—there was little attempt to make qualitative evaluations or dynamic interpretations of the findings. Nevertheless, one is justified in attempting—in fact, is obligated to attempt—to relate these data to the dynamics of personality.

A. EXPERIMENTAL VARIABLES

An effort will be made to summarize the effects produced upon the experiencing subjects by the different variables herein studied. Too, an attempt is made to understand the differences among the three examiners in terms of the different effects they so consistently produced in the test results. While these procedures have highly speculative components, every effort is made to hold the speculations close to the actual data, to translate into dynamic terms the actual findings of this experiment.

Influence of repetition of the test. The mere repetition of the Rorschach was the least important variable in the entire study, accounting for the smallest total number of important *t*-values, only eight in all. The categories showing change with successive administrations are, for the most part, such as can be quite easily accounted for. One is not surprised to find the average time per response consistently decreasing with repetition, this change accounting for two administrative *t*-values. On being successively confronted with the same stimuli, subjects needed no time to adjust to the stimuli; they could employ mere recall as a substitute for perception, apperception, and conceptualization. Furthermore, there is the strong possibility that the subjects, on once learning the total demand or expectancy offered by the test-challenge, simply functioned in line with our cultural speed-value, meeting the total requirements of the situation with as little expenditure of time as could be managed.

We have elsewhere indicated that our subjects frequently showed moderately compulsive tendencies. As a defense mechanism, the compulsive tendencies would be expected to be most operative when the subjects felt most challenged or threatened. One influence of repetition of the test on this dynamic pattern would be reduction of threat or challenge and consequent reduction in display of the compulsive defense. Three of our eight administration *t*-values grow out of reduced use of the whole blot in concept formation on successive tests. This phenomenon would seem to need no further comment.

Repetition of the Rorschach induced a successive and consistent increase in the use of "refined control." Again, one does not have to delve into deep dynamics of personality to understand this finding. Our intelligent subjects merely demonstrated their ability to improve their mastery over a challenging situation with each successive association with the test-task.

The remaining measurable influence of repetition on the test results is concerned with M, human movement responses. On taking the test for the second time, our subjects manifested greater equilibrium, more inner adjustment, a higher level of imaginative thinking. This is in line with the previously noted increase in security, the display of refined control over the situation which attended successive administrations. The third administration of the same test, however, failed to stimulate our subjects to display this sign of the superior, well-adjusted person. There is a measurable decrease in human movement responses on the third administration. One may speculate that the subjects were inhibited on the first administration, were less inhibited and more secure on the next association with the blots, hence free to demonstrate optimal capacity to absorb and creatively utilize stimuli, but were perhaps just bored with the third presentation of the same blots, bored to the point of not bothering to behave optimally.

The suggestion that boredom attended the third testing situation is somewhat supported by the spontaneous comments of many of the subjects during the third session: "These again?" "I've already done this twice." "Same old thing—a butterfly," etc., etc.

Effect of Examiner A. Among administrators, A elicited responses which reveal the following functioning of the subjects, as indicated by rank order of means: Fewest number of responses, shortest average time per response, least degree of emotional adjustment or social adjustment (FC), least amount of emotional lability (CF), smallest measure of emotionality (sumC), least expression of sensitivity (Fc), least tendency to use all possible environmental stimuli (C′), least stimulation of critical or perfectionist attitudes toward concepts (Ad and Hd), lowest frequencies in all location areas except W% wherein A's subjects show the highest mean.

The signs on which A's mean frequencies were highest in rank order suggest the following reactions to the effect of this administrator on the subjects: Greatest amount of crude control (F%), most frequent manifestation of unhealthy, uncontrolled direct emotional interaction with the environment (C), strongest tendency toward compulsive behavior (W%).

The pattern which seems to form, as one reviews these summarized effects of Administrator A on the subject's Rorschach records, somewhat resembles what one might expect of a person confronted with a threatening, frustrating situation. If this total effect may be considered a mirror of the administrator's personality, then Examiner A would be described as a cold, forbidding, frustrating, threatening figure, these personality components permeating the test-situation regardless of the deliberate and varied role-playing attempted.

There is no way of checking the validity of this thumb-nail sketch of A's personality components as reflected in her effect on Rorschach records. The writer, however, did ask two psychologically sophisticated persons, acquainted with all three examiners, to give subjective descriptions of each. Both described A as the coldest, most inflexible, and most solid of the examiners. One added the adjective "masculine" and the phrase "castrating type of female."

Effect of Examiner B. Administrator B's results fell in the middle position on rank order of means with the majority of measures analyzed in this study. The relative effect of her personality on the administrations is revealed in part, perhaps, by the very paucity of extreme positions achieved under her administrations. Following are the measurable effects: smallest amount of introspection (FK), lowest indication of maturity or creative imagination (M), and least evidence of bouyancy or free expression of primitive drives (FM).

The subjects, under B's administrations, achieved rank order of 1 on only two significant means of categories: highest total degree of emotionality (sumC) and most refined control (FK + F + Fc/R).

The pattern reflected in the mirror of effects suggests that B may possess personality traits that are emotionally exciting to the subjects; at the same time, this excitement apparently is well controlled and does not provoke undue anxiety or tension, neither does it stimulate intellectual activity.

It will be remembered that Administrator B is the youngest of the three examiners. She was subjectively described as the most feminine of the group, the "softest," most nearly the "ideal protecting mother-figure." One person described her as essentially "seductive."

Effect of Examiner C. Administrator C stimulated in subjects the least amount of either crude or refined control (F% and FK + F + Fc/R), the lowest measure of uncontrolled emotionality (C), and the least indication of "whole compulsion" (W%).

The means of the significant measures showing highest rank order under C's administrations are the following: Most responses with shortest average time per response, most introspection and unfixed anxiety (FK and K); best social and emotional adjustment (FC), most evidence of creative imagination (M) and of buoyancy (FM), highest indication of sensitivity (Fc), freest use of all possible stimuli (C'), most evidence of ease in relating to people (H), greatest evidence of critical or perfectionist attitudes toward productions (Ad and Hd), greatest use of all blot location areas except W% wherein C's subjects show the lowest mean.

The effect of Examiner C on the results of the Rorschach are more complex than the effects of the other examiners. One may speculate that C provided more of an intellectual than an emotional stimulation to the subjects.

There would seem to be evidence of challenge with attendant anxiety, but there is also evidence of easy rapport, social adjustment, and less need for control devices in the situation with C.

C is the eldest of the three examiners. She was subjectively described as the most flexible of the three, as more feminine than A but less than B. One person described her as exuberant, "bubbling," the other as "very sympathetic."

Before leaving these speculations on the effects of the various examiners, it should be pointed out that Administrator A quite consistently approximates the pattern of the negative administrations with sixteen agreements out of a possible thirty-one. Administrator B most nearly approximates the pattern of the neutral administrations with fourteen agreements out of thirty-one. Administrator C almost duplicates the pattern of the positive administration with twenty-six agreements out of the possible thirty-one.

One may speculate that the basic personalities of the examiners, which permeated all testing situations regardless of the varied affective roles they played, are in fact related: A = negative; B = neutral; C = positive. Or one might infer that Administrators A and B, for example, in deliberately structuring the positive administrations actually created a situation somewhat like that which was consistently and unintentionally created by C in all administrations, that A and C, in attempting to be neutral succeeded only in resembling B's essential personality, and that B and C in structuring negative situations succeeded merely in resembling A's basic pattern. The former interpretation seems more likely. Whichever interpretation appears more reasonable, the facts and figures serve further to underline the importance of examiner differences.

Effect of positive administrations. This highly permissive situation was deliberately structured to give subjects the feeling of acceptance; the atmosphere was one of approval from beginning to end. This procedure brought about significant changes in the Rorschach behavior of the subjects, as has been previously noted. Let us summarize the effect of these positive administrations:

More responses were elicited, suggesting greater productivity in the more permissive situation. These responses tended to incorporate all possible stimuli presented. There was a greater display of intellectual activity, of creative imagination, plus evidence of increased thinking of a popular or communal type. Stereotypy of thinking was markedly low during the positive administrations. There was evidence of increased resistance against feelings of personal inadequacy plus a rise in tension-tolerance and in self-questioning, or introspection. Finally, there was marked evidence of a greater ease in relating to other human beings.

Effect of negative administrations. The negative test-situations were non-permissive, rejecting; an atmosphere of disapproval prevailed throughout. The effect of this environmental tone on the Rorschach records is reflected in a definite increase in stereotypy of thinking and a decrease in thinking that is in harmony with community thinking. There is a low incidence of intellectual activity of the imaginative or creative sort. Too, there is evidence of withdrawal from emotional stimuli, as measured by a decrease in the number of responses to the all-color cards. There is a marked rise in self-questioning, or introspection, plus evidence of resistance against feelings of personal inadequacy.

Effect of neutral administrations. The chief value in the experimental design of the neutral set of Rorschachs is that of a control factor. Since these tests were administered in the standard manner, without affectively loaded pre-tests, they serve somewhat as a measure of the reactions to the Rorschach which one might expect to find under ordinary clinical situations. The results on the neutral Rorschachs, however, cannot be construed to have the same meaning as is ordinarily attributed to the results of control groups in psychological experimentation. A third of our subjects had had one affectively loaded Rorschach before experiencing the neutral situation; two thirds had had two affectively loaded experiences with the test before receiving the neutral administration. It would be folly to assume that all of these neutral administrations provided identical test-situations for our subjects, that there was no carry-over from previous experiences with the administrative tone in which the blots were presented. Nevertheless, our neutral administrations do offer a modicum of evidence as to how subjects react to the test when standard testing conditions prevail.

The neutral situation elicited fewer responses than the positive, and these responses showed higher stereotypy of content than occurred on the positive administrations. There was less interest in utilizing all environmental stimuli, diminished ease in interpersonal relationship, and diminution of intellectual creativity on the neutral—as compared with the positive—administrations. Lower tension-tolerance and less resistance to feelings of inadequacy were also apparent in the neutral, over the positive, administrations. A lower resistance reaction was evident on the neutral administrations when compared with the negative situations. Less introspection was apparent on the neutral than on the positive administrations, and there was greater reaction to the emotional stimulation of all-color cards.

B. IMPLICATIONS FOR FURTHER INVESTIGATION

This study does not supply the answer to a question which grows out of the findings: What kind of personality was possessed by each of the three administrators? Since administrator differences appeared as the greatest contributing factor to the variation in the Rorschach records, one would like to know what specific and measurable factors in an examiner's personality will bring about what specific and measurable factors in a subject's Rorschach protocol. One wonders if a Rorschach psychogram of the three examiners would resemble the composite mean profiles of the subjects in every way or in any way. These problems should be investigated.

The present study was designed in such a way that a subject could withdraw without suffering too great a penalty. Consequently, several of the individuals who reacted intensely to the negative administration withdrew from the project without finishing the three tests. Their records, of course, could not be included in this study. This entire experiment should be repeated with a group of subjects over whom the examiner can exercise greater control. The fact that differences were revealed as a function of the negative administration makes one wonder how much more significant these differences might have been—and what additional differences might have appeared—if the records of the intensely affected subjects could have been incorporated in the data.

The experimental design of the present study required that each subject not only experience three different affective loadings of the test situation but also experience three different examiners. Two separate investigations should be made as a supplement to the present study. It would be well to know whether the same kind and amount of fluctuation of scoring symbols and M: sumC balance would occur if a single examiner tested a group of subjects under varied affectively loaded situations or if several examiners successively tested a group of subjects under the same affectively loaded circumstances. This latter study should, in fact, be broken into at least two studies, one investigating the results of a series of positively loaded situations, and the other exploring the results of a series of negatively loaded administrations.

In order to minimize the personal equation and thereby to study in purer form the influence of negative and positive rapport factors on Rorschach performances, one could repeat this experiment with the following variations: neutral, positive, and negative administrations could be administered in group form, according to the design herein used, with directions or instructions given by a single examiner through the medium of phonographic recordings. This examiner would, of course, have to cut three records, each affectively differently loaded. While such a procedure could not effectively incorporate the particular card-sorting pre-tests used in this study as tone-setters for the administration, other equally simple devices could be created. In fact, the findings of the present study suggest that no such elaborate preamble is necessary to instill feelings of acceptance or rejection. A cold reception proved adequate to disturb our subjects to the point of misunderstandings and errors.

The significant findings for the group of male college sophomores justify a repetition of this entire experiment with other age groups and with female subjects. While our subjects were randomly selected, they were not selected from the population as a whole but from a rather small stratum of a very small and highly selected population—college sophomores. Our group was shown to deviate from population norms in several instances; e.g., in compulsive tendencies and pedantic approach. One may only speculate on the extent to which other findings in this experiment are a function of the select group from which the subjects were drawn. Would a similar study, with subjects representing a cross section of the population as a whole, show more or less variation, show the same or different kinds of instability?

All of these questions, and many more, must eventually be answered in the laboratory if we are to refine our use of the most popular and pragmatically valuable of the projective techniques: The Rorschach Ink Blot Test. This study is a small step in a direction which must, and certainly will, be taken by other students who realize that the practical success of the Rorschach must be supported by laboratory verification. This area is rich in experimental problems sufficient to excite at least a generation of students.

VI. Summary and Conclusions

This investigation has attempted to explore the stability or variability of the numerous response-determinants of subjects' concept on the Rorschach Ink Blot Test, to discover the extent to which mere repetition of the test, a change of administrators, or an alteration of the affective tone of the testing situation would bring about alterations in number and content of responses, in determinants, and in location areas.

Related studies are extremely few and their contradictory results are explainable as a function of their decidedly different experimental designs. A single study, that of the Army Air Forces, is closely related to the present experiment in its analysis of variation in number of responses as a function of examiner-differences.

What other response categories are subject to fluctuation as a function of examiner-differences? If examiners studiously attempt to structure three different affectively loaded testing situations, will there be consistent differences, or any differences, as a function of these deliberately varied rapport situations? Will mere repetition of the Rorschach significantly alter any of the scoring categories, regardless of administrator or of affective loading of the administration? If so, which scoring categories are sensitive to such variation?

Thirty-six male college sophomores between the ages of nineteen and twenty-seven participated in a series of three Rorschach tests, administered without testing of the limits. Each test was administered by a different female, and each testing situation was affectively differently loaded. One test was given in the standard manner without pre-tests and without any attempt to give the subject a marked feeling of acceptance or rejection. Another test was administered following two pre-tests during which, by manner and tone of voice, the subject was made to feel rejected and a failure. Still another test was administered after a similar pre-test situation during which the subject was made to feel accepted and successful. Each examiner gave twelve tests first, second and third; twelve tests positively loaded, negatively loaded, and neutral without affective loading. Each subject's different test was administered by a different examiner. An equal number (twelve) of negative, positive, and neutral tests was given on the first, second, and third administrations and by the three different examiners. This plan netted thirty-six Rorschach protocols on each of the three administrations, thirty-six by each of the different examiners, and thirty-six under each of the three different affective loadings of the testing situation. The 108 Rorschach protocols were scored and separately analyzed according to the number of the administration, the administrator, and the type of administration.

On the basis of the analyses of the 108 Rorschach records, the following findings are reported: Subjects who were coldly received tended to misunderstand, and make errors in following directions on simple card-sorting tests. Subjects warmly greeted did not misunderstand, request repetition of, or make errors in following simple directions.

The Experience Balance, or M : sumC ratio, was unstable, only 30% of the subjects maintaining a constant balance throughout the variations in administration. The remainder shifted emphasis from one side of the ratio to the other at least once.

Ten, thirty-one, and forty-eight t-ratios were found at the 1 per cent, 5 per cent, and 10 per cent levels of confidence respectively. Of these forty-eight measurable differences, eight were a function of repetition of the test, thirteen a function of the variation in affective loading of the test situation, and twenty-seven a function of examiner differences.

Of the twenty-three Rorschach response-categories subjected to statistical analysis, three were relatively unaffected by the extra-test, or "situational" stimuli: Dd + S%, Fk, and A. The other twenty categories showed frequency differences at least once at the 1 per cent, 5 per cent, or 10 per cent levels of confidence under at least one of the experimentally varied situations.

In conclusion, performance on the Rorschach, as measured by the frequency of responses in the Rorschach categories, varies significantly with repetition of the test, with variation in the negative or positive rapport conditions of the administration, and with examiner differences. In the present study, the largest and most frequent variations in Rorschach performance were associated with examiner differences.

APPENDIX

Explanation of Scoring Symbols
*Used in this Study**

LOCATION

W   Whole blot
W, S   Whole blot and white space used (tabulated as main W and additional S)
D   Large usual detail
D, S   White space used in addition to D (tabulated as main D and additional S)
d   Small usual detail
Dd   Unusual detail (or unusual combinations of usual areas)
S   White space

CONTENT

H   Human figures
Hd   Parts of human figures, not anatomical
A   Animal figures
Ad   Parts of living animals

POPULARITY

P   Popular responses

DETERMINANTS

R   Response
M   Figures in human-like action
FM   Animals in animal-like action
m   Abstract or inanimate movement
k   Shading as three dimensional expanse projected on a two dimensional plane
K   Shading as diffusion
FK   Shading as three-dimensional expanse in vista or perspective
F   Form only, not enlivened
Fc   Shading as surface appearance or texture, differentiated
C'   Achromatic surface color
FC   Definite form with bright color
CF   Bright color with indefinite form
C   Color only

$$\text{sumC} = \frac{FC + 2CF + 3C}{2}$$

** After Klopfer, Bruno and Helen H. Davidson, *The Rorschach Method of Personality Diagnosis.* Individual Record Blank (New York: World Book Company, 1942).*

REFERENCES

1. BECK, S. J. *Rorschach's test: I Basic processes.* New York: Grune & Stratton, 1944.
2. BECK, S. J. *Rorschach's test: II. A variety of personality pictures.* New York: Grune & Stratton, 1945.
3. BELLAK, L. The concept of projection. *Psychiatry,* 1944, *7,* 365–366.
4. BERGMAN, M. S., GRAHAM, H., & LEAVITT, H. C. Rorschach exploration of consecutive hypnotic chronological age level regressions. *Psychosom. Med.,* 1947, *9,* 20–28.
5. BOCHNER, RUTH, & HALPERN, FLORENCE. *The clinical application of the Rorschach test.* New York: Grune & Stratton, 1945.
6. BRUSSEL, J. A., & HITCH, K. S. The Rorschach method and its uses in military psychiatry. *Psychiat. Quart.,* 1942, *16,* 3–27.
7. BUHLER, CHARLOTTE, BUHLER, K., & LEFEVER, D. W. *Development of the basic Rorschach score.* Los Angeles: mimeographed ed., 1948.
8. BUHLER, CHARLOTTE, & LEFEVER, D. W. A Rorschach study on the psychological characteristics of alcoholics. *Quart. J. Stud. Alcohol,* 1947, *8,* 197–261.
9. COFER, C. N. Psychological test performance under hyoscine: A case of post-infectious encephalopathy. *J. Gen. Psychol.,* 1947, *36,* 221–228.
10. DOUGLAS, ANNA GERTRUDE. A tachistoscopic study of the order of emergence in the process of perception. *Psychol. Monogr.,* 1947, *61,* No. 6.
11. FOSBERG, I. A. How do subjects attempt fake results on the Rorschach test? *Rorschach Res. Exch.,* 1943, *7,* 119–121.
12. FOSBERG, I. A. Rorschach reactions under varied instructions. *Rorschach Res. Exch.,* 1938, *3,* 12–31.
13. HALL, CALVIN S. Diagnosing personality by the analysis of dreams. *J. Abnorm. Soc. Psychol.,* 1947, *42,* 68–79.
14. HEIDER, F. Social perception and phenomenal causality. *Psychol. Rev.,* 1944. *51,* 358–374.
15. HERTZMAN, M., & PEARCE, JANE. The personal meaning of the human figure in the Rorschach. *Psychiatry,* 1947, *10,* 413–422.
16. HSÜ, E. H. The Rorschach responses and factor analysis. *J. Gen. Psychol.,* 1947, *37,* 129–138.
17. HUNT, W. A. The future of diagnostic testing in clinical psychology. *J. Clin. Psychol.,* 1946, *2,* 311–317.
18. JACOB, Z. Some suggestions on the use of content symbolism. *Rorschach Res. Exch.,* 1944, *8,* 40–41.
19. KADINSKY, D. Human whole and detail responses in the Rorschach test. *Rorschach Res. Exch.,* 1946, *10,* 140–144.
20. KAMMAN, G. R. The Rorschach as a therapeutic agent. *Amer. J. Orthopsychiat.,* 1944, *14,* 21–27.
21. KLOPFER, B., & KELLEY, D. M. *The Rorschach technique.* New York: World Book Co., 1946.

22. LEVINE, K. N., GRASSI, J. R., & GERSON, M. J. Hypnotically induced mood changes in the verbal and graphic Rorschach: A case study. *Rorschach Res. Exch.,* 1943, *7,* 130–144.

23. LEVINE, K. N., GRASSI, J. R., & GERSON, M. J. Hypnotically induced mood changes in the verbal and graphic Rorschach. Part II: The response records. *Rorschach Res. Exch.,* 1944, *8,* 104–124.

24. LINDNER, R. M. Content analysis in Rorschach work. *Rorschach Res. Exch.,* 1946, *10,* 121–129.

25. LINDNER, R. M. Some significant Rorschach responses, *J. Crim. Psychopathol.,* 1944, *5,* 775–778.

26. LINDQUIST, E. F. *Statistical analysis in educational research.* Boston: Houghton Mifflin, 1940.

27. LUCHINS, A. S. Situational and attitudinal influences on Rorschach responses. *Amer. J. Psychiat.,* 1947, *103,* 780–784.

28. PIOTROWSKI, Z. A comparative table of the main Rorschach symbols. *Psychiat. Quart.,* 1942, *16,* 28–37.

29. RORSCHACH, H. *Psychodiagnostics. A diagnostic test based on perception.* Berne, Switzerland: Hans Huber, 1942. English ed. by Paul Lemkau and Bernard Kronenberg.

30. SCHACHTEL, E. G. Subjective definitions of the Rorschach test situations and their effect on test performance. *Psychiatry,* 1945, *8,* 419–448.

31. SCHACHTEL, E. G. Review, *The Rorschach technique,* by Bruno Klopfer. *Psychiatry,* 1942, *5,* 604–606.

32. U.S. ARMY AIR FORCES AVIATION PSYCHOLOGY PROGRAM RESEARCH REPORT, J. P. GUILFORD, editor. *Printed classification tests.* Report No. 5. Washington, D.C.: Government Printing Office, 1947. Chapter 24, Clinical type procedures.

33. WILKINS, W. L. & ADAMS, A. J. The use of the Rorschach test under hypnosis and under sodium amytal in military psychiatry. *J. Gen. Psychol.,* 1947, *36,* 131–138.

III

Scoring

J. R. Wittenborn

STATISTICAL TESTS OF

CERTAIN RORSCHACH

ASSUMPTIONS, *Analyses of*

Discrete Responses

THE CUSTOMARY procedures employed in the evaluation of a subject's responses to the Rorschach ink blots involve a variety of assumptions. Some of the assumptions are explicitly stated in the Rorschach literature and others are merely implied by common practices. Although the validity of the Rorschach technique for personality appraisal is indicated by clinical findings and certain types of studies, the assumptions employed in the Rorschach psychodiagnosis have not been subjected to direct validation. There are considerations which make particularly important the validation of the assumptions per se.

1. Since the assumptions have not been tested, the possibility exists that some of them are invalid. If some of the assumptions cannot be validated,

Reprinted from *J. Consult. Psychol.*, 1949, *13*, 257–267, by permission of the American Psychological Association and the author.

aspects of scoring or interpretation based on the questionable assumptions should be employed with reservation or perhaps eliminated from standard procedures.

2. Many of the assumptions employed in Rorschach procedures cannot be found among the established facts and theories of American academic psychology. If the Rorschach assumptions are valid, their relevance to the psychology of personality organization and to the psychology of perception could be of extraordinary significance.

Analysis A. An Examination of the Functional Similarity of Responses Which Have Common Determinants

In scoring a Rorschach protocol, it is customary to classify each response with respect to several classes of factors, such as content, portion of ink blots interpreted, and ink-blot characteristics determining the response. There are standard categories within each of the classes of factors. When a response is scored the content category in which it falls, as well as its location category and its determinant category, is designated by the scorer. As a second step in scoring, the total number of responses falling in each category is ascertained. Regardless of the precise manner in which the categories are used, the device of categorizing the responses and then finding the total number of responses in each category carries two implications:

I. That all of the responses falling in a given category are similar in some behavioral respect.

II. That the psychological significance of responses falling in a given category is different in some respect from responses placed in other categories.

These assumptions are implicit for example in the distinction that is made between color and human movement responses. The importance of the distinction between human movement and color responses was first emphasized by Rorschach, and the observance of this distinction has remained a basic feature of Rorschach psychodiagnosis. Because of the basic significance ascribed to these two types of responses, it was decided to employ this distinction in testing the foregoing assumptions of intracategory similarity and intercategory difference.

It would be erroneous to suppose that any absolute or relative quantity of color or movement responses is unalterably and invariably associated with a particular total personality appraisal. Movement and color have an invariable abstract meaning for the personality, but for total personality appraisals this is added to, detracted from, or modified by other characteristics of the response and other aspects of the protocol. This is analogous to clinical practice wherein the psychologist's evaluation may be based on the Rorschach indications, other test data, and data from the case history; the relative contribution ascribed to the Rorschach in the total personality evaluation is determined to some degree by the other findings, but this does not render a Rorschach finding meaningless. By the same token the qualifying role of such factors as form level and content do not make the concept of a movement response meaningless nor make inconsequential an assumption that movement responses include a constant, functionally similar element.

THE PLAN OF EXPERIMENT

If Assumption I is a true proposition, it follows that several measurements of the tendency to perceive human movement would be positively related. If several measures of a given response category were not positively interrelated, it would be difficult to justify an assumption that differences in number of responses of that category expressed differences in a personality attribute. It also follows from Assumption II that several measures of a given response category would be more highly interrelated with each other than they would be related with measures of some other category.

In order to employ these deductions in an experimental test of the assumptions, it is necessary to devise several measures of the tendency to give responses falling in the respective categories. For example, it is possible to regard any response falling within a given category as evidence of a tendency to give responses in that category, and it is equally possible to regard failure to give a particular response falling in a given category as evidence of a tendency not to give responses falling in the category. Employing this approach, it is possible to secure a large number of plus or minus scores for any response category. If making or not making a particular response which belongs to a given category is to be a measure for a tendency to make respectively many or few responses which fall in that category, it is important that the particular response be well specified. This poses an important methodological problem.

One of the outstanding characteristics of Rorschach responses is their highly individual quality, their extreme variability from person to person. This makes conventional statistical treatment of Rorschach data awkward because of the difficulty in securing a sufficiently large number of roughly identical responses. For example, out of a group of one hundred normal subjects many, if not all, would report human movement responses, but relatively few would have more than two or at the most three identical responses in common.

In the present study an attempt has been made to reduce this difficulty by use of the Harrower-Erickson check list (6). This check list comprises a sheet of paper upon which are printed three groups of ten possible responses for each of the ten cards. There are three hundred possible responses in all. The technique of administration provides that the ten cards be projected on a screen in the usual serial order. The check list is designed so that the subject may check or underline responses which indicate what he has seen on the card. Although this technique of administration and manner of responding to the cards is obviously different from the standard technique for administering the Rorschach test, this device provides a uniform, common response list for all subjects and thus makes possible a tabular treatment of responses to ink blots. The limitation of this procedure as a method for personality appraisal (3, 5, 7) is not necessarily disadvantageous to the present experiment which is an examination of the consequences of certain restricted assumptions and is not otherwise concerned with the problem of the validity of the Rorschach method in general or the validity of other Rorschach assumptions.

The following experimental hypotheses were tested by a statistical analysis of data provided by the Harrower-Erickson check list:

A. The tendency for controlled color responses (FC and CF) to be associated with other controlled color responses (FC and CF) is greater than the tendency for such color responses to be associated with human movement responses.

B. The tendency for human movement (M) responses to be associated with other human movement (M) responses is greater than the tendency for such responses to be associated with controlled color responses (FC and CF).

RESULTS

The subjects for the investigation were 247 Yale University freshmen, all the members of a small entering class. The check list was administered as a part of a guidance battery. The responses selected for analysis had to meet several requirements. The responses had to be sufficiently common to afford a basis for statistical tests. The permissible range of response frequency was arbitrarily set from 28 to 220. The exact range was influenced by efforts to meet certain other requirements, e.g., an effort was made to include responses from all cards; different responses to the same portion of the card which could therefore be construed as mutually exclusive were (with two noted exceptions) avoided. The responses finally selected are listed in Table I.

The color responses comprise two groups which differ in the degree to which they are influenced by the form characteristics of the card. Responses numbers 8, 9 and 10 are strongly influenced by form and would be scored FC, whereas responses 11, 12 and 13 are less influenced by form and would be scored CF by most workers. The color responses are not strictly comparable with respect to the location of the response; for example, responses 8 and 10 clearly involve large details of the cards, whereas with the exception of response 9, which is probably based on the whole card, the others are less definite in their exact location. For the most part the human movement responses are based on most if not all of the total area of the respective ink blots. Responses 1, 6 and 7 are based on colored cards and they may involve color to some degree. This possibility is greatest for response 1; clowns (or equivalent movement responses for card II) are commonly given a specific identification which employs the red color. It is possible to control these complicating and extraneous factors by restricting comparisons to certain of the selected responses. For example, human movement responses 3, 4 and 7 comprise practically all of the ink blot and cannot involve color because the blots are achromatic. Similarly, responses 11, 12 and 13 are homogeneous in that they tend to involve most of the card and would usually be scored CF.

In order to test the experimental hypotheses, each response was correlated with every other one. Two different statistical devices were employed to examine the relationships. The χ^2 test of independence was first used. The size of χ^2 is not determined by the degree of relationship, but since the frequency with which χ^2 of any given size may occur by chance is known, χ^2 may be used as a test for the significance of the correlation, i.e., the lack of independence between two responses may be evaluated by means of the χ^2 test. The result of this analysis is shown in Table I.

In order to get some appreciation of the strength of the significant relationships revealed by the χ^2 test, tetrachoric correlations between the responses were computed. The correlations were determined by means of a chart (4). Since the tetrachoric correlation is an appropriate statistic only when the dichotomized variables are normally distributed, its use for the present purpose may be questioned; whether the strength of a tendency to give a Rorschach response is normally distributed or not is a speculative question. At any rate the indications provided by the tetrachoric correlations are in agreement with those provided by the χ^2 test. The tetrachoric correlations between all possible pairs of responses are given in Table II.

TABLE I

Chi-Square Test of Independence Between Rorschach Responses

No.	Response	Card No.	Resp. Group	1	2	3	4	5	6	7	8	9	10	11	12
1	Two Clowns	II	a	2.1											
2	Two Men Pulling Something Apart	III	a	3.6	1.3										
3	Man Seen From Below	IV	c	3.2	3.3	14.7									
4	A Fan Dancer	V	c	13.4	.2	1.4	1.3								
5	Two Women Talking	VII	a	3.3	.9	5.1	2.3	5.5							
6	Two Witches	IX	a	.8	.9	14.7	5.9	4.6	10.4						
7	Two People	X	a	.1	.5	8.3	12.4	1.4	14.8	3.6					
8	A Red Bow Tie	III	a	.07	.1	2.1	1.9	.8	1.6	8.2	2.1				
9	An Emblem	VIII	a	.1	.0	2.4	5.4	.1	1.8	1.0	9.6	3.2			
10	Colored Map of California	X	a	8.3	.3	.0	.5	16.1	1.7	.2	.0	.4	1.5		
11	Red and Black Ink	II	a	4.4	.0	3.5	1.5	1.0	9.7	.8	6.4	.2	9.2	.2	
12	Fire and Ice	VIII	b	2.7	.2	.2	8.0	.7	.8	.8	.5	1.1	1.3	1.3	3.8
13	Forest Fire	IX	b												

6.63 = 1% level   3.84 = 5% level   2.71 = 10% level

TABLE II

Tetrachoric Correlations Between Rorschach Responses

No.	Response	Card No.	Resp. Group	1	2	3	4	5	6	7	8	9	10	11	12
1	Two Clowns	II	a												
2	Two Men Pulling Something Apart	III	a	.11											
3	Man Seen From Below	IV	c	.20	.20										
4	A Fan Dancer	V	c	.21	.16	.42									
5	Two Women Talking	VII	a	.32	-.01	.16	.17								
6	Two Witches	IX	a	.20	.20	.22	.23	.26							
7	Two People	X	a	.08	-.10	.40	.27	.30	.33						
8	A Red Bow Tie	III	a	.00	-.14	.30	.37	.15	.43	.23					
9	An Emblem	VIII	a	.08	-.07	.13	.14	.02	.15	.30	.15				
10	Colored Map of California	X	a	.00	-.05	.14	.24	.03	.20	.10	.20	.22			
11	Red and Black Ink	II	a	-.38	.01	-.10	-.10	-.50	.07	.06	-.01	.02	.13		
12	Fire and Ice	VIII	b	.33	.05	.34	.16	.20	.40	.33	.31	.07	.31	.09	
13	Forest Fire	IX	b	.20	-.05	-.07	.44	.20	.07	.22	-.10	.21	.02	-.15	.20

Two conclusions seem equally appropriate from an examination of either Table I or Table II:

1. Among the intercorrelations there is no obvious pattern which conforms with a pattern predictable from either Hypothesis I or II.
2. The number of significant correlations exceeds the number that would be expected by pure chance.

Although it would be unwarranted on the basis of the present data to make any conclusive statements concerning the general status of Assumptions I and II, the hypotheses generated by them for this experiment are not clearly verified. If the Rorschach were analogous to the typical mental test wherein the score is based on many responses of a given kind and evaluation of the individual is based on differences in many score units, a high degree of interitem consistency would not be necessary. But such is not the case, and in view of the considerable psychological significance ascribed to small variations in number of human movement or color responses, highly consistent interresponse evidence for the hypotheses may be expected. The scant evidence for the assumptions is a challenge to their status and strongly indicates the need for further investigation.

The fact that among the responses there are numerous relatively large and significant interrelationships which were not predicted by the hypotheses indicates need for a broader examination of the patterning of Rorschach responses. It is possible that the interrelationships among Rorschach responses have a well defined and meaningful pattern which if discovered would contribute to our understanding and use of the Rorschach technique.

Although from a casual examination of Tables I and II it appears that the evidence which the present data provide for the assumptions is unequal to the important manner in which they are employed in practice, any evidence of a trend toward correspondence between the requirements of the hypotheses and the nature of the data should not be overlooked.

Accordingly, Table III was prepared to summarize the findings and from this summary several statements may be offered:

1. There is no consistent functional similarity among the human movement responses or among the color responses, i.e., most of the movement responses are not significantly interrelated and similarly most of the color responses are not significantly interrelated.

2. The pattern among the most significant relationships is in a direction predictable from the hypotheses.

TABLE III

Distribution of Chi-Squares and Tetrachoric Correlation Coefficients

χ^2	Per Cent of the 42 Possible Comparisons of Human Movement with Human Movement	Per Cent of the 42 Possible Comparisons of Human Movement with Color*	Per Cent of the 30 Possible Comparisons of Color with Color
Less than 2.71	42	69	67
2.71 and above (10% level)	58	21	33
3.84 and above (5% level)	38	19	27
6.635 and above (1% level)	19	15	13
Tetrachoric *r*			
Less than .20	33	62	60
.20 or above	67	38	40
.30 or above	24	21	13
.40 or above	10	05	00

* Two of the significant χ^2 are for negative relationships (see Tables I and II).

3. The hypotheses are not clearly verified and the assumptions may be false.

As a result of the analysis it is concluded that in these data the tendencies required by hypotheses A and B are negligible. A variety of considerations may be adduced to account for negligible evidence for experimental hypotheses. Among them the following may be included:

1. The assumptions may be at fault.

a) The assumptions may be false. (The present findings merely challenge the assumptions.)

b) The assumptions may describe a very slight trend. (The present evidence does suggest that the trend is much less marked than might be inferred from Rorschach practices.)

c) The statement of the assumptions may be faulty. (One of the purposes of research is to arrive at correctly stated assumptions, and the refutation of hypotheses is the basis for reformulation of assumptions.)

2. The experimental hypotheses may not be the logical consequences of the assumptions.

a) The hypotheses may involve assumptions other than those under examination. (The present experiment does involve assumptions regarding the meaning and scalability of a response.)

b) The hypotheses may be incorrectly deduced, e.g., so as to be in conflict with other possible deductions.

3. The experimental interpretation may be faulty.

a) The data may be partially or wholly irrelevant to the hypotheses. (The present data may be inappropriate to a general examination of Rorschach assumptions, but they are considered appropriate to the present assumptions.)

b) The data may be influenced by constant, uncontrolled effects (either the group situation or the list of possible responses may have an untoward effect on the individual's responses).

c) Relative to the magnitude of the trend to be examined, errors of measurement and other variable extraneous factors may be large and thus obscure the findings. (This possibility is not eliminated in the present investigation, e.g., other aspects of the personality not expressed through movement or color may vary from response to response and from individual to individual.)

Analysis B. An Examination of the Functional Similarity of a Large Number of Check List Responses

The major conclusions of Analysis A may be stated as follows:

1. Among the intercorrelations there is no obvious pattern which conforms with a pattern predictable from either Hypothesis I or Hypothesis II.

2. The number of significant correlations exceeds the number that would be expected by pure chance.

These conclusions, particularly the latter one, provide the point of departure for a second analysis. Since there is a greater number of significant intercorrelations among the Rorschach responses than chance alone would provide, it is possible that the pattern of the intercorrelations could be anticipated to some degree from a consideration of certain beliefs and practices concerning the Rorschach. As indicated in the discussion of the results of Analysis A, the consistent behavioral significance among human movement or among color responses may be relatively small compared with the variations among the responses due to other inconsistent factors, e.g., a group of responses selected because they all involve color may differ greatly in other respects. For example, some of the responses will involve the whole card whereas others will be based on a small detail, and the contents of some of the responses may be man-made objects while others may be plants, etc. It may be reasoned, therefore, that the intercorrelations among responses which have more than one scoring category in common will be higher than the intercorrelations among responses which have but one or no common scoring category. These considerations lead to a third hypothesis for testing the provisions of Assumptions I and II.

Hypothesis C: The degree to which Rorschach responses will be intercorrelated is a function of the number of scoring categories the responses have in common.

Since it is obviously infeasible to study the interrelationships among all of the 300 responses possible in the Harrower-Erickson check list, some selection was necessary. In selecting the responses for Analysis II several factors were considered:

1. The responses must be sufficiently common to make statistical analysis feasible.
2. The manner in which they are scored must be unambiguous.
3. They must be pertinent to common Rorschach practices and assumptions.
4. Whenever possible, the responses to be studied should be selected from the first group of 10 possible responses for each card or at least the response of a given type selected for a card was the first one listed for each card.
5. Within these restrictions the responses selected should represent a variety, and not be limited to one or two types.

As a result of these considerations, twenty-seven check list responses were selected from the records of a small Yale freshman class of 247 and intercorrelated by the tetrachoric method.

As a second step in the analysis, a location, determinant, and content scoring was made for each response. The scoring for each response was then compared with the scoring for every other response and for each response four lists were prepared:[1]

a) The responses which agreed in three respects (had location, determinant, and content in common).
b) The responses which agreed in two respects.
c) The responses which agreed in one respect.
d) The responses which agreed in no respect (had no common scoring category).

On the basis of these four lists, four distributions of correlation coefficients were made:

a) The three-degree-of-correspondence distribution compromised all the correlations between each response and every other response which had identical scoring categories (Table IV).
b) The two-degree-of-correspondence distribution comprised all the correlations

1. The correlations between responses based on a common card were not included in the analysis.

between each response and every other response wherein two scoring categories were shared (Table IV).

c) The one-degree-of-correspondence distribution comprised all the correlations between each response and every other response having but one common scoring category (Table IV).

d) The zero-degree-of-correspondence distribution comprised all of the correlations between each response and every other response having no common scoring category (Table IV).

TABLE IV

**Frequency Distributions of Correlation Coefficients Between Responses
with Varying Numbers of Aspects in Common**

Frequency Distributions of Correlation Coefficients Between Responses With

Interval of r	Three Aspects Same	Two Aspects Same	One Aspect Same	No Aspect Same	Total Distr.
+.4 – +.5	2	4	14	4	24
+.3 – +.4	12	6	18	18	54
+.2 – +.3	20	18	70	22	130
+.1 – +.2	28	10	74	50	162
.0 – +.1	14	12	92	36	154
−.1 – .0	8	4	42	18	72
−.2 – −.1	—	2	28	10	40
−.3 – −.2	—	—	—	—	—
−.4 – −.3	—	—	—	—	—
−.5 – −.4	—	—	2	—	2
−.6 – −.5	—	—	—	—	—
−.7 – −.6	—	—	—	—	—
−.8 – −.7	—	—	—	—	—
−.9 – −.8	—	—	2	—	2
	N = 84	N = 56	N = 342	N = 158	N = 640
	M = +.176	M = +.184	M = +.108	M = +.130	M = +.129
	S = .123	S = .147	S = .168	S = .143	S = .176

Hypothesis C is tested by means of the χ^2 test shown in Table V. This table shows that there is a significant tendency for the number of response categories common to pairs of Rorschach responses to be positively related with the size of the correlations between the paired responses. The trend does not appear to be a continuous one, however, and as a means of examining it more minutely, each degree of correspondence was compared with every other one. Responses which have two or three common scoring categories have probable higher intercorrelations than responses which have one or less common scoring categories. There is no significant difference between the size of the correlations between responses which have two common categories and the responses which have three common categories: nor is the difference between the size of the correlations between responses having one common category and the size of the correlations between responses having no common categories significant. These findings are taken as evidence for Hypothesis C.

TABLE V

**Chi-square Between Values of Correlation Coefficients and Number
of Response-Aspects in Common**

Number of Respects in which Responses are Same

Value of r	3	2	1	0	Total
	Frequency	Frequency	Frequency	Frequency	
.20 plus	34 (28)	28 (19)	102 (114)	44 (52)	208
.0 – .2	42 (41)	22 (27)	166 (167)	86 (77)	316
Less than .0	8 (15)	6 (10)	74 (61)	28 (28)	116
Total	84	56	342	158	640

$$n = 6 \qquad \chi^2 = 18.932 \qquad P = .01$$

The relatively small differences between the size of the correlations in each of the four distributions (Table IV) and the variability of each of the distributions is meager support for the practice of categorizing the small number of responses provided by the usual Rorschach protocol. The large number of zero or negative correlations between responses which have two or even three scoring categories suggests that the trend provided by Assumption I is indeed weak. The number of correlations above .30 between responses which have one or even no common category suggests that the distinction between responses having different scoring categories (Assumption II) could be of little or no practical value in appraising individuals on the basis of these data.

DISCUSSION

As a result of the Analysis B two conclusions are permissible:

1. There is a statistically significant tendency for Rorschach responses which have two or three scoring categories in common to be more highly intercorrelated than responses which have but one or no common scoring categories. Thus Hypothesis C is verified.

2. The tendency for the correlations between responses to vary directly with the number of common scoring categories is no negligible as to be associated with a large number of gross exceptions. The number and size of the exceptional correlations is such as to challenge the propriety of the prac-

tice of scoring the Rorschach check list responses on the basis of location, determinant, and content.

The present study has been concerned with the functional similarity of responses which are scored in a highly similar if not identical manner. The relevance of this analysis is based on the presumption that responses which receive an identical designation on the basis of a complex categorization should have a strong, consistent, demonstrable, functional similarity if the categorization has implications for making distinctions between people. It is similarly argued that responses which are placed in dissimilar scoring categories should have a relatively low degree of functional similarity. The result of the present analysis is not in conformance with these expectations, and the value of the practice of scoring Rorschach responses on the basis of location, determinant, and content is hereby questioned. It is important to note that the data employed in the present study were secured by the use of a check list was necessary to a study such as the present one, and it is to be emphasized that the inability of the examiner to make qualitative judgments of the examinee's behavior, to make an inquiry, test limits, and conduct a searching interview with the client regarding his background and present difficulties (such interviews appear to be the rule, rather than the exception with Rorschach examiners) is beside the point of the present study. There are, however, two possible respects in which the check list technique would elicit atypical data:

1. Actually seeing the possible responses may in some cases suggest a response which would not be made in the standard situation.

2. The presence of others in the testing situation may result in responses which might otherwise not appear.

These possibilities impose a limitation in the degree to which the present results may be generalized to the standard individual Rorschach procedure.

Summary of Analyses A and B

Analyses A and B comprise an examination of the responses of 247 students to a Rorschach check list. The analyses were designed to determine empirically the status of certain hypotheses generated by two assumptions which are relevant to practices in Rorschach scoring and interpretation. The assumptions from which the hypotheses were deduced are:

Assumption I, All the responses falling in a given Rorschach scoring category are similar in some behavioral respects.

Assumption II, The psychological significance of responses falling in a given scoring category is different from that of responses in other categories.

Analysis A was designed to examine the status of Hypotheses A and B. The analysis of the data offers negligible support for the validity of these hypotheses:

Hypothesis A, The tendency for controlled color responses (FC and CF) to be associated with other controlled color responses (FC and CF) is greater than the tendency for such color responses to be associated with human movement responses.

Hypothesis B, The tendency for human movement (M) responses to be associated with other human movement (M) responses is greater than the tendency for such responses to be associated with controlled color responses (FC and CF).

Analysis B provided a test for Hypothesis C:

Hypothesis C, The degree to which Rorschach responses will be inter-correlated is a function of the number of scoring categories the responses have in common.

The evidence for Hypothesis C met a criterion for a high order of statistical significance. Nevertheless, the trend was slight and marked by numerous important exceptions (see Table IV). Although the data support Hypothesis C they may be interpreted as comprising a challenge to the clinical value of current Rorschach scoring procedures rather than as an indication that the procedures are economical and highly efficacious in attempts at appraising the individual.

The data employed in the present study are check-list data. Had they afforded strong support for the hypotheses, the implications would have been readily generalized to include responses elicited by individual methods of Rorschach examination. Since the data failed to offer strong support for the hypotheses, however, the findings are regarded with caution. Analyses must be designed which can be conducted with material from individually conducted protocols. It is possible that exposing a list of alternative responses to a subject biases him (particularly if he is suggestible), and may detract from trends which could be clearly demonstrated in material from individually administered Rorschach tests. It seems unlikely, however, that well-defined patterns of response could be revealed in one testing situation and altogether obscured in another. It is suggested, therefore, that the present data may be taken as evidence that the provisions of Assumptions I and II will not be sufficiently marked in individually administered protocols to warrant the confident use which is constantly made of them.

The scant support which the Hypotheses A, B, and C receive is taken as indication that the usual abstract scoring procedures are of no value in attempts to appraise the behavioral significance of Rorschach responses elicited by check-list procedures.

REFERENCES

1. BALINSKY, B. The multiple choice group Rorschach test as a means of screening applicants for jobs. *J. Psychol.*, 1945, *19*, 203–208.

2. BECK, S. J. *Rorschach's test*. New York: Grune and Stratton, 1945. Vols. I and II.

3. CHALLMAN, R. C. The validity of the Harrower-Erickson Multiple Choice test as a screening device. *J. Psychol.*, 1945, *20*, 41–48.

4. CHESIRE, L., SAFFIR, M. AND THURSTONE, L. L. *Computing diagrams for the tetrachoric correlation coefficient*. Chicago: Univ. of Chicago Bookstore, 1938.

5. ENGLE, T. L. The use of the Harrower-Erickson Multiple Choice test in differentiating between well adjusted and maladjusted high school pupils. *J. Educ. Psychol.*, 1946, *37*, 550–556.

6. HARROWER-ERICKSON, M. R., AND STEINER, M. E. *Large scale Rorschach techniques*. Springfield, Ill.: Charles C Thomas, 1945.

7. JENSEN, M B. AND ROTTER, J. B. The validity of the multiple choice Rorschach test in Officer Candidate selection. *Psychol. Bull.*, 1945, *42*, 182–185.

8. KLOPFER, B. AND KELLEY, D. M. *The Rorschach technique*. Yonkers, N.Y.: World Book Co., 1942.

9. LAWSHE, C. H., JR. AND FORSTER, MAX H. Studies in projective techniques: I. The reliability of a multiple choice group Rorschach test. *J. Appl., Psychol.*, 1947, *31*, 199–211.

10. RAPAPORT, D. *Diagnostic psychological testing*. Chicago: Year Book Pub., 1945. Vols. I and II.

11. RORSCHACH, H. *Psychodiagnostics*. Berne: Hans Huber, 1942.

12. WINFIELD, M. C. The use of the Harrower-Erickson Multiple Choice Rorschach test with a selected group of women in military service. *J. Appl. Psychol.*, 1946, *30*, 481–487.

J. R. Wittenborn

A FACTOR ANALYSIS OF

RORSCHACH SCORING

CATEGORIES

THE PRESENT study was undertaken for the purpose of testing three hypotheses. These hypotheses were developed during the course of a series of investigations concerned with the use of the Rorschach test.

Several of the analyses which have been published in the present series of studies (4, 5) provide evidence that the traditional distinction between Rorschach responses based primarily on the perception of human movement, and Rorschach perceptual responses based on an employment of color, is congruent with the manner in which various manifestations of these two classes of responses are intercorrelated. In this respect, at least, the universally observed scoring distinction between the movement and color responses is justifiable. The distinctions between the movement and color responses provided by the various interrelationships examined were relative and far from absolute, however. Inasmuch as there is a variety of different Rorschach determinant scores, it is possible that the distinctions

Reprinted from *J. Consult. Psychol.*, 1950, *14*, 261–267, by permission of the American Psychological Association and the author.

revealed between the human movement and color scores are minor relative to the distinctions that exist between some of the other determinant scores. This, however, is not implied in the Rorschach literature. As a matter of fact, in most writings the distinction between human movement and color receives a primary emphasis. Accordingly, one would not predict that this distinction would be obscured by other marked and broadly relevant distinctions between Rorschach determinants. The magnitude of the distinction between the human movement response score and the color response score may be evaluated by comparing it with the magnitude of the distinctions which exist between other classes of response. Such a comparison is relevant to Rorschach theory and may have some practical implications.

Under certain conditions, a factor analysis of the intercorrelations among various commonly employed Rorschach scoring categories should reveal the difference between the human movement and the color responses. This possibility is stated formally in Hypothesis I.

Hypothesis I: In a factor analysis of the various Rorschach response categories, the pattern of factorial composition for the human movement response will be different from the pattern of factorial composition for responses involving the use of color.

In order for the factor analysis to be relevant to Hypothesis I, it is necessary for both the human movement response score and some of the color response scores to show large correlations with several scoring categories, i.e., it is necessary for both human movement and color scores to have an important amount of common factor variance. If, under this condition, the analysis does not reveal evidence for Hypothesis I, the distinctions between the human movement and the color responses which have been revealed in earlier analyses may be considered to be minor relative to the distinctions which exist between other response categories.

As a result of a few different fragmentary clues provided by earlier analyses (3, 5), it was inferred that some of the Rorschach responses differed from each other with respect to the degree of perceptual control characterizing them. Although the exact nature of this "control" was not and is not clearly specified, human movement responses and large detail responses were conceived as involving a high order of perceptual control, whereas whole responses and color-form responses were considered to be alike[1] in that they involve a flexible perceptual approach requiring appreciably less

---

1. To what degree the suspected behavioral similarity between color-form and whole responses is due to a possible prevalence of whole color-form responses to one or two cards is unknown, but the concept of uncontrolled perceptual responses as expressed in Hypothesis II is extended beyond such specific possibilities and the concept must stand or fall on its broad implications.

perceptual discipline. A low order of perceptual control is tentatively conceived to be manifested by responses which are incautious, possibly spontaneous or impulsive, to a degree which results in a relative disregard for or an unawareness of the purely formal, literal, or concrete response possibilities. In order to apply this conceptualization broadly, the pure color, the pure texture, and the pure diffusion response categories may be added to the whole and the color-form response categories. Similarly, in order to broaden the tentatively conceived class of responses which expresses a high order of perceptual control, the pure form responses and the other detail response categories are added to the human movement and the large detail response categories. This conceptualization requires that the pattern of intercorrelation among the response categories should be organized in the manner specified by Hypothesis II.

Hypothesis II: The whole, color-form, pure color, pure texture, and pure diffusion response categories are intercorrelated in a manner which yields a factor different from the factor which is most important in determining the common factor variance of the pure form, human movement, and the various detail response categories.

A classification of responses on the basis of the degree to which they require perceptual control is closely akin to the common practice of evaluating responses on the basis of the degree to which they reflect spatially definite well-conceived formal percepts. The conceptualization responsible for Hypothesis II is somewhat different from the usual form-level evaluation in that it is intended to emphasize distinctions in perceptual approach rather than distinctions in perceptual quality or plausibility. It also makes no provision for the qualitative distinctions among the texture, diffusion, and color determinants. It implies that the distinctions between responses which are based upon the degree of perceptual control transcend the distinctions among the different classes of determinants. Hypothesis II, if a true hypothesis, may invite a shift in emphasis from the qualitative distinctions between certain classes of determinants to a system of distinctions based on perceptual control; it does not preclude, however, that there are discernible systematic distinctions among whole, uncontrolled color, uncontrolled texture, and uncontrolled diffusion responses.

Both as a result of clinical applications of the Rorschach method and researches concerning the psychological significance of Rorschach responses, the writer has come to suspect that although the general productivity of the patient greatly influences the score for most response categories, it does not influence the score for the various response categories equally. If productivity is an important determiner of the frequency with which responses fall in the various response categories, the possibility exists that most of the reliable variance of some of the scoring categories is due primarily to the general productivity of the patients. For the purposes of the present experiment, this possibility is formally stated by Hypothesis III.

Hypothesis III: The Rorschach scoring categories will be correlated with the total number of responses (R) in such a manner as to result in a general or quasi-general factor of productivity.

If Hypothesis III is supported by the present data, it becomes possible to examine the validity of Hypothesis IV which has practical implication for the use of the Rorschach test.

Hypothesis IV: Response-scoring categories differ greatly in the degree to which their common-factor variance is due to a productivity factor.

Hypothesis IV is worth examining because the degree to which the various scoring categories are independent of general productivity is unknown, and if the various scoring categories differ markedly in this respect, it would suggest, all other things being equal, that the scoring categories most independent of productivity be accorded a more uniquely significant meaning than those which reflect primarily the productivity of the patient, i.e., the recognition of response categories which are primarily measures of productivity would contribute to efficient and economical scoring procedures and

TABLE 1

Definitions of Scoring Categories

Variable No.	Symbol	Definition
1	W	Whole blot
2	D	Large usual detail
3	d	Small usual detail
4	Dd	Unusual detail
5	S	White space
6	M	Figures in human-like action (human, mythological, or animal)
7	FM	Animals in animal-like action
8	m	Abstract or inanimate movement
9	K	Shading as diffusion (smoke, clouds)
10	FK	Shading as three-dimensional expanse in vista or perspective
11	F	Form only, not enlivened
12	Fc	Shading as surface appearance or texture, differentiated
13	c	Shading as texture, undifferentiated
14	C'	Achromatic surface color
15	FC	Definite form with bright color
16	CF	Bright color with indefinite form
17	C	Color only
18	P	Popular responses
19	O	Original responses, found not more than once in one hundred records
20	R	Total number of responses

TABLE 2

Intercorrelations Among Scoring Categories

No.	Symbol	1	2	3	4	5	6	7	8	9	10	11	12	13	14	15	16	17	18	19
1	W																			
2	D	−194																		
3	d	−228	669																	
4	Dd	−138	608	749																
5	S	−143	464	512	660															
6	M	−041	498	560	665	616														
7	FM	−058	625	429	381	288	359													
8	M	115	403	351	297	287	379	375												
9	K	255	330	246	259	155	269	281	425											
10	FK	203	275	238	221	232	154	201	240	411										
11	F	−052	693	705	762	635	438	285	202	147	198									
12	Fc	100	587	583	605	519	579	326	450	349	153	460								
13	c	144	138	116	108	097	113	136	182	310	193	108	191							
14	C'	016	466	510	503	508	532	345	468	310	114	377	546	076						
15	FC	023	541	429	457	374	342	361	563	181	028	305	571	−084	464					
16	CF	410	241	090	114	−008	−108	−025	113	353	285	179	117	251	089	133				
17	C	170	178	072	137	066	−020	075	098	259	270	039	098	261	109	177	235			
18	P	−095	208	266	163	034	177	221	363	198	−005	025	357	187	206	356	−033	216		
19	O	−011	436	570	579	565	624	303	456	305	135	415	646	181	379	550	046	172	659	
20	R	093	879	783	813	598	629	581	478	429	379	797	710	195	551	584	315	224	188	551

reduce unrecognized sources of error necessarily inherent in practices which involve the multiple employment of the same variable which unrecognized appears in different guises.

Subjects and Procedures

As a means of testing the three hypotheses, twenty-one different Rorschach scores were intercorrelated for a sample of ninety-two Yale undergraduates and the intercorrelations were submitted to a centroid analysis. The Rorschach scoring categories employed are shown in Table 1, and their intercorrelations in Table 2. The variables may be recognized as comprising the principal scoring categories of the Klopfer system. The intercorrelations were computed by the Pearson product-moment method, which requires that the variables be linearly related to each other. An examination of numerous scatter diagrams between a variety of scoring categories gave no indication that the relationships were nonlinear. All of the distributions of the scoring categories were positively skewed, however. Had the skewness in some instances been negative, it is possible that the linearity of some of the interrelationships among the scoring categories would have been distorted. Some of the scores occurred infrequently and were not found in

TABLE 3

Centroid Factors

No.	I	II	III	IV	h²
1	087	472	134	−417	.422
2	788	−291	159	094	.740
3	745	−353	085	184	.721
4	773	−378	122	079	.762
5	629	−341	−049	−038	.516
6	656	−301	−191	094	.566
7	540	−127	−013	196	.346
8	601	151	−296	−122	.487
9	521	409	101	053	.452
10	383	277	323	096	.337
11	664	−385	350	−071	.717
12	765	−098	−166	−120	.637
13	284	375	144	197	.333
14	649	−122	−225	−137	.505
15	613	−102	−308	−289	.565
16	283	400	461	−274	.528
17	274	358	148	110	.237
18	384	261	−456	308	.518
19	744	032	466	109	.784
20	941	−216	277	−064	1.013

every protocol. It is not customary to apply the product-moment coefficient to variables having such a small range[2]; nevertheless, it is felt that a system of intercorrelations such as provided by Table 2 permits an evaluation of the hypotheses in question.

The four factors yielded by the centroid analysis are presented in Table 3. The factors in Table 3 may be rotated to the position described in Table 5 by an employment of the transformation matrix shown in Table 4. All of

TABLE 4

Transformation Matrix*

	I	II	III	IV
I′	556	104	−721	−403
II′	195	586	−197	761
III′	316	635	537	−425
IV′	744	−494	349	281

* In one of the rotations .709 was erroneously substituted for .707 in the sine and cosine. For this reason the rotated factors are not perfectly orthogonal (the departure from orthogonality is quite minute) and the communalities in Table 5 do not correspond perfectly with those of Table 3.

the various rotations were selected by an application of the usual criteria, i.e., maximizing the number of zero loadings and minimizing the negative loadings. The test clusters responsible for rotated factors II′, III′, and IV′ are relatively independent of each other. The clustering tendency responsible for factor I′ is not wholly distinct from that responsible for factor IV′. If the present study were concerned with factors per se, it would be necessary to rotate factors I′ and IV′ obliquely with respect to each other and it would be possible to make other minor improvements in the rotated factors.

From an examination of Table 5 it may be seen that, with certain qualifications, Hypothesis I is a true hypothesis. Variable 6, the human movement variable, draws most of its common factor variance from the factor IV′; it also draws a substantial quantity of its factor variance from factor I′. The factorial composition of variable 6 is quite different from that of variables 16 and 17, the color-form and the pure color response variables; most

2. In general it may be observed that the variables that have the smallest range tend to have relatively small correlations. This is not surprising, but this difficulty cannot be resolved in any simple manner. Since all the correlations are based upon the same sample, the usual considerations regarding heterogeneity of sample are not applicable nor is it clearly appropriate to regard the difficulty as a result of broad categories because an attempt to correct the variables in question for a broad category effect would involve ascribing statistically a refinement and sensitivity which actually does not characterize the scores. Since the present investigation is concerned with the conceptual implications of the Rorschach *scoring procedures,* it was decided to study the scores directly with whatever imperfections they may possess and not attempt statistically to refine them or their intercorrelations.

TABLE 5

Rotated Factor Matrix

No.	Symbol	I'	II'	III'	IV'	h2
1	W	169	−015	576	−239	.420
2	D	255	023	110	812	.737
3	d	242	061	−021	810	.719
4	Dd	271	−035	036	827	.760
5	S	365	−007	−028	609	.505
6	M	433	061	−127	597	.564
7	FM	217	183	−001	515	.346
8	m	612	171	179	235	.491
9	K	238	361	456	236	.450
10	FK	−030	246	429	288	.328
11	F	105	−220	183	786	.711
12	Fc	583	033	141	526	.637
13	c	014	397	321	132	.278
14	C'	565	−005	065	426	.505
15	FC	669	−100	086	318	.566
16	CF	−024	−010	707	097	.510
17	C	039	318	347	109	.235
18	P	445	552	−089	084	.518
19	O	709	339	−041	406	.784
20	R	327	292	336	885	1.088

of their common factor variance may be explained in terms of factor III'. On the basis of the present analysis, however, the form-color response variable (number 15) is more similar in its factorial composition to the human movement variable than it is to the other color variables. The factorial composition of the form-color response is not at all similar to the factorial composition of the color-form and the pure color responses. The form-color response is different from the human movement response in that it draws most of its common factor variance from factor I' and is only secondarily dependent on factor IV', which is the chief source of the common factor variance of the human movement response variable. It is interesting to observe that the factorial composition of the form-color response is quite similar to the factorial composition of the achromatic color responses (variable 14), the form-texture responses (variable 12), and to a lesser degree the inanimate movement (variable 8) and the human movement (variable 16) responses. This pattern of relationships is scarcely predictable from the Rorschach literature and the scoring and interpretive practices of Rorschach workers. The present sample suggests that the superficial logical similarity between the form-color and the color-form responses may have little behavioral basis. If the pattern of relationships revealed in the present sample can be verified in other samples, it may be desirable to consider a revision of our current beliefs concerning the behavioral or personality significance of the form-color response.

An examination of factor III' shows it to be the factor required by Hypothesis II. Factor III' may be seen to be determined by the classes of response (whole, pure vista, pure texture, color-form and pure color) which were judged by the writer on a priori grounds to be similar in that they presumably require a loose, informal, spontaneous perceptual approach not governed primarily by the most obvious spatial characteristics of the ink blot. Factor III' is also seen to be correlated with variable 10, the form-vista variable; although no prediction concerning variable 10 was made. Variable 20, total productivity (R), participates to some degree in factor III'. This is not an untoward result and obviously does not detract from the meaning of factor III'.

A most impressive feature of Table 5 is its failure to correspond with the qualitative classifications of Rorschach determinants (movement [M, FM, m], vista [K, FK], texture [c, Fc] and color [C, CF, FC]) which are emphasized so insistently in the literature and about which elaborate and tediously arbitrary scoring distinctions have been devised. For example, the factorial compositions of the form-vista, pure vista, pure texture, and pure color response variables are strikingly similar to each other and involve primarily factors II' and III'. The form-color and form-texture response variables have a highly similar factorial composition which does not involve factors II' and III', but instead draws upon factors I' and IV'. Thus, we see that qualitatively similar Rorschach response determinant variables not only fail to cluster together in a manner to form factors, but they have dissimilar factorial compositions and responses which fall in one particular qualitative determinant classification are inclined to resemble most certain responses which belong to some other class of determinants. Findings such as these suggest that the behavioral or personality significance traditionally ascribed to many of the specific Rorschach scoring categories may be incorrect in its emphasis even if valid to a degree.

Factor IV' seems to satisfy the requirements of Hypothesis III. This would be more obvious if factors I' and IV' were rotated obliquely with each other, or if the reference vector corresponding to factor IV' were projected through variable 20. Nevertheless, Hypothesis IV may be discussed in terms of factor IV'. The relative importance of general productivity may also be discerned by an examination of the intercorrelations, Table 2. For the most part, the variables which are important to factor IV' also have substantial loadings with factor I' and in general these variables have a highly similar factorial composition; specifically, all of the various detail scores are highly similar to each other and to a striking degree are similar in factorial composition to all of the scores which are based on responses which primarily emphasize form. At any rate, either the correlations with variable 20 (total number of responses, given in Table 2) or the loadings of the various scores on factor IV in which variable 20 is so important may be taken as evidence that many of the Rorschach response scores are for the most part highly similar to each other and are also a measure of the productivity of the subject in the Rorschach situation. All of the various types of scores are not equally affected by the general productivity of the patient. Some of the Rorschach scores, particularly those which have high loadings with factors II′ and III′, show important evidence of having a behavioral significance quite different from the behavioral significance of the general productivity of the subject.

It may be noted that variable 18, the number of popular responses, is less important in the productivity factor than variable 19, the number of original responses. This probably arises from the fact that there is a limited number of popular responses; because of their popularity the percentage of popular responses for moderately productive subjects would be as great or greater than the percentage of popular responses for highly productive subjects. Similarly, since originality of responses is based on a frequency of occurrence criterion, the subjects producing the largest number of responses, all other things equal, have a greater chance of producing original responses.

In general, the manner in which variables are intercorrelated depends upon patterns of differences among the individuals comprising the sample. The pattern of differences among the individuals comprising the present sample is in some respects reminiscent of clinically familiar personality patterns. This is particularly true in the case of the variables which cluster together in a manner to form factor III′. The tendency to give numerous whole responses and to give responses in general which are spontaneous, impressionistic, and not exclusively formal and literal in their spatial aspects has often been found to characterize the so-called hysterical personality. Such perceptual tendencies on the Rorschach are also often considered to be characteristic of the classical personality trait of extroversion. To what degree either the hysterical personality or the extrovert personality produces a relatively large number of the kinds of Rorschach responses which determine factor III′ would not be difficult to determine. As a matter of fact, it would be very simple from the arithmetic standpoint to weight the types of responses contributing to factor III′ in a manner to yield a scale of the response tendency or characteristic responsible for the factor. If this were done, the behavioral significance of this scale could be explored by correlating it with results or other personality tests and with different clinical and behavioral criteria.

The Rorschach responses responsible for factor IV', viewed as a group, are also reminiscent of a familiar personality reaction pattern which has considerable clinical interest. Specifically, Rorschach protocols produced by ruminative, obsessive, compulsive individuals are commonly characterized by a preponderance of detailed responses, relatively numerous human movement, animal movement and pure form responses, a high level of productivity and a tendency to avoid informal responses such as those contributing to factor III'.

The participation of W responses in factor III' may be puzzling to some readers and they may be inclined to suspect that its presence in factor III' is due to a tendency for K, c, CF, and C to be determinants for whole responses. To what degree this is true cannot be established from the present analysis but in an earlier study (3) several whole responses to achromatic cards were found to be highly correlated with the CF responses to chromatic cards 8 and 9.

Conclusions

As a means of evaluating certain hypotheses concerning the behavioral similarities and dissimilarities of Rorschach responses, twenty-one of the basic scores of the Klopfer system were intercorrelated and submitted to a centroid analysis. The intercorrelations could be accounted for in four factors and after a series of orthogonal rotations several clustering tendencies became conspicuous. As a result of this analysis and within the limitations of the sample of ninety-two students employed, the following conclusions are offered:

1. The factorial composition of the human movement response category is distinctly different from the factorial composition of the color-form and the pure color response categories. The color-form and the pure color responses have a highly similar factorial composition.

This result combined with the results of earlier studies (4, 5) comprises considerable justification for the traditional distinction (between human movement and the color responses) which is emphasized in the scoring of the Rorschach test and in an interpretation of Rorschach protocols.

2. The factorial composition of the form-color response category is quite different from the factorial composition of the color-form and color response categories. This result suggests that the common practice of regarding the three classes of color responses as similar in their implications for the affective features of human behavior should be viewed with reservations. In the present study, the factorial composition of the form-color response cate-

gory is more similar to the factorial composition of the human movement response category than it is to the other color response categories.

3. Factor III′ in the present study fulfills the requirement of Hypothesis II which states, "The whole, color-form, pure color, pure texture, and pure diffusion response categories are intercorrelated in a manner which yields a factor different from the factor which is most important in determining the common factor variance of the pure form, human movement, and the various detail response categories." The evidence for the validity of Hypothesis II suggests that it may be profitable to employ a new Rorschach scoring principle which is based on a weighted combination of the response categories which contribute to factor III′.

4. Factor IV′ may be offered in support for both Hypothesis III ("The Rorschach scoring categories will be correlated with the total number of responses [R] in such a manner as to result in a general or quasi general factor of productivity") and Hypothesis IV ("Response scoring categories differ greatly in the degree to which their common factor variance is due to a productivity factor"). There are two possible practical implications for factor IV′:

a) Factor IV′ may be produced by the obsessive, compulsive personalities in the sample and when its contributing response categories are appropriately weighted, it may provide a scale which has some clinical value.

b) This factor has implications for the current use of the Rorschach test inasmuch as it implies that some of the separately interpreted scoring categories overlap each other and should receive relatively less weight than they now do.

5. In general, the present study suggests that an incorrect emphasis may have influenced the development of current Rorschach scoring procedures and interpretive practices. For example, many of the scoring categories which belong to the various broad classes of determinants, e.g., color, texture, or diffusion have a quite dissimilar factorial composition and in general the manner in which the various determinant scoring categories cluster together could not be predicted by an employment of the usual beliefs concerning behavioral implications of determinants.

REFERENCES

1. KLOPFER, B. AND KELLEY, D. M. *The Rorschach technique.* Yonkers, N.Y.: World Book Co., 1942.

2. WITTENBORN, J. R. Certain Rorschach response categories and mental abilities. *J. Appl. Psychol.,* 1949, *33,* 330–338.

3. WITTENBORN, J. R. A factor analysis of discrete responses to the Rorschach ink blots. *J. Consult. Psychol.*, 1949, *13*, 335–340.

4. WITTENBORN, J. R. Statistical tests of certain Rorschach assumptions: Analyses of discrete responses. *J. Consult. Psychol.*, 1949, *13*, 257–267.

5. WITTENBORN, J. R. Statistical tests of certain Rorschach assumptions. The internal consistency of scoring categories. *J. Consult. Psychol.*, 1950, *14*, 1–19.

J. R. Wittenborn

STATISTICAL TESTS OF

CERTAIN RORSCHACH

ASSUMPTIONS ⸱ *The Internal*

Consistency of Scoring Categories

I N THE first publication of this series, *Analyses of Discrete Responses* (13), two reasons were given for examining the implications of some of the Rorschach assumptions:

1. Since the assumptions have not been tested, the possibility exists that some of them are invalid. If some of the assumptions cannot be validated, aspects of interpretations based on the questionable assumptions should be employed with reservation or perhaps eliminated from standard procedures.

2. Many of the assumptions employed in Rorschach procedures cannot be found among the established facts and theories of American academic psychologists. If the Rorschach assumptions are valid, their relevance to the

Reprinted from *J. Consult. Psychol.*, 1950, *14*, 1–19, by permission of the American Psychological Association and the author.

psychology of personality organization and to the psychology of perception could be of extraordinary significance.

In scoring a Rorschach protocol, it is customary to classify each response with respect to several classes of factors, such as content, portion of ink blot interpreted, and ink-blot characteristics determining the response. There are standard categories within each of the classes of factors. When a response is scored, the content category in which it falls, as well as its location category and its determinant category, is designated by the scorer. As a second step in scoring, the total number of responses falling in each category is ascertained. Regardless of the precise manner in which the categories are used, the device of categorizing the responses and then finding the total number of responses in each category carries two implications:

I. That all of the responses falling in a given category are similar in some behavioral respect.

II. That the psychological significance of responses falling in a given category is different in some respect from responses placed in other categories.

These assumptions are implicit, for example, in the distinction that is made between human movement and color responses. This distinction was first emphasized by Rorschach (9), and its observance has remained a basic feature of Rorschach psychodiagnosis. Because of the basic significance ascribed to these two types of responses, it was decided to employ this distinction in testing the foregoing assumptions of intracategory similarity and intercategory difference.

If Assumption I is a true proposition, it follows that several measurements of the tendency to perceive human movement would be positively related. If several measures of a given response category were not positively interrelated, it would be difficult to justify an assumption that differences in number of responses of that category expressed differences in a personality attribute. It also follows from Assumption II that several measures of a given response category would be more highly interrelated with each other than they would be related with measures of some other category.

The following experimental hypotheses have been tested by statistical analyses (A and B) of data provided by the Harrower-Erickson multiple choice check list (3), the analyses were based on a sample of 247 undergraduates:

A. The tendency for controlled color responses (*FC* and *CF*) to be associated with other controlled color responses (*FC* and *CF*) is greater than the tendency for such color responses to be associated with human movement (*M*) responses.

B. The tendency for human movement (*M*) responses to be associated with other human movement (*M*) responses is greater than the tendency for such responses to be associated with controlled color responses (*FC* and *CF*).

C. The degree to which Rorschach responses will be intercorrelated is a function of the number of scoring categories the responses have in common.

The major conclusions of the Analyses (A and B) of the check list data may be stated as follows (13):

1. Among the intercorrelations between pairs of discrete check list responses there is no obvious pattern which conforms with a pattern predictable from either Hypothesis A or Hypothesis B.

2. There is a statistically significant tendency for Rorschach responses which have two or three scoring categories in common to be more highly correlated than pairs of responses which have but one or no common scoring categories. Thus Hypothesis C is verified. Nevertheless, the tendency for the correlations between responses to vary directly with the number of common scoring categories is so negligible as to be associated with a large number of gross exceptions.

3. In general, the number and size of the exceptional correlations is such as to challenge the value of scoring the Rorschach responses on the basis of abstract categories.

As a result of these findings, it was decided to submit the discrete check list responses to a factor analysis (Analysis C) which could provide an answer to the following questions:

1. The intercorrelations among the responses could not be satisfactorily predicted by certain deductions from Assumption I and II: is there some structure, some systematic clustering effect among the check list responses or are their relationships haphazard and unpatterned?

2. If there is a discernible pattern of relationships among the check list responses, will it be congruent with any current practice or belief concerning the Rorschach?

From the factor analysis (14), which involved 18 responses and was based upon 247 students, the following conclusions may be offered:

1. The analysis yielded relatively independent factors, most of which retained their composition when rotated obliquely. Nevertheless, an inspection of the factors yielded by both orthogonal and oblique methods of rotation does not offer evidence in support of some of the common beliefs concerning the Rorschach responses, particularly those which are reflected in abstract scoring practices.

2. The data suggest that response content (with its implied associations and projections) may play an important role in determining the functional

similarities and dissimilarities of certain responses, particularly those which involve movement.

Because of its known practical limitations, a Rorschach multiple choice check list per se is of restricted interest; nevertheless, the form lends itself to quantitative analyses which in turn yield hypotheses relevant to and readily tested by the individual form of the test. With perhaps some exceptions it may reasonably be supposed that the responses which the individual has checked on the check list comprise a sample of the perceptions which may be elicited from him by the ink blots. Therefore, in the absence of specific contra-indications, it is justifiable to generalize the results of certain statistical analyses (which are convenient only with data yielded by the check list form of the test) to relevant assumptions which have implications for all forms of the test. Consequently, inferences from the preliminary studies have been employed in the formulation of hypotheses which are tested in the present study with data yielded by the individual Rorschach procedure.

The Plan of the Present Investigation

In the present study three different analyses are employed for the purpose of testing eleven different hypotheses, almost all of which were generated primarily by Assumptions I and II. In order to facilitate the presentation and to clarify the nature of the study each of the three analyses will be presented separately with a formal statement of the hypotheses to be tested, a description of the subjects employed, a terse presentation of the statistical test results, and a brief discussion of the apparent status of the hypotheses.

ANALYSIS D

In order to test the consequences of Assumptions I and II, it is necessary to secure several different measures or quantifiable groupings of the scoring categories in question. This has been accomplished in Analysis D by determining for each card the number of responses falling in a given scoring category. Thus each card may be considered to yield its own evidence of the individual's tendency to give responses which belong to a given scoring category.

A measure of a response tendency based on a single card involves certain considerations which should be made explicit:

1. Such measures of a response tendency are but a fraction of the total protocol score for that response tendency. Accordingly, the reliability of such a measure

cannot be expected to approach the reliability of the total score for the response tendency (i.e., scoring category) in question.

2. Moreover, such measures of a response tendency cannot be expected to be equally reliable from card to card. Therefore, perfect evidence for the assumptions of intracategory similarity and intercategory difference should not be expected.

3. Although the frequency of responses of a given category is known to vary conspicuously from card to card, this is not expected to affect the tests of the internal consistency (i.e., the correlation between two variables is independent of any constant difference between them).

4. Regardless of the exact manner in which responses of a given category are fractionated, the resulting subgroups will differ from each other in some qualitative respect. These qualitative differences will obviously detract from the evidence for intracategory similarity. Some readers may be inclined to seize upon such qualitative differences and argue that they disqualify a fractional analytic examination of Rorschach assumptions. It is to be emphasized, however, that such qualitative differences are the prime justification for studies of internal consistency such as the present one; if such qualitative differences are so great as to obscure completely the trends required by the hypothesis, then the trends specified in the hypothesis may be rejected as irrelevant and perhaps the nature of the qualitative differences may be considered to be the proper subject for analysis.

Analysis D is designed to test two hypotheses:

D. There will be more significant interrelations *among* the number of human movement responses for cards I, II, III, VII, IX, and X than there will be *between* the number of human movement responses for these same cards (I, II, III, VII, IX, and X) and the number of color responses (total of *FC, CF,* and *C*) for cards II, III, VIII, IX, and X.

E. There will be more significant interrelationships *among* the number of color responses (total of *FC, CF,* and *C*) for cards II, III, VIII, IX, and X than there will be *between* the number of human movement responses for cards I, II, III, VII, IX and X and the number of color responses (*FC, CF,* and *C*) for cards II, III, VIII, IX, and X.

Hypotheses D and E were tested by means of data provided by the following three samples:

Sample I—Comprises a group of ninety-five Yale undergraduates who voluntarily served as subjects for a Ph.D. candidate, Mrs. Florence Schumer, who administered and scored the Rorschach tests in a manner closely conforming to that of Klopfer (4).

Sample II—Comprises forty-five Yale undergraduates who had consulted the writer for guidance and therapy. All could be described as moderately neurotic but none was incapacitated by his symptoms nor in apparent danger of entering a psychotic episode. The Rorschach test protocols employed were prepared by Klopfer's methods.

Sample III—Comprises a group of 100 patients who had been treated on either an out-patient or an in-patient basis in the clinics of the psychiatric service of the New Haven Hospital. Almost all of these patients could be described as ill, and at least one-third were psychotic or had suffered a psychotic episode. Most of the examiners were close adherents to the Klopfer method, although several of them were equally familiar with the methods of Beck. (The scores employed in the analysis were determined in conformance with Klopfer.)

It is always possible that findings based on a particular sample, regardless of its composition, will be considered by some readers as inappropriate for testing such an instrument as the Rorschach. Basing analyses on several groups which are clearly different in the quality of their personal adjustment affords an important control.

The data for each sample were of such a nature as to make the following statistical tests feasible:

Sample I—55 χ^2 tests were made comprising the following groups:

1. 15 χ^2 tests, based on all possible interrelationships among the number of human movement responses for cards I, II, III, VII, IX and X.

2. 10 χ^2 tests based on all possible interrelationships among the number of color responses for each of the colored cards, II, III, VIII, IX, and X.

3. 30 χ^2 tests based on all possible interrelationships between the number of human movement responses for cards I, II, III, VII, IX, and X and the number of color responses for cards II, III, VIII, IX, and X.

Sample II—45χ^2 tests were made comprising the following groups:

1. 10 χ^2 tests based on all possible relationships between the number of human movement responses for cards I, III, VII, IX, and X. (Because of the small size of sample B an analysis of the human movement responses for card II was not made.)

2. 10 χ^2 tests based on all possible interrelationships among the total number of color responses for each of the colored cards, II, III, VIII, IX, and X.

3. 25 χ^2 tests based on all possible interrelationships between the number of human movement responses for cards I, III, VII, IX, and X, and the number of color responses for cards II, III, VIII, IX, and X.

Sample III—55 χ^2 tests were made comprising groups of χ^2 tests which were arranged identically with those provided by sample I.

The 155 χ^2 tests provided by the analysis of samples I, II, and III are summarized in Table 1 below. These data have the following implications:

1. Since almost half (eighteen out of forty) of the interrelationships among groups of human movement responses would occur by chance less than 10 per cent of the time, Hypothesis D is considered to be a true hypothesis. That is to say, there is a discernible degree of mutual consistency among human movement responses, and as a consequence it is inferred that the human movement response category is a behaviorally relevant category in the sense that it refers to demonstrably similar ways of reacting to ink-blot stimuli. Since human movement responses comprise functionally similar behavioral features, quantification of them is an appropriate procedure. The consistency among groups of human movement responses (as well as

TABLE 1

**A Summary of the Results of Chi-Square Tests Required by Hypotheses "D" and "E,"
Showing the Distribution of Significance Levels for All Groups Compared**

Sample	Significance level distribution of the comparison for each of the three possible combinations of the determinant groups		
	M vs. M	M vs. C	C vs. C
Sample I			
1% level	3	1	1
5% level	6	5	4
10% level	6	6	6
99% level			
(All comparisons for Sample I)	15	30	10
Sample II			
1% level	2	0	6
5% level	3	0	8
10% level	4	0	8
99% level			
(All comparisons for Sample II)	10	25	10
Sample III			
1% level	4	1	2
5% level	6	1	5
10% level	8	2	6
99% level			
(All comparisons for Sample III)	15	30	10
All Samples Combined			
1% level	9	2	9
5% level	15	6	17
10% level	18	8	20
99% level			
(All comparisons for all samples)	40	85	30
Approximate fraction significant at 10% level	$\frac{1}{2}$	$\frac{1}{10}$	$\frac{2}{3}$

their relative independence from groups of color responses) may be taken as evidence that the total human movement response score could bear a valid relationship to an important feature of the personality which could not be predicted from a knowledge of the individual's color responses.

2. The similarity among small groups of human movement responses is not of a high order, and it is not invariably consistent. Since exceptions to the hypothesis exist, the common clinical practice of ascribing a particular

meaning (or a particular personality implication) to small differences in the number of human movement responses is obviously hazardous and probably unjustified. That is to say, small groups of human movement responses do not invariably have the same meaning or the same behavioral implications; it is gratuitous to ascribe any particular difference between two individuals as a consequence of observed small differences (one or two responses) between them with respect to the number of human movement responses they produce.

3. Hypothesis E is also a true hypotheses. Two-thirds of the interrelationships among groups of color responses are so marked that they would occur less than 10 per cent of the time by chance (i.e., significant at the 10 per cent level). Since less than one-tenth of interrelationships between groups of human movement responses and groups of color responses are significant at as high a level, the practice of combining the number of color responses into a total score which is interpreted differently from the human movement total score appears to be justified. Moreover, since the color scores are related with each other, it is quite possible that the total color response scores could bear an important degree of relationship with some other response score, e.g., a measure of some practically important feature of personality. It is evident from the data that small groups of responses to the color cards may not always have the same meaning. It is interesting to note, however, that the consistency with which a particular meaning may be ascribed to responses to the different color cards appears to be substantially greater than the consistency of meaning which may be ascribed to the human movement responses elicited by different cards.

4. The status of Hypotheses D and E does not appear to be dependent upon the exact nature of the sample employed inasmuch as the findings for all three samples appear to have the same implications for the two hypotheses.

5. There is no evidence that the pattern of significant χ^2 tests is consistent from sample to sample. Accordingly, it may not be concluded that there is a greater similarity among the human responses (or among the color responses) for any particular group of cards than there is for any other group of cards. This lack of consistency from sample to sample is in keeping with the interpretation that the number of insignificant χ^2 tests is an expression of a generally low level of intercard relationships among color or among human movement determinant scores.

ANALYSIS E

In Analysis D hypotheses generated by the assumptions of intracategory similarity and intercategory difference among abstract Rorschach scoring categories were examined for two determinants, human movement and color. The hypotheses, D and E, required a demonstrable degree of similarity among groups of responses which had a common determinant but which were different with respect to the card which elicited them. For Analysis D the consequences of the assumption of similarity among responses with a common determinant were tested by means of an experimental design wherein differences due to the location of the responses were distributed among the groups in an uncontrolled manner. Such differences obviously reduce the sensitivity of the analysis, but they probably do not result in im-

TABLE 2

The Confidence Levels (Based on the Chi-Square Test) at Which the Statistical Hypothesis of "No Relationship" May be Refuted for Various Pairs of Response Grouping

Deter-minant	Loca-tion	Sam-ple	M			FC			CF		
			D	W	X	D	W	X	D	W	X
M	D	I									
		III									
	W	I	1%								
		III	5%								
	X	I	1%	—							
		III	10%	5%							
FC	D	I	(5%)*	—	—						
		III	(—)	—	10%						
	W	I	—	(—)	—	(5%)					
		III	—	(—)	5%	—					
	X	I	10%	—	(5%)	10%	—				
		III	—	—	(1%)	—	5%				
CF	D	I	(5%)	—	—	(—)	—	10%			
		III	(—)	—	10%	(5%)	10%	5%			
	W	I	—	(10%)	—	—	(1%)	—	10%		
		III	—	(—)	—	—	(—)	—			
	X	I	—	—	(—)	—	—	(10%)	—	—	
		III	—	—	(5%)	—	5%	(1%)	5%	—	

* Some of the confidence levels are enclosed in parentheses. The comparisons to which they refer are between groups with the same location. They are employed in Analysis F and not in Analysis E.

portant systematic differences between the groups which were being tested. Since the response groups employed in Analysis D were determined by the cards, differences due to the card (e.g., content differences resulting from the nature of the stimulus material) vary systematically from group to group and to some degree detract from the apparent validity of the hypotheses.

Analysis E is designed somewhat differently. Like Analysis D, E is concerned with testing hypotheses which state the consequences of Assumptions

I and II with respect to the human movement and color determinants. In Analysis E, however, intercategory differences due to content (due to card) are uncontrolled, and may randomly reduce the sensitivity of the tests of relationship whereas the groups differ systematically with respect to location. Accordingly, differences due to the location factor systematically reduce the demonstrable magnitude of the relationship between the groups. In Analysis E three location groupings are employed: (1) The W group comprises all of the human movement or all of the color responses in the protocol which are scored as whole responses. (2) The D group comprises all the movement or color responses of the protocol which are scored as based upon one of the large details of the card. (3) The X group comprises all other movement or color responses which were not scored as whole responses or as large detail responses; for the most part the X group comprises responses based upon small or rarely used portions of the card. Since fewer groups are employed in Analysis E than in Analysis D, in Analysis E a larger number of responses is available for each group. As a consequence, it is possible for the color responses to be subdivided so that the provisions of Assumptions I and II may be examined as they apply to the degree to which color responses are controlled by form. Analysis E makes use of the data provided by samples I and III described in Analysis D. The data from these two samples were employed independently in testing the following hypotheses.

Hypothesis F—Groups of human movement responses which are different from each other with respect to their location (W, D, or X) are more consistently correlated with each other than they are with groups of color responses (FC and CF) which are different from the groups of human movement responses not only with respect to determinant but also are different from the human movement responses with respect to location.

Hypothesis G—Groups of color responses (FC and CF) which are different from each other with respect to their location (W, D, or X) are more consistently correlated with each other than they are with groups of human movement responses which are different from the groups of color responses not only with respect to determinant but also are different from the color responses with respect to location.

Hypothesis H—Groups of FC responses which are different from each other with respect to location are more consistently correlated with each other than they are with groups of CF responses which are different from the FC responses with respect to location as well as with respect to the degree to which the response is controlled by form (FC and CF are here employed to represent the responses which they commonly designate in the Klopfer scoring system).

Hypothesis I—Groups of CF responses which are different from each other with respect to location are more consistently correlated with each other than they are with groups of FC responses which are different from the CF responses with respect to location as well as with respect to the degree to which the response is controlled by form (CF and FC are here employed to represent the responses which they commonly designate in the Klopfer scoring system).

The χ^2 tests required by hypotheses F, G, H, and I are summarized in Table 2. In the instance where the relationship between the groups of responses is so small as to occur more often than 10 per cent of the time by chance the confidence level is omitted from the table; these cases are indicated by a dash. Since the data for samples I and III were analyzed independently, the results for each sample are shown. The significance of the relationship between any two particular groups may be readily found in the Table by locating the row for one of the groups in question and the column for the other group; the point at which the respective row and column intersect gives the significance of the relationship between the two groups.

Confidence levels in Table 2 which are relevant to Hypothesis F are summarized in Table 3. Since five of the six possible interrelationships among the groups of human movement responses (three comparisons for each of the two samples involved) are significant at the 10 per cent confidence level and since only four of the twenty-four possible interrelationships between human movement and color response groups are equally significant, Hypothesis F is considered to be a true hypothesis. The evidence for Hypothesis F is noticeably more consistent than the evidence in favor of the analo-

TABLE 3

A Summary of the Results of the Chi-Square Tests Required by Hypothesis "F," Showing the Distribution of Significance Levels for the Groups Compared

	M vs. M	M vs. C
Samples I and III		
1% level	2	0
5% level	4	1
10% level	5	4
99% level (All location groups combined)	6	24
Approximate fraction significant at 10% level	⅚	⅙

gous hypothesis, D. Some of this difference may be due to the greater reliability inherent in the larger groups employed in Hypothesis F. It seems more probable, however, that the difference is a result of the difference between the designs employed in Analyses D and E. The support provided Hypothesis F favors the practice of using the total number of human movement responses as a quantification for a particular response mode. The total number of human movement responses appears to be an internally consistent feature of behavior in the Rorschach situation and accordingly could possess an important degree of validity for some personality criterion.

The confidence levels relevant to the status of Hypothesis G are similarly summarized in Table 4. It is apparent that significant relationships between two groups of responses which involve color are twice as prevalent as they are between two groups of responses which do not have the same determinant. It is interesting to note that despite the fact that the groups employed in Hypothesis G are presumably more reliable than those employed in Hypothesis E, the evidence for Hypothesis G is not as conspicuous as the evidence for the analogous Hypothesis E. The difference, probably a feature of the design of the analyses, will be discussed in a succeeding section. The

TABLE 4

A Summary of the Results of the Chi-Square Tests Required by Hypothesis "G," Showing the Distribution of Significance Levels for the Groups Compared

	C vs. C	M vs. C
Samples I and III		
1% level	0	0
5% level	5	1
10% level	9	4
99% level (All location groups combined)	24	24
Approximate fraction significant at 10% level	⅓	⅙

evidence for Hypothesis G provided by the present analysis supports the practice of combining the color responses into a total score and suggests that the tendency to respond to color in Rorschach situations represents a consistent human trait or behavior attribute which is different from the tendency to offer human movement responses.

TABLE 5

A Summary of the Results of Chi-Square Tests Required by Hypothesis "H," Showing the Distribution of Significance Levels for the Groups Compared

	FC vs. FC	FC vs. CF
Samples I and III		
1% level	0	0
5% level	2	2
10% level	3	4
99% level (All location groups combined)	6	12
Approximate fraction significant at 10% level	½	⅓

The summarized material in Table 5 suggests that Hypothesis H could be a true hypothesis but the distinction is not clear; there is no evidence among the data provided by Table 2 to support Hypothesis I. Nevertheless, these data are not considered as a challenge to the practice of distinguishing between the *CF* and the *FC* score.

The rather modest evidence in Analysis E for consistency among the color responses is in contrast with the fact that in Analysis D two-thirds of the interrelationships among the color responses were found to be significant. This contrast is interpreted as a consequence of the difference between the two experimental designs and will receive a more nearly complete discussion in a subsequent section.

ANALYSIS F

Analysis F like Analysis E employs samples I and III which were described and employed in Analysis D. In other respects, however, Analysis F is greatly different from Analyses D and E. Analyses D and E were concerned with hypotheses which specified consequences of Assumptions I and II for the Rorschach scoring distinction between responses involving human movement and those involving color. Analysis F is concerned with hypotheses which have to do with distinctions in Rorschach scoring which are based upon the portion of the card presumably eliciting the response. In Analysis E the portions of the card eliciting the response (commonly referred to in scoring as the location factor) were described with respect to three subdivisions. These subdivisions are employed in the present analysis also and comprise the following groups:

I. The number of responses based on the whole card, W.
   (a) W responses with the M determinant.
   (b) W responses with the CF determinant.
   (c) W responses with the CF determinant.

II. The number of responses based on the large details of the card, D.
   (a) D responses with the M determinant.
   (b) D responses with the FC determinant.
   (c) D responses with the CF determinant.

III. The number of responses which have a location score other than W or D; in the present study the location of these responses is designated by the letter X.
   (a) X responses with the M determinant.
   (b) X responses with the FC determinant.
   (c) X responses with the CF determinant.

In the case of Hypothesis K differences due to card and to content are uncontrolled, but differences due to the determinants vary systematically from group to group and systematically detract from the apparent magnitude of the relationship between the groups.

Hypothesis K—Response groups which belong to the same scoring category with respect to location (but are different with respect to determinant) are more consistently related among themselves than they are with response groups which belong to a different location category (and are different with respect to determinant).

Confidence levels for the relationships relevant to Hypothesis K may be found in Table 2 and for the convenience of the reader are summarized in Table 6. On the basis of the present data, Hypothesis K is considered to be a true hypothesis. Nevertheless, only one-half of the interrelationships among groups of responses which have the same location but a different determinant are significant at the 10 per cent level. The evidence of functional similarity among groups of responses which have the same location is of academic interest and is in keeping with the practice of counting and interpreting separately those responses which are elicited by different portions of the card. Rorschach examiners commonly ascribe a personality difference between individuals as a result of small observed differences with respect to the number of whole or large detail responses; the data and the analyses of this study may *not* be taken as a justification for this practice. As a matter of fact, they may better be taken as cause for viewing such practice with suspicion.

TABLE 6

Levels of Significance of Relationship Distributed for Response Groups Which Have the Same Location and Distributed for Response Groups Which Have a Different Location

	Significance of Relationships Between Groups Having the Same Location	Significance of Relationships Between Groups Having a Different Location
1% level	1	0
5% level	5	1
10% level	6	4
99% level (All comparisons)	12	24
Approximate fraction significant at 10% level	½	⅙

The *FC* and *CF* categories, although scored differently, were not shown in Analysis E to be conspicuously or consistently different from each other. In Rorschach theory they are considered to be expressions of the same general class of response and are commonly combined to yield a total color response score. In keeping with the conception of the FC and CF as merely gradations within the response to color category they have been combined in a preliminary analysis (8) as well as in Analysis D of the present series. Viewing the *FC* and *CF* responses as having a determinant in common results in the statement of Hypothesis L which like the foregoing hypotheses is generated primarily from Assumptions I and II. For the purpose of testing Hypothesis L groups of responses which have *FC* as their determinant are considered to have the same determinant as groups of responses for which the determinant is actually *CF*. Thus it is possible to interpret certain of the parenthetical values in Table 2 as confidence levels for relationships between response groups which are the same with respect to both determinant and location features.

Hypothesis L—Responses which have both a common location and a common determinant category are more consistently related with each other than are responses which have either a location or a determinant factor in common.

Hypothesis L has an interesting relevance to Assumptions I and II because it states that similarities among responses which are due either to common location or determinant categories are cumulative, and in this respect it is similar in its implications to Hypothesis C, which was tested in an earlier study and is stated in the introduction to the present paper.

The significance levels relevant to Hypothesis L are distributed in Table 7. The significance levels distributed in the first row of Table 7 are based upon relationships between response groups which are identical with respect to location and are similar with respect to determinant, i.e., the groups compared all have color as a determinant but the groups compared are different

TABLE 7

Distribution of Significance Levels

	1% Level	5% Level	10% Level	99% Level (All Comparisons)	Approximate Fraction Significant At 10% Level
Relationships between groups of responses which have a common location and a quasi-common determinant	2	3	4	6	$\frac{2}{3}$
Relationships between groups of responses which have a location only in common	1	5	6	12	$\frac{1}{2}$
Relationships between groups of responses which have a common determinant, either quasi or strictly defined	2	9	13	30	$\frac{1}{2}$
Relationships between groups of responses which have neither a location nor a determinant category in common	0	1	4	24	$\frac{1}{6}$

with respect to the degree to which color is controlled by form. The second row in Table 7 comprises a distribution of significance levels determined between groups of responses which are identical with respect to location only. The third row comprises a distribution of significance levels between groups of responses which are different from each other with respect to location and are identical with respect to determinant (groups which are strictly identical with respect to determinant as well as those which have a quasi-common determinant are both included). The last row in Table 7 is a distribution of significance levels for the relationships between groups of responses which have neither a location nor a determinant category in common. It may be seen from an examination of Table 7 that the distributions of levels of significance are arranged in a manner in keeping with the provisions of Hypothesis L.

ANALYSIS G

Analysis G employs data provided by samples I and III. The hypotheses tested in Analysis D are homogeneous with respect to design and implication, as were those tested in Analyses E and F. In the present analysis the hypotheses tested, M and N, have their origins in preceding studies and in Rapaport (8) and Rorschach (9).

The Rorschach literature does not state explicitly whether location factors or determinant factors are more important in the abstract scoring of Rorschach responses, nor is there any evidence in the literature which could be taken as a definite indication that determinant factors are more (or less) consistent in influencing the psychological significance of the response than are the location factors. In the factor analysis of discrete responses to the Rorschach check list (8) no evidence was produced to indicate that determinant factors played a more important role in influencing the interrelationships among the responses than did the location factors. The relevance of this question to the kind of data employed in the present analysis is stated in Hypothesis M.

Hypothesis M—The portion of significant relationships among groups of responses which have a common determinant but differ with respect to location is as great as the portion of significant relations between groups of responses which have the same location but are different with respect to determinant.

Table 8 provides a summary of the significance levels which are relevant to Hypothesis M. It is apparent that the data available for the present analysis do not challenge the status of the hypothesis. In general it appears that the consistency among groups of responses which have a common determi-

TABLE 8

Distribution of Significance Levels

	1% Level	5% Level	10% Level	99% Level (All Comparisons)	Approximate Fraction Significant At 10% Level
Relationships between groups of responses which have a common location (D, W, or X)	1	5	6	12	½
Relationships between groups of responses which have a common determinant (M, FC, or CF)	2	7	10	18	½

nant is of about the same order as that among groups of responses which have a common location. It should be emphasized, however, that the number and diversity of comparisons involved in the present analysis is not sufficient to confer any general validity to Hypothesis M; it can only be stated that Hypothesis M is not challenged by the available data.

It is a common belief among workers who have had intensive experience with the Rorschach that the personality significance of the human movement response varies somewhat with the exact nature of the human movement which is perceived. It is also commonly observed among Rorschach workers that the cards differ with respect to the kinds of human movement responses they elicit (5, 6). These common informal beliefs based on the clinical experience of Rorschach workers are in good agreement with the results of the factor analysis of discrete responses (14). If these beliefs growing out of clinical practice as well as the implications of the factor analysis are valid, it would be predicted that:

Hypothesis N—The interrelationships among groups of human movement responses which are based on different cards would be less marked and less consistent than interrelationships among groups of human movement responses which are not based on different cards and which do not maximize this source of differences in content.

In the case of the large detail responses and the whole responses, one would not often expect the nature of the perceived human movement to be contingent upon the subject's willingness to use the whole card in preference to merely a large portion of it in forming his response. In general it seems plausible to suppose that the location scoring designation of a response has less to do with its content than the card which elicited the response. This seems particularly plausible inasmuch as the exact location designation of a human movement response seems to be more often determined by combinatory or relatively incidental features of the response than by the exact nature of the *human movement* feature of the response. The foregoing considerations are of interest because they predict the shift in the prevalence of significant relationships between human movement response groups observed upon comparison of Table 1 (Analysis D) with Table 2 (Analysis E). Hypothesis N is considered to be a true hypothesis and its status and implications are further discussed in the following section.

Discussion

The nature of the procedure employed in testing the hypotheses requires comment. It is to be noted that all of the hypotheses require a comparison of two samples of interrelationships. The interrelationships comprising each sample were based upon groups of responses which were not independent of each other; they instead were related to each other to an unknown but varying degree. Estimation of the sampling distributions of the χ^2 statistic for such samples of interrelationships would be inconvenient, if not prohibitively difficult. Accordingly, the chance frequency of any particular difference between the sample distributions of the χ^2 statistics is unknown, and it is not possible to specify the confidence level with which the null statement of the hypotheses may be refuted. In the case of each of the hypotheses, it is possible to state only whether the difference between the distributions of the χ^2 statistic for the two samples of relationships is in a direction predictable by the hypothesis. Regardless of the subjective confidence which the reader may have in the status of any of the hypotheses, it should be noted that the evidence is favorable to all the hypotheses except possibly those involving the distinction between the *FC* and *CF* responses. Accordingly, the acceptance of Assumptions I and II as true propositions (within the requirements of the stated hypotheses and the characteristics of the Rorschach samples employed) should not be regarded as reckless or incautious.[1]

In evaluating the present analyses and their implications for Rorschach practices, it should be noted that despite the relatively large samples employed, a large fraction of the relationships required by the hypotheses are insignificant. Since there is no apparent pattern which leads to a distinction between the significant and insignificant χ^2 tests for a given sample of relationships, the relationships exceptional to the requirements of the hypotheses are considered to be a result of either the unreliability of the response groups or of a modest degree of intrinsic relationship among the responses

1. The assumptions do not require that the Rorschach scoring categories are optimal for classifying responses and the present study is not designed to indicate the nature of the optimal or most economical scoring categories.

which have a common abstract scoring category. In any event, the present data are in no sense a justification for the common practice of ascribing important personality differences between individuals as a result of small differences in the frequency with which color responses, movement responses, whole responses, or large detailed responses appear in the Rorschach protocols of the individuals. How large such differences must be before they may be justifiably used in the evaluation of individuals, if they may ever be so used, cannot be precisely inferred from the present analyses. Obviously, important differences between people cannot be predicted on the bases of one or two abstract response scores. (It is conceivable, however, that the *content* of a single response or the conditions under which it is elicited, may have an important validity.) Thus with respect to the first question which prompted this series of studies, it may be stated that some important provisions of Assumptions I and II afford a partial prediction of the pattern of interrelationships among the Rorschach responses. This may be taken as an indication favorable to some of the abstract scoring practices, but the data must also be taken as distinctly unfavorable to certain common clinical practices involving these abstract response scores.

The results of the analyses are particularly relevant to the second general question instigating these studies. The manner in which responses having a common abstract scoring category tend to cluster together, and tend to distinguish themselves from responses having other types of abstract scoring features, suggests that the modes of perceptual response to which some of the abstract scoring features refer may be members of a fairly broad and stable class of perceptual response modes, and may actually be evidences of practically significant classes of human attributes (relatively stable response patterns). Such response patterns, like most response patterns, would be a reflection of certain important features of the conditions of the individual's existence. If the total constellation of such response patterns were known, abstract classes of perceptual responses could possibly be of value in inferring some of the important conditions of the individual's prior existence and of perhaps greater value in predicting the conditions under which certain types of behavior could be elicited in the future.

Evidence for the assumptions of intracategory similarity and intercategory difference among responses with a common scoring designation is not of academic interest only. The evidence for the assumptions not only hints at the existence of unexplored perceptual response attributes but more specifically is an indication that the total score for some of the response categories could be of valid means of predicting a personality characteristic. As a matter of fact the present series of studies is in certain respects a validation of the Rorschach test. The present studies have sought evidence of the validity of the Rorschach by means of tests of internal consistency. In situations where no dependable, quantified criteria are available for validating a test, the possibility of a test's being valid may be explored by examining its internal consistency. If the numerous component features of a test are found to be unrelated with each other, the total score of the test cannot be validly related to any simple criterion.

In a preceding paragraph, it was suggested that the tendency to perceive human movement in response to the Rorschach cards could comprise a portion of a broad sample of response patterns which were not restricted to the Rorschach situation. If the human movement response is so conceived, the nature of the general class of responses under which it may be subsumed becomes of interest. Speculation concerning such a class of responses may be guided somewhat by consideration of the conditions which determine or qualify the human movement response. In clinical practice it is commonly observed that the presence or absence of human movement responses having a particular content is determined by fantasies, conflicts or repressions of the individual (7). As a matter of fact, the relationship between the content of the human movement perceived and the content of the individual's fantasies is considered by many clinicians to be conspicuous. In the factor analysis of discrete Rorschach responses there was some evidence that the interrelationships among responses, including those involving human movement, were determined in part by content. In the present paper, there is an important difference between Tables 1 and 2 with respect to the prevalence of significant relationships among groups of human movement responses. Only half of the interrelationships among human movement response groups which differed from each other with respect to card were significant at the 10 per cent level whereas all but one of the interrelationships among human movement response groups which differed from each other with respect to location were significant at the 10 per cent level of confidence. This shift may be interpreted as an expression of the importance of content in determining the human movement response. This interpretation emerges from these considerations: By virtue of their form the cards differ importantly among themselves with respect to the kinds of human movement responses readily elicited; that is to say, the human movement content which the form of the card favors appears to determine the frequency with which certain individuals perceive human movement in the respective card; such differences due to card content are obscured, however, in interrelationships among response groups which differ systematically with respect to location, but do not differ systematically with respect to card (content).

Thus it appears that individual differences in the readiness with which a human movement is perceived is a function of the nature of the stimulus material. Inasmuch as there is a discernible correspondence between the objective form of the card and the human movement responses elicited, it is suggested that people differ in the readiness with which they perceive different kinds of human behavior.

The tendency of the individual to see or not to see certain kinds of human acts or attitudes in the Rorschach cards may be an instance of his readiness to see or not to see evidence for these human acts or attitudes in other situations. If this general pattern of speculation is correct, and it appears to be congruent with Rorschach's interpretation of the human movement response (9), the following assumptions may be regarded as tentative indications of relationships between the Rorschach human movement perceptual response tendency and perceptual tendencies characteristic of the individual in other situations requiring responses involving human acts or attitudes:

III. Any predominant content among the human movement responses elicited by the Rorschach cards should be demonstrably related to the content of human behavior perceptions elicited by situations wherein varied alternative perceptions are possible.

IV. A person who produces a relatively large number of human movement responses on the Rorschach will tend in other situations (wherein varied alternative perceptions are possible) to produce a relatively high number of responses involving human acts, attitudes or attributes.

These assumptions are not offered as clinical aids; as a matter of fact, much clinical practice presupposes their validity. Their value lies in the possibility that upon definition of terms they may be interpreted in the form of hypotheses which specify experimental procedures.

A thorough study of the human movement responses would involve devising a wide variety of tests which sample separate aspects or phases of the broad hypothetical class of responses which include, in addition to human movement responses, other types of responses, e.g., the expression of suppressed or repressed fantasy material. These tests would be included in a battery which would also include tests for other human attributes which might be confused with the hypothetical classification of responses. If the hypothetical class of responses is properly conceived and adequately sampled by tests, a factor analysis of the intercorrelations among the tests should provide evidence relative to the status of the Assumptions III and IV.

A similar design could possibly provide an advantageous means for examining the nature and implications of responses which are based on color. The present series of investigations appears to offer few hints concerning the nature of the color responses. A few tangential observations may be made, however. It should be noted for example, that color responses in Table 1 (Analysis D) are more consistently related with each other than those given in Table 2 (Analysis E). It appears that the differences in content due to the nature of the card do not detract from the interrelationships among the color responses whereas differences due to the amount of the card involved (i.e., location) do detract from the interrelationships among color responses. This suggests that the implications of color responses may be more a function of the size of the area of the card involved in the response than the nature (content) of the response. It is of interest to observe in the factor analysis (14) that the *FC* response appeared in the same factor with responses based upon large details whereas *CF* responses occurred in factors involving the whole card responses.

It would be in keeping with a portion of the meaning generally ascribed to the color responses to hypothesize a continuum which describes the degree to which perceptions vary from the extreme of rigid control and formalization (e.g., simple form responses) through various levels of control (e.g., *FC* and *CF*) to perceptions which are uncontrolled by and incongruent with formal considerations (e.g., *C*). Because of their very nature, relatively uncontrolled responses (*CF*) may be inconsistent and less highly related with each other than the relatively controlled responses (*FC* and *F*). The idea of a hypothetical continuum of perceptual control expressed in the Rorschach cards by the degree to which color responses are controlled by form is important in the Rorschach method and it is of interest to note that, by an employment of a very tenuous reasoning, correspondence between the present findings and this important assumption is discernible. For example in Table 2, it may be seen that the *FC* responses are more highly related with the *M* response (*M* responses are highly dependent on form) than are the *CF* responses. Obviously, the present data are inadequate to the task of even tentatively defining the color response, but it is of interest that an interpretation of the present findings which is in keeping with the control concept of the color responses can be construed. If Rorschach responses based on small or rare details are considered to be most controlled and whole responses are considered to be least controlled, additional evidence for this hypothetical continuum can be construed from some other results; e.g., it may be observed in Table 2 that the whole responses show the smallest number of consistent interrelationships whereas responses involving the *X* location (made up principally of small details) shows the largest number of significant relationships. It should be observed, however, that the slight difference in the number of significant relationships to which this paragraph refers may well be due to chance.

Regardless of the validity of the foregoing conjectures, if degree of control in perceptual responses is conceived as a human attribute, it should be possible after definition of the word "control" to formulate a variety of quantifiable instances of this perceptual attribute (instances from the Rorschach as well as from other situations) and study the relative consistency of their interrelations in the presence of measures of other attributes, the nature of which might be confused with the hypothetical control attribute. Factor analysis offers a suitable statistical approach for such a study.

At present neither the meaning nor the practical import of the human movement response or of the color response is objectified. Authoritative statements concerning them do not fully agree, and such statements comprise terms which for the most part are obscure or circularly defined. This probably is largely due to the fact that few unambiguous quantitative criteria for different aspects of the personality are available (quantified criteria for some Rorschach scores have been reported [2] but as far as the writer is aware are not described). Since such objective criteria for defining the meaning of the Rorschach responses are lacking, their meaning is not only unspecified but must vary from psychologist to psychologist and from day to day. (The uncanny competence of some clinicians is no more relevant to this problem than the incompetence of others.)

This state of affairs is important, not only from the standpoint of psychology as a behavioral science or from the standpoint of the problems in teaching it creates, but (since all of the subjective concepts of the implications of human movement and of color responses cannot be equally valid) it is important from the standpoint of the patient's welfare.

Research oriented toward the validation of these responses has produced promising but unsatisfactory evidence of validity. Since Rorschach validation research has had the handicap of questionable criteria, the following approaches to this important problem may be suggested:

1. The systematic development of objective, quantified criteria for personality characteristics important in the validation of the tests.

2. An hypothetic-deductive approach wherein an explicit unambiguous interpretation of a response group is given; numerous tests generated by this interpretation are prepared; intercorrelations of these tests are examined for mutual consistency; and the explicit interpretation rejected as invalid if the resultant tests are not mutually consistent.

The present discussion will be recognized as favoring the second of the two suggested alternatives.

Summary and Conclusion

Three samples comprising a total of 240 individually administered Rorschach tests were employed in testing a series of hypotheses generated by the following assumptions:

I. That all of the responses falling in a given category are similar in some behavioral respect.

II. That the psychological significance of responses falling in a given category is different in some respect from responses placed in other categories.

As a result of the application of a variety of analytical designs the following conclusions may be offered.

1. Within the requirements of the stated hypotheses and the characteristics of the samples employed, Assumptions I and II may be accepted as true hypotheses.

2. Human movement responses comprise functionally similar behavioral elements and quantification of them is an appropriate procedure. The consistency among groups of human movement responses (as well as their relative independence from groups of color responses) may be taken as evidence that the total human movement response score could bear a valid relationship to an important feature of the personality which could not be predicted from a knowledge of the individual's color responses.

3. The practice of combining the number of color responses into a total score which is interpreted differently from the human movement total score appears to be justified. Moreover, since the color scores are related with each other, it is quite possible that the total color response scores could bear an important degree of relationship with some other response score, e.g., a measure of some practically important feature of personality.

4. The evidence of functional similarity among groups of responses which have the same location is in keeping with the practice of counting and interpreting separately those responses which are elicited by different portions of the card.

5. The present data are in no sense a justification for the common practice of ascribing important personality differences between individuals as a result of small differences in the frequency with which color responses, movement responses, whole responses or large-detail responses appear in the Rorschach protocols of the individuals. How large such differences must be before they may be justifiably used in the evaluation of individuals, if they may ever be so used, cannot be precisely inferred from the present analyses. Obviously, important differences between people cannot be predicted on the bases of one or two abstract response scores.

6. Responses which have both a common location and a common determinant factor are more consistently related with each other than are responses which have either a location or a determinant factor in common.

7. The portion of significant relationships among groups of responses which have a common determinant but differ with respect to location ap-

pears to be as great as the portion of significant relations between groups of responses which have the same location but are different with respect to determinant.

8. The data offered no strong support for the practice of distinguishing between the *CF* and the *FC* responses. The findings are not interpreted as comprising a direct challenge to this practice, however.

9. It appears that individual differences in the readiness with which a human movement is perceived is a function of the nature of the stimulus material.

10. The implications of color responses may be more a function of the size of the area of the card involved in the response than the nature (content) of the response.

11. The whole responses show the smallest number of consistent interrelationships whereas responses involving the *X* location (made up principally of small details) shows the largest number of significant relationships.

In the discussion it is suggested that an employment of a hypothetic-deductive approach for the investigation of the validity of the Rorschach and other projective tests may at present prove to be the most feasible.

REFERENCES

1. BECK, S. J. *Rorschach's test.* New York: Grune & Stratton, 1945. Vols. I and II.
2. GUSTAVE, A. Estimation of Rorschach scoring category by means of an objective inventory. *J. Psychol.,* 1946, *22,* 253–260.
3. HARROWER-ERICKSON, MOLLY R. AND STEINER, MATILDA E. *Large scale Rorschach techniques.* Springfield, Ill.: Charles C Thomas, 1945.
4. KLOPFER, B. AND KELLEY, D. M. The Rorschach technique. Yonkers, N.Y.: World Book, 1942.
5. LINDNER, R. M. Some significant Rorschach responses. *J. Crim. Psychopathol.,* 1943–44, *5,* 775–778.
6. LINDNER, R. M. Content analysis in Rorschach work. *Rorschach Res. Exch.,* 1946, *10,* 121–129.
7. PIOTROWSKI, Z. The M, FM, and m responses as indication of changes in personality. *Rorschach Res. Exch.,* 1936–37, *1,* 148–156.
8. RAPAPORT, D. *Diagnostic psychological testing.* Chicago: Year Book Publishers, 1945. Vols. I and II.
9. RORSCHACH, H. *Psychodiagnostics.* Berne: Hans Huber, 1942.
10. THORNTON, G. R. AND GUILFORD, J. P. The reliability and meaning of erlebnis-typus scores in the Rorschach test. *J. Abnorm. Soc. Psychol.,* 1946, *31,* 324–330.

11. WITTENBORN, J. R. Certain Rorschach response categories and mental abilities. *J. Appl. Psychol.*, 1949, *33*, 330–338.

12. WITTENBORN, J. R. Statistical tests of certain Rorschach assumptions: Analyses of discrete responses. *J. Consult. Psychol.*, 1949, *13*, 257–267.

13. WITTENBORN, J. R. A factor analysis of discrete responses to the Rorschach ink blots. *J. Consult. Psychol.*, 1949, *13*, 335–340.

14. WITTENBORN, J. R. AND SARASON, S. B. Exceptions to certain Rorschach criteria of pathology. *J. Consult. Psychol.*, 1949, *13*, 21–27.

Irwin J. Knopf

RORSCHACH SUMMARY SCORES

IN DIFFERENTIAL DIAGNOSIS[1]

T HE DISCREPANCY between reports of clinical experience and research data has been a serious dilemma in Rorschach circles for a number of years. On the one hand, many clinicians have been impressed with the usefulness and the validity of the Rorschach method in a range of applications, while, on the other, research findings have not in the main supported this confidence. One such application has been the considerable use of the Rorschach as an aid in differentiating psychiatric disorders.

Formulated on the assumption that differences in psychiatric conditions would be reflected in Rorschach data, early investigations were primarily concerned with descriptive reports of the typical Rorschach performance of one or more psychiatric populations. As a result, statistical and/or experimental controls were not generally employed, but instead, clinical description was accepted without more rigorous verification. Later, some workers attempted to isolate the qualitative differences purported between patient groups and yet preserve the "holistic" nature of the test findings by deriving patterns or signs which collectively seemed to discriminate among nosologi-

Reprinted from *J. Consult. Psychol.*, 1956, *20*, 99–104, by permission of The American Psychological Association and the author.

1. A portion of this paper was presented at the American Psychological Association meetings in New York, 1954.

cal groups. Thus, a variety of signs were reported, for example, signs which were found in brain-damaged individuals, in psychoneurotics, in schizophrenics, and which were useful as indices of adjustment in the evaluation of psychotherapy (17, 18, 14, 8, 22, 15). However, when many of these signs were employed in subsequent investigations, the significant discriminations reported earlier were not corroborated (16, 3, 21, 7, 11). The fact that signs derived in the original investigations provided better discrimination within the initial sample than within subsequent populations is not too surprising. In some of these studies, signs were obtained by selecting for prediction those few aspects of Rorschach performance which showed the highest relationships from among the available predictors which had a low correlation with the criterion. Such a procedure tends to capitalize on chance fluctuations within the sample, and consequently may result in a spuriously high multiple-correlation coefficient. When signs which were derived in this manner are applied to subsequent populations, it can be expected that the coefficient will be of lower magnitude and of less predictive value than that obtained in the parent population.

Other investigators have studied the extent to which Rorschach single summary scores can discriminate among psychiatric groups. Wittenborn and Holzberg (23) studied thirty-nine summary scores with five patient groups and found that one score (*CF*) significantly discriminated the manic from the depressed patients. Freidman (6) evaluated the discriminative effectiveness of Rorschach scores with two groups of normal adults and 30 schizophrenics. He found eight Rorschach variables which significantly differentiated the schizophrenics from both groups of normal subjects. Reiman (19) evaluated eighty-six scores with replicated samples of ambulatory schizophrenics and neurotics. The results indicate that six scores were significant at the .10 level of confidence or better between the clinical groups for both samples. Kobler and Steil (12) reported no statistical differences of any consequence between the Rorschach scores of the paranoid and depressive subgroups of involutional melancholic patients.

While the findings with respect to single summary scores are predominantly negative, unequivocal evaluation of these data is difficult. Most studies were able to obtain a few scores which discriminated among psychiatric groups. However, in some instances, the positive findings could be expected by chance because of the large number of tests of significance computed. It should also be noted that although a variety of Rorschach scores have been reported as differentiating diagnostic groups, there has not been a great deal of consistency for these scores to appear repeatedly as diagnostic from study to study. In addition, certain methodological limitations such as small samples, incomplete statistical or experimental controls, and vaguely defined diagnostic criteria have complicated the interpretation of the results.

In the light of the ambiguous nature of the research findings, and the extensive application of the instrument, the need for a systematic evaluation of the Rorschach as a psychodiagnostic technique seems indicated. An investigative program of this sort is under way at the Iowa Psychopathic Hospital. The present study represents one major phase of this research program, and it specifically deals with the problem of determining the extent to which Rorschach summary scores can differentiate psychiatric groups.

Procedure

Our subjects were selected on the basis of the following criteria: (a) chronological age of fifteen or older; (b) unanimous agreement among psychiatrists as to diagnosis both on admission to and discharge from the hospital; (c) diagnosis was restricted to psychoneurosis (Pn), psychopathy (Pp), or schizophrenia (Sc); (d) diagnosis was independent of the Rorschach data,[2] and (e) the number of Rorschach responses (R) would not contribute to a significant difference in the mean number or the variance of responses for the three groups.

Initially, over 800 case records of patients who were fifteen years or older, and who were given the Rorschach test during the six-year period from 1948 to 1953, were examined in order to check on the agreement and consistency of the psychiatric diagnosis. Each case folder contained an initial diagnostic impression usually made by a psychiatric resident or a staff psychiatrist, an admission and staff diagnosis, and a final discharge staff diagnosis, both of which were made by several residents and one or more staff psychiatrists. In this way 339 Rorschach records were obtained, and the number of responses per record was determined. Statistical tests showed no significant difference between the mean number of responses for the three groups, while the variances between the groups were significantly different. Inspection of the data indicated that two cases in the Pn group, each with 153 responses, were contributing greatly to the heterogeneity of variance. Consequently they were withdrawn from the sample and statistical tests of means and variances were recomputed. The groups showed no differences in either the total number of responses or variances, so that the effects of R on other Rorschach scores for the three groups were considered approximately equal.

2. It was not possible to obtain complete independence of diagnosis and Rorschach data. However, this criterion was met to the extent that the initial impression and the admission staff diagnosis were made prior to the Rorschach administration.

TABLE 1

Frequencies of Subclinical Types Within Each Major Diagnostic Group

Psychoneurotics		Psychopaths		Schizophrenics	
Mixed	31	Psychopathic pers.	38	Paranoid	46
Anxiety	30	Path. sexuality	18	Simple	13
Psychasthenia	28	Path. emotionality	14	Hebephrenic	8
Hysteria	22	Psychotic episodes	12	Mixed	7
Neurasthenia	5	Neurotic traits	8	Catatonic	4
Impulse neurosis	5	Inadequate type	7	Acute	3
Hypochondriasis	4	Asocial trends	3	Defect state	1
Psychosomatic	2	Alcoholism	2	Unclassified	18
Reactive depress.	2	Paranoid tendencies	2		
Unclassified	2	Exhibitionism	1		
		Malingering	1		
Total	131		106		100

A total of 337 Rorschach protocols meeting all the criteria and obtained from 131 *Pn*'s, 106 *Pp*'s, and 100 *Sc*'s comprised the basic data for this study. In order to assure equal treatment of the data for all subjects, each protocol was rescored according to the scoring system described by Hertz (9).[3] The incidence of clinical types which were included within each of the three major diagnostic groups is presented in Table 1. Additional subject characteristics of the three groups are given in Table 2. From this it will be noted

TABLE 2

Subject Characteristics for the Three Groups (*N* = 337)

Sex	Psychoneurotics (56 M, 75 F)		Psychopaths (79 M, 27 F)		Schizophrenics (57 M, 43 F)	
	Mean	SD	Mean	SD	Mean	SD
Age	27.3	8.6	26.9	9.8	27.7	9.6
Educ.	11.7	2.5	11.1	2.5	12.4	3.2
Length of hosp. (days)	58.1	43.7	40.5	37.5	55.8	45.3

that there was an unequal number of males and females in each group, and that this was most discrepant in the *Pp*'s. The small differences in age between the groups were not statistically reliable, although the differences in education and length of hospitalization were significant at the .01 level of confidence. The educational level of the *Sc*'s was slightly higher than that of the *Pn*'s and *Pp*'s, while the length of hospitalization was slightly shorter for the *Pp*'s than for the other two groups. Data were also available with re-

3. The author wishes to express his appreciation to Donald Spangler for rescoring each Rorschach protocol.

gard to the subject's previous admission and illness. Thirty-seven per cent of the *Pn* group had been ill prior to this admission, whereas 24 per cent of the *Pp*'s and 23 per cent of the *Sc*'s had been ill previously. Generally these figures indicate that approximately 72 per cent of the total sample were first admissions at the time of the Rorschach administration, and that their condition was not, for the most part, considered chronic.

Medians, means, and standard deviations were computed for each clinical group on the following summary scores: *R, W%, D%, Dr%, S, F%, F +% * of 80, *F +% * of 60, *M, FM, Fm, FC, CF, C, Fch, chF, ch, Fch', ch'F, ch', Fc, cF, c, A%, Ad, H%, Hd,* Nature, Blood, Sex, Anatomy, Object, Fire, Position, Contamination, *P, O%,* and Rejection. Inspection of these figures indicated marked differences in the medians and the means for many of the scores, supporting previous observations that most Rorschach scores are not distributed normally (4, 5). In addition almost half of the scoring categories had medians of zero and means of less than 1.0, which not only suggests that these scores occurred very rarely, but also that they have very limited utility in individual differential diagnosis. With the exception of the *c, ch',* Position, and Contamination scores which occurred very infrequently, chi-square tests of independence were employed to evaluate the significance of differences between the groups for the remaining thirty-four summary scores. The over-all median derived from the total sample (337) for each score was used as the empirical cutoff point. Yates's correction for continuity was applied to the data wherever cell frequencies were lower than ten (13). The null hypothesis was retained with those chi-square values which did not meet the minimum requirement of the .05 level of confidence.

Results

Although tests of significance were not computed, the incidence of occurrence of contaminated and position responses will be presented because some Rorschach workers have regarded these responses as diagnostically important in that they are almost always associated with schizophrenia or psychosis (1, 2, 10, 20). Our data, however, indicate that these responses can and do occur in other psychiatric conditions. For example, we found contaminated responses in nine *Sc*'s, two *Pn*'s, and one *Pp,* and position responses in two *Sc*'s, five *Pn*'s, and one *Pp.* Moreover, when we consider that only twelve patients out of the total sample of 337 produced contaminated responses and only eight patients produced position responses, it is apparent that diagnostic classification cannot be effectively made solely on the basis of the presence or absence of these responses.

TABLE 3

Medians, Means, and Sigmas for the Larger Clinical Groups on the Significant Scores and the Probability Values Obtained from Intergroup Comparisons

Score	Pn (N = 131)			Pp (N = 106)			Sc (N = 100)			Intergroup chi-square value probabilities*		
	Mdn	Mean	SD	Mdn	Mean	SD	Mdn	Mean	SD	Pn-Pp	Pp-Sc	Pn-Sc
Dr%	11.0	14.4	13.8	6.5	10.0	11.4	15.0	15.8	12.8		.01	
A%	50.0	48.0	17.4	51.0	50.2	18.0	44.0	43.4	17.0		.01	
FM	2.0	2.7	2.4	2.0	2.6	2.5	2.0	2.0	2.0			.02
P	5.0	5.1	2.2	5.0	5.2	2.5	4.0	4.1	2.0			.02
Sex	0.0	0.5	1.2	0.0	0.2	1.0	0.0	0.9	2.8	.01	.01	
Anatomy	1.0	2.5	3.3	1.0	1.7	2.4	1.0	2.6	4.3	.01	.01	

* Only probability values at or beyond the .05 levels are reported.

The over-all chi-square tests applied to each Rorschach score for the three clinical groups resulted in significant values for the following six scores: $Dr\%$, $A\%$, FM, P, Sex, and Anatomy. Three additional chi-square values were computed for each of these significant scores to determine more specifically which group or groups the scores discriminated among. Table 3 lists the medians, means, and standard deviations for these scores, as well as the probability level obtained from the separate comparisons of the clinical groups. Most apparent from this table is the failure of any one score to discriminate among all three groups, although three scores were discriminative in two comparisons. It will also be noted that five scores significantly differentiated the Pp's from the Sc's, whereas only two scores differentiated the Pn's from the Pp's, and the Pn's from the Sc's. Inspection of the data and reference to the medians and means listed in Table 3 indicates the direction of significance. There were more Pp's who were lower on $Dr\%$, and higher on FM than Sc's; more Pn's who were lower on $Dr\%$, and higher on $A\%$ than Sc's; more Pn's who were higher on FM than Sc's; more Pp's and Pn's who were higher on P than Sc's; and more Pn's and Sc's who were higher on Sex and Anatomy responses than Pp's.

The $F + \%$ score is often regarded as important in differentiating psychotic from non-psychotic subjects. However, the over-all median value of 80 per cent which was obtained from the total sample did not discriminate among the clinical groups. Beck (2) has suggested 60 per cent as a diagnostically useful cutoff point, and consequently this score was employed with the present data. The chi-square values indicated significant differences between the Sc's and the Pn's, and the Pp's and Pn's at the .001 and .05 levels of confidence respectively, while no significant difference was obtained between the Pp's and the Sc's. Recognizing that there are differences in the Hertz and Beck scoring systems which include $F +$ tables and procedures for computing $F + \%$, these findings nevertheless suggest that Beck's empirical cutoff point of 60 per cent may also be discriminative with Hertz's scoring method.

In evaluating the results, it seemed important to consider the extent to which chance factors could account for the significance of differences between the groups for the seven Rorschach scores. Having computed thirty-four over-all chi-square values, we can expect approximately two to be significant merely by chance at the .05 level of confidence. In the light of this possibility, a more rigorous examination of the stability of the present findings seemed essential. Therefore, 150 cases, fifty from each clinical group, were randomly selected from the total parent sample of 337. Statistical treatment and the analysis of the data for this sample was the same as that previously described for the parent population. Chi-square values were ob-

TABLE 4

Medians, Means, and Sigmas for the Clinical Groups of 50 Cases on the Significant Scores and the Probability Values Obtained from Intergroup Comparisons

Score	Pn (N = 50)			Pp (N = 50)			Sc (N = 50)			Intergroup chi-square value probabilities*		
	Mdn	Mean	SD	Mdn	Mean	SD	Mdn	Mean	SD	Pn-Pp	Pp-Sc	Pn-Sc
Dr%	8.0	12.7	13.0	7.0	9.9	11.1	14.0	16.5	13.2		.01	.05
M	1.0	1.8	2.2	1.0	1.8	1.5	1.0	1.6	2.8		.01	
Fch'	1.0	1.1	1.5	0.0	0.5	1.3	0.0	0.5	1.0	.01	.01	.05
P	5.0	4.9	2.2	5.0	5.2	2.4	4.0	4.0	2.0			
Sex	0.0	0.6	1.6	0.0	0.1	0.4	0.0	1.0	2.5		.02	
Anatomy	1.0	2.6	3.2	1.0	1.5	1.9	2.0	2.8	2.9	.05	.01	

* Only probability values at or beyond the .05 levels are reported.

tained separately for the thirty-four Rorschach scores, and only those scores which were significant on both samples were regarded as stable.

The analysis of the data for the new sample revealed that the $Dr\%$, M, Fch', P, Sex, and Anatomy scores significantly differentiated the groups at the .05 level of confidence or better. The medians, means, and standard deviations for each score together with the probability levels obtained from the separate comparisons of the groups are shown in Table 4. These results indicate the Pp's and the Sc's were significantly differentiated by five scores, whereas only two scores differentiated the Pn's from the Pp's, and the Pn's from the Sc's. In comparing these findings with those obtained from the parent sample, we find, that only the $Dr\%$, P, Sex, and Anatomy scores significantly discriminated the clinical groups on both samples, and thus met the criterion of stability. While all four stable scores discriminated the Pp's from the Sc's, these scores were less sensitive in differentiating the Pn's from the Sc's, and the Pn's from the Pp's in that only one score for each comparison was found to be significant with both samples ($Dr\%$ and Sex, respectively).

Summary and Conclusions

To determine the extent to which Rorschach summary scores could discriminate among psychiatric populations, a total of 337 carefully selected Rorschach records obtained from 131 Pn's, 106 Pp's, and 100 Sc's were analyzed. Chi-square tests of independence were computed on thirty-four Rorschach summary scores for the total sample, and also for a second sample of 150 cases drawn randomly from the parent sample. Only scores which were discriminative on both samples were considered stable. The results showed that:

1. Most Rorschach summary scores are not normally distributed.

2. Almost half of the scoring categories had medians of zero and means of less than 1.0, not only indicating the rareness of these responses but also underscoring the limited utility of these scores for differential diagnosis.

3. Contaminated and position responses can and do occur, albeit infrequently, in all three groups and cannot be regarded as pathognomonic of psychosis or schizophrenia.

4. On an over-all basis, four scores: $Dr\%$, P, Sex, and Anatomy significantly discriminated among the groups on both samples at or beyond the .05 level of confidence.

5. When specific tests of significance were made, no single summary score significantly differentiated all three clinical groups.

6. For practical purposes, Rorschach summary scores cannot be regarded as effective in differentiating psychiatric groups.

REFERENCES

1. BECK, S. J. *Rorschach's test:* I. *Basic processes.* (2nd ed.) New York: Grune & Stratton, 1950.

2. BECK, S. J. *Rorschach's test:* II. *A variety of personality pictures.* New York: Grune & Stratton, 1947.

3. CRONBACH, L. J. Statistical methods applied to Rorschach scores: A review. *Psychol. Bull.,* 1949, *46,* 393–431.

4. BERKOWITZ, M., & LEVINE, J. Rorschach scoring categories as diagnostic "signs." *J. Consult. Psychol.,* 1953, *17,* 110–112.

5. FISKE, D. W., & BAUGHMAN, E. E. Relationships between Rorschach scoring categories and the total number of responses. *J. Abnorm. Soc. Psychol.,* 1953, *48,* 25–32.

6. FREIDMAN, H. A comparison of a group of hebephrenic and catatonic schizophrenics with 2 groups of normal adults by means of certain variables of the Rorschach test. *J. Proj. Tech.,* 1952, *16,* 352–360.

7. HAMLIN, R. M., ALBEE, G. W., & LELAND, E. M. Objective Rorschach "signs" for groups of normal, maladjusted, and neuropsychiatric subjects. *J. Consult. Psychol.,* 1950, *14,* 276–282.

8. HARROWER-ERICKSON, MOLLY R. The values and limitations of the so-called "neurotic signs." *Rorschach Res. Exch.,* 1942, *6,* 109–114.

9. HERTZ, MARGUERITE R. Scoring the Rorschach ink-blot test. *J. Genet. Psychol.,* 1938, *52,* 15–64.

10. KLOPFER, B., & KELLEY, D. M. The Rorschach technique. Yonkers, N.Y.: World Book Co., 1946.

11. KNOPF, I. J. The Rorschach test and psychotherapy. *Amer. J. Orthopsychiat.,* 1956, *26.*

12. KOBLER, F. J., & STEIL, AGNES. The use of the Rorschach in involutional melancholia. *J. Consult. Psychol.,* 1953, *17,* 365–370.

13. LEWIS, D., & BURKE, C. J. The use and misuse of the chi-square test. *Psychol. Bull.,* 1949, *46,* 433–489.

14. MIALE, FLORENCE, & HARROWER-ERICKSON, MOLLY R. Personality structure in psychoneuroses. *Rorschach Res. Exch.,* 1940, *4,* 71–74.

15. MUENCH, G. A. An evaluation of nondirective psychotherapy by means of the Rorschach and other indices. *Appl. Psychol. Monogr.,* 1947, No. 13.

16. NADEL, A. B. A qualitative analysis of behavior following cerebral lesions. *Arch. Psychol., N.Y.,* 1938, *32,* No. 224.

17. PIOTROWSKI, Z. A. On the Rorschach method and its application in organic disturbances of the central nervous system. *Rorschach Res. Exch.,* 1936–37, *1,* 23–40.

18. PIOTROWSKI, Z. A. The Rorschach ink-blot method in organic disturbances of the central nervous system. *J. Nerv. Ment. Dis.*, 1937, *86*, 525–537.

19. REIMAN, G. W. The effectiveness of Rorschach elements in the discrimination between neurotic and ambulatory schizophrenics. *J. Consult. Psychol.*, 1953, *17*, 25–31.

20. RORSCHACH, H. *Psychodiagnostics*. New York: Grune & Stratton, 1951.

21. RUBIN, H., & LONSTEIN, M. A cross validation of suggested Rorschach patterns associated with schizophrenia. *J. Consult. Psychol,* 1953, *17*, 371–372.

22. THIESEN, J. W. A pattern analysis of structural characteristics of the Rorschach test in schizophrenia. *J. Consult. Psychol.*, 1952, *16*, 365–370.

23. WITTENBORN, J. R., & HOLZBERG, J. D. The Rorschach and descriptive diagnosis. *J. Consult. Psychol.*, 1951, *15*, 460–463.

IV

Validity

Leonard I. Schneider

RORSCHACH VALIDATION

Some Methodological Aspects

Introduction

I<small>T IS</small> generally agreed in clinical circles that the Rorschach psycho-diagnostic method is the most comprehensive device in the clinician's repertoire for ascertaining personality patterns. However, it is also agreed that results are highly dependent upon the skill of the interpreter. This is due to the fact that the relationships between the data yielded by the test and personality variables have not been clearly ascertained and stated. Consequently, the user of the method must rely upon a body of guesses as to the relationships involved—including those which have accumulated in the literature, plus his own experience with the test in particular, and knowledge of normal and abnormal personality in general.

Considerable space in psychological literature was at one time devoted to the question of whether or not such a state of affairs was desirable. More recently the majority of those concerned with use of the instrument have supported the position that the Rorschach needs validation (1, 2, 6, 8, 15, 16, 17, 21, 26, 30, 32, 35, 36, 39). However, the variety of opinions on the requirements for Rorschach validation are as numerous as are the theoretical and methodological positions in the entire field of psychology—as the following quotations will demonstrate.

Reprinted from *Psychol. Bull.,* 1950, *47,* 493–508 by permission of the American Psychological Association and the author.

Harrison (15) claims that rigid validation procedures may be applicable to cognitive aspects of the personality but not the affective aspects. He maintains that "there must be sacrifice of objectivity and spurious precision with more reliance being put upon insight and ingenuity in the forging of tools for personality investigation." Clinical validation, he claims, is ample evidence for the present, though controlled experimentation may in the future produce more definite knowledge. Rapaport (26) and Brosin and Fromm (6) call for experimental investigation of "what form level means" by use of Gestalt experiments of form genesis and prägnance. Brosin and Fromm state further that ". . . the question of what may constitute the basis for correspondence between the responses and the personality of the subject; and the nature of the equivalence between the perceptual patterns and the general personality patterns, seem to obtain the most fruitful suggestions from Gestalt Psychology."

Sargent (32) claims that "factors taken out of context have little meaning. For the reason that it is not the absolute amount of one determinant but its relation to the whole pattern which gives it significance in the individual protocol." Thus, for her, validity studies can proceed along two lines: (1) correspondence of Rorschach impression of the total personality with impressions independently arrived at, and (2) predictive capacity which she thinks is the sounder approach due to the fact that correlations based upon inter-judge agreement are minimized by "each analyst understanding correctly different aspects of the personalities under inspection."

Macfarlane (21) lists five validation methods: (1) correlation with outside criteria, (2) projective data vs. case history data, (3) through time consistencies, (4) collateral experimental approach, and (5) degree of success in prediction, which she offers as the most fruitful method. In support of this method she says:

> The writer's opinion is that the utilization of the interpretation and predictive judgments of widely experienced clinicians later checked for predictive success, will offer at this stage the most productive leads. If an experienced clinician is able to predict with considerable success, then the data on which he bases his correct intuitive predictions can be inspected and validly weighted configurations can be established, quantified, and made available to less experienced people. Also, his wrong and partially right predictions in conjunction with the right ones can serve for finer and more differentiating criteria.

Frank (8) holds that validation must be concerned with the aggregate of part functions since he believes that there may be lawfulness at that level but not between the discrete part functions and outside criteria. Like Harrison, he appears to believe in the acceptability of intermediate gross validation, for he says:

If it appears that the subject projects similar patterns or configurations upon widely different materials and reveals in his life history the sequence of experiences that make these projections psychologically meaningful for his personality, then the procedures may be judged sufficiently valid to warrant further experimentation and refinement.

Thurstone (35), in a recent polemic against the scientific laxity of Rorschach workers, calls for validation data that will enable a Rorschach interpreter to predict the style of response an individual is likely to give to different types of life situations. Hertz (16, 17) has been quite outspoken about the need for validating data. She suggests four methods: (1) direct experimentation, (2) comparison with extensive individual case studies, (3) comparison with independent, objective data, and (4) comparison with known diagnoses and clinical pictures. In her earlier article (16), she states that concentration on one individual in the tradition of the clinician would be scientifically productive.

Varvel (36) has offered some specific suggestions for validation procedures. He mentions the possibility of finding the relationship between the autokinetic phenomenon and Rorschach personality types, checking Rorschach factors against data obtained from the Dembo situation, use of drugs and post-hypnotic suggestion to measure the effects on Rorschach protocols of these experimentally produced states, and simultaneous recording with the Luria technique, pneumograph and Rorschach responses.

In 1935 Beck (1) wrote that the value of the Rorschach method was not on the basis of successful penetration into personality as yet, but as a suggestion that human nature could be passed through a prism and analyzed into component elements. He cautioned, however, that it must be recognized, ". . . that the same trait is not necessarily equivalent in two different kinds of personalities, or in another way, the same diagnostic index may have different diagnostic value depending on the larger background of the personality in which it appears." In 1942 (2) he wrote that Klopfer's argument that standardization of the Rorschach implied devising of numerical formulae for the several whole personality entities, was a fallacy. He pointed out that two issues were confused in Klopfer's position. One was the personality as a whole governed by the laws which unit personalities follow and the second was the component elements, ". . . whether we are contemplating the psychological traits or the impersonal Rorschach factors which stand for these traits." Of the latter, Beck claimed that they can and must be isolated and subjected to experimentally controlled observation independently of the problems relating to the whole personality. "The criteria of the two are different and validation is within two totally different spheres of reference."

Point of View

As is obvious from this sampling, a position on the most fruitful approach to take in future Rorschach validation work is dependent upon one's theoretical and methodological biases in the broader problems within the fields of science and psychology. Accordingly, before embarking on a set of criticisms and suggestions, it is necessary in the interest of clarity to make an explicit statement of position on the crucial issues involved.

Validity is here considered to be measured by a statement of the degree of concomitant variation between two independent variables, one of which is designated as the criterion variable. The data obtained from a validity investigation indicate the degree of predictability of the magnitude of one variable, given the magnitude of the other. In the problem of Rorschach validation, then, the usefulness of the results will depend upon the criterion chosen. The requisites for an acceptable criterion variable are: (1) amenability to the assignment of numerals with a high degree of reliability which represents a relative statement of the degree of presence of the variable, and (2) known or hypothesized relationships between the criterion variable and other variables useful in work with personality. Use of the term "numerals" in (1) above indicates another bias. The writer believes that the variables of personality are lawfully related to relevant environmental variables and since laws are numerical statements for optimal serviceability, it is necessary to quantify the variables in order to find the laws. This is deemed a requirement for a science of psychology. Finding the laws depends in part upon a methodological approach geared to finding lawful relationships. It then becomes an empirical matter as to whether or not the lawfulness is "out there."

In the case of the Rorschach it is held as a working hypothesis that many of the variables of personality can be measured by it, the task being to ascertain the tenability of the hypothesis by making a series of verifiable hypotheses relating clearly defined personality variables to each of the factors or groups of factors found in a Rorschach protocol. It is also held that the laws describing the functioning of the whole personality are of the same class as those relating component parts to environmental variables. In describing the whole personality, what is needed is a composite law expressing the component parts and their interaction. Again, this may be true or false according to future empirical findings. Its immediate value lies in focusing on a search for relationships that can be expressed in a single system of laws. As a practical matter, it is probably more fruitful to start with component parts until more of the relevant variables for the total personality are ascertained. The rest of this paper will be devoted to an application of this orientation in an attempt to clarify some of the methodological problems inherent in Rorschach validation.

Levels of Inference

From a similar theoretical and methodological background, Steisel and Cohen (34) have elaborated on Beck's differentiation of the levels of inference used in interpreting from Rorschach protocols. To clarify the problems of Rorschach valdiation they differentiate three levels of inference, each of which require validation.

Level I covers the inferences drawn from the raw response record for purposes of arriving at the appropriate scoring symbols and constructing an adequate psychogram.

Level II represents the descriptive statements which can be made by inspection of the psychogram, sequence analysis and analysis of specific verbalizations.

Level III includes the comprehensive, coherent personality diagnoses which may include the classification of the subject in some nosological group.

This can be considered a vertical schema ascending in order of degree of complexity (the number of variables involved in attempts to validate the inferences made). However, it can be pointed out that Level I does not involve the problem of validity as herein defined. Steisel and Cohen's Level I can more adequately be defined as entailing the problem of reliability, that is, the setting up of symbols each with a definition which summarizes certain aspects of a given response. The problem is to find the definition which will yield the highest degree of agreement in the case where several observers using the same definition for a given symbol are tested for the degree of concurrence of their applications of the symbol in question.

Having established that certain symbols can be applied with a satisfactory degree of reliability, Level II is reached. Level II represents the inferences as to specific processes or mechanisms which can be made about a personality. The raw data for these are found mostly in the psychograms (factors such as $F + \%$, M, C, $W : M$, etc.) though material such as symbolism, pathognomic signs, and sequence analysis (19) may also be used. As a point of departure some of the Rorschach studies sometimes referred to as validation studies in the literature will be classified in terms of the Rorschach variables used and the method employed. Each study will be evaluated in terms of the notion of validity expressed above.

LEVEL I: PSYCHOLOGICAL PROCESSES
REPRESENTED BY PSYCHOGRAM FACTORS

1. Hypnosis. Sarbin (31) took Rorschach protocols from a single subject under four different conditions. Two of these conditions were with the hypnotic suggestion that the patient was Mme. Curie, and then Mae West; a third condition was that of hypnosis with no suggestion; and the fourth condition was in the waking state. He found that each of the three artificial situations produced changes in several of the psychogram factors and he attributed the changes to induced sets. However, this does not qualify as a validity study in that the relationship between the particular stimuli used to induce the sets, and changes resulting, are not known.

Levine, Grassi, and Gerson (20) used hypnosis in a Rorschach study with an improved method. They obtained a Rorschach protocol under normal conditions and then under several conditions of hypnotically induced affective changes. They suggested certain situations (under hypnosis) the psychological consequences of which were predicted on the basis of clinical experience. The Rorschach protocols obtained under the experimental conditions reflected changes in psychogram factors for each of the induced conditions. Further, the changes obtained in each case reflected the Rorschach factors usually associated with the respective affective conditions induced. Validity of the results in this case, is, of course, dependent upon the accuracy with which a group of judges can predict the psychological correlates of certain situations. Accurate prediction in such cases is dependent in part upon knowledge of the differential reactions of a large group of subjects to the same situation. Thus the relationship between the factors of the emotionally charged situation and the personality involved must be known in order to predict for small groups. Also, since it is known that hypnotizability is related to certain aspects of personality, results of such studies cannot legitimately be generalized beyond groups that can be hynotized.

Bergmann, Graham, and Leavitt (4) used Rorschach protocols in conjunction with hypnotic age level regressions. The authors do not claims this to be a Rorschach validity study. They acknowledge using Rorschach personality pictures obtained at the various suggested age levels to validate the extent of regression, in that superficial regression would not be expected to reflect a complete change in Rorschach patterns. However, were the extent of regression under hypnosis established by use of independent measures other than Rorschach, then Rorschach factors could be validated by this procedure. Detailed histories of certain levels of individual development could be obtained and a group selected on the basis of optimum uniformity.

On the basis of the personality features held in common for the individuals of this group, predictions could be made as to the relevant Rorschach factors that would be obtained under hypnotic regression to the respective levels of similarity. However, such a roundabout method is warranted only if there is a demonstrable need for an approach to the study of personality such as that used by Bergmann, Graham, and Leavitt.

In general, it might be said of use of hypnosis for Rorschach validation that considerably more data are needed to demonstrate how much of the personality changes are produced by the nature of the situation (i.e., effect of submission of the passive individual to the assertive hypnotist) and how much by the specific suggestions used.

2. *Drugs.* The studies reported in the literature (13, 18, 27, 37, 38) relating Rorschach factors to administration of drugs do not qualify as validation studies in that the laws describing the relationship between the drugs used (mescaline, histamine, amytal) and personality factors measured independently of the Rorschach are not known. The data reported suggest that the reactions obtained depend in part upon features of the predrug personality. Guttman (13) states, ". . . there is need of a searching investigation in terms of the subject's setting and individual equipment before specificity of reaction can be established." Until the laws relating a single drug with personality reactions are found, this method will not be serviceable in Rorschach validation work.

3. *Operationally Defined Situations.* As Williams points out (39) this method requires: (1) setting up of an "independent and standardized criterion situation which would yield a quantitative index to an operationally defined aspect of personality, and (2) examination of the validity of those Rorschach factors primarily associated with this personality process in terms of the criterion measure." He assembled the definitions offered for intellectual control and designed a situation to measure this. He used as his measure decrement in performance of a task requiring intellectual factors under stress compared with performance under optimum conditions. Thus, the definition of intellectual control is in terms of the operations used to measure it. He administered a standard Rorschach to each of his subjects and used as the Rorschach index of intellectual control $F + \%$ and integration of form with color on the basis of hypotheses stated by Beck and Rapaport. He acknowledged the fact that other factors also were used in Rorschach interpretation and that he was operating at what is considered in this paper to be Level II. His results tend to bear out the hypothesized relationships between the selected Rorschach factors and the operationally defined aspects of personality. Structurally, this study conforms with the tenets presented here. However, he overlooked the fact that a linear rela-

tionship between intellectual control and $F + \%$ is not hypothesized by Beck and Rapaport for emotionally charged situations. An $F + \%$ above the optimum hypothetically represents an overcontrol due to inhibition and anxiety, compulsiveness, and rigidity or strong superego. Consequently, it might be hypothesized: (1) that overly-acute form perception is a defense against affective instability and as such might be related to loss of control under affective stress, and (2) that the threshold for affective stress would be lower than that for an individual with a lower but optimal $F + \%$. Therefore, it might be more in line with expectancy to adjust for $F + \%$ above the empirical mean for a standardization population, rather than consider it to be a continuous distribution with respect to intellectual control under stress.

Another study with a similar methodological basis provides a focus for the problem of the usefulness of the independent variable with which the Rorschach factors are correlated. Steisel (33) attempted to demonstrate a relationship between the factors on the Rorschach commonly hypothesized to be related to suggestibility, and performance in the autokinetic and Hull body sway situations. The relationship between suggestibility and performance in these situations is not as universally acceptable as is the relationship between intellectual control and the situation used by Williams. Therefore, acceptance of Steisel's results as bearing upon suggestibility as a personality variable depends upon the demonstration of a relationship between his two criterion measures and another independent measure of suggestibility. Insofar as his concept of suggestibility is operationally defined in terms of these two indices it is a defensible method at the current stage of development of Rorschach validation; i.e., if he had found a relationship between his selected variables it would then be a fruitful problem to experiment with the autokinetic phenomenon and Hull body sway technique to find their relationship to other independently defined aspects of personality. Even if they should be found related to aspects other than suggestibility, Steisel's data would be useful.

Rockwell, Welch, Kubis, and Fisichelli (28) report an experiment concerned with color shock. They define shock in terms of the neurological conception as a condition of lowered excitability. They measured shock by taking a continuous reading of the palmar skin response during Rorschach administration and described the changes expected with "shock" present and those expected with startle. Thus, their measure constitutes an operational criterion for shock and startle. They found that shock, as neurophysiologically conceived, does occur on those cards and in those subjects where it is expected, whereas startle does not. On the basis of these results they reject the Beck criteria for "color shock" which are based on expectation of a startle reaction to the color cards. This is a rather clear-cut example of an operationally defined situation devised to test two antithetical hypotheses. Acceptance of their interpretation depends upon evidence for relationship between the neurological conception of shock and Rorschach's conception of emotional inhibition. Assuming this relationship, it then remains to be determined what conditions the startle response (or more properly the Rorschach criteria for its presence) is related to—as a problem for those interpreters who use the "startle" criteria.

4. Empirical Sign Studies. The studies that fall into this group are concerned with demonstration of a relationship between certain single psychogram factors or groups of factors and effectiveness of various therapeutic techniques. (The sign studies concerned with relationship of Rorschach factors to psychiatric diagnostic categories will be dealt with in the series of Level III studies.)

In 1940 Piotrowski (23) published data which resulted from a study of two groups of schizophrenics, one of which showed improvement following insulin therapy while the other did not. He compared the pretreatment Rorschach protocols, and found that the presence of a response which included color as a determinant (*FC, CF,* or *C*) and for which there is a concrete or emotional association, i.e., other than color denomination, occurred significantly more frequently in the records of those who subsequently improved than those who did not. He reported that 81 per cent of the improved group met this criterion. Halpern (14) in a study of similar design found that the pretreatment Rorschach psychograms of those patients who subsequently improved with insulin therapy manifested greater productivity and those factors associated with "wider emotional range and greater capacity for empathy." Graham (9) with a study similarly designed found that those who improve with insulin give more responses determined by the chiaroscuro aspects of the inkblots. Benjamin (3) gives a preliminary report of a follow-up study of insulin-treated schizophrenics for whom he had pretreatment Rorschach protocols. Though his data are unquantified, he states that the preliminary suggestion is that the appearance of low $F + \%$, *DdW* and *DW,* and highly irregular sequence are associated with poor prognosis.

In these studies the criterion variable is judged improvement, and consequently judgment of improvement must be based upon clear-cut reliable criteria. Also, a clear statistical statement of the relationship between degrees of improvement and the signs reported to discriminate between "improved" and "unimproved" is required for an acceptable statement of validity. The above studies do not meet these criteria, but the results suggest possible relationships to be checked by more rigorous methods.

In an investigation concerned with factors related to success of metrazol therapy with a group of psychotics, Morris (22) improved on the method in the preceding studies. He provided for more clear-cut criteria for judgment of improvement and then selected critical points for his signs by referring his findings to the chi-square distribution for a statistical statement of his results.

The significance of this group of studies lies in the attempt to establish the usefulness of the Rorschach for prediction under restricted, specified conditions. However, they contribute little to validation of the Rorschach in terms of the second validity criterion, which calls for correlation between Rorschach variables and independent measures of personality for which a relationship with other personality measures is known. Should it later be demonstrated that improvement following insulin or metrazol administration is related to certain dimensions of personality, then the signs found in the above studies can be used as a basis for statements about these new dimensions insofar as the studies from which they result are experimentally sound. It should be pointed out that though these studies may not be of immediate optimal value for Rorschach validation, this does not mean they are equally questionable from the standpoint of other theoretical and/or practical considerations, such as the ones for which they were designed. They are on the same continuum only with respect to the first criterion of validity and are cited here merely to clarify the issues involved in Rorschach validation per se.

LEVEL II: PSYCHOLOGICAL PROCESSES
REPRESENTED BY FACTORS OTHER THAN
THOSE IN THE PSYCHOGRAM

1. Symbolism. Earl (7) reported an experiment in which he investigated the validity of the usual interpretations for certain content categories frequently obtained in the Rorschach protocols of disturbed subjects. He was primarily interested in water responses and selected a group of feeble-minded males aged thirteen to fifteen who were inmates of a residential school and had markedly immature personalities with severe conflict over masturbation. He selected those words with water content and all content words which occurred with the determinants M, FM, m, K, FK, and KF in the pre-experiment protocols. He then put his subjects in an hypnotic trance and told them, "I am going to tell you to think of something. As soon as you think of it something quite different will come into your mind. . . . I want you to say at once what it is. . . ." He then gave as stimulus words the words taken from the subject's own record which were suspected of being symbolic, interspersed among banal responses from his own record. He found that all the crucial words used for expressing a response the determinant of which was *m,* had symbolic significance. All responses having water as primary or secondary content "produced anxiety symbolized or overt in the hypnotized subjects." In interpreting his study he suggests that no common symbolic significance exists, at least among children, and that these responses, however determined, are associated with profound anxiety and it may be suspected that primitive sexual stirrings are always present.

The nature of his sample and small N (5 subjects) places serious restrictions on interpretations of these data. It would be desirable to have a control group of "stable" individuals so as to measure relative occurrence of water responses, and to compare the associations offered in the experimental situations by those "normal" cases in which water responses do occur with the responses of the experimental group. It might also be possible to do this type of work by use of word association without hypnosis, thereby freeing it from the limitations of hypnotic validation studies discussed above. By use of such a method, it is reasonable to expect that affective disturbances associated with the responses suspected of symbolic usage could be demonstrated. However, it is a more difficult problem to ascertain consistency for the particular material being symbolized by a given symbol. Demonstration of such consistency may require an approach which integrates data for responses with data on behavioral indices which are associated with aspects of the inkblots. An example of an attempt to associate a behavioral index with features of the blot is Blake's empirical study of ocular activity (5) during administration of the Rorschach technique. He found that number and duration of fixations was related to properties of the cards. Card VI, for example, elicits the largest number of fixations for the top center detail. Card VI as a whole also elicits longer fixations during the initial inspection period than is true of the other cards in the sequence. It is also known that the top center detail of Card VI elicits the largest number of manifest sex responses and is suspected of producing symbolized sex responses as well as disturbances of sequence, form, control, etc., which are referred to as "sex shock." Therefore, it might prove fruitful to select those areas of the several cards which yield the highest number of fixations and use the responses offered for them in a method similar to that used by Earl. One might use a large group of normals and investigate the number of times a particular word is substituted in the word association experiment for the response offered during Rorschach administration.

2. *Empirical Sign Studies.* In 1941 Piotrowski (24) published a paper which presented six signs relevant to predicting the prognosis of schizophrenics given insulin therapy. It is unlike the similar studies reported above in that five of his signs are not found in the usual psychogram. He

presented six signs which are reported to be indicators of a good prognosis: Generic Term, Variety, Evidence, Color Response, Indirect Color Approach, and Demurring. He offers what seems to be adequate criteria for determining presence of responses with these attributes, designates the method of determining improvement (psychiatric staff decision), and claims 93.3 per cent correct prediction by use of three or more signs as the criterion for good prognosis. As in the other studies of this type it remains to be demonstrated that prognosis for schizophrenics with insulin therapy is lawfully related to certain specified personality variables or processes. On the basis of his own data, Piotrowski offers an hypothesis in terms of intellectual regression to account for the differences between schizophrenics who improve with insulin and those who do not. Those who improve have undergone emotional regression; those who do not improve have undergone intellectual regression during their pretreatment illness. Assuming that there are operations with which to measure intellectual regression (other than Rorschach variables), this hypothesis then becomes subject to experimental verification. If verified, Piotrowski's signs would then become valid indicators of emotional regression (though the converse could not be assumed a priori in the case of absence of the signs). This is an illustration of how a sign study which, though not of itself a complete validation process, might lead to a series of studies the end result of which is validation of Rorschach variables. However, before results such as Piotrowski's are followed up, it would be advisable to select a new group of schizophrenics about to be treated with insulin shock and test the accuracy of the prediction of his signs. This would guard somewhat against the possibility that his original results were influenced by variables other than those to which he attributed his results.

LEVEL III: COMPREHENSIVE
PERSONALITY DIAGNOSES

At this level an attempt is made to relate variables of the Rorschach protocol to groups with various diagnostic labels. The emphasis is on a complete personality pattern rather than the component processes as far as the validity criterion is concerned. Thus one might measure the degree of relationship between diagnosis arrived at by use of the Rorschach and diagnoses made by any other means such as other clinical tests, psychiatric observation, a combination of tests, interviews and observations, or case history. Several such studies have been reported in the literature with results supposedly supporting the validity of the Rorschach as a diagnostic tool. However, the instability of current diagnostic groupings makes them unsuitable for use as validity criteria. Diagnostic practices differ from institution to institution and even from psychiatrist to psychiatrist in the same institution. A further criticism of this type of study can be made in terms of efficiency which would hold even if stability of diagnostic groupings were granted. The number of variables involved in arriving at a Rorschach diagnosis is large. Some of them might be highly related to the criterion and some not at all related. If the relationship of each variable (used in the Rorschach diagnosis) to the criterion variable is not known, then no statements can be made on possible improvements of the method of diagnosis. It is an all or none conclusion where there is ample reason for suspecting that some of the variables in combination might be more effectively used than others. Guirdham (10, 11, 12) has indicated one way to handle this problem in his work with epileptics and depressives in which he sought complexes of Rorschach variables each of which had some power to differentiate the groups in question from other nosological groups. He empirically tried numerical relationships between these variables until he found an index which provided optimum differentiation. The logical development of such an approach would lead to statistical analysis of a large number of Rorschach records from a variety of diagnostic groups, with each Rorschach variable being put into a separate multiple regression equation for each diagnostic category. Such an approach would constitute a sign method and, although a high order one, would still be subject to the limitations of sign approach as a validity method discussed earlier in this paper (i.e., the variables used for prediction are not selected on the basis of degree to which they enter into relationships with other variables of personality).

Piotrowski (25) has outlined three approaches to Rorschach diagnosis of mild forms of schizophrenia which can be applied to the general problems of Level III validation. He discusses first pathognomonic signs such as contamination, fluctuations in form level, and position responses. The limitations of this approach he lists as use of too small a part of the total record, and the observed fact that a large porportion of schizophrenics produce none of the signs, and thus absence of the signs does not mean schizophrenia is not present. He takes up next tabular diagnostic procedures which are based on Rorschach components that can be counted. It consists in establishing the differences in the frequency with which the scoring symbols occur in the records of schizophrenic and nonschizophrenic subjects. He indicates his preference for what he calls a systematic diagnostic procedure which "rests on principles which interrelate the components of the Rorschach method, expressing their mutual dependencies, and arranging them into a dynamic system." By this means he implies that the interrelated variables he uses are based on valid interrelationships among Rorschach symbols, e.g., that the more human percepts, the larger the percentage of sharply perceived forms.

His criticism of the pathognomonic and tabular procedures are well taken as far as he goes, but he overlooks the fact that the interrelationships used for the systematic procedure are not validated in the strict sense. Their "validation" rests on unquantified clinical observations. Further, the search for such relationships as used by Piotrowski requires a deduction as to component processes from what is known about the unit personality of schizophrenics. Such a search would be warranted only if the component processes for a given diagnosis were known. With regularly occurring relationships between given diagnostic categories and component processes we would have stable diagnostic categories, provided there were also operations to measure them. If these operations were in dependent of the Rorschach variables. However, in such an ideal situation Rorschach validation would then conform with the description for Level validation.

Conclusions

In view of the foregoing considerations, the position is taken here that Rorschach validating procedures can be most fruitfully treated as problems in relating Rorschach variables to independent measures of component personality processes. There is no body of facts that can be invoked to prove this contention. It rests on principles of methodology concerned with the demonstration of valid relationships which are acceptable within a scientific framework. The merit of this approach applied to the Rorschach will be substantiated or discredited by the results obtained from its use. If procedures are used with provision for precise statement of results which are repeatedly obtained under the specified conditions, the Rorschach becomes a surer clinical device and it will facilitate psychological research. The clinician frequently protests that the experimental psychologist deals with artificial situations which are in no way related to the behavior which must be dealt with in the clinical problems of diagnosis and treatment. If the relationship between one or more Rorschach variables and component personality factors could be demonstrated, then those factors could be subjected to controlled experimentation with the Rorschach used to measure the changes that occur under varied conditions. It might also be possible to develop relationships between certain manipulable conditions and the origin of some of the personality components. Thus a single measuring instrument, satisfactorily validated, could help to establish a connection between experimental results and clinical problems. It would seem particularly useful to aim toward this possibility in view of the widely held hypothesis that the Rorschach test samples a larger number of variables of personality than any other single instrument.

In conclusion, it should be made explicit that the point of view on validation presented here does not do violence to the experienced interpreter's demands that each Rorschach factor be interpreted in terms of the other factors for any given record. What is required is specific statement of any particular constellation that is believed to be related to some measurable aspect of behavior, and then an appropriate test of this statement.

BIBLIOGRAPHY

1. BECK, S. J. Problems of further research in the Rorschach test. *Amer. J. Orthopsychiat.*, 1935, 5, 100–115.

2. BECK, S. J. Error, symbol and method in the Rorschach test. *J. Abnorm. Soc. Psychol.*, 1942, 37, 83–103.

3. BENJAMIN, J. D. A method for distinguishing and evaluating formal thinking disorders in schizophrenia. In J. S. Kasanin (Ed.), *Language and thought in schizophrenia*. Berkeley and Los Angeles: Univ. of California Press, 1946.

4. BERGMANN, M. S., GRAHAM, H., & LEAVITT, H. C. Rorschach exploration of consecutive hypnotic age level regressions. *Psychosom. Med.*, 1947, 9, 20–28.

5. BLAKE, R. R. Ocular activity during administration of the Rorschach test. *J. Clin. Psychol.*, 1948, 4, 159–170.

6. BROSIN, H. W., & FROMM, ERIKA O. Some principles of Gestalt psychology in the Rorschach experiment. *Rorschach Res. Exch.*, 1942, 6, 1–15.

7. EARL, C. J. C. A note on the validity of certain Rorschach symbols. *Rorschach Res. Exch.*, 1941, 5, 51–61.

8. FRANK, L. K. Projective methods for the study of personality. *J. Psychol.*, 1939, 8, 389–413.

9. GRAHAM, VIRGINIA T. Psychological studies of hypoglycemia therapy. *J. Psychol.*, 1940, 10, 327–358.

10. GUIRDHAM, A. The Rorschach test in epileptics. *J. Ment. Sci.*, 1955, 81, 870–893.

11. GUIRDHAM, A. Simple psychological data in melancholia. *J. Ment. Sci.*, 1936, 82, 649–653.

12. GUIRDHAM, A. The diagnosis of depression by the Rorschach test. *Brit. J. Med. Psychol.*, 1936, 16, 130–145.

13. GUTTMAN, E. Artificial psychoses produced by mescaline. *J. Ment. Sci.*, 1936, 82, 203–221.

14. HALPERN, FLORENCE. Rorschach interpretation of the personality structure of schizophrenics who benefit from insulin therapy. *Psychiat. Quart.*, 1940, 14, 826–833.

15. HARRISON, R. The thematic apperception and Rorschach methods of personality investigation in clinical practice. *J. Psychol.*, 1943, 15, 49–74.

16. HERTZ, MARGUERITE R. Rorschach: twenty years after. *Psychol. Bull.*, 1942, 49, 529–572.

17. HERTZ, MARGUERITE R. The Rorschach method: science or mystery. *J. Consult. Psychol.*, 1943, 7, 67–80.

18. KELLEY, D. M., LEVINE, K., PEMBERTON, W., & LILLIAN, K. K. Intravenous sodium amytal medication as an aid to the Rorschach method. *Psychiat. Quart.*, 1941, 15, 68–73.

19. KLOPFER, B., & KELLEY, D. *The Rorschach Technique.* New York: World Book Co., 1942.

20. LEVINE, K. N., GRASSI, J. R., & GERSON, M. J. Hypnotically induced mood changes in the verbal and graphic Rorschach: a case study. *Rorschach Res. Exch.*, 1943, 7, 130–144.

21. MACFARLANE, JEAN W. Problems of validation inherent in projective methods. *Amer. J. Orthopsychiat.*, 1942, 12, 405–410.

22. MORRIS, W. W. Prognostic possibilities of the Rorschach method in metrazol therapy. *Amer. J. Psychiat.*, 1943, 100, 222–230.

23. PIOTROWSKI, Z A. A simple experimental device for the prediction of outcome of insulin therapy in schizophrenia. *Psychiat. Quart.*, 1940, 14, 267–273.

24. PIOTROWSKI, Z. A. The Rorschach method as a prognostic aid in the insulin shock treatment of schizophrenics. *Psychiat. Quart.*, 1941, 15, 807–822.

25. PIOTROWSKI, Z. A. Experimental psychological diagnosis of mild forms of schizophrenia. *Rorschach Res. Exch.*, 1945, 9, 189–200.

26. RAPAPORT, D. In Rorschach forum report. *Rorschach Res. Exch.*, 1939, 3, 107–110.

27. ROBB, R. W., KOVITZ, B., & RAPAPORT, D. Histamine in the treatment of psychosis. *Amer. J. Psychiat.*, 1940, 97, 601–610.

28. ROCKWELL, P. V., WELCH, L., KUBIS, J., & FISICHELLI, V. Changes in palmar skin resistance during the Rorschach test. I. Color shock and psychoneurotic reactions. *Monthly Rev. Psychiat. Neurol.*, 1947, 113, 9–152.

29. RORSCHACH, H. *Psychodiagnostics.* (Trans. by P. Lemkau & B. Kronenberg.) New York: Grune and Stratton (distr.), 1942.

30. ROSENZWEIG, S. Outline of a cooperative project for validating the Rorschach test. *Amer. J. Orthopsychiat.*, 1935, 5, 121–123.

31. SARBIN, T. R. Rorschach patterns under hypnosis. *Amer. J. Orthopsychiat.*, 1939, 9, 315–318.

32. SARGENT, HELEN D., Projective methods: their origins, theory and applications in personality research. *Psychol. Bull.*, 1945, 42, 257–293.

33. STEISEL, I. An experimental investigation of the relationships between some measures of the Rorschach test and certain measures of suggestibility. Unpublished doctoral dissertation, Univ. Iowa, 1949.

34. STEISEL, I., & COHEN, B. D. The problem of validation of the Rorschach test with special reference to the method of direct experimentation. Unpublished paper, 1947.

35. THURSTONE, L. L., The Rorschach in psychological science. *J. Abnorm. Soc. Psychol.,* 1948, 43, 471–475.

36. VARVEL, W. A. Suggestions toward the experimental validation of the Rorschach test. *Bull. Menninger Clin.,* 1937, 1, 220–226.

37. WERTHAM, F., & BLEULER, M. Inconstancy of the formal structure of the personality; experimental study of the influence of mescaline on the Rorschach test. *Arch. Neurol. Psychiat.,* 1932, 28, 52–70.

38. WILKINS, W. L., & ADAMS, A. J. The use of the Rorschach test under sodium amytal and under hypnosis in military psychiatry. *J. Gen. Psychol.,* 1947, 36, 131–138.

39. WILLIAMS, M. An experimental study of intellectual control under stress and associated factors. *J. Consult. Psychol.,* 1947, 11, 21–29.

James O. Palmer

A DUAL APPROACH TO

RORSCHACH VALIDATION

A Methodological Study

I. The Two Approaches—
A General Statement of the Problem[1]

A. INTRODUCTION

THE NUMEROUS investigations of the validity of the Rorschach have been reviewed very thoroughly in three articles by Hertz (5, 6, 7), and the validity of the TAT has been similarly summarized by Tomkins (19). However, a brief restatement of the methods used by various investigators in establishing the validity of projective techniques may serve as an orientation to the particular questions considered in the present study. Thus far, the authorities who

Reprinted from *Psychol. Monogr.*, 1951, *8* (Whole No. 325), 1–27, by permission of the American Psychological Association and the author.

1. This study was conducted under the auspices of the Veterans Administration Regional Office, San Francisco, while the author was in training in the Clinical Psychology Training Program of the Veterans Administration. The author is therefore deeply indebted to the Veterans Administration for making this study possible. The opinions stated in this report are, however, those of the author and do not necessarily reflect the viewpoint of the Veterans Administration.

have reviewed this problem have been concerned primarily with the types of evidence used for the validation of projective techniques. Hertz (5) distinguished four main types of validation studies, as providing different kinds of evidence: (a) *clinical studies,* in which the usefulness of these techniques is illustrated in the analysis of case histories, therapy, etc.; (b) *experimental studies,* in which changes in the test results are shown to accompany controlled changes in the individual's pattern of behavior; (c) *studies of defined groups,* in which certain patterns of test results are established as associated with the characteristic behavior of known groups; and (d) *predictive studies,* in which the degree of agreement is measured between the description of personality derived from the results of a projective technique and that obtained from an analysis of some criterion, for example, a life history.

Although various writers (Tomkins [17], Macfarlane [12], and Symonds and Krugman [16]) have granted the possibility of approaching the validation of projective techniques in various ways, they have, at the same time, been careful to emphasize that the chosen method must take into account the nature of the technique being validated, particularly the concept of personality underlying the use of this technique. The most comprehensive argument concerning this point has been presented by Frank (3) in his classic discussion of the scientific basis of projective techniques. He pointed out that the "personality" which projective techniques are designed to evaluate is a *framework of* intervening concepts, a framework that relates the details of the individual's manifest behavior in terms of a *pattern* of motivations and attitudes. Macfarlane (12) also has considered this use of *interrelated* constructs to be a central problem "inherent in the validation of projective techniques." The point stressed by Frank is that personality as a configuration of functioning processes cannot be meaningfully broken up into isolated traits, but that part functions can only be described in terms of their interrelationships within the whole pattern. From this viewpoint, a description of personality derived from the results of a projective technique would require a method of validation which could test the accuracy of this description as a whole unit.

This assumption concerning the relationship between personality descriptions derived from projective techniques, and the method employed for their validation constituted the point of departure of the present research. In the light of this concept of personality, two divergent predictive approaches to validation were applied to an established projective technique, the Rorschach. One of these approaches, the matching method, was designed specifically to test the validity of description of personality as whole units. The other approach, which attempts to validate these descriptions item by item, does not necessarily take into account the Gestalt nature of these descriptions. The general intent of this study was to test the relative applicability of these two methods in investigating the validity of a projective technique.

B. THE INTERPRETATION AS
THE OBJECT OF VALIDATION

Before proceeding with the description of these two methods, it may be well to emphasize that this study is concerned with methods of validating the *interpretation* or description of personality as derived from the responses of the subject, rather than with consideration of specific *scores* or discrete responses. While there are merits in dealing with the so-called objective data of projective tests, this author agrees with such authorities as Hertz (6) and Marfarlane (12) that behind such scoring systems lie implicit assumptions about personality functioning. It thus appears to this author more reasonable to deal directly with these interpretative assumptions and avoid the current controversies concerning scoring categories and their discrete meanings. The question of whether or not a set of idiosyncratic responses represents in a rough manner the general pattern of functioning of the individual, and of how this question may be answered, seems a legitimate object of study.

C. THE MATCHING APPROACH

It was clearly apparent to Vernon (19), even during the developmental stage of projective techniques, that there was a need for a statistical approach which would treat their interpretation as a single, whole unit. With this specific problem in mind, he developed what has become known in the literature as the *matching method*. As Vernon (18), Hunter (9), and Krugman (11) have used it, this method consists of the following procedures: An interpretative report from a projective technique and a case analysis are prepared, independently, for each individual in a given sample. The sample is divided into small groups, ranging from five to ten subjects, known as *matching groups*. The interpretative reports and case analyses of each group[2] are presented, unidentified as to subject, to several judges who then attempt to match each of the test reports to the corresponding case analysis of the same individual's life history. Validity is then expressed in terms of the success of this matching. Chapman (1) derived the statistics for deter-

---

2. While most investigators have used matching groups consisting of an equal number of reports and case analyses, the matching groups may be uneven, e.g., ten interpretations to five analyses, or five to one.

mining the chance variation and the significance of the success of matching. Vernon (19) has added a formula for a coefficient of contingency, *C,* permitting a statement of the degree of relationship between the test and the criterion as implied in the success of the matching.

Vernon (18) admitted that his method was "only a coarse beginning" to the validation of projective techniques and suggested two additional steps to this procedure: (*a*) the homogeneity of the matching groups must be determined (obviously, a group of very similar reports would be more difficult to match than a group of very dissimilar reports); and (*b*) the reliability of the matching judges should be determined.

The application of the matching method to the validation of projective techniques has produced varying results. In his original study on the Rorschach, Vernon (18) reported an average contingency coefficient, *C,* of .833 ± .0315. Vernon noted that "the actual size of the *C* depends very largely on the degree of heterogeneity or distinctiveness of the subjects in each group. As far as possible, a normal degree of heterogeneity was aimed at" by randomly selecting the cases for the groups out of the whole sample (18, p. 213). However, Vernon's matching groups may have been more heterogeneous than he assumed, as is suggested by the results of later studies, Hunter (9), in a study of fifty school children, reported that only five Rorschach reports were matched correctly by all four judges, and that each judge, singly, was successful in only 30 to 40 per cent of the matchings. She concluded, therefore, that matching was "of doubtful value" . . . "Calculated to differentiate only extreme cases" (9). Although this investigator did not state her method of selecting the matching groups, she did remark that the personality sketches were all very similar.

The chief objection to the matching method, however, is that it permits, at best, only a very general statement about the accuracy of an interpretative report, namely, the statement that on the whole the report is similar to the personality pattern depicted by the criterion. While it is reassuring to know that an essentially meaningful interpretation may be drawn from a projective technique, it would be even more satisfactory to know how well the personality configuration is delineated in an interpretative report. If the interpretative report is, in general, similar to the case analysis, successful matching may occur, even though the accuracy of many of the statements within the report is dubious. In fact, Cronbach (2) considered that the matching method depends too much on the presence or absence of small clues. A proponent of the matching method might argue that, if the same personality pattern is, in general, described in both the interpretative report and in the case analysis, then the statements about particular functions of the personality would be likely to be similar in both descriptions.

Unfortunately, the matching method does not provide any tests of this argument.

D. AN ITEM ANALYSIS METHOD

In a study of the validity of the TAT, Harrison (4) introduced a procedure which simultaneously checked both the *degree* and *area* of the accuracy of his interpretations. His interpreters wrote out an "itemized analysis" of the test protocols, i.e., lists of separate interpretative statements, and the case analyses were prepared in a similar fashion. The judges then compared the two sets of statements, *item by item,* denoting each item of the interpretation as "right," "wrong," or "?." This index of validity was significantly higher for his sample of interpretations than for a random group of interpretations, or for a group of "mock" reports, matched randomly with the same criterion. Cronbach (2)[3] described a validation design for projective techniques which is quite comparable to that employed by Harrison. Cronbach's conclusions, which might also be said to apply to Harrison's method, were that his type of approach (*a*) yielded a statistically sound test of significance, (*b*) "identifies objectively the accurate and inaccurate aspects of the prediction," and (*c*) permitted "identification of the types of cases for whom prediction is relatively accurate" (2, p. 373).

It should be noted that in this procedure, the proof of validity hinges on the premise that the judges accept the statements of the interpretation as being similar to the items in the case analysis. The criterion for being "similar" is not stated in either of these articles, and from this procedure, no conclusion can be drawn as to the *degree* of similarity between the two sets of items. This degree of similarity might be measured by a rating scale of agreement, as used by Krugman (11). The ultimate step in this validation procedure would be to demonstrate that the personality of the individual as inferred from the test and from a life situation could be described by the same statements, e.g., on a rating scale or on a check list of commonly used statements.

The feature of this "item analysis" method of greatest import to our discussion is that on the surface it contradicts the assumption by Frank (3) and Vernon (18, 19), namely, that, since these descriptions deal with an integrated personality structure, they could not be validated piece by piece. This seeming contradiction might be explained, however, by the hypothesis that *the validity of these separate items depends on the validity of the whole description.* In the strictest sense, this hypothesis would mean that separate statements within the interpretative report would be valid *only* if the whole

3. Since Cronbach's article was published after the present study was completed, the particular design which he introduced was not originally considered in this investigation.

interpretation were valid. At least, it would indicate that if the interpretation as a whole is accurate, then the isolated statements drawn from the interpretative reports would be *more likely* to be accurate. It should be emphasized that this hypothesis refers to the validation of interpretations which stress the *relationships* between the various functionings within the personality as a whole.

However, the studies of Harrison (4) and by Cronbach (2) do not supply any direct evidence in support of this hypothesis, since neither study provided a test of the accuracy of the interpretations as integrated, whole reports. Harrison did not state whether or not certain of his cases had significantly lower "validity indices." Although Cronbach concluded that his procedure allowed "the identification of the types of cases for whom prediction is relatively accurate," he did not describe these cases in the part of his study reported to date. It is possible that in both of these studies, some interpretations were inaccurate in the description of the personality as a whole, and that, therefore, the items drawn from these interpretations failed to attain significance.

Unfortunately, it cannot be determined from either Harrison's or Cronbach's articles exactly on what basis the interpretations were broken down into isolated items. One main criticism of these two studies is that no rationale is presented as a basis for the selection of the items. In fact, Harrison did not adopt a dynamic, structural approach to personality in his interpretations, but stated that his approach to personality was "eclectic and emphasized common sense psychology" in contrast to Murray's (13) theories or to psychoanalysis. Nor did Cronbach describe the theoretical bias of his Rorschach interpreters, although he did indicate that a more complete report would follow his introductory article. Exactly what types of statements about personality were validated, or might be validated, in this fashion remains undetermined. There is no assurance that this methodological design is applicable to the validation of interpretations based on a dynamic theory of personality.

E. PURPOSES AND PROCEDURES OF
THE PRESENT STUDY

The purposes of the present study were:

1. To test the hypothesis (discussed above) that the validity of separate statements about personality, inferred from projective techniques, depends on the accuracy of the interpretation as a whole.

2. To determine whether a test of the validity of isolated statements is

applicable to interpretations based on a dynamic, structural concept of personality.

3. To determine whether the personality of the individual as inferred from the test protocol and from the criterion situation could be described by the same set of statements.

II. The Test, the Criterion, and the Sample

A. THE SELECTION OF THE RORSCHACH TECHNIQUE

In order to study the applicability of two methods of validation, it was essential that these approaches be tested on a projective technique of relatively accepted validity. After due consideration, the Rorschach technique was chosen, mainly on the strength of a comparatively longer and more varied background of validation studies. For a complete review of these investigations of the validity of the Rorschach, the reader is referred to the three articles by Hertz (5, 6, 7).

Predictive studies of the accuracy of Rorschach interpretation have not been as numerous, nor have the results been as uniformly positive, as those reported for the other types of approaches. Other than the studies using the matching method—which is under consideration here—most statistical studies have attempted to correlate isolated Rorschach signs with manifest behavior, usually with negative results. In regard to these studies, Hertz remarked. "The abortive dissection of the psychogram in the search for static factors in isolation has distorted the [Rorschach] method" (6, p. 549).

In addition to summarizing the various studies containing evidence of the validity of the Rorschach, Hertz presented many positive criticisms of these studies and recommendations for further investigation. In particular, she stressed the need for more experimental and differential studies to evaluate the various hypotheses underlying the interpretation of the Rorschach. The main purpose of her review was to stimulate sound experimental design in these studies.

1. The Administration of the Test. The method of administration followed the procedure described by Klopfer and Kelley (10). All the examiners took particular pains to secure a thorough "inquiry" into the features of the blots which elicited the subjects' responses. Probing and suggestive questions were avoided, however, until the "testing of the limits." Twenty-one of the subjects were tested by the author; the other seven subjects had been previously tested by other experienced administrators.

2. The Protocols. The validity of a Rorschach interpretation depends both on the quantity and quality of the subject's responses. Most of these records offer a wealth of variegated responses as raw data for the interpreter. The completeness of the records was, to some extent, assured by the technique of administration, i.e., by the thorough inquiry. The quality of the protocols may also have been affected by the nature of the sample; possibly the patients had been selected for psychotherapy because they were comparatively more responsive and less restricted in their functioning.

B. THE SUBJECTS

In three Veterans Administration installations, the Rorschach was administered to all patients who were currently receiving psychotherapy and to whom the Rorschach had not previously been given. Of these twenty-eight subjects, eleven were in a neuropsychiatric hospital, eleven were from an outpatient clinic, and six were attending a nearby university clinic. These subjects ranged in age from nineteen to forty-two years, with a mean age of twenty-eight years. Ten of the patients were classified as psychotic, sixteen as neurotic, and two had other diagnoses. Except for the differences in diagnostic classification (see further discussion below), the character of this sample did not appear to have any direct bearing on the study of these two methods of validation.

C. THE CRITERION

Obviously, the validation of a projective technique depends on the use of a criterion description which is comparable in nature to the test interpretation, and which is based on an adequate study of the individual. While the functioning of the individual's personality may be inferred from his manifest behavior as summarized in a life history or factual case study, this functioning may be observed even more directly and intimately in a psychotherapeutic study, i.e., in the individual's expression of his feelings and attitudes during psychotherapy, and in his emotional reactions to the psychotherapeutic situation. This criterion has been used in at least two major clinical validations of projective techniques: Hertz and Rubenstein (8), and Tomkins (17). It was also recommended by Rosenzweig (15) in his outline for a comprehensive study of the validity of the Rorschach.

In the present study, the Rorschach interpretations were compared, in the two validation methods, with the therapists' impressions of their patients. The seventeen therapists acted as the judges in both validation experiments, i.e., they selected the Rorschach reports which matched their patients in the matching experiment and described their patients in terms of the choices on the item check list. Thus, the validation judges were able to evaluate the Rorschach interpretations on the basis of an intimate and extensive knowledge of the subject, instead of having to reply on the basis of a summarized sketch compiled by a disinterested party.

The therapy which the patients were receiving was psychoanalytic in nature, i.e., its purpose was to reveal to the patient his unconscious attitudes and motivations through an analysis of his emotional reaction to the therapeutic situation itself. The purpose of this therapeutic study of the patient's underlying attitudes and motivations may be considered equivalent to the aim of Rorschach interpretation. In fact, these therapists frequently requested a Rorschach report on their patients' personalities as an aid in planning treatment (excepting the patients who were subjects of this experiment). A majority of the therapists were also expert in the administration and interpretation of the Rorschach technique.

In the main, the therapists' impressions of their patients were derived from frequent contact with them. The total number of therapeutic interviews at the time the therapist made his judgment ranged from 6 to 90, with a median of 19 interviews: only 4 subjects were interviewed less than 10 times, while 8 had been interviewed over 30 times. In 20 of the 28 cases, the Rorschach was administered when therapy was in a beginning stage, i.e., before the fifth interview: the median number of interviews at the time of testing was 1, with a range of 0 to 40. A median of 15 weeks elapsed between the time of testing and the time of judgment; in no case was there less than a 7-week interval, and in 2 cases, the interval was over 30 weeks. During this period, the therapists interviewed their patients between 5 and 80 times, with a median of 11 interviews occurring between testing and judging. As to the frequency of these interviews, 6 of the cases were seen 3 or more times weekly, 5 others were seen twice weekly, and all but 2 patients were seen regularly at least once a week. These 2 cases were interviewed frequently, but at irregular intervals. The minimum opportunity which a therapist had to observe his patient was 6 interviews, occurring at irregular intervals, over a period of 16 weeks. The maximum observation occurred in a case where the patient was interviewed 90 times, 3 times a week, over a 30-week period. In summary, it may be said that the therapists' impressions were derived after extensive and frequent contacts with the subjects and may be considered comparable, in their theoretical approach to personality, to the Rorschach interpretations.

III. The Matching Approach

In brief, the matching experiment consisted of the following procedures:

1. Interpretative reports were prepared from each of the Rorschach records by one interpreter (the author).

2. The reliability of these reports was checked in two ways: by having the reports matched to the protocols, and by having them matched to a duplicate set of reports which had been prepared by another psychologist.

3. In order to test the reliability of the therapists in their matching technique, they were given a group of five sample interpretations from which they had to select the one which matched a corresponding sample case analysis.

4. For each patient, a matching group was chosen, consisting of the interpretation of that patient's Rorschach, referred to hereafter as the *experimental* interpretation; and of four other interpretative reports, to be referred to as *alternates*.

5. Each therapist was then asked to select, from the group of five reports, the one report which he believed most closely represented his patient; subsequently, the therapist made a second choice among the remaining four reports.

A. THE NATURE OF THE INTERPRETATIONS

In order to standardize the method of interpretation and the style of the interpretative reports, all the protocols were interpreted by one person, the author. These interpretations were based solely on an individual's responses to the test material and on his behavior during the administration of the test.[4] The method of interpretation followed that outlined in Klopfer and Kelley (10), particularly in the scoring of the responses and in the preliminary analysis of the psychogram. The conceptual framework employed throughout this process of interpretation was, broadly speaking, psychoanalytical. As far as possible, these descriptions were couched in everyday idiom, and both Rorschach and psychoanalytic terms were avoided.

B. THE RELIABILITY OF THE INTERPRETATIONS

Since all of the interpretative reports employed in the matching experiment were prepared by one person, it was necessary to determine whether these interpretations were reliable in the same sense that the consistency and accuracy with which one scores a psychometric instrument might be checked. As a rough test of this reliability, three judges, skilled in Rorschach interpretation, attempted to match the report to the protocols, in groups of five each. Since this study was directed at the reliability or consistency of fully verbalized interpretations rather than of standardized symbols or *scores*, no attempt was made to check the author's scoring. These judges were

4. The patient's behavior during the testing (as distinguished from his responses to the materials) was not recorded. Since most of the records were interpreted some time after the test administration, little if any account was taken of this factor.

instead presented with the *unscored* responses and asked to match these directly to the author's statements about the various subjects' personalities. All three judges were 100 per cent successful in this matching.

Despite this positive result, it was possible to question the reliability of these interpretations, i.e., whether they were similar to descriptions derived by some other interpreter. As a further check on this reliability, the protocols were interpreted independently by another psychologist.[5] Three judges matched, with complete success, the first five interpretations of this second set of reports with the five corresponding intepretations by the author. Since this result coincided with the results of Krugman's (11) more comprehensive study of Rorschach reliability, the success of this single matching was considered sufficient indication of the reliability of the interpretations used in the present study.

C. THE RELIABILITY OF THE THERAPISTS
IN MATCHING

Prior to the matching of the Rorschach interpretations in the main part of this research, the therapists were briefly trained in the use of the matching technique. In order to check the reliability of the therapists in matching, the author prepared a case analysis on a patient not included in the validation study. This patient's Rorschach record was interpreted independently by the interpreter who had participated in the study of the reliability of the interpretations. Using this case analysis as a criterion, ten of the therapists attempted to select this experimental interpretation from among four alternative interpretations (previously prepared by this other interpreter).

On this trial, six of the therapists matched the sample interpretation correctly on their first choice, and three others indicated it as their second choice. In this instance, successful matching on first choice could be expected by chance in two cases, i.e., two out of ten times. When first and second choices were considered, chance matchings might occur in four instances in ten matchings. According to the tables of "General Term of Poisson's Exponential Expansion" in Pearson (14)[6] the obtained results of both the

5. The author wishes to acknowledge the patient assistance of Mr. Mervin Freedman, Mr. Patrick Sullivan, and Mr. William Cook of The University of California who acted as the judges here, and of Mr. Allen Dittmann, who prepared the second set of reports.

6. Throughout this study, many of the resultant proportions of chance agreement were so small that their distribution was thought to be considerably skewed and platykurtic. The use of a standard error of a proportion and its interpretation in terms of the normal probability integral would have yielded erroneous probabilities. It was thought, however, that the computation of exact binomial probabilities would have required more effort than their usefulness justified, so approximations to these probabilities were obtained from the Poisson distributions. This distribution is useful in approximately binomial probabilities when p is small in comparison to q, but where the possible number (of agreements, in our case) is finite.

first choices alone (six correct matchings) and of the two choices combined (nine correct matchings) are significant beyond the 5 per cent level of confidence. Admittedly, this limited study of the reliability of the therapists in matching a single case was not completely comparable to the matching study of the validity of the twenty-eight cases, as described below. Still, in view of the positive results of this brief reliability study, it seems reasonable to expect that these therapists would be approximately reliable in other matching experiments—particularly one in which they would be more familiar with the criterion, i.e., their own patients.

D. SELECTION OF THE MATCHING GROUPS

As noted in Section I, the results of a matching study depends to a large extent on the variability among the descriptive reports which constitute the matching groups. In contrast to previous investigations which also made use of the matching method, the present research included an attempt to control the heterogeneity of the matching groups. This particular step in the present research may, therefore, bear some detailed explanation.

The purpose of this step in the matching procedure was to select matching groups having the same degree of heterogeneity. It seemed desirable that the *alternate interpretations* to be included in a group with the experimental interpretation *should be neither very different from nor very similar to that experimental interpretation.* To achieve this degree of heterogeneity, it was necessary to compare each interpretation with all other interpretations which might appear within a group as an alternate. In order to estimate the differences between interpretations, the following rough rating scale was adopted:

SS—Both interpretative reports describe the same basic personality features but may differ in specific characteristics.

S—Both reports describe similar basic personality features but may differ in specific characteristics.

SO—Both reports describe some similar basic features *and* some similar specific characteristics, but also differ slightly in both respects.

O—Both reports differ as to basic features but present some similar specific characteristics.

OO—Both reports differ in all respects.

N—The reports are not comparable.

For the sake of convenience, the first fifteen reports collected from the sample were rated on this scale prior to the last thirteen reports. Three judges[7] rated these reports on the above scale; each judge made an inde-

7. The author appreciates the assistance of Mr. Timothy Leary and Mr. Walter Klopfer in this task.

pendent rating first, followed by a final pooled rating by all three judges. These ratings were made on the over-all description of the personality rather than any specific cues. Thus, two interpretations discussing latent homosexual trends as important to the personality picture but differing in most other respects, i.e., in basic personality structures, might be rated at least *O,* if not *OO.*

In selecting the matching groups, reports which rated *SO* with the experimental report were given preference; a few reports compared as *O* or *S* were also used in some groups, but none of those extremely different or similar were included. Thus, the matching groups were of appropriate heterogeneity with regard to the experimental report.

E. THE SEQUENCE IN WHICH THE
TWO APPROACHES WERE USED

Since both the matching and the check list judgments were made by the same judges (i.e., the therapists), the sequence in which the two techniques were tested carried a possible contamination: a therapist who matched his case before using the check list might be influenced by the selected report when the time came for him to make choices on the check list. Or, if he used the check list first, he might acquire a set for the matching of the report. Although such bias could not be wholly prevented, its possible effect was taken into account by systematically varying the order in which the therapist performed the two tasks. Therefore, in fourteen of the cases (seven in each half of the sample), the therapist selected the report before he made choices on the check list—the sequence being reversed in the other fourteen cases. The possibility of this type of bias was further lessened by the fact that the therapists always made the two judgments separately, with an intervening period of two to three weeks.

F. HOW THE THERAPIST
MADE HIS SELECTIONS

Each therapist was presented with one matching group for each of his patients. Each group consisted of five reports (one of which was derived from his own patient's Rorschach). The therapist was instructed to select the one report which matched his patient. After this first choice was made, the therapist was asked to name a second choice from the remaining four reports. The selection of a second choice was requested in order to allow for partial errors in matching, particularly in those instances when a judge might be undecided as to which of two similar reports to select.

Another factor which had to be considered in this procedure was the possibility that the patient's personality had been altered by the therapy which intervened between the time the Rorschach was administered and the time the therapist made his selection. Therefore, as he made his selection, the therapist was reminded of the date of the test administration, and he was asked to consider the patient's personality as it had been at that previous time.

G. RESULTS OF THE MATCHING

In eleven of the twenty-eight cases, the therapists correctly selected the interpretation of their patient's Rorschach as a first choice from the matching groups; only two more were correctly selected as second choices. In terms of chance expectancy (using Poisson's tables) this result is significant beyond the 3 per cent level of confidence. Using Vernon's (19) formula for the coefficient of contingency, C is equal to .434 ± .078.

Although this matching was above chance, the relationship between the Rorschach and criterion, indicated by this C, was considerably lower than reported in previous studies. Vernon (18) found a C of .833 ± .047.[8] Krugman (11) reported a C of .850. Both studies differ from the present investigation in two important aspects:

1. They did not specifically control the heterogeneity of their matching groups. It seems reasonable to presume that in the present study the control of this factor created a more difficult task for the judges, and consequently a more acute test of the Rorschach reports.

2. The previous studies used equal numbers of reports and case analyses, while the present investigation employed a five-to-one matching. Thus, in the present study, the judges were forced to differentiate among five reports, with only one criterion as a basis of judgment; in this sense, the chance of success was probably much smaller than in the previous studies.

Considering the factor of a more differentiating task for the judges, who therefore had less chance for successful matching, the degree of validity obtained in the present study may perhaps be regarded as comparatively more significant than the findings in the previous studies which did not include these controls.

The results of the matching experiment might also have been affected by other variables in the nature of the sample or in any of the procedures used in collecting and presenting the data. Seven variables were considered as possibly affecting the results of this matching, namely: (*a*) the type of installation (hospital or outpatient); (*b*) the psychiatric diagnosis (psychotic or "other neuropsychiatric disorder"); (*c*) the total numbers of interviews

---

8. Vernon reported a *PE* of .0314, converted here for purposes of comparison to a standard error.

(above or below the median of 19); (*d*) the numbers of interviews after test-ing (median or 11 interviews); (*e*) the frequency of the interviews (weekly or more frequent); (*f*) the order in which the Rorschachs were administered (a difference in results was indicated between the two halves of the sample); and (*g*) the judgment which the therapist made first (matching or check list). A study of the effect of these seven variables was made to discover if they had any possible relationship to the matching results (see Table 1).

TABLE 1

Differences in the Proportions of Cases Matched Correctly, Between Various Characteristics of the Sample, and Between Various Procedures in Matching

Groups Compared	*N*	Cases Matched Correctly No.	Cases Matched Correctly Prop.	Diff.	*CR*	*P*
Hospital patients	11	4	.36	.05 ± .27	<1	
Outpatients	17	7	.41			
Psychotic patients	10	2	.20	.30 ± .14	2.15	.03
Other NP patients	18	9	.50			
Total interviews:						
Over 19	14	5	.36	.07 ± .18	<1	
Under 19	14	6	.43			
Interviews after testing:						
Over 11	14	6	.43	.07 ± .18	<1	
Under 11	14	5	.36			
Frequency of interviews:						
Once weekly	15	6	.40	.02 ± .18	<1	
Over once weekly	13	5	.38			
Cases 1–15	15	2	.13	.56 ± .16	3.5	<.01
Cases 16–28	13	9	.69			
Check list first	14	7	.50	.14 ± .19	<1	
Matching first	14	5	.36			

Only one of these differences, the order in which the Rorschach tests were administered—and interpreted—is significant at less than the 1 per cent level of confidence. A possible explanation of this difference is that the reports in the last half of the sample might have been more incisive descrip-tions than the first fifteen interpretations. The ratings of heterogeneity, which were made in the procedure for selecting the matching groups, pro-vided some measure of the qualitative differences among the reports—at least within each of the two halves of the sample, but, unfortunately, not over the entire sample. The results of this rating procedure, as shown in Table 2, indicate that in both halves of the sample, a significantly greater number of the comparisons were rated as different from one another (*O* or *OO*) than might be expected if the distribution of ratings had been even; on the other hand, the percentage of *S* and *SS* ratings was much less than expected. Thus, the efforts of the interpreter to achieve distinctive reports were sustained within each half of the samples. Whether or not this distinctiveness increased progressively from one half of the sample through the next cannot be stated conclusively inasmuch as not each interpretation was paired with every other interpretation throughout the whole sample. However, in view of the fact that no significant difference existed between the two halves of the sample in the proportion of *O* + *OO* ratings, it may be considered that the cases of the second half were no more distinctive, as compared among themselves, than those of the first half.

TABLE 2

Differences Between Obtained and Expected Ratings of *S* + *SS* and *O* + *OO*
(Assuming an Expected Chance Distribution of Equal Proportions of *SS* + *S*,
***SO* + *X* and *OO* + *O*.)**

Cases	Comparisons	Rating	Obtained	Per Cent Obtained	Per Cent Expected	Diff.	*CR*	*P*
1–15	105	S + SS	16	15.2	33 + 4.47	−17.8	3.73	<.01
		O + OO	44	48.8		+10.8	2.06	<.05
16–28	78	S + SS	9	11.5	33 + 4.9	−21.5	4.39	<.01
		O + OO	38	48.7		+15.7	3.21	<.01

The second of these variables which showed a significant difference in the matching results was the diagnostic classification of the patients. Fewer of the cases diagnosed "psychotic" were matched correctly than those classed as "neurotic" or in other neuropsychiatric categories. Although the number of patients in these classifications was too small for further computation of differences, it was noted that seven of the ten psychotic cases fell in the first half of the sample. These results, if meaningful, would indicate that the interpretations of the Rorschach of the psychotic patients may have been less differentiating ones. In view of the fact that psychotic patients (other than paranoid types) often give vague and diffuse responses, it is to be expected that these interpretations would be less meaningful and distinctive. Such responses from the psychotic patients are consonant with the theory of personality used here, i.e., that inadequate perceptual differentiation is equated with psychoses. However, this concept is not helpful in distinguishing one psychotic patient from another, as was required of the matching judges. If the judges operated on the basis of this concept also, then the criteria may have been as nondifferentiating as the Rorschach. Further study of the psychotic individual may be required, by both the Rorschach and other methods of observation, before a higher validity of interpretation can be demonstrated by the matching method.

IV. The Check List Approach

The check list approach consisted of the following steps:

1. A list of thirty-four multiple choice items was constructed, consisting of statements commonly used in interpretative reports and in psychotherapeutic analysis.

2. The reliability of the therapists in the use of this check list was determined, using a sample case analysis as criterion.

3. Four Rorschach interpreters independently checked their choices on the multiple choice items for the twenty-eight Rorschach protocols. The reliability of these Rorschach judges was determined by computing the significance of the number of agreements between these judges, for each item.

4. The therapists checked choices on each item on the basis of their impression of their patients. The validity of the Rorschach judges' choices was then determined by computing the significance of the number of times that they agreed with the therapists on each item.

A. SELECTION OF THE ITEMS

In order to obtain a list of multiple choice items representative of the many abstractions used in Rorschach interpretation, each of the major categories of personality utilized in the interpretative reports was represented by at least one item. These six major areas of personality were as follows: (a) inner drives and attitudes, (b) emotional reactions and relationships, (c) sensitivity to emotional stimuli, (d) intellectual functioning and reality testing, (e) sexual attitudes and identification, and (f) anxiety and defenses against anxiety. Each of these major categories or areas was further considered in four subdivisions or "dimensions": (a) the *frequency* or extent to which these areas were represented in his reaction to the test materials or to psychotherapy, (b) the characteristic *type* or nature of each area, (c) the *role* which each area played in the total pattern of the personality, (d) the *control* or manner in which the individual handled the attitude or reaction in question.

The questions asked in the interpretative reports concerning the individual's attitudes toward his identity and his inner motivations were represented on the check list by those items referring to fantasy life and inner drives, as follows:

(Quantity) No. 17. "Expression by the individual of his inner needs and drives, i.e., his striving for satisfaction of these drives, is: almost completely absent," to "directly impulsive, showing an infantile lack of control."

(Role) No. 23. "Such inner fantasy life as the individual may allow himself is utilized for, or functions in his personality structure as: A. An internalization of certain unacceptable feelings, not permitted in overt behavior, e.g., for introjection of hostility in an intrapunitive manner. B. An attempt to organize and handle outer behavior in an integrated manner. C. A retreat from nearly all environmental frustrations, especially those in interpersonal relationships, with a handling of such relationships on a fantasy level. D. Very little, being poorly developed. E. Very little, being a source of anxiety in itself."

(Control) No. 13. "The method by which the individual handles and controls his inner emotional drives is chiefly: A. By fantasy solutions—possibly by divorcing such feelings from reality. B. By creative use of his energies, in a sublimated manner. C. By repressing them in a rigid and constricted manner. D. By direct release in overt behavior. E. By attempting to intellectualize, depersonalize or otherwise detach them from him emotionally."

Closely related to this general area of inner motivation are the individual's attitudes toward his sexual functioning, which were sampled on the check list by the following items:

(Quantity) No. 6. "The extent to which the individual enters into heterosexual relationships: is almost completely nil," to "is so exaggerated as to pervade much of the individual's behavior."

(Type) No. 30. "The following attitude may be considered as the 'basic' one with which the individual regards his own sexual or 'sexualized' behavior: A. As an aggressive (sadist) act. B. As a dangerous (castrating) act. C. As a passive, receptive (incorporative) act. D. As a demonstration of potency, an egotistic self-assertion, (autoerotic or exhibitionistic). E. As normal and acceptable (genital supremacy) ." (A–D assume infantile sexual fixations or conflicts.)

No. 32. "The individual's general identification in most sexual and social roles is: A. With a dominant male figure. B. With a dominant female figure. C. With a passive male figure. D. With a passive female figure. E. Without a definite character and/or extremely ambivalent."

(Role) No. 10. "Homosexual relationships are utilized by the individual for, or play a role in his personality as: A. An integrated and mature part of his social behavior. B. A denial of rejection by other males. C. A denial of rejection by females. D. A minor role (e.g., for further satisfaction of narcissistic needs). E. An assertion of identification as to sexual role."

(Control) No. 24. "The chief method by which the individual handles his homosexual relationships is: A. By fairly overt emotional attachments possibly including sexual satisfactions. B. By repression of such feelings and/or avoidance of such relationships. C. By sublimating such feelings into socially acceptable channels of behavior. D. By retreating into fantasy solutions. E. By intellectually detaching the emotional aspects, depersonalization."

No. 34. "The individual handles, or reacts to, possible heterosexual relationships (or needs for such relationships) chiefly by: A. A retreat into fantasy (without necessarily breaking with reality). B. By accepting social restrictions, and sublimating where necessary. C. By repressing such drives, and/or depersonalizing them, detaching the emotional aspects of such relationships. D. By affective outburst—such as overt anxiety and panic, etc. E. By breaking with reality."

The manner in which the individual perceives and accepts the pressure of his environment was represented in the following items, which dealt with interpersonal relationships and emotional reactions:

(Quantity) No. 27. "The degree to which the individual allows himself to become involved in emotional relationships with others is: a very limited involvement of any type," to "a purely volatile and explosive reaction."

(Type) No. 25. "The emotional tone or affect which the individual displays in his emotional attachments with others is most often: A. Warm and spontaneous. B. (Absent.) C. Cold and detached. D. Hostile and oppositional. E. Forced and artificial.

(Role) 33. "Involvement in active emotional, interpersonal relationships serves the individual as, or plays a role in his personality structure as: A. A method of compensating for the inadequacies felt within himself. B. A release mechanism for the satisfaction of inner drives. C. A minor role—in an intraversive adjustment, under accumulated frustration or increasing environmental stimulation only. D. (None.) E. As a mature and integrated part of his behavior."

(Control) No. 19. "The principal method by which the individual handles and controls his emotional reactions in his interpersonal relationships is: A. By integrating them in a mature manner with other personal needs. B. By rigidly avoiding and denying the emotional aspects (isolation of emotion). C. By ignoring the reality of such an emotion and autistically withdrawing into fantasy solutions. D. By immature, and possibly aggressive, reactions. E. By depersonalizing such situations through intellectualizing or rationalizing."

Four other items were constructed requiring judgment relative to the individual's sensitivity to environmental stimulation:

(Quantity) No. 8. "The extent to which the individual allows himself to be receptive to the affective feelings of others, or to other emotional stimulation: A. Is limited and tenuous, chiefly when socially approved. B. Is practically absent. C. Is such that the individual is acutely aware of the emotional aspects of a situation. D. Shows a well-balanced and integrated sensitivity and tact. E. Shows a tendency to be unduly sensitive."

(Type) No. 9. "The individual's most characteristic reaction to the affective feelings of others and to the emotional stimulation from his environment, is: to be indifferent and disinterested," to "to be overtly sensuous."

(Role) No. 16. "Sensitivity to the emotions of others or to other emotional stimuli is utilized by the individual for, or plays a role in his personality as: A. (None.) B. A counterreaction to repressed hostility. C. A withdrawal from frustration, from a more active emotional involvement. D. An integrated part of a mature handling of social relationships. E. A primary source of guilt and anxiety."

(Control) No. 2. "The way in which the individual controls and handles possible sensitivity to emotional stimulation, especially to the feelings of others, is usually: A. By rigid repression and restriction of such sensitivity. B. By attributing such stimulation to his own inner needs (by introjection). C. By reactively denying such feelings in aggressive, hostile behavior. D. By divorcing such feelings from reality and/or by fantasy solutions. F. By acceptance and integration of such sensitivity in social relationships.

From the area of intellectual functioning and of reality testing, the following items were derived:

(Quantity) No. 1. "The wealth of the individual's intellectual activity may be characterized as generally: impoverished, and tending to be perserverative," to "having a wide range of interests, often being rich and original in content." No. 7. "The individual's intellectual productivity may be estimated as generally: very limited," to "extensive."

(Type) No. 15. "The individual's intellectual approach to a problem or situation: A. Usually shows a tendency to abstract and overgeneralize, without sufficient attention to everyday affairs. B. Tends to be overly critical, analytical, possibly picayunish. C. Usually shows a fair ability to conceptualize, but with adequate attention to practical concrete matters. D. May contain some evidence of delusional thought processes, forcing relationships between facts or distorting reality. E. Is most often a matter-of-fact approach, tending to be overly concrete."

No. 18. "The individual's ties to reality may be classified as chiefly: very strong, as never permitting any vagueness" through "adequate—but not overly concerned with reality testing," through "so tenuous as to easily become inadequate" to "quite inadequate and/or absent."

(Role) No. 22. "Intellectual functioning is utilized by the individual for, or has a principal function in his personality structure as: A. A rigid defense against the release of inner drives and/or emotional ties with others, by depriving them of their emotional tone. B. A mature and normal mode of controlling himself and his environment. C. As an aid to autistic thinking, e.g., in delusional types of solutions. D. A highly aggressive, critical defense mechanism. E. Only a minor role, e.g., as an aid to immediate satisfaction of narcissistic needs."

(Control) No. 5. "The individual's contact with reality appears weakest: A. In his creative, inner fantasy life. B. In his active, and potentially aggressive, interpersonal relationships. C. In his sensitivity to emotional stimulation. D. In seemingly impersonal situations (to which affect has been displaced). E. In his release of instinctual drives."

The items included on the check list under the rubric of *anxiety* correspond in part to those considerations given ego-functioning above:

(Quantity) No. 28. "The degree to which the individual shows feelings of generalized disturbance may be estimated as: seldom more than a minimal and occasional uneasiness," to "states of overwhelming panic."

(Type) No. 3. "The individual's expression of feelings of generalized disturbance may be characterized as: A. A free-floating type of anxiety state. B. A feeling of inner tension and conflict-guilt feelings. C. Overt depression. D. A sense of frustration and disappointment. E. (Relatively absent.)"

(Role) No. 21. "The effect of anxiety and/or guilt feelings on the individual's personality structure constitutes: no noticeable effect," to "a gross breakdown of most functioning."

The different defenses were considered more specifically in the following items:

(Projection) No. 4. "Projection of guilt feelings onto others or the environment is used by the individual as a method of averting anxiety to the following degrees: very rarely," to "extensively."

(Rationalization) No. 11. "The individual uses rationalization and justification as an intellectual evasion of anxiety to the following degree: very rarely," to "extensively."

(Obsession) No. 12. "The individual uses compulsive behavior or obsessive thinking as a magical ritualistic denial of anxiety to the following degree: very rarely," to "extensively."

(Displacement) No. 14. "The individual attempts to avert anxiety by displacement of emotional content to some more 'neutral' situation: very rarely," to "extensively."

(Withdrawal) No. 20. "The individual attempts to avert anxiety by fantasy solutions and/or by withdrawal from contact with reality to the following degree: very rarely," to "extensively."

(Normal reaction) No. 26. "The individual uses anxiety as a normal 'warning signal' of possible frustration: very rarely," to "extensively."

(Acting out) No. 29. "The individual attempts to avert anxiety by 'acting out' of frustrations onto the environment, by negativism and aggression, etc.: very rarely," to "extensively."

(Isolation) No. 31. "The individual attempts to avert anxiety by rigid isolation of all emotional aspects of a situation: very rarely," to "extensively."

B. ARRANGEMENT OF THE ITEMS ON THE LIST

It is possible that, if the items had been presented in the logical order of the scheme shown above, a judge's choice on one item might directly influence his choices on succeeding items, especially those within the same major category. In order to lessen the sequential effect, the items were presented in a random arrangement.

C. THE NUMBER AND ORDER OF THE CHOICES

For the sake of uniformity, five choices were listed for each statement. As was discovered afterward, this uniform number of choices was an unnecessary restriction; in many instances, a larger number of choices would have offered the judges more opportunity to describe their patients, and in a more accurate manner. In many instances, also, these five choices formed an obvious continuum, e.g., from "extensively" to "rarely," or "well adjusted" to "very disturbed," etc. Since a judge's choices on one item might well be influenced by the position on this continuum of his choices on previous items, the order of choices was varied in a random manner from item to item.

D. THE INSTRUCTIONS

The judges were instructed to make two choices on each item for each patient. Second choices were requested, because (*a*) it was possible that a pair of judges might agree, given two choices each, even though they might not agree on a first choice; and (*b*) some judges felt less forced in their judgments when allowed two choices.

E. RELIABILITY OF THE THERAPISTS IN THE
USE OF THE CHECK LIST

Reliability of the therapists in the use of the check list was determined in the same manner as was their reliability in the matching procedure. Using a sample case analysis (described above) as a criterion, ten of the therapists indicated choices on each item of the list. The therapists had previously had some training in the use of this type of list, in a trial run of a preliminary form. A rough estimate of the reliability of these therapists was obtained by assuming the agreement to be satisfactory when five or more therapists indicated the same first choice on an item—as describing this sample case history. When any two judges indicated the same two choices on any item, either as first or second choice, this was also noted as an agreement. For these "pairs" of choices, satisfactory agreement on an item was assumed when four or more judges used the same pair. On twenty of the items, five or more judges employed the same pair of choices. Although this reliability study was admittedly limited, it seems reasonable to assume that similar results might have been obtained if a more extensive study had been possible. Strictly speaking, the results of this step in the check list approach can only be taken to indicate that the therapists were able to agree satisfactorily on a majority of the items, using one sample case as a basis of judgment.

F. RELIABILITY OF THE RORSCHACH JUDGES
IN THE USE OF THE CHECK LIST

The twenty-eight Rorschach records of the sample were judged independently on the check list by four experienced Rorschach interpreters.

These judges[9] received a brief training in the use of this check list on a sample Rorschach protocol. The reliability of these Rorschach judges in the use of the check list was considered in terms of the number of agreements, i.e., the number of times they indicated the same choice on an item regarding the same individual. For each item, the twenty-eight first choices of each judge were compared with those of every other judge—two judges at a time. Thus, six sets of comparisons were made for each item. The first choices of each pair of judges were tabulated on a five-square table, such that the agreements fell on the diagonal. The degree of agreement expected by chance was then computed on the assumption that the two sets of judgments were independent, subject to the restriction of the observed marginal totals. Since in most instances this chance degree of agreement was a relatively small proportion of the total number of cases—usually less than one-third—the significance of the difference between this number of agreements expected by chance and the number of agreements actually obtained was again read from the tables of Poisson's distribution (14). Where the expected number of agreements was larger than one-third of the total number of cases, the significance of this difference was computed in terms of the standard error of a proportion.

All in all, the four judges of the Rorschach agreed significantly about one-third of the time. Of the 204 comparisons for first choices (the choices of six pairs of judges compared on 34 items), 78 resulted in agreement at the 10 per cent level or beyond; 51 of these were significant at the 5 per cent or beyond; and 26 at the 2 per cent level or better. For the two choices combined, 63 of the obtained agreements were significant at the 10 per cent level or beyond; 43 of these at the 5 per cent level; and 31 at the 2 per cent level or better. If we consider the rather abstruse wording of some of these items and the limitations on the number of choices, this degree of agreement is considerable. The large percentage of lack of agreement is not surprising in view of the fact that the judges were attempting to make almost *unqualified* statements about personality from such a restricted sampling of behavior, i.e., responses to ten ink-blot pictures. The alternative or second choice did not appreciably increase the agreement between the judges.

Further analysis of the agreement and lack of agreement indicates that a fair number of items may be called reliable. If three significant agreements, i.e., agreement by three pairs of judges, be granted as indicating satisfactory reliability for an item, then about one-third of the 34 items may be called reliable—12 for first choices and 11 for the combined choices. An appreci-

9. Mr. Walter Klopfer, Mr. J. Neil Campion, Jr., and Dr. Claire Thompson of the University of California were kind enough to devote many hours assisting the author in making these judgments.

able part of the lack of agreement may have been attributable to some particular pair of judges. However, it was found that all pairs of judges agreed to about the same degree. The degree of agreement within each area and within each dimension, as shown in Table 3, is summarized *as a proportion of the total number of comparisons* made in that area or dimension which showed significant agreement. The area in which the proportion of agreement was highest was intellectual functioning (.667). This particular area has been given close attention in the interpretative method of Klopfer and Kelley (10). Besides, it has also been thoroughly discussed in the current literature; therefore, the comparatively strong agreement shown here is not surprising. Two items which were included in this area, but which failed to have three or more agreements (Nos. 5 and 18) should properly belong to reality testing in general, rather than to specific intellectual functioning. Undoubtedly, a better definition of *reality testing* should have been reached by the judges.

The judges agreed reasonably well on another area: the one dealing with the individual's inner life, including his motivations and incorporated attitudes (.611). The significance of this agreement lies in the fact that this area is not as easily interpreted as that of intellectual functioning. This result might be explained by the hypothesis that the Rorschach is designed to tap these inner drives more than it does other areas. However, the degree of agreement about these inner drives does not appear to be much stronger than that about outer emotional reactions (.417) or sensitivity (.458). (The actual number of agreements was too small to permit statistical comparison.)

The lower percentage of agreement regarding emotional reactions and sensitivity may be traced to the disagreement among the judges about the dimensions of *type* and *role*. These two dimensions in these areas were the most difficult to restrict to five choices, and it seemed that greater agreement might have occurred if more choices had been provided.

Although the agreement on items concerning sexual attitudes (.277) might also have been improved by expanding the number of choices, the basic difficulty was more likely the confusion over the concepts employed in these items, particularly the concept "homosexual." This term was intended to refer to any type of attitude toward the same sex, rather than just to overt sexual behavior. Although the judges understood this broader connotation, they tended to limit their thinking about it to the latter, more common meaning.

The notably low proportion of agreement on the items pertaining to anxiety and defenses (.166) (see Table 4) is again explicable by the fact of the limited number of choices. To paraphrase: all anxiety is scarcely divisible into five parts! A more serious source of disagreement was found to be

TABLE 3

Distribution of Significant Agreement Between Rorschach Interpreters According to Area and Dimension of Personality Functioning

Area	No. of Comparisons	Proportion of Agreement	Frequency		Type		Role		Control	
			Items	No. of Agreements	Items	No. of Agreements	Items	No. of Agreements	Items	No. of Agreements
Inner drives	18	.611	17	2	—	—	23	4	13	5
Sexual attitudes	36	.277	6	0	30	3	10	0	34	4
					32	1			24	2
Emotional reactions	24	.417	27	4	25	2	33	1	19	3
Sensitivity	24	.458	8	3	9	1	16	1	2	6
Reality testing	36	.667	1	6	15	6	22	3	5	2
			7	5	18	2				
Anxiety reactions	18	.166	28	2	3	1	21	0	—	
Number of comparisons			42		42		36		36	
Proportion of agreement			.524		.328		.250		.606	

the poor definition of terms in this area. Even after the use of the check list had been reviewed among the judges, such terms as "displacement" were not consistently applied; note the significant disagreements on this item (No. 14) particularly. Several of the judges expressed the opinion that the items referring to defenses often overlapped in meaning or were otherwise confusing.

TABLE 4

Distribution of Significant Agreements Between Rorschach Interpreters, According to Type of Defense

Defense	Item No.	No. of Agreements
Projection	4	2
Rationalization	11	0
Obsession	12	1
Displacement	14	−2
Withdrawal	20	0
Normal warning	26	2
Acting out	29	1
Isolation	31	2
Total no. of comparisons		48
Proportion of agreement		.166

Viewing the results according to *dimension,* the highest agreement occurred on those items concerning the individual's handling or *control* of his functioning (.606). Next on the scale of agreement came the dimension of *frequency* (.524). These results indicate that Rorschach interpreters can agree among themselves on the two following aspects: the way in which an individual controls his impulses, and the degree to which he uses any particular control or defense or expresses an attitude.

The difference in the percentage of agreement between *control* (.606) and *role* (.250) assumes an importance when one considers that both dimensions deal with *relationships* between reactions. Thus, the judges were in much better agreement as to the *control* relationship between various areas of personality than they were concerning the relative importance and relationship of a particular reaction or attitude in the individual's overall functioning. This lack of agreement about the concept of *role* may be due partially to inadequate phrasing of the items or limitations in the number of choices. But the fact should also be pointed out that Rorschach interpretation underscores this concept of *control,* and that, too often, little attention is given the importance of such control or defense in the "economics" of the personality.

Thus, if it be granted that Rorschach theory emphasizes the perceptual functioning of the ego, then the comparatively higher reliability on the items covering *intellectual functioning* and *control* was to be expected. Conversely, these results may be taken to show a lack of agreement on those aspects which are less clearly defined in Rorschach theory, namely, the contentual factors, such as sexual attitudes and types of anxiety.

G. RESULTS OF VALIDATION
ON THE CHECK LIST

The choices on each item by each of the four Rorschach judges were tabulated with those of the therapists—one pair of judges at a time; four differences between the obtained frequencies of agreement and that expected by chance were derived for first choices, and the significance of these differences was noted in terms of the approximation to binomial probabilities read from Poisson's tables.

Considering first choices alone, only nine of the 136 comparisons (four comparisons on the thirty-four items) resulted in significant differences, at the 10 per cent level of confidence or beyond. No significant agreement appeared for the combined choices (first and second choices together). Only five of the differences on first choices were "positive differences," i.e., the obtained agreement was larger than that expected by chance, while four were "negative differences," i.e., the obtained agreement being smaller than chance. Since, in a distribution of 136 differences, 13.6 might be expected to show such significance by chance, this small number of significant agreements cannot be considered to be of any statistical importance. The differences did not seem to occur in any meaningful pattern: no more than one difference occurred on any one item; almost an equal number of such differences occurred for each pair of judges; and these differences did not appear to have any relation to the scheme of personality areas and dimensions.

In general, these results support the hypothesis that the check list type of approach is not applicable to the validation of the interpretations of projective techniques when these techniques are interpreted by means of a dynamic concept of personality. Such statements as those used in this check list are apparently meaningless, except in the context of an integrated descriptive report.

Undoubtedly, the amount of agreement between the Rorschach judges and the therapists was dependent on the degree to which these two sets of judges agreed separately among themselves. The reliability studies discussed above showed that when one set of judges used one kind of data, either Rorschach records or therapy, the agreement in that instance was satisfactory. In terms of the number of items which showed significant agreement, the Rorschach judges agreed among themselves 35 per cent of the time, i.e., on twelve items, while the therapists agreed among themselves fifty-eight per cent of the time, or on twenty items. In view of these reliabilities, there would seem to be some chance of obtaining higher validity. At the same time, one might inquire as to why these isolated statements were not applicable to the *validation* of Rorschach interpretation when they appear to be applicable to the study of its *reliability*.

Qualitative examination of the reliability of the Rorschach judges and of the therapists may serve to explain why there was agreement within each respective set of judges but little agreement between the two sets. In fact, the results of this reliability study may aid in the exploration of the relationships between the isolated statements and the whole reports.

As has been noted in the above discussion, the Rorschach judges agreed among themselves on those statements referring to the concepts which are most clearly defined in Rorschach theory, namely, in the area of *intellectual functioning* and on the dimension of *control*. Although several other basic concepts are commonly recognized in Rorschach interpretation, these two concepts may be considered as the "axis" from which the whole pattern of the personality is evolved. It must be acknowledged that when other concepts are introduced in an interpretation, they are not based entirely on the relationship between those two primary inferences. However, the analysis of clues in the Rorschach protocol associated with other concepts than intellectual functioning or control is strongly influenced by the conclusions about these two concepts.

Although the therapists used the same general framework of concepts as adopted by the Rorschach interpreters, there was no direct evidence as to which particular concepts within this framework were central in each therapist's thinking. Since the therapy dealt principally with emotional relationships and with the analysis of emotional reactions, one might expect that the concepts concerned with this area of the personality determined the therapist's orientation. Thus, in considering a patient's personality as observed during therapy, the therapist might be inclined to give weight only to such intellectual functioning as was directly related to the patient's emotional life.

Although the Rorschach interpreter and the therapist may have had different concepts and clues in mind as they analyzed their respective observations of the patient's reactions, they were both attempting to infer a total picture of the individual's functioning, i.e., his personality structure. Each set of judges used their particular clues and concepts consistently and reliably when considering their respective data. The two sets of judges did not agree significantly on the concepts which were not central to their separate considerations, especially when these concepts were isolated from the context of the whole structural pattern—as was required on the check list. On the other hand, when the total picture of the individual was taken into consideration, agreement between the therapists and the Rorschach interpreter was obtained, as was demonstrated in the matching experiment.

V. The Relationship Between the Two Approaches

We return to the hypothesis which assumed that validity of (or agree-ments on) specific statements is more likely to be found when the whole de-scriptive report is validated. Bearing in mind that of the twenty-eight whole reports in this study, only eleven were satisfactorily matched or validated, then little or no validity could be expected throughout the check list *for the entire sample*. On the other hand, more agreement would be expected on the check list items for those eleven cases on whom there was also agree-ment on the whole reports. In order to test this hypothesis, the sample was divided into two groups, based on the results of the matching experiments, i.e., the eleven cases correctly matched, and the seventeen cases in which matching was unsuccessful.

As one test of the hypothesis, the significance of the agreements between the Rorschach and criterion judges was calculated separately for these two groups on each item of the check list. This division yielded no significant agreement for any one of the items for either group, whether considering the first choices separately or the combined choices. These results were not surprising, considering the results of the validation of these items for the sample as a whole. In addition, a positive agreement significantly above chance was contraindicated because of the small number of cases in each of the two groups.

A preliminary analysis of the data indicated that the obtained agree-ments on the check list for the eleven matched cases were consistently greater than those for the other seventeen cases, although not enough to be statis-tically significant. This possible difference was again tested by contrasting the obtained agreements and disagreements for both groups on fourfold chi-square tables. Since the number of agreements on first choices was too small to permit this comparison for any item, a chi-square test was made on the first and second choices combined. No significant results were obtained on the whole. Only eleven of the 136 comparisons attained significance be-yond the 10 per cent level of confidence. Five of these chi-squares indicated a difference in the expected directions, i.e., the correctly matched group had more agreements but six were in the opposite direction, i.e., the group not correctly matched possessed greater agreement on the check list item in question than did the cases correctly matched. There was no indication that these results were associated with any particular pair of judges or with any definite area of content of the items.

The absence of *any* significant degree of difference between these two groups of cases indicates that the agreement between the Rorschach and therapy judges on the specific items had no relation to their agreement on the whole reports. The lack of significant agreement between the Rorschach judges and the therapists on the check list, for the whole sample, therefore, cannot be attributed to the presence of any group of cases in the sample which were not validly interpreted as whole reports.

VI. Summary

A. THE CHECK LIST APPROACH

The check list approach was employed in this study for two purposes: (*a*) to study the possibilities of validating a projective technique on a set of isolated interpretative statements, and (*b*) to determine whether the behavior of the individual on the test and in a life situation could be described by the same statement. The results of validating an accepted projective technique, the Rorschach, on this check list indicate that this approach is not applicable to the validation of such projective techniques. In view of the fact that both the Rorschach interpreters and the therapists used this check list reliably when describing their respective observations, the main conclusion is that the check list approach may be applicable to the study of personality descriptions only when a common set of concepts is maintained as a reference point for inferring the total pattern of the individual's functioning.

In general, these findings support the contentions of Vernon (19), Frank (3), and other investigators who have argued that a description of the interrelated functioning of an individual can be validated only as a whole. In particular, it has been demonstrated that a total and integrated picture of the individual's personality may be valid, even though there may be no more than chance agreement between the judgments of a test interpreter and a criterion in regard to isolated statements about the individual's functioning.

This check list approach was a more rigid and exacting test of the validity of separate interpretative statements than the "item analysis" design employed by Harrison (4) and by Cronbach (2). In the first place, neither of these investigators attempted to test whether the behavior of the individual in both the test situation and in the life situation could be described by a common set of statements. Secondly, in this check list approach, the isolated statements were selected according to a definite rationale, i.e., the scheme of "area" and "dimensions" of personality.

The results of the present study indicate that the behavior of the individual in both the test situation and a life situation could not be satisfactorily described by the same statement. Since the "item analysis" method does not make this demand on the test, it is probably a sounder approach. However, in the use of an "item analysis" approach it is recommended that the rationale for selecting statements from the whole reports be clearly stated.

B. THE MATCHING APPROACH

The chief advantage of the matching approach, according to Vernon (18), is that for whole interpretative reports, this approach tests the validity of the most essential features of the interpretation of projective techniques, i.e., the accuracy with which the *interrelated pattern* of the individual's functioning is described. The findings of the present study support Vernon's contention. By means of the matching approach, validity was demonstrated for descriptions of personality which emphasized these interrelationships. On the other hand, no validity was obtained when isolated interpretative statements were applied in which the relationships between various functionings of the personality were not elaborated.

One of the major concerns in the present study of the matching approach was the effect of the heterogeneity of the matching groups. This study indicated that use of matching groups of an "optimum" heterogeneity resulted in a smaller number of successful matchings than were obtained in previous studies using randomly selected groups. Since the matching approach is essentially a test of *interindividual* differentiation, careful attention must be paid to the nature of the sample of individuals from whom a particular individual is to be differentiated.

The chief criticism directed against the matching approach has been that it does not provide a test of the accuracy with which various part-functionings within this whole pattern are delineated. The present study attempted, without success, to test this *intra-individual* differentiation of an interpretation, by means of the check list approach. Since the completion of the present study, an "item analysis" design has been suggested by Cronbach (2) which, if used in conjunction with a matching approach, may provide a thorough statistical method for the validation of projective techniques.

REFERENCES

1. CHAPMAN, D. W. The statistics of correct matching. *Amer. J. Psychol.*, 1934, *46*, 287–298.

2. CRONBACH, L. J. A validation design for qualitative studies of personality. *J. Consult. Psychol.*, 1948, *12*, 365–375.

3. FRANK, L. K. Projective methods for the study of personality. *J. Psychol.*, 1939, *8*, 398–413.

4. HARRISON, R. Studies in the use and validity of the TAT with mentally disordered patients. II. A quantitative validity study by the method of blind analysis. *Character & Pers.*, 1940, *9*, 122–138.

5. HERTZ, MARGUERITE R. The validity of the Rorschach method. *Amer. J. Orthopsychiat.*, 1941, *11*, 512–520.

6. HERTZ, MARGUERITE R. Rorschach: twenty years after. *Psychol. Bull.*, 1942, *39*, 529–572.

7. HERTZ, MARGUERITE R. The Rorschach method: Science or mystery? *J. Consult. Psychol.*, 1943, *7*, 67–79.

8. HERTZ, MARGUERITE R., AND RUBENSTEIN, B. A comparison of three blind Rorschach analyses. *Amer. J. Orthopsychiat.*, 1939, *9*, 295–315.

9. HUNTER, M. E. The practical value of the Rorschach test in a psychological clinic. *Amer. J. Orthopsychiat.*, 1939, *9*, 278–294.

10. KLOPFER, B., AND KELLEY, D. M. *The Rorschach technique.* New York: World Book Co., 1942.

11. KRUGMAN, JUDITH I. A clinical validation of the Rorschach with problem children. *Rorschach Res. Exch.*, 1942, *5*, 61–70.

12. MACFARLANE, JEAN W. Problems of validation inherent in projective methods. *Amer. J. Orthopsychiat.*, 1942, *12*, 405–410.

13. MURRAY, H. A., AND ASSOCIATES. *Explorations in personality: A clinical and experimental study of fifty men of college age.* New York: Oxford Univ. Press, 1938.

14. PEARSON, K. *Tables for statisticians and biometricians.* Cambridge, Eng.: Cambridge Univ. Press, 1914.

15. ROSENZWEIG, S. An outline of a cooperative project for validating the Rorschach test. *Amer. J. Orthopsychiat.*, 1935, *5*, 395–403.

16. SYMONDS, P. M., & KRUGMAN, M. Projective methods in the study of personality. *Rev. Educ. Res.*, 1944, *14*, 81–93.

17. TOMKINS, S. S. *The Thematic Apperception Test.* New York: Grune and Stratton, 1947.

18. VERNON, P. E. The significance of the Rorschach test. *Brit. J. Med. Psychol.*, 1935, *15*, 199–217.

19. VERNON, P. E. Matching methods as applied to the investigation of personality. *Psychol. Bull.*, 1936, *33*, 149–177.

Lee J. Cronbach
Paul E. Meehl[1]

CONSTRUCT VALIDITY IN

PSYCHOLOGICAL TESTS

VALIDATION OF psychological tests has not yet been adequately conceptualized, as the APA Committee on Psychological Tests learned when it undertook (1950–54) to
specify what qualities should be investigated before a test
is published. In order to make coherent recommendations
the Committee found it necessary to distinguish four types of validity, established by different types of research and requiring different interpretation. The chief innovation in the Committee's report was the term *construct
validity*.[2] This idea was first formulated by a subcommittee (Meehl and
R. C. Challman) studying how proposed recommendations would apply to
projective techniques, and later modified and clarified by the entire Committee (Bordin, Challman, Conrad, Humphreys, Super, and the present
writers). The statements agreed upon by the Committee (and by committees

Reprinted from *Psychol. Bull.*. 1955, *52*, 281–302, by permission of the American Psychological Association and the authors.

1. The second author worked on this problem in connection with his appointment to
the Minnesota Center for Philosophy of Science. We are indebted to the other members of
the Center (Herbert Feigl, Michael Scriven, Wilfrid Sellers), and to D. L. Thistlethwaite of
the University of Illinois, for their major contributions to our thinking and their suggestions for improving this paper.

2. Referred to in a preliminary report (58) as *congruent validity*.

of two other associations) were published in the *Technical Recommenda-tions* (59). The present interpretation of construct validity is not "official" and deals with some areas where the Committee would probably not be unanimous. The present writers are solely responsible for this attempt to explain the concept and elaborate its implications.

Identification of construct validity was not an isolated development. Writers on validity during the preceding decade had shown a great deal of dissatisfaction with conventional notions of validity, and introduced new terms and ideas, but the resulting aggregation of types of validity seems only to have stirred the muddy waters. Portions of the distinctions we shall discuss are implicit in Jenkins' paper, "Validity for what?" (33), Gulliksen's "Intrinsic validity" (27), Goodenough's distinction between tests as "signs" and "samples" (22), Cronbach's separation of "logical" and "empirical" validity (11), Guilford's "factorial validity" (25), and Mosier's papers on "face validity" and "validity generalization" (49, 50). Helen Peak (52) comes close to an explicit statement of construct validity as we shall present it.

Four Types of Validation

The categories into which the *Recommendations* divide validity studies are: predictive validity, concurrent validity, content validity, and construct validity. The first two of these may be considered together as *criterion-oriented* validation procedures.

The pattern of a criterion-oriented study is familiar. The investigator is primarily interested in some criterion which he wishes to predict. He administers the test, obtains an independent criterion measure on the same subjects, and computes a correlation. If the criterion is obtained some time after the test is given, he is studying *predictive validity*. If the test score and criterion score are determined at essentially the same time, he is studying *concurrent validity*. Concurrent validity is studied when one test is proposed as a substitute for another (for example, when a multiple-choice form of spelling test is substituted for taking dictation), or a test is shown to correlate with some contemporary criterion (e.g., psychiatric diagnosis).

Content validity is established by showing that the test items are a sample of a universe in which the investigator is interested. Content validity is ordinarily to be established deductively, by defining a universe of items and sampling systematically within this universe to establish the test.

Construct validation is involved whenever a test is to be interpreted as a measure of some attribute or quality which is not "operationally defined." The problem faced by the investigator is, "What constructs account for variance in test performance?" Construct validity calls for no new scientific approach. Much current research on tests of personality (9) is construct validation, usually without the benefit of a clear formulation of this process.

Construct validity is not to be identified solely by particular investigative procedures, but by the orientation of the investigator. Criterion-oriented validity, as Bechtoldt emphasizes (3, p. 1245), "involves the *acceptance* of a set of operations as an adequate definition of whatever is to be measured." When an investigator believes that no criterion available to him is fully valid, he perforce becomes interested in construct validity because this is the only way to avoid the "infinite frustration" of relating every criterion to some more ultimate standard (21). In content validation, *acceptance* of the universe of content as defining the variable to be measured is essential. Construct validity must be investigated whenever no criterion or universe of content is accepted as entirely adequate to define the quality to be measured. Determining what psychological constructs account for test performance is desirable for almost any test. Thus, although the MMPI was originally established on the basis of empirical discrimination between patient groups and so-called normals (concurrent validity), continuing research has tried to provide a basis for describing the personality associated with each score pattern. Such interpretations permit the clinician to predict performance with respect to criteria which have not yet been employed in empirical validation studies (cf. 46, pp. 49–50, 110–111).

We can distinguish among the four types of validity by noting that each involves a different emphasis on the criterion. In predictive or concurrent validity, the criterion behavior is of concern to the tester, and he may have no concern whatsoever with the type of behavior exhibited in the test. (An employer does not care if a worker can manipulate blocks, but the score on the block test may predict something he cares about.) Content validity is studied when the tester *is* concerned with the type of behavior involved in the test performance. Indeed, if the test is a work sample, the behavior represented in the test may be an end in itself. Construct validity is ordinarily studied when the tester has no definite criterion measure of the quality with which he is concerned, and must use indirect measures. Here the trait or quality underlying the test is of central importance, rather than either the test behavior or the scores on the criteria (59, p. 14).

Construct validation is important at times for every sort of psychological test: aptitude, achievement, interests, and so on. Thurstone's statement is interesting in this connection:

In the field of intelligence tests, it used to be common to define validity as the correlation between a test score and some outside criterion. We have reached a stage of sophistication where the test-criterion correlation is too coarse. It is obsolete. If we attempted to ascertain the validity of a test for the second space-factor, for example, we would have to get judges [to] make reliable judgments about people as to this factor. Ordinarily their [the available judges'] ratings would be of no value as a criterion. Consequently, validity studies in the cognitive functions now depend on criteria of internal consistency . . . (60, p. 3).

Construct validity would be involved in answering such questions as: To what extent is this test of intelligence culture-free? Does this test of "interpretation of data" measure reading ability, quantitative reasoning, or response sets? How does a person with A in Strong Accountant, and B in Strong CPA, differ from a person who has these scores reversed?

Example of construct validation procedure. Suppose measure X correlates .50 with Y, the amount of palmar sweating induced when we tell a student that he has failed a Psychology I exam. Predictive validity of X for Y is adequately described by the coefficient, and a statement of the experimental and sampling conditions. If someone were to ask, "Isn't there perhaps another way to interpret this correlation?" or "What other kinds of evidence can you bring to support your interpretation?" we would hardly understand what he was asking because no interpretation has been made. These questions become relevant when the correlation is advanced as evidence that "test X measures anxiety proneness." Alternative interpretations are possible; e.g., perhaps the test measures "academic aspiration," in which case we will expect different results if we induce palmar sweating by economic threat. It is then reasonable to inquire about other *kinds* of evidence.

Add these facts from further studies: Test X correlates .45 with fraternity brothers' ratings on "tenseness." Test X correlates .55 with amount of intellectual inefficiency induced by painful electric shock, and .68 with the Taylor Anxiety scale. Mean X score decreases among four diagnosed groups in this order: anxiety state, reactive depression, "normal," and psychopathic personality. And palmar sweat under threat of failure in Psychology I correlates .60 with threat of failure in mathematics. Negative results eliminate competing explanations of the X score; thus, findings of negligible correlations between X and social class, vocational aim, and value-orientation make it fairly safe to reject the suggestion that X measures "academic aspiration." We can have substantial confidence that X does measure anxiety proneness if the current theory of anxiety can embrace the variates which yield positive correlations, and does not predict correlations where we found none.

Kinds of Constructs

At this point we should indicate summarily what we mean by a construct, recognizing that much of the remainder of the paper deals with this question. A construct is some postulated attribute of people, assumed to be reflected in test performance. In test validation the attribute about which we make statements in interpreting a test is a construct. We expect a person at any time to possess or not possess a qualitative attribute (amnesia) or structure, or to possess some degree of a quantitative attribute (cheerfulness). A construct has certain associated meanings carried in statements of this general character: Persons who possess this attribute will, in situation X, act in manner Y (with a stated probability). The logic of construct validation is invoked whether the construct is highly systematized or loose, used in ramified theory or a few simple propositions, used in absolute propositions or probability statements. We seek to specify how one is to defend a proposed interpretation of a test; *we are not recommending any one type of interpretation.*

The constructs in which tests are to be interpreted are certainly not likely to be physiological. Most often they will be traits such as "latent hostility" or "variable in mood," or descriptions in terms of an educational objective, as "ability to plan experiments." For the benefit of readers who may have been influenced by certain eisegeses of MacCorquodale and Meehl (40), let us here emphasize: Whether or not an interpretation of a test's properties or relations involves questions of construct validity is to be decided by examining the entire body of evidence offered, together with what is asserted about the test in the context of this evidence. Proposed identifications of constructs allegedly measured by the test with constructs of other sciences (e.g., genetics, neuroanatomy; biochemistry) make up only *one* class of construct-validity claims, and a rather minor one at present. Space does not permit full analysis of the relation of the present paper to the MacCorquodale-Meehl distinction between hypothetical constructs and intervening variables. The philosophy of science pertinent to the present paper is set forth later in the section entitled, "The nomological network."

The Relation of Constructs to "Criteria"

CRITICAL VIEW OF THE CRITERION IMPLIED

An unquestionable criterion may be found in a practical operation, or may be established as a consequence of an operational definition. Typically, however, the psychologist is unwilling to use the directly operational approach because he is interested in building theory about a generalized construct. A theorist trying to relate behavior to "hunger" almost certainly invests that term with meanings other than the operation "elapsed-time-since-feeding." If he is concerned with hunger as a tissue need, he will not accept time lapse as *equivalent* to his construct because it fails to consider, among other things, energy expenditure of the animal.

In some situations the criterion is no more valid than the test. Suppose, for example, that we want to know if counting the dots on Bender-Gestalt figure five indicates "compulsive rigidity," and take psychiatric ratings on this trait as a criterion. Even a conventional report on the resulting correlation will say something about the extent and intensity of the psychiatrist's contacts and should describe his qualifications (e.g., diplomate status? analyzed?).

Why report these facts? Because data are needed to indicate whether the criterion is any good. "Compulsive rigidity" is not really intended to mean "social stimulus value to psychiatrists." The implied trait involves a range of behavior-dispositions which may be very imperfectly sampled by the psychiatrist. Suppose dot-counting does not occur in a particular patient and yet we find that the psychiatrist has rated him as "rigid." When questioned the psychiatrist tells us that the patient was a rather easy, free-wheeling sort; however, the patient *did* lean over to straighten out a skewed desk blotter, and this, viewed against certain other facts, tipped the scale in favor of a "rigid" rating. On the face of it, counting Bender dots may be just as good (or poor) a sample of the compulsive-rigidity domain as straigtening desk blotters is.

Suppose, to extend our example, we have four tests on the "predictor" side, over against the psychiatrist's "criterion," and find generally positive correlations among the five variables. Surely it is artificial and arbitrary to impose the "test-should-predict-criterion" pattern on such data. The psychiatrist samples verbal content, expressive pattern, voice, posture, etc. The psychologist samples verbal content, perception, expressive pattern, etc. Our proper conclusion is that, from this evidence, the four tests and the psychiatrist all assess some common factor.

The asymmetry between the "test" and the so-designated "criterion" arises only because the terminology of predictive validity has become a commonplace in test analysis. In this study where a construct is the central concern, any distinction between the merit of the test and criterion variables would be justified only if it had already been shown that the psychiatrist's theory and operations were excellent measures of the attribute.

Inadequacy of Validation in Terms of Specific Criteria

The proposal to validate constructural interpretations of tests runs counter to suggestions of some others. Spiker and McCandless (57) favor an operational approach. Validation is replaced by compiling statements as to how strongly the test predicts other observed variables of interest. To avoid requiring that each new variable be investigated completely by itself, they allow two variables to collapse into one whenever the properties of the operationally defined measures are the same: "If a new test is demonstrated to predict the scores on an older, well-established test, then an evaluation of the predictive power of the older test may be used for the new one." But accurate inferences are possible only if the two tests correlate so highly that there is negligible reliable variance in either test, independent of the other. Where the correspondence is less close, one must either retain all the separate variables operationally defined or embark on construct validation.

The practical user of tests must rely on constructs of some generality to make predictions about new situations. Test *X* could be used to predict palmar sweating in the face of failure without invoking any construct, but a counselor is more likely to be asked to forecast behavior in diverse or even unique situations for which the correlation of test *X* is unknown. Significant predictions rely on knowledge accumulated around the generalized construct of anxiety. The *Technical Recommendations* state:

> It is ordinarily necessary to evaluate construct validity by integrating evidence from many different sources. The problem of construct validation becomes especially acute in the clinical field since for many of the constructs dealt with it is not a question of finding an imperfect criterion but of finding any criterion at all. The psychologist interested in construct validity for clinical devices is concerned with making an estimate of a hypothetical internal process, factor, system, structure, or state and cannot expect to find a clear unitary behavioral criterion. An attempt to identify any one criterion measure or any composite as *the* criterion aimed at is, however, usually unwarranted (59, p. 14–15).

This appears to conflict with arguments for specific criteria prominent at places in the testing literature. Thus Anastasi (2) makes many statements of the latter character: "It is only as a measure of a specifically defined criterion that a test can be objectively validated at all. . . . To claim that a test measures anything over and above its criterion is pure speculation" (p. 67). Yet elsewhere this article supports construct validation. Tests can be profitably interpreted if we "know the relationships between the tested behavior . . . and other behavior samples, none of these behavior samples necessarily occupying the preeminent position of a criterion" (p. 75). Factor analysis with several partial criteria might be used to study whether a test measures a postulated "general learning ability." If the data demonstrate specificity of ability instead, such specificity is "useful in its own right in advancing our knowledge of behavior; it should not be construed as a weakness of the tests" (p. 75).

We depart from Anastasi at two points. She writes, "The validity of a psychological test should not be confused with an analysis of the factors which determine the behavior under consideration." We, however, regard such analysis as a most important type of validation. Second, she refers to "the will-o'-the-wisp of psychological processes which are distinct from performance" (2, p. 77). While we agree that psychological processes are elusive, we are sympathetic to attempts to formulate and clarify constructs which are evidenced by performance but distinct from it. Surely an inductive inference based on a pattern of correlations cannot be dismissed as "pure speculation."

SPECIFIC CRITERIA USED TEMPORARILY:
THE "BOOTSTRAPS" EFFECT

Even when a test is constructed on the basis of a specific criterion, it may ultimately be judged to have greater construct validity than the criterion. We start with a vague concept which we associate with certain observations. We then discover empirically that these observations covary with some other observation which possesses greater reliability or is more intimately correlated with relevant experimental changes than is the original measure, or both. For example, the notion of temperature arises because some objects feel hotter to the touch than others. The expansion of a mercury column does not have face validity as an index of hotness. But it turns out that (a) there is a statistical relation between expansion and sensed temperature; (b) observers employ the mercury method with good interobserver agreement; (c) the regularity of observed relations is increased by using the thermometer (e.g., melting points of samples of the same materials vary little on the thermometer; we obtain nearly linear relations between mercury measures and pressure of a gas). Finally, (d) a theoretical structure involving unobservable microevents—the kinetic theory—is worked out which explains the relation of mercury expansion to heat. This whole process of conceptual enrichment begins with what in retrospect we see as an extremely fallible "criterion"—the human temperature sense. That original criterion has now been relegated to a peripheral position. We have lifted ourselves by our bootstraps, but in a legitimate and fruitful way.

Similarly, the Binet scale was first valued because children's scores tended to agree with judgments by schoolteachers. If it had not shown this agreement, it would have been discarded along with reaction time and the other measures of ability previously tried. Teacher judgments once constituted the criterion against which the individual intelligence test was validated. But if today a child's IQ is 135 and three of his teachers complain about how stupid he is, we do not conclude that the test has failed. Quite to the contrary, if no error in test procedure can be argued, we treat the test score as a valid statement about an important quality, and define our task as that of finding out what other variables—personality, study skills, etc.—modify achievement or distort teacher judgment.

Experimentation to Investigate Construct Validity

VALIDATION PROCEDURES

We can use many methods in construct validation. Attention should particularly be drawn to Macfarlane's survey of these methods as they apply to projective devices (41).

Group differences. If our understanding of a construct leads us to expect two groups to differ on the test, this expectation may be tested directly. Thus Thurstone and Chave validated the Scale for Measuring Attitude Toward the Church by showing score differences between church members and nonchurchgoers. Churchgoing is not *the* criterion of attitude, for the purpose of the test is to measure something other than the crude sociological fact of church attendance; on the other hand, failure to find a difference would have seriously challenged the test.

Only coarse correspondence between test and group designation is expected. Too great a correspondence between the two would indicate that the test is to some degree invalid, because members of the groups are expected to overlap on the test. Intelligence test items are selected initially on the basis of a corerspondence to age, but an item that correlates .95 with age in an elementary school sample would surely be suspect.

Correlation matrices and factor analysis. If two tests are presumed to measure the same construct, a correlation between them is predicted. (An exception is noted where some second attribute has positive loading in the first test and negative loading in the second test; then a low correlation is expected. This is a testable interpretation provided an external measure of either the first or the second variable exists.) If the obtained correlation departs from the expectation, however, there is no way to know whether the fault lies in test A, test B, or the formulation of the construct. A matrix of intercorrelations often points out profitable ways of dividing the construct into more meaningful parts, factor analysis being a useful computational method in such studies.

Guilford (26) has discussed the place of factor analysis in construct validation. His statements may be extracted as follows:

"The personnel psychologist wishes to know 'why his tests are valid.' He can place tests and practical criteria in a matrix and factor it to identify 'real dimensions of human personality.' A factorial description is exact and stable; it is economical in explanation; it leads to the creation of pure tests which can be combined to predict complex behaviors." It is clear that factors here function as constructs. Eysenck, in his "criterion analysis" (18), goes farther than Guilford, and shows that factoring can be used explicitly to test hypotheses about constructs.

Factors may or may not be weighted with surplus meaning. Certainly when they are regarded as "real dimensions" a great deal of surplus meaning is implied, and the interpreter must shoulder a substantial burden of proof. The alternative view is to regard factors as defining a working reference frame, located in a convenient manner in the "space" defined by all behaviors of a given type. Which set of factors from a given matrix is "most useful" will depend partly on predilections, but in essence the best construct is the one around which we can build the greatest number of inferences, in the most direct fashion.

Studies of internal structure. For many constructs, evidence of homogeneity within the test is relevant in judging validity. If a trait such as *dominance* is hypothesized, and the items inquire about behaviors subsumed under this label, then the hypothesis appears to require that these items be generally intercorrelated. Even low correlations, if consistent, would support the argument that people may be fruitfully described in terms of a generalized tendency to dominate or not dominate. The general quality would have power to predict behavior in a variety of situations represented by the specific items. Item-test correlations and certain reliability formulas describe internal consistency.

It is unwise to list uninterpreted data of this sort under the heading "validity" in test manuals, as some authors have done. High internal consistency may *lower* validity. Only if the underlying theory of the trait being measured calls for high item intercorrelations do the correlations support construct validity. Negative item-test correlations may support construct validity, provided that the items with negative correlations are believed irrelevant to the postulated construct and serve as suppressor variables (31, pp. 431–436; 44).

Study of distinctive subgroups of items within a test may set an upper limit to construct validity by showing that irrelevant elements influence scores. Thus a study of the PMA space tests shows that variance can be partially accounted for by a response set, tendency to mark many figures as similar (12). An internal factor analysis of the PEA Interpretation of Data Test shows that in addition to measuring reasoning skills, the test score is strongly influenced by a tendency to say "probably true" rather than "certainly true," regardless of item content (17). On the other hand, a study of item groupings in the DAT Mechanical Comprehension Test permitted rejection of the hypothesis that knowledge about specific topics such as gears made a substantial contribution to scores (13).

Studies of changeover occasions. The stability of test scores ("retest reliability," Cattell's "N-technique") may be relevant to construct validation. Whether a high degree of stability is encouraging or discouraging for the proposed interpretation depends upon the theory defining the construct.

More powerful than the retest after uncontrolled intervening experiences is the retest with experimental intervention. If a transient influence swings test scores over a wide range, there are definite limits on the extent to which a test result can be interpreted as reflecting the typical behavior of the individual. These are examples of experiments which have indicated upper limits to test validity: studies of differences associated with the examiner in projective testing, of change of score under alternative directions ("tell the truth" vs. "make yourself look good to an employer"), and of coachability of mental tests. We may recall Gulliksen's distinction (27): When the coaching is of a sort that improves the pupil's intellectual functioning in school, the test which is affected by the coaching has validity as a measure of intellectual functioning; if the coaching improves test-taking but not school performance, the test which responds to the coaching has poor validity as a measure of this construct.

Sometimes, where differences between individuals are difficult to assess by any means other than the test, the experimenter validates by determining whether the test can detect induced intra-individual differences. One might hypothesize that the Zeigarnik effect is a measure of ego involvement, i.e., that with ego involvement there is more recall of incomplete tasks. To support such an interpretation, the investigator will try to induce ego involvement on some task by appropriate directions and compare subjects' recall with their recall for tasks where there was a contrary induction. Sometimes the intervention is drastic. Porteus finds (53) that brain-operated patients show disruption of performance on his maze, but do not show impaired performance on conventional verbal tests and argues therefrom that his test is a better measure of planfulness.

Studies of process. One of the best ways of determining informally what accounts for variability on a test is the observation of the person's process of performance. If it is supposed, for example, that a test measures mathematical competence, and yet observation of students' errors shows that erroneous reading of the question is common, the implications of a low score are altered. Lucas in this way showed that the Navy Relative Movement Test, an aptitude test, actually involved two different abilities: spatial visualization and mathematical reasoning (39).

Mathematical analysis of scoring procedures may provide important negative evidence on construct validity. A recent analysis of "empathy" tests is perhaps worth citing (14). "Empathy" has been operationally defined in many studies by the ability of a judge to predict what responses will be given on some questionnaire by a subject he has observed briefly. A mathematical argument has shown, however, that the scores depend on several attributes of the judge which enter into his perception of *any* individual, and that they therefore cannot be interpreted as evidence of his ability to interpret cues offered by particular others, or his intuition.

THE NUMERICAL ESTIMATE OF

CONSTRUCT VALIDITY

There is an understandable tendency to seek a "construct validity coefficient." A numerical statement of the degree of construct validity would be a statement of the proportion of the test score variance that is attributable to the construct variable. This numerical estimate can sometimes be arrived at by a factor analysis, but since present methods of factor analysis are based on linear relations, more general methods will ultimately be needed to deal with many quantitative problems of construct validation.

Rarely will it be possible to estimate definite "construct saturations," because no factor corresponding closely to the construct will be available. One can only hope to set upper and lower bounds to the "loading." If "creativity" is defined as something independent of knowledge, then a correlation of .40 between a presumed test of creativity and a test of arithmetic knowledge would indicate that at least 16 per cent of the reliable test variance is irrelevant to creativity as defined. Laboratory performance on problems such as Maier's "hatrack" would scarcely be an ideal measure of creativity, but it would be somewhat relevant. If its correlation with the test is .60, this permits a tentative estimate of 36 per cent as a lower bound. (The estimate is tentative because the test might overlap with the irrelevant portion of the laboratory measure.) The saturation seems to lie between 36 and 84 per cent; a cumulation of studies would provide better limits.

It should be particularly noted that rejecting the null hypothesis does not finish the job of construct validation (35, p. 284). The problem is not to conclude that the test "is valid" for measuring the construct variable. The task is to state as definitely as possible the degree of validity the test is presumed to have.

The Logic of Construct Validation

Construct validation takes place when an investigator believes that his instrument reflects a particular construct, to which are attached certain meanings. The proposed interpretation generates specific testable hypotheses, which are a means of confirming or disconfirming the claim. The philosophy of science which we believe does most justice to actual scientific practice will now be briefly and dogmatically set forth. Readers interested in further study of the philosophical underpinning are referred to the works by Braithwaite (6, especially Chapter III), Carnap (7; 8, pp. 56–69), Pap (51), Sellars (55, 56), Feigl (19, 20), Beck (4), Kneale (37, pp. 92–110), Hempel (29; 30, Sec. 7).

THE NOMOLOGICAL NET

The fundamental principles are these:

1. Scientifically speaking, to "make clear what something *is*" means to set forth the laws in which it occurs. We shall refer to the interlocking system of laws which constitute a theory as a *nomological network*.

2. The laws in a nomological network may relate (*a*) observable properties or quantities to each other; or (*b*) theoretical constructs to observables; or (*c*) different theoretical constructs to one another. These "laws" may be statistical or deterministic.

3. A necessary condition for a construct to be scientifically admissible is that it occur in a nomological net, at least *some* of whose laws involve observables. Admissible constructs may be remote from observation, i.e., a long derivation may intervene between the nomologicals which implicitly define the construct, and the (derived) nomologicals of type *a*. These latter propositions permit predictions about events. The construct is not "reduced" to the observations, but only combined with other constructs in the net to make predictions about observables.

4. "Learning more about" a theoretical construct is a matter of elaborating the nomological network in which it occurs, or of increasing the definiteness of the components. At least in the early history of a construct the network will be limited, and the construct will as yet have few connections.

5. An enrichment of the net such as adding a construct or a relation to theory is justified if it generates nomologicals that are confirmed by observation or if it reduces the number of nomologicals required to predict the same observations. When observations will not fit into the network as it

stands, the scientist has a certain freedom in selecting where to modify the network. That is, there may be alternative constructs or ways of organizing the net which for the time being are equally defensible.

6. We can say that "operations" which are qualitatively very different "overlap" or "measure the same thing" if their positions in the nomological net tie them to the same construct variable. Our confidence in this identification depends upon the amount of inductive support we have for the regions of the net involved. It is not necessary that a direct observational comparison of the two operations be made—we may be content with an intranetwork proof indicating that the two operations yield estimates of the same network-defined quantity. Thus, physicists are content to speak of the "temperature" of the sun and the "temperature" of a gas at room temperature even though the test operations are nonoverlapping because this identification makes theoretical sense.

With these statements of scientific methodology in mind, we return to the specific problem of construct validity as applied to psychological tests. The preceding guide rules should reassure the "toughminded," who fear that allowing construct validation opens the door to nonconfirmable test claims. *The answer is that unless the network makes contact with observations, and exhibits explicit, public steps of inference, construct validation cannot be claimed.* An admissible psychological construct must be behavior-relevant (59, p. 15). For most tests intended to measure constructs, adequate criteria do not exist. This being the case, many such tests have been left unvalidated, or a finespun network of rationalizations has been offered as if it were validation. Rationalization is not construct validation. One who claims that his test reflects a construct cannot maintain his claim in the face of recurrent negative results because these results show that his construct is too loosely defined to yield verifiable inferences.

A rigorous (though perhaps probabilistic) chain of inference is required to establish a test as a measure of a construct. To validate a claim that a test measures a construct, a nomological net surrounding the concept must exist. When a construct is fairly new, there may be few specifiable associations by which to pin down the concept. As research proceeds, the construct sends out roots in many directions, which attach it to more and more facts or other constructs. Thus the electron has more accepted properties than the neutrino; *numerical ability* has more than *the second space factor*.

"Acceptance," which was critical in criterion-oriented and content validities, has now appeared in construct validity. Unless substantially the same nomological net is accepted by the several users of the construct, public validation is impossible. If A uses *aggressiveness* to mean overt assault on others, and B's usage includes repressed hostile reactions, evidence which convinces B that a test measures *aggressiveness* convinces A that the test does not. Hence, the investigator who proposes to establish a test as a measure of a construct must specify his network or theory sufficiently clearly that others can accept or reject it (cf. 41, p. 406). A consumer of the test who rejects the author's theory cannot accept the author's validation. He must validate the test for himself, if he wishes to show that it represents the construct as *he* defines it.

Two general qualifications are in order with reference to the methodological principles 1–6 set forth at the beginning of this section. Both of them concern the amount of "theory," in any high-level sense of that word, which enters into a construct-defining network of laws or lawlike statements. We do not wish to convey the impression that one always has a very elaborate theoretical network, rich in hypothetical processes or entities.

Constructs as inductive summaries. In the early stages of development of a construct or even at more advanced stages when our orientation is thoroughly practical, little or no theory in the usual sense of the word need be involved. In the extreme case the hypothesized laws are formulated entirely in terms of descriptive (observational) dimensions although not all of the relevant observations have actually been made.

The hypothesized network "goes beyond the data" only in the limited sense that it purports to *characterize* the behavior facets which belong to an observable but as yet only partially sampled cluster; hence, it generates predictions about hitherto unsampled regions of the phenotypic space. Even though no unobservables or high-order theoretical constructs are introduced, an element of inductive extrapolation appears in the claim that a cluster including some elements not-yet-observed has been identified. Since, as in any sorting or abstracting task involving a finite set of complex elements, several nonequivalent bases of categorization are available, the investigator may choose a hypothesis which generates erroneous predictions. The failure of a supposed, hitherto untried, member of the cluster to behave in the manner said to be characteristic of the group, or the finding that a nonmember of the postulated cluster does behave in this manner, may modify greatly our tentative construct.

For example, one might build an intelligence test on the basis of his background notions of "intellect," including vocabulary, arithmetic calculation, general information, similarities, two-point threshold, reaction time, and line bisection as subtests. The first four of these correlate, and he extracts a huge first factor. This becomes a second approximation of the intelligence construct, described by its pattern of loadings on the four tests. The other three tests have negligible loading on any common factor. On this evidence the investigator reinterprets intelligence as "manipulation of words." Subsequently it is discovered that test-stupid people are rated as unable to express their ideas, are easily taken in by fallacious arguments, and misread complex directions. These data support the "linguistic" definition of intelligence and the test's claim of validity *for* that construct. But then a block design test with pantomime instructions is found to be strongly saturated with the first factor. Immediately the purely "linguistic" interpretation of Factor I becomes suspect. This finding, taken together with our initial acceptance of the others as relevant to the background concept of intelligence, forces us to reinterpret the concept once again.

If we simply *list* the tests or traits which have been shown to be saturated with the "factor" or which belong to the cluster, no construct is employed. As soon as we even *summarize the properties* of this group of indicators—we are already making some guesses. Intentional characterization of a domain is hazardous since it selects (abstracts) properties and implies that new tests sharing those properties will behave as do the known tests in the cluster, and that tests not sharing them will not.

The difficulties in merely "characterizing the surface cluster" are strikingly exhibited by the use of certain special and extreme groups for purposes of construct validation. The P_d scale of MMPI was originally derived and cross-validated upon hospitalized patients diagnosed "Psychopathic personality, asocial and amoral type" (42). Further research shows the scale to have a limited degree of predictive and concurrent validity for "delinquency" more broadly defined (5, 28). Several studies show associations between P_d and very special "criterion" groups which it would be ludicrous to identify as "*the* criterion" in the traditional sense. If one lists these heterogeneous groups and tries to characterize them intentionally, he faces enormous conceptual difficulties. For example, a recent survey of hunting accidents in Minnesota showed that hunters who had "carelessly" shot someone were significantly elevated on P_d when compared with other hunters (48). This is in line with one's theoretical expectations; when you ask MMPI "experts" to predict for such a group they invariably predict P_d or M_a or both. The finding seems therefore to lend some slight support to the construct validity of the P_d scale. But of course it would be nonsense to *define* the P_d component "operationally" in terms of, say, accident proneness. We might try to subsume the original phenotype and the hunting-accident proneness under some broader category, such as "Disposition to violate society's rules, whether legal, moral, or just *sensible*." But now we have ceased to have a neat operational criterion, and are using instead a rather vague and wide-range class. Besides, there is worse to come. We want the class specification to cover a group trend that (nondelinquent) high school students judged by their peer group as least "responsible" score over a full sigma higher on P_d

than those judged most "responsible" (23, p. 75). Most of the behaviors contributing to such sociometric choices fall well within the range of socially permissible action; the proffered criterion specification is still too restrictive. Again, any clinician familiar with MMPI lore would predict an elevated P_d on a sample of (nondelinquent) professional actors. Chyatte's confirmation of this prediction (10) tends to support *both:* (*a*) the theory sketch of "what the P_d factor is, psychologically"; and (*b*) the claim of the P_d scale to construct validity for this hypothetical factor. Let the reader try his hand at writing a brief phenotypic criterion specification that will cover both trigger-happy hunters and Broadway actors! And if he should be ingenious enough to achieve this, does his definition also encompass Hovey's report that high P_d predicts the judgments "not shy" and "unafraid of mental patients" made upon nurses by their supervisors (32, p. 143)? And then we have Gough's report that *low* P_d is associated with ratings as "good-natured" (24, p. 40), and Roessell's data showing that high P_d is predictive of "dropping out of high school" (54). The point is that all seven of these "criterion" dispositions would be readily guessed by any clinician having even superficial familiarity with MMPI interpretation; but to mediate these inferences explicitly requires quite a few hypotheses about dynamics, constituting an admittedly sketchy (but far from vacuous) network defining the genotype *psychopathic deviate.*

Vagueness of present psychological laws. This line of thought leads directly to our second important qualification upon the network schema. The idealized picture is one of a tidy set of postulates which jointly entail the desired theorems; since some of the theorems are coordinated to the observation base, the system constitutes an implicit definition of the theoretical primitives and gives them an indirect empirical meaning. In practice, of course, even the most advanced physical sciences only approximate this ideal. Questions of "categoricalness" and the like, such as logicians raise about pure calculi, are hardly even stable for empirical networks. (What, for example, would be the desiderata of a "well-formed formula" in molar behavior theory?) Psychology works with crude, half-explicit formulations. We do not worry about such advanced formal questions as "whether all molar-behavior statements are decidable by appeal to the postulates" because we know that no existing theoretical network suffices to predict even the *known* descriptive laws. Nevertheless, the sketch of a network is there; if it were not, we would not be saying *anything* intelligible about our constructs. We do not have the rigorous implicit definitions of formal calculi (which still, be it noted, usually permit of a multiplicity of interpretations). Yet the vague, avowedly incomplete network still gives the constructs whatever meaning they do have. When the network is very incomplete, having many strands missing entirely and some constructs tied in only by tenuous threads, then the "implicit definition" of these constructs is disturbingly loose; one might say that the meaning of the constructs is underdetermined. *Since the meaning of theoretical constructs is set forth by stating the laws in which they occur, our incomplete knowledge of the laws of nature produces a vagueness in our constructs* (See Hempel [30]; Kaplan [34]; Pap [51]). We will be able to say "what anxiety is" when we know all of the laws involving it; meanwhile, since we are in the process of discovering these laws, we do not yet know precisely what anxiety is.

Conclusions Regarding the Network After Experimentation

The proposition that *x* per cent of test variance is accounted for by the construct is inserted into the accepted network. The network then generates a testable prediction about the relation of the test scores to certain other variables, and the investigator gathers data. If prediction and result are in harmony, he can retain his belief that the test measures the construct. The construct is at best adopted, never demonstrated to be "correct."

We do not first "prove" the theory, and then validate the test, nor conversely. In any probable inductive type of inference from a pattern of observations, we examine the relation between the total network of theory and observations. The system involves propositions relating test to construct, construct to other constructs, and finally relating some of these constructs to observables. In ongoing research the chain of inference is very complicated. Kelly and Fiske (36, p. 124) give a complex diagram showing the numerous inferences required in validating a prediction from assessment techniques, where theories about the criterion situation are as integral a part of the prediction as are the test data. A predicted empirical relationship permits us to test all the propositions leading to that prediction. Traditionally the proposition claiming to interpret the test has been set apart as the hypothesis being tested, but actually the evidence is significant for all parts of the chain. If the prediction is not confirmed, any link in the chain may be wrong.

A theoretical network can be divided into subtheories used in making particular predictions. All the events successfully predicted through a subtheory are of course evidence in favor of that theory. Such a subtheory may be so well confirmed by voluminous and diverse evidence that we can reasonably view a particular experiment as relevant only to the test's validity. If the theory, combined with a proposed test interpretation, mispredicts in this case, it is the latter which must be abandoned. On the other hand, the accumulated evidence for a test's construct validity may be so strong that an instance of misprediction will force us to modify the subtheory employing the construct rather than deny the claim that the test measures the construct.

Most cases in psychology today lie somewhere between these extremes. Thus, suppose we fail to find a greater incidence of "homosexual signs" in the Rorschach records of paranoid patients. Which is more strongly disconfirmed—the Rorschach signs or the orthodox theory of paranoia? The negative finding shows the bridge between the two to be undependable, but this is all we can say. The bridge cannot be used unless one end is placed on solider ground. The investigator must decide which end it is best to relocate.

Numerous successful predictions dealing with phenotypically diverse "criteria" give greater weight to the claim of construct validity than do fewer predictions, or predictions involving very similar behaviors. In arriving at diverse predictions, the hypothesis of test validity is connected each time to a subnetwork largely independent of the portion previously used. Success of these derivations testifies to the inductive power of the test-validity statement, and renders it unlikely that an equally effective alternative can be offered.

IMPLICATIONS OF NEGATIVE EVIDENCE

The investigator whose prediction and data are discordant must make strategic decisions. His result can be interpreted in three ways:

1. The test does not measure the construct variable.

2. The theoretical network which generated the hypothesis is incorrect.

3. The experimental design failed to test the hypothesis properly. (Strictly speaking this may be analyzed as a special case of 2, but in practice the distinction is worth making.)

For further research. If a specific fault of procedure makes the third a reasonable possibility, his proper response is to perform an adequate study, meanwhile making no report. When faced with the other two alternatives, he may decide that his test does not measure the construct adequately. Following that decision, he will perhaps prepare and validate a new test. Any rescoring or new interpretative procedure for the original instrument, like a new test, requires validation *by means of a fresh body of data.*

The investigator may regard Interpretation 2 as more likely to lead to eventual advances. It is legitimate for the investigator to call the network defining the construct into question, if he has confidence in the test. Should the investigator decide that some step in the network is unsound, he may be able to invent an alternative network. Perhaps he modifies the network by splitting a concept into two or more portions, e.g., by designating types of *anxiety,* or perhaps he specifies added conditions under which a generalization holds. When an investigator modifies the theory in such a manner, he is now required to *gather a fresh body of data* to test the altered hypotheses. This step should normally precede publication of the modified theory. If the new data are consistent with the modified network, he is free from the fear that his nomologicals were gerrymandered to fit the peculiarities of his first sample of observations. He can now trust his test to some extent, because his test results behave as predicted.

The choice among alternatives, like any strategic decision, is a gamble as to which course of action is the best investment of effort. Is it wise to modify the theory? That depends on how well the system is confirmed by prior data, and how well the modifications fit available observations. Is it worth while to modify the test in the hope that it will fit the construct? That depends on how much evidence there is—apart from this abortive experiment—to support the hope, and also on how much it is worth to the investigator's ego to salvage the test. The choice among alternatives is a matter of research planning.

For practical use of the test. The consumer can accept a test as a measure of a construct only when there is a strong positive fit between predictions and subsequent data. When the evidence from a proper investigation of a published test is essentially negative, it should be reported as a stop sign to discourage use of the test pending a reconciliation of test and construct, or final abandonment of the test. If the test has not been published, it should be restricted to research use until some degree of validity is established (1). The consumer can await the results of the investigator's gamble with confidence that proper application of the scientific method will ultimately tell whether the test has value. Until the evidence is in, he has no justification for employing the test as a basis for terminal decisions. The test may serve, at best, only as a source of suggestions about individuals to be confirmed by other evidence (15, 47).

There are two perspectives in test validation. From the viewpoint of the psychological practitioner, the burden of proof is on the test. A test should not be used to measure a trait until its proponent establishes that predictions made from such measures are consistent with the best available theory of the trait. In the view of the test developer, however, both the test and the theory are under scrutiny. He is free to say *to himself privately,* "If my test disagrees with the theory, so much the worse for the theory." This way lies delusion, unless he continues his research using a better theory.

The test developer who finds positive correspondence between his proposed interpretation and data is expected to report the basis for his validity claim. Defending a claim of construct validity is a major task, not to be satisfied by a discourse without data. The *Technical Recommendations* have little to say on reporting of construct validity. Indeed, the only detailed suggestions under that heading refer to correlations of the test with other measures, together with a cross reference to some other sections of the report. The two key principles, however, call for the most comprehensive type of reporting. The manual for any test "should report all available information which will assist the user in determining what psychological attributes account for variance in test scores" (59, p. 27). And, "The manual for a test which is used primarily to assess postulated attributes of the individual should outline the theory on which the test is based and organize whatever partial validity data there are to show in what way they support the theory" (59, p. 28). It is recognized, by a classification as "very desirable" rather than "essential," that the latter recommendation goes beyond present practice of test authors.

The proper goals in reporting construct validation are to make clear (*a*) what interpretation is proposed, (*b*) how adequately the writer believes this interpretation is substantiated, and (*c*) what evidence and reasoning lead him to this belief. Without *a* the construct validity of the test is of no use to the consumer. Without *b* the consumer must carry the entire burden of evaluating the test research. Without *c* the consumer or reviewer is being asked to take *a* and *b* on faith. The test manual cannot always present an exhaustive statement on these points, but it should summarize and indicate where complete statements may be found.

To specify the interpretation, the writer must state what construct he has in mind, and what meaning he gives to that construct. For a construct which has a short history and has built up few connotations, it will be fairly easy to indicate the presumed properties of the construct, i.e., the nomologicals in which it appears. For a construct with a longer history, a summary of properties and references to previous theoretical discussions may be appropriate. It is especially critical to distinguish proposed interpretations from other meanings previously given the same construct. The validator faces no small task; he must somehow communicate a theory to his reader.

To evaluate his evidence calls for a statement like the conclusions from a program of research, noting what is well substantiated and what alternative interpretations have been considered and rejected. The writer must note what portions of his proposed interpretation are speculations, extrapolations, or conclusions from insufficient data. The author has an ethical responsibility to prevent unsubstantiated interpretations from appearing as truths. A claim is unsubstantiated unless the evidence for the claim is public, so that other scientists may review the evidence, criticize the conclusions, and offer alternative interpretations.

The report of evidence in a test manual must be as nearly complete as any research report, except where adequate public reports can be cited. Reference to something "observed by the writer in many clinical cases" is worthless as evidence. Full case reports, on the other hand, may be a valuable source of evidence so long as these cases are representative and negative instances receive due attention. The report of evidence must be interpreted with reference to the theoretical network in such a manner that the reader sees why the author regards a particular correlation or experiment as confirming (or throwing doubt upon) the proposed interpretation. Evidence collected by others must be taken fairly into account.

Validation of a Complex Test "As a Whole"

Special questions must be considered when we are investigating the validity of a test which is aimed to provide information about several constructs. In one sense, it is naïve to inquire "Is this test valid?" One does not validate a test, but only a principle for making inferences. If a test yields many different types of inferences, some of them can be valid and others invalid (cf. Technical Recommendation C2: "The manual should report the validity of each type of inference for which a test is recommended"). From this point of view, every topic sentence in the typical book on Rorschach interpretation presents a hypothesis requiring validation, and one should validate inferences about each aspect of the personality separately and in turn, just as he would want information on the validity (concurrent or predictive) for each scale of MMPI.

There is, however, another defensible point of view. If a test is purely empirical, based strictly on observed connections between response to an item and some criterion, then of course the validity of one scoring key for the test does not make validation for its other scoring keys any less necessary. But a test may be developed on the basis of a theory which in itself provides a linkage between the various keys and the various criteria. Thus, while Strong's Vocational Interest Blank is developed empirically, it also rests on a "theory" that a youth can be expected to be satisfied in an occupation if he has interests common to men now happy in the occupation. When Strong finds that those with high engineering interest scores in college are preponderantly in engineering careers nineteen years later, he has partly validated the proposed use of the engineer score (predictive validity). Since the evidence is consistent with the theory on which all the test keys were built, this evidence alone increases the presumption that the *other* keys have predictive validity. How strong is this presumption? Not very, from the viewpoint of the traditional skepticism of science. Engineering interests may stabilize early, while interests in art or management or social work are still unstable. A claim cannot be made that the whole Strong approach is valid just because one score shows predictive validity. But if thirty interest scores were investigated longitudinally and all of them showed the type of validity predicted by Strong's theory, we would indeed be caviling to say that this evidence gives no confidence in the long-range validity of the thirty-first score.

Confidence in a theory is increased as more relevant evidence confirms it, but it is always possible that tomorrow's investigation will render the theory obsolete. The *Technical Recommendations* suggest a rule of reason, and ask for evidence for each *type* of inference for which a test is recommended. It is stated that no test developer can present predictive validities for all possible criteria; similarly, no developer can run all possible experimental tests of his proposed interpretation. But the recommendation is more subtle than advice that a lot of validation is better than a little.

Consider the Rorschach test. It is used for many inferences, made by means of nomological networks at several levels. At a low level are the simple unrationalized correspondences presumed to exist between certain signs and psychiatric diagnoses. Validating such a sign does nothing to substantiate Rorschach theory. For other Rorschach formulas an explicit a priori rationale exists (for instance, high $F\%$ interpreted as implying rigid control of impulses). Each time such a sign shows correspondence with criteria, its rationale is supported just a little. At a still higher level of abstraction, a considerable body of theory surrounds the general area of *outer control,* interlacing many different constructs. As evidence cumulates, one should be able to decide what specific inference-making chains within this system can be depended upon. One should also be able to conclude—or deny —that so much of the system has stood up under test that one has some confidence in even the untested lines in the network.

In addition to relatively delimited nomological networks surrounding *control* or *aspiration,* the Rorschach interpreter usually has an overriding theory of the test as a whole. This may be a psychoanalytic theory, a theory of perception and set, or a theory stated in terms of learned habit patterns. Whatever the theory of the interpreter, whenever he validates an inference from the system, he obtains some reason for added confidence in his overriding system. His total theory is not tested, however, by experiments dealing with only one limited set of constructs. The test developer must investigate far-separated, independent sections of the network. The more diversified the predictions the system is required to make, the greater confidence we can have that only minor parts of the system will later prove faulty. Here we begin to glimpse a logic to defend the judgment that the test and its whole interpretative system is valid at some level of confidence.

There are enthusiasts who would conclude from the foregoing paragraphs that since there is some evidence of correct, diverse predictions made from the Rorschach, the test as a whole can now be accepted as validated. This conclusion overlooks the negative evidence. Just one finding contrary to expectation, based on sound research, is sufficient to wash a whole theoretical structure away. Perhaps the remains can be salvaged to form a new structure. But this structure now must be exposed to fresh risks, and sound negative evidence will destroy it in turn. There is sufficient negative evidence to prevent acceptance of the Rorschach and its accompanying interpretative structures as a whole. So long as any aspects of the overriding theory stated for the test have been disconfirmed, this structure must be rebuilt.

Talk of areas and structures may seem not to recognize those who would interpret the personality "globally." They may argue that a test is best validated in matching studies. Without going into detailed questions of matching methodology, we can ask whether such a study validates the nomological network "as a whole." The judge does employ some network in arriving at his conception of his subject, integrating specific inferences from specific data. Matching studies, if successful, demonstrate only that each judge's interpretative theory has some validity, that it is not completely a fantasy. Very high consistency between judges is required to show that they are using the same network, and very high success in matching is required to show that the network is dependable.

If inference is less than perfectly dependable, we must know which aspects of the interpretative network are least dependable and which are most dependable. Thus, even if one has considerable confidence in a test "as a whole" because of frequent successful inferences, one still returns as an ultimate aim to the request of the technical recommendation for separate evidence on the validity of each type of inference to be made.

Recapitulation

Construct validation was introduced in order to specify types of research required in developing tests for which the conventional views on validation are inappropriate. Personality tests, and some tests of ability, are interpreted in terms of attributes for which there is no adequate criterion. This paper indicates what sort of evidence can substantiate such an interpretation, and how such evidence is to be interpreted. The following points made in the discussion are particularly significant.

1. A construct is defined implicitly by a network of associations or propositions in which it occurs. Constructs employed at different stages of research vary in definiteness.

2. Construct validation is possible only when some of the statements in the network lead to predicted relations among observables. While some observables may be regarded as "criteria," the construct validity of the criteria themselves is regarded as under investigation.

3. The network defining the construct, and the derivation leading to the predicted observation, must be reasonably explicit so that validating evidence may be properly interpreted.

4. Many types of evidence are relevant to construct validity, including content validity, interitem correlations, intertest correlations, test-"criterion" correlations, studies of stability over time, and stability under experimental intervention. High correlations and high stability may constitute either favorable or unfavorable evidence for the proposed interpretation, depending on the theory surrounding the construct.

5. When a predicted relation fails to occur, the fault may lie in the proposed interpretation of the test or in the network. Altering the network so that it can cope with the new observations is, in effect, redefining the construct. Any such new interpretation of the test must be validated by a fresh body of data before being advanced publicly. Great care is required to avoid substituting a posteriori rationalizations for proper validation.

6. Construct validity cannot generally be expressed in the form of a single simple coefficient. The data often permit one to establish upper and lower bounds for the proportion of test variance which can be attributed to the construct. The integration of diverse data into a proper interpretation cannot be an entirely quantitative process.

7. Constructs may vary in nature from those very close to "pure description" (involving little more than extrapolation of relations among observation-variables) to highly theoretical constructs involving hypothesized entities and processes, or making identifications with constructs of other sciences.

8. The investigation of a test's construct validity is not essentially different from the general scientific procedures for developing and confirming theories.

Without in the least *advocating* construct validity as preferable to the other three kinds (concurrent, predictive, content), we do believe it imperative that psychologists make a place for it in their methodological thinking, so that its rationale, its scientific legitimacy, and its dangers may become explicit and familiar. This would be preferable to the widespread current tendency to engage in what actually amounts to construct validation research and use of constructs in practical testing, while talking an "operational" methodology which, if adopted, would force research into a mold it does not fit.

REFERENCES

1. AMERICAN PSYCHOLOGICAL ASSOCIATION. *Ethical standards of psychologists.* Washington, D.C.: American Psychological Association, Inc., 1953.

2. ANASTASI, ANNE. The concept of validity in the interpretation of test scores. *Educ. Psychol. Measmt.,* 1950, *10,* 67–78.

3. BECHTOLDT, H. P. Selection. In S. S. Stevens (ed.), *Handbook of experimental psychology.* New York: Wiley, 1951. Pp. 1237–1267.

4. BECK, L. W. Constructions and inferred entities. *Phil. Sci.,* 1950, *17.* Reprinted in H. Feigl and M. Brodbeck (eds.), *Readings in the philosophy of science.* New York: Appleton-Century-Crofts, 1953. Pp. 368–381.

5. BLAIR, W. R. N. A comparative study of disciplinary offenders and non-offenders in the Canadian Army. *Canad. J. Psychol.,* 1950, *4,* 49–62.

6. BRAITHWAITE, R. B. *Scientific explanation.* Cambridge Univer. Press, 1953.

7. CARNAP, R. Empiricism, semantics, and ontology. *Rév. Int. de Phil.,* 1950, II, 20–40. Reprinted in P. P. Wiener (ed.), *Readings in philosophy of science.* New York: Scribner's, 1953. Pp. 509–521.

8. CARNAP, R. *Foundations of logic and mathematics. International encyclopedia of unified science,* I, No. 3. Pages 56–69 reprinted as "The interpretation of physics" in H. Feigl and M. Brodbeck (eds.), *Readings in the philosophy of science.* New York: Appleton-Century-Crofts, 1953. Pp. 309–318.

9. CHILD, I. L. Personality. *Annu. Rev. Psychol.,* 1954, *5,* 149–171.

10. CHYATTE, C. Psychological characteristics of a group of professional actors. *Occupations,* 1949, *27,* 245–250.

11. CRONBACH, L. J. *Essentials of psychological testing.* New York: Harper, 1949.

12. CRONBACH, L. J. Further evidence on response sets and test design. *Educ. Psychol. Measmt.,* 1950, *10,* 3–31.

13. CRONBACH, L. J. Coefficient alpha and the internal structure of tests. *Psychometrika,* 1951, *16,* 297–335.

14. CRONBACH, L. J. Processes affecting scores on "understanding of others" and "assumed similarity." *Psychol. Bull.,* 1955, *52,* 177–193.

15. CRONBACH, L. J. The counselor's problems from the perspective of communication theory. In Vivian H. Hewer (ed.), *New perspectives in counseling.* Minneapolis: Univer. of Minnesota Press, 1955.

16. CURETON, E. E. Validity. In E. F. Lindquist (ed.), *Educational measurement.* Washington, D.C.: American Council on Education, 1950. Pp. 621–695.

17. DAMRIN, DORA E. A comparative study of information derived from a diagnostic problem-solving test by logical and factorial methods of scoring. Unpublished doctor's dissertation, Univer. of Illinois, 1952.

18. EYSENCK, H. J. Criterion analysis—an application of the hypothetico-deductive method in factor analysis. *Psychol. Rev.,* 1950, *57,* 38–53.

19. FEIGL, H. Existential hypotheses. *Phil. Sci.,* 1950, *17,* 35–62.

20. FEIGL, H. Confirmability and confirmation. *Rév. Int. de Phil.,* 1951, *5,* 1–12. Reprinted in P. P. Wiener (ed.), *Readings in philosophy of science.* New York: Scribner's, 1953. Pp. 522–530.

21. GAYLORD, R. H. Conceptual consistency and criterion equivalence: a dual approach to criterion analysis. Unpublished manuscript (PRB Research Note No. 17). Copies obtainable from ASTIA-DSC, AD-21 440.

22. GOODENOUGH, FLORENCE L. *Mental testing.* New York: Rinehart, 1950.

23. GOUGH, H. G., MCCLOSKY, H., & MEEHL, P. E. A personality scale for social responsibility. *J. Abnorm. Soc. Psychol.,* 1952, *47,* 73–80.

24. GOUGH, H. G., MCKEE, M. G., & YANDELL, R. J. Adjective check list analyses of a number of selected psychometric and assessment variables. Unpublished manuscript. Berkeley: IPAR, 1953.

25. GUILFORD, J. P. New standards for test evaluation. *Educ. Psychol. Measmt.,* 1946, *6,* 427–439.

26. GUILFORD, J. P. Factor analysis in a test-development program. *Psychol. Rev.,* 1948, *55,* 79–94.

27. GULLIKSEN, H. Intrinsic validity. *Amer. Psychologist,* 1950, *5,* 511–517.

28. HATHAWAY, S. R., & MONACHESI, E. D. *Analyzing and. predicting juvenile delinquency with the MMPI.* Minneapolis: Univer. of Minnesota Press, 1953.

29. HEMPEL, C. G. Problems and changes in the empiricist criterion of meaning. *Rév. Int. de Phil.,* 1950, *4,* 41–63. Reprinted in L. Linsky, *Semantics and the philosophy of language.* Urbana: Univer. of Illinois Press, 1952. Pp. 163–185.

30. HEMPEL, C. G. *Fundamentals of concept formation in empirical science.* Chicago: Univer. of Chicago Press, 1952.

31. HORST, P. The prediction of personal adjustment. *Soc. Sci. Res. Council Bull.,* 1941, No. 48.

32. HOVEY, H. B. MMPI profiles and personality characteristics. *J. Consult. Psychol.,* 1953, *17,* 142–146.

33. JENKINS, J. G. Validity for what? *J. Consult. Psychol.,* 1946, *10,* 93–98.

34. KAPLAN, A. Definition and specification of meaning. *J. Phil.,* 1946, *43,* 281–288.

35. KELLY, E. L. Theory and techniques of assessment. *Annu. Rev. Psychol.,* 1954, *5,* 281–311.

36. KELLY, E. L., & FISKE, D. W. *The prediction of performance in clinical psychology.* Ann Arbor: Univer. of Michigan Press, 1951.

37. KNEALE, W. *Probability and induction.* Oxford: Clarendon Press, 1949. Pages 92–110 reprinted as "Induction, explanation, and transcendent hypotheses"

in H. Feigl and M. Brodbeck (eds.), *Readings in the philosophy of science.* New York: Appleton-Century-Crofts, 1953. Pp. 353–367.

38. LINDQUIST, E. F. *Educational measurement.* Washington, D.C.: American Council on Education, 1950.

39. LUCAS, C. M. Analysis of the relative movement test by a method of individual interviews. *Bur. Naval Personnel Res. Rep.,* Contract Nonr–690 (00), NR 151–13, Educational Testing Service, March 1953.

40. MACCORQUODALE, K., & MEEHL, P. E. On a distinction between hypothetical constructs and intervening variables. *Psychol. Rev.,* 1948, *55,* 95–107.

41. MACFARLANE, JEAN W. Problems of validation inherent in projective methods. *Amer. J. Orthopsychiat.,* 1942, *12,* 405–410.

42. MCKINLEY, J. C., & HATHAWAY, S. R. The MMPI: V. Hysteria, hypomania, and psychopathic deviate. *J. Appl. Psychol.,* 1944, *28,* 153–174.

43. MCKINLEY, J. C., HATHAWAY, S. R., & MEEHL, P. E. The MMPI: VI. The K scale. *J. Consult. Psychol.,* 1948, *12,* 20–31.

44. MEEHL, P. E. A simple algebraic development of Horst's suppressor variables. *Amer. J. Psychol.,* 1945, *58,* 550–554.

45. MEEHL, P. E. An investigation of a general normality or control factor in personality testing. *Psychol. Monogr.,* 1945, *59,* No. 4 (whole no. 274).

46. MEEHL, P. E. *Clinical vs. statistical prediction.* Minneapolis: Univer. of Minnesota Press, 1954.

47. MEEHL, P. E., & ROSEN, A. Antecedent probability and the efficiency of psychometric signs, patterns or cutting scores. *Psychol. Bull.,* 1955, *52,* 194–216.

48. *Minnesota Hunter Casualty Study.* St. Paul: Jacob Schmidt Brewing Company, 1954.

49. MOSIER, C. I. A critical examination of the concepts of face validity. *Educ. Psychol. Measmt,* 1947, *7,* 191–205.

50. MOSIER, C. I. Problems and designs of cross-validation. *Educ. Psychol. Measmt.,* 1951, *11,* 5–12.

51. PAP, A. Reduction-sentences and open concepts. *Methods,* 1953, *5,* 3–30.

52. PEAK, HELEN. Problems of objective observation. In L. Festinger and D. Katz (eds.), *Research methods in the behavioral sciences.* New York: Dryden Press, 1953. Pp. 243–300.

53. PORTEUS, S. D. *The Porteus maze test and intelligence.* Palo Alto: Pacific Books, 1950.

54. ROESSEL, F. P. MMPI results for high school drop-outs and graduates. Unpublished doctor's dissertation, Univer. of Minnesota, 1954.

55. SELLARS, W. S. Concepts as involving laws and inconceivable without them. *Phil. Sci.,* 1948, *15,* 287–315.

56. SELLARS, W. S. Some reflections on language games. *Phil. Sci.,* 1954, *21,* 204–228.

57. SPIKER, C. C., & MCCANDLESS, B. R. The concept of intelligence and the philosophy of science. *Psychol. Rev.,* 1954, *61,* 255–267.

58. Technical recommendations for psychological tests and diagnostic techniques: preliminary proposal. *Amer. Psychologist,* 1952, *7,* 461–476.

59. Technical recommendations for psychological tests and diagnostic techniques. *Psychol. Bull. Supplement*, 1954, *51*, 2, Part 2, 1–38.

60. THURSTONE, L. L. The criterion problem in personality research. *Psychometric Lab. Rep.*, No. 78. Chicago: Univer. of Chicago, 1952.

Reliability

Marguerite R. Hertz

THE RELIABILITY OF THE

RORSCHACH INK-BLOT TEST[1]

HE RORSCHACH Ink-blot Test[2] has been applied in many fields—abnormal psychology, psychiatry, mental tests, psychology of perception, heredity, childhood and adolescence, educational psychology and vocational guidance. The technique, the symptomatic value of the various categories and the interpretation of the test as a whole have been subject to extensive investigation. The method has been found of value in making personality studies of school children and adults, in studying racial differences, adolescent changes in personality, and the influence of environment and heredity on mental make-up, also in diagnosing general intelligence, types of intelligence and grades of mental deficiency. It has likewise been studied in connection with various other typological systems—constitutional types, eidetic types, graphological types and form-color types. It has been used to reveal imagination, inventiveness, fantasy living, poetic talent, and various aesthetic values, and to detect mental and moral defects, schizophrenic, neurotic, psy-

Reprinted from *J. Appl. Psychol.*, 1934, *18*, 461–477, by permission of the American Psychological Association and the author.

1. Published through the courtesy of the Richman Fund.

2. For a description of the method, reference should be made to Rorschach (18), Rorschach and Oberholzer (19). Summaries of the method may be found in Behn-Eschenburg (4), Enke (5), Soukup (20), Müller (12), Oeser (14), Löpfe (10), Loosli-Usteri (9), Pfahler (15), Beck (2, 3), Vernon (22), and Hertz (8).

chotic traits and the like. Finally it has been used as a clinical instrument for making diagnosis and has been found of value in psychoanalysis.[3]

A review of the literature discloses a shocking scarcity of data on the reliability of the method. With few exceptions, it has not even been challenged. Despite extensive investigation and application little thought seems to have been given to the problem of whether or not it diagnoses personality consistently and reliably. Without doubt the results of the studies made with the method depend upon its reliability and must be interpreted with caution until that is established. Before the Rorschach test can be used as an instrument of measurement and diagnosis, it must show consistency of results when applied repeatedly to the same individuals under similar conditions.

The Problem of Reliability

A number of factors make for inconsistency of results. They include 1) lack of standardization of procedure, 2) too limited a sampling of the individual's behavior, 3) unreliability of the sampling of the individual's behavior because of the variability of his performance, and 4) lack of objectivity in scoring.

It was observed in working with the Rorschach Test that there appeared to be great variability in the reactions of divers individuals to the test and that such wide and variable performance might not give an accurate index in the reactions of the same individual at different sittings. It was thought that such wide and variable performance might not give an accurate index of the individual's habitual behavior or personality. It was of greatest importance, therefore, to study the variability-performance factor to determine whether the sample of the individual's behavior appearing at one sitting was consistent with that at another time.

It was likewise thought that ten pictures might be too small a number of components for a test instrument to elicit a good sampling of behavior. Behavior under the test conditions might not be sufficiently extensive to give a satisfactory and reliable score.

Finally, it was observed from preliminary work with the test that the scoring was highly subjective and might be too dependent upon the "intuition" of the examiner at the expense of its reliability.

All these factors had to be taken into consideration, in studying the reliability of the ink-blot test.

3. Subsequent investigations of the Rorschach method are summarized by Beck (2, 3), Vernon (22), and Hertz (8).

Reliability is generally reported in terms of the coefficient of correlation, i.e., the correlation of the scores of the same individuals upon two successive and similar tests. In the absence of duplicate tests either the same material is used twice or the split test method is employed in which the test is divided into halves as comparable as possible, the score determined on each half, and those half scores correlated thus giving the reliability of half of the test.

Methods Used in Other Investigations

Two studies are reported in which the Rorschach blots were given twice. Mira (11) applied the test to a group of subjects twice a fortnight apart. In certain groups he observed consistency of response. He considered the amount of change indicative of the stability of the individual. He does not include any statistical evidence of these findings. In like manner, Wertham and Bleuler (25) gave two applications of the test to determine differences in reactions of individuals under normal circumstances and when under the drug, mescaline. They reported comparatively close agreement in the two sets of responses, with one exception. The slight differences which did occur, did not materially affect the interpretation as a whole. In this study, also, no statistical computations are presented.

Behn-Eschenburg (4) reported the use of a parallel series of ink-blots which gave the same results as the standard Rorschach series. His claim is not, however, statistically substantiated. Other series of blots supposed to be similar to the original Rorschach blots have been used by Roemer (16, 17), Struve (21), Gordon and Norman (7) and Weil (23). These have not, however, been standardized against the Rorschach series, and there is no statistical evidence that they are actually similar in nature, equally difficult, and basically measuring the same factors.

The only statistical study to the writer's knowledge which specifically deals with the reliability of the method is that of Vernon (22). With ninety subjects, twenty-five male students of Yale University, forty-eight male students of Harvard, and seventeen male and female adults in England, he used the corrected split-half method and tested the reliability of the Rorschach categories. He divided each subject's scores into two halves of five blots, I, III, V, VI, and X in one series, and II, IV, VII, VIII, and IX, in a second series, correlated them and used the Spearman-Brown correction to show the predicted correlation of the whole test with a second similar test. Scores for his three groups of subjects were tabulated separately. He obtained the highest correlation for the number of responses (R) + 0.91, indicating that if a parallel series were available, the average subject might attain the same total number of responses as on the original set. The reliabilities of the other scores were not as satisfactory, the per cent W (see Table II for symbols) being 0.74, the percentage of M, O, and P falling between 0.70 and 0.60, and the other scores less, indicating that scores might be very different for the two sets. (See Table IV.) Vernon ascribes this unsatisfactory reliability of the different categories especially to the subjectivity of the scoring and to the shortness of the test. Because of this latter failing he recommends a parallel set or additional blots. He further states that psychometric standards of reliability do not "properly apply to the test" because Rorschach never intended each separate category to be isolated and treated as a quantitative variable. On the contrary he specifically insisted that no diagnosis should be made without considering the total psychogram. Vernon admits, however, "that if the test is to be regarded as a test at all, or if it claims any objective validity, it must in the future be modified in such a way that the reliabilities of the chief categories of response may achieve a level of at least 0.70–0.80."[4]

In the investigation of the Rorschach Test planned by the Brush Foundation[5] the split-test method was used in the preliminary experiment described in a previous paper.[6] Briefly, the test was administered to seventy subjects constituting a miscellaneous "normal" group, to thirty patients referred to the Psychological Clinic of Western Reserve University, and to fifty patients from the Neuropsychiatric Clinic of Lakeside Hospital, Cleveland, in two sittings, a set of odd-numbered blots being given at one time and after an interval of one to two weeks, the set of even-numbered blots. The answers were scored for those general test factors which required no norms or frequency tabulations, namely for the per cent W, per cent D (any detail answers), percentage of DS, M, C (any color answers), and per cent F (any form answers). The test factors were studied without their qualifications and their differentiations. The corrected coefficients for these factors showed a fairly high reliability in the three groups. Table I reproduces the reliability coefficients for the factors studied.

It was because the test in this general form showed satisfactory reliability that the experiment proper was set up. It was thought that if the procedure could be made more uniform and the scoring more objective, the reliability of the test could be definitely established.

4. Vernon, P. E. The Rorschach Ink-blot Test. *British J. Med. Psychol.*, XIII, Part III, 1933, p. 184.

5. Research was begun by the writer while a Fellow in Psychology at the Brush Foundation, Western Reserve University, and continued under the direction of Dr. L. Dewey Anderson. The Foundation is now called the Developmental Health Inquiry of the Associated Foundations.

6. Hertz, M. The Standardization of the Procedure and of the Scoring of the Rorschach Ink-blot Test. Western Reserve Library, Cleveland, Ohio.

TABLE I

Reliability Coefficients for Rorschach Scores with Correction*

	No. of S.	%W	%D	%DS	%M	%C	%F
Miscellaneous	70	.66	.72	.60	.58	.62	.86
correction*		.80	.83	.75	.73	.77	.91
Psychological Clinic	25	.71	.69	.60	.24	.36	.55
correction*		.83	.82	.75	.39	.53	.71
Neuropsychiatric Clinic	50	.71	.61	.65	.55	.88	.81
correction*		.85	.76	.78	.71	.93	.69

* Brown-Spearman Prophecy Formula $r_{12} = \dfrac{2r}{1+r}$

Standardization of the Ink-blot Test

Reference must be made to the previous paper for details as to standardization of the method of administering the test and of the method of scoring.[7] Suffice it to say here that revision was made of certain steps in the procedure to insure standardized conditions. Record blanks, summary sheets and diagrams were rearranged and improved, a trial blot was introduced into the procedure, time of exposure of each blot was limited to two minutes, uniform directions were given, and the test situation was kept as uniform as possible. The test was given to 300 students of Patrick Henry Junior High School, Cleveland, 150 boys and 150 girls, ages ranging from 12, 6 to 16, 5. The test records obtained were subjected to statistical analysis and definite quantitative and qualitative criteria were determined for scoring the Rorschach test factors. Responses were tabulated for each ink blot, the tabulations constituting "Frequency Tables." These tables represented the standard of normality for the specific age group and were used in scoring W, D, Dr, Do, F, O, I and P. The scoring method was found to be reliable as judged by the extent of agreement between the scores of one judge and those of another on 100 records selected at random.

Procedure in Determining the Reliability of the Test

It was decided to use the split-test method again in determining the reliability of the ink-blot test as had been done in the preliminary work. Two

7. *Ibid.*

applications of the original set were not advisable since factors of familiarity and practice would enter and prejudice results. No parallel series of blots was available. The split-test method was the only method left.

This procedure has its limitations. The assumption is made that halves of the test are approximately equivalent in difficulty, content, and similar respects. When the Rorschach test was divided into a set of five odd-numbered cards (Set A) and another set of five even-numbered cards (Set B), it was observed that the latter contained one colored blot more than the former. It is to be noted that Vernon's sets (22) were not strictly comparable for the same reason. Second, there are several test factors of diagnostic significance which very obviously could not be studied with this method because their existence depends upon the original progression of the series, the *succession* for example. These factors had to be omitted from this study because of the method of approach.

Using the split-test method was justified because it seemed to be the only method available. No test factors which depended upon the progression of the series were included in this treatment. This method further would reveal the influence of the variability-performance factor, the adequacy of the instrument, and of the standardization of the procedure in reference to the test factors selected for study.

Computation of the Coefficients of Reliability

One hundred records were selected at random from the group of three hundred. Scores of each of these were divided into two parts, Set A containing scores of the answers to the odd numbered cards and Set B containing scores of the responses to the even numbered cards. The two sets of scores were summarized. In all there were two hundred half sets of scores.

The two sets of scores were compared for the following factors:

1. Total number of responses
2. Total number of whole responses
3. Percentage of whole answers
4. Number of normal detail answers
5. Percentage of normal detail answers
6. Number of rare detail answers
7. Percentage of rare detail answers
8. Number of oligophrenic details
9. Percentage of oligophrenic details

10. Number of normal details, rescoring and not considering the oligophrenic category
11. Percentage of normal details, rescoring and not considering the oligophrenic category
12. Number of rare details rescoring and omitting consideration of the oligophrenic category
13. Number of white space details
14. Percentage of white space details
15. Number of good forms
16. Percentage of good forms on the basis of the total responses
17. The %F+ factor of Rorschach
18. Number of movement answers
19. Percentage of movement answers
20. Number of chiaroscuro responses
21. Percentage of chiaroscuro responses
22. Number of color answers of any kind
23. Percentage of color answers of any kind
24. Color score factor of Rorschach
25. Number of animal answers
26. Percentage of animal answers
27. Number of human answers
28. Percentage of human answers
29. Number of answers referring to anatomy
30. Percentage of anatomical answers
31. Number of good original answers
32. Percentage of good original answers
33. Number of popular responses
34. Percentage of popular responses
35. Number of forms verbally mentioned, called "items"
36. The "Erlebnistypus" as suggested by each set

In Table II are presented the reliability coefficients of certain of these factors with correction according to the Brown-Spearman formula.

The Rorschach factors appear to be reliable in most cases. Percentage of anatomical, original, and chiaroscuro answers showed the highest reliability (.9). Satisfactory coefficients (.8) were obtained likewise for number of responses, percentage of whole, rare detail, oligophrenic detail, space detail, color, animal and human form answers, and number of items. Percentage of normal detail, good form, and movement answers and the color score obtained coefficients approximating .70. The lowest coefficient (.6) in the group was that for percentage of popular answers. The normal detail and the rare detail factors appeared to have greater reliability when the oligophrenic detail was omitted. The oligophrenic detail, however, showed high reliability in itself.

Comparing *Erlebnistypen* suggested by each half of the test, the percentage of correspondence is 73.

Comparison with Results in Preliminary Experiment

In the preliminary work, reliability coefficients were found for the percentage of whole, detail, space detail, movement and color answers, treated generally without consideration of qualifications. The split-test method was used, each half of the test being given at a separate sitting.

TABLE II

Reliability Coefficients of Rorschach Test Factors $(N = 100)$

Sym.	Test Factors	Coeff.	P.E.±	Correction*
R	Total number of responses	+.812	.014	+.890
%W	Percentage of *whole* answers	+.717	.032	+.835
%D	Percentage of *normal detail* answers	+.600	.043	+.750
%Dr	Percentage of *rare detail* answers	+.752	.029	+.859
%Do	Percentage of *oligophrenic detail* answers	+.686	.040	+.813
%D	Percentage of *normal detail* answers (No Do)	+.678	.039	+.808
%Dr	Percentage of *rare detail* answers (No Do)	+.814	.024	+.897
%DS	Percentage of *space detail* answers	+.767	.030	+.868
%F	Percentage of *good forms* in relation to R	+.677	.039	+.807
%F+	Percentage of *good forms* in relation to F	+.576	.051	+.730
%M	Percentage of *movement* answers	+.594	.043	+.745
%F(C)	Percentage of *chiaroscuro* answers	+.847	.024	+.917
%C	Percentage of *color* answers	+.677	.039	+.810
C	*Color Score*	+.640	.039	+.763
%A	Percentage of *animal* answers	+.708	.035	+.829
%H	Percentage of *human* answers	+.756	.029	+.861
%Anat.	Percentage of *anatomical* forms	+.944	.013	+.971
%O+	Percentage of *original* answers	+.837	.024	+.911
%P	Percentage of *popular* answers	+.495	.051	+.666
Items	Total number of *Items* given	+.761	.017	+.864

Percentage of correspondence between
personality types   73%

* Brown-Spearman Prophecy Formula $r_{12} = \dfrac{2r}{1+r}$

The reliability coefficients with the final results here were for the same factors in more refined form. The same procedure was used except that the test was given in one sitting.

The two sets of coefficients are therefore not comparable. However, they are placed side by side in Table III for observation.

The reliability of the whole, space detail and color answers appear to have been increased. The detail factor is not at all comparable of course, since in the final experiment it referred to normal details as statistically determined whereas in the preliminary work it meant any detail answer.

TABLE III

Coefficients of Reliability (as Corrected) in Preliminary and Final Experiments

Group	No. of S.	%W	(%D)	%DS	%M	%C
Preliminary						
Normal	70	.80	(.83)*	.75	.73	.77
Final						
Patrick Henry	300	.89	(.80)*	.87	.76	.81

* Not comparable.

Comparison with Results Obtained by Vernon (22)

Table IV reproduces the correlations found by Vernon, averaged for his three groups. It is to be noted that his reliabilities are considerably lower than those obtained in this investigation. His average is 0.54 while the coefficients in the present study average 0.829. The number of responses and the percentage of whole answers appear to be reliable in both studies. The percentage of original answers given irrespective of qualification as used in Vernon's study has a much lower reliability (0.60) than the percentage of good original answers as herein obtained (0.911). The percentage of popular answers obtains unsatisfactory reliability in both studies. It is to be noted that the %F+ in the present study has a much higher reliability (.73) than the same factor in Vernon's study (.33). This is likewise true of the %A which has a reliability of .829 here while it attained only .48 in the other study. Again the color score appears more reliable (.763) than the sum color score per cent of Vernon.

Possibly the standardization of the procedure, especially limitation of the time of exposure, and standardization and increased objectivity of the scoring can account in part for the better results herein obtained.

TABLE IV

Vernon's Reliabilities of Scores on the Rorschach Test $(N = 90)$

Test Factors	Average for Three Groups
W%	0.74
F+%	0.33
M%	0.62
SumC%*	0.34
A%	0.48
O%*	0.60
P%	0.64
Aver.	0.54
R	0.91

* Note—It is to be noted that these factors are not comparable to similar factors in the present investigation. Color score here is on a percentage basis, whereas in this study, only the percentage of color answers given and the sum color score were used. Again, Vernon used the percentage of original answers given while the percentage of good original answers is herein employed.

In determining the reliability of the *Erlebnistypus,* Vernon used the formula $\frac{M - Sum\ C}{R}$ as an index of the degree of introversiveness and extra-tension. He obtained an average split-half reliability (corrected) of 0.55, a result which did not bear out Rorschach's contention that the single test is adequate to diagnose the personality type. According to our results, a correspondence of 73 per cent was obtained between the types found on each half of the test, which tended to confirm Rorschach.

Summary of the Reliability of the Rorschach Test

1. The coefficients of reliability of the test factors obtained by the corrected split-test method may be considered satisfactory, since they compare favorably with most of the correlations reported in the literature for intelligence tests or tests of mechanical abilities.

2. The ten component pictures of the Rorschach series are sufficient to elicit a fair sampling of an individual's behavior or personality in terms of the above test factors.

3. Personality traits or behavior patterns in terms of the above factors tend to be consistent and follow a stable and unitary pattern. Hence these patterns may be considered as an accurate index to the individual's habitual responses to the test, and the variability performance factor, though it ap-

pears important, evidently does not militate against the reliability of the test.

4. Comparison of the indices of reliability in the preliminary experiment where some general test factors were considered, and in the final work where test factors were studied in their several differentiations and where there was refinement of technique, indicates that the reliability of the test was increased after the procedure was standardized and the scoring was made more objective.

Intercorrelations of the Rorschach Test Factors

Despite the fact that Rorschach does not introduce any statistical data in his manual, he does indicate certain definite relationships between the various test factors. An examination of these would serve as a further check on the reliability of the method.

Behn-Eschenburg (4), already referred to, compared the average scores of each test factor of his extreme groups to ascertain if Rorschach's relationships obtained. He did not use the method of correlation. He reported positive correspondence between W and M, per cent F+ and FC, also between per cent F+ and Mr; negative correspondence between W and Dr, per cent A and M, Dr and DS, and between per cent F+ and Dr.

Vernon (22) studied the interrelations of the different test factors by the method of correlation and reported statistically unreliable results. He again attempted to account for these unsatisfactory results in terms of Rorschach's assertions that the relationships are to be found only in the "normal person" and are at times broken down or even completely reversed by emotional disturbances. Since the normal person according to Rorschach is the hypothetical person who never can be found (if he was, he would be abnormal) one should not expect to find the schematic relationships enumerated by him.

Table V contains the correlations which obtain among different factors selected for study in the present investigation.[8]

Comparing the whole answer factor with the others, the highest relationship appears between the movement and the color score and the percentage of good original answers. It corresponds least with the percentage of good forms. Rorschach found the direct proportion between the whole an-

---

8. For treatment of the relationship between the Rorschach test factors and intelligence, see Hertz, M. Validity of the Rorschach Test: Intellectual Factors. Western Reserve University, Library, Cleveland, Ohio.

TABLE V

Intercorrelations* of the Rorschach Test Factors $(N = 300)$

	IQ	%F+	%O+	Items	%A	Color Score	Whole Ans.	Move. Ans.
IQ		.460	.398	.186	−.108	.209	.241	.259
%F+	.460		.263	−.003	−.007	.072	.108	.173
%O+	.398	.263		.390	−.436	.305	.380	.509
Items	.186	−.003	.390		−.281	.294	.240	.482
%A	−.108	−.007	−.436	−.281		−.311	−.246	−.294
Color Score	.209	.072	.305	.294	−.311		.393	.177
Whole Ans.	.241	.108	.390	.240	−.246	.393		.424
Move. Ans.	.259	.173	.509	.482	−.294	.177	.424	

* P.E. of the coefficients of correlation for r
  $0.0 - 0.2 \pm .0380$
  $0.3 - 0.5 \pm .0323$

swer and the movement which is suggested here.[9] He did not find clear proportions between W and F or between W and C.[10] Present data agree in that they do not indicate high correspondence between these factors. Experience with the test bears out the fact that W need not necessarily be associated with good form imagery. Subjects frequently gave whole answers without consideration of the exactness of the forms involved. This is pointed out in the study of the feebleminded group[11] who, of all the groups studied, gave the highest percentage of whole answers with the lowest percentage of good forms. Again, many normal subjects gave few whole answers with a high percentage of good forms. Data here presented suggest that the more whole answers given, the less the stereotypy and the more originality and productivity, which again is in accord with Rorschach's finding.

The movement factor appears to vary directly with the percentage of good original answers and with the number of items. This appears to be in accord with Rorschach's estimate of this factor.

"The number of M rises with the productivity of the intelligence, with the wealth of associations, and with the ability to complete new associative connections."[12]

"A direct proportion exists between movement and original answers."[13] Further, a low negative correlation is likewise obtained with the percentage

9. Rorschach, H. *Psychodiagnostik*. Pp. 30 and 54.
10. *Ibid.*, p. 30.
11. Hertz, M. Validity of the Rorschach Test: Intellectual Factors. Western Reserve University Library, Cleveland, Ohio.
12. Hertz, M. Validity of the Rorschach Test: Intellectual Factors. Western Reserve University Library. P. 15.
13. *Ibid.*, p. 80.

of stereotypy, again showing the adverse relationship suggested by Rorschach.

"Stereotyped and feeble-minded persons have no movement answers."[14]

"The number of movement answers stands in direct proportion . . . to the variability of the responses, hence in reverse proportion to the animal per cent. And the direct proportion between the number of good original answers and the movement answers stand out even more clearly."[15]

The coefficient of correlation obtained between M and per cent F+ (+.173) does not substantiate Rorschach when he reports:

"With normal subjects, a clear proportion exists between the number of M and the keenness of the form imagery."[16]

Rorschach adds, however, that this direct proportion may be upset wherever emotional disturbances enter.[17] In like manner, Rorschach is not confirmed when he indicates a direct proportion between movement and color factors, but again he indicates exceptions.[18]

Rorschach indicated a proportion between per cent F+ and C,[19] but practically no relationship is indicated by present data. Again, Rorschach finds this correspondence may be reversed by normal subjects with nervous or artistic leanings.[20] The inverse relationship between color and stereotypy indicated by Rorschach is confirmed by the correlation of −.311 which was obtained.

"Only the stabilized show no color . . . the less color, the more stabilized and the more stereotyped the individual."[21]

Present data also indicate a positive relationship of +.305 with the per cent 0+ which bears this out.

The percentage of stereotypy appears negatively related to per cent 0+, to the number of items, the color score, whole and movement answers. The highest relationships obtained are with the per cent 0+ (−.436) and the color score (−.311). These facts are all suggested by Rorschach. He indicates that artistic and imaginative people have a low per cent A, while the stereotyped and the feeble-minded have a high per cent A.[22]

It should be noted that the number of items shows highest correlation with the per cent 0+ and the movement answers. This factor was introduced into the present study and was not suggested by Rorschach.

14. *Ibid.*, p. 15.
15. *Ibid.*, p. 55.
16. *Ibid.*, p. 17.
17. *Ibid.*, pp. 17 and 54.
18. *Ibid.*, p. 21.
19. *Ibid.*, p. 21.
20. *Ibid.*, p. 21.
21. *Ibid.*, p. 22.
22. *Ibid.*, p. 36, Table VI.

Summary for the Intercorrelations
of the Rorschach Test Factors

1. Intercorrelations range from −.436 to +.509.

2. The whole answer factor shows highest correspondence with movement, color score, and percentage of good original answers.

3. The movement factor is best related to the good original answers and corresponds likewise to items and number of whole answers.

4. The color score is positively related to per cent 0+ and W and negatively related to per cent A.

5. The per cent A shows a negative relationship to all the other factors especially with the per cent 0+, the C and the W.

6. The items factor is best related to movement and originality.

7. While definite conclusions cannot be made, the figures suggest many of the findings which Rorschach reported.

General Conclusion

Statistical treatment of the results obtained with the Rorschach test in its modified and standardized form shows the test to be a reliable instrument.

BIBLIOGRAPHY

1. BECK, S. J. Personality Diagnosis by Means of the Rorschach Test. *Amer. J. Orthopsychiat.*, 1930, 1, 81–88.

2. ———. The Rorschach Test and Personality Diagnosis. I. Feeble-minded. *Amer. J. Psychiat.*, 1930, 10, 19–52. Also in *Institute for Child Guidance Studies* (L. G. Lowrey), pp. 222–261. N. Y.: Commonwealth Fund, 1931.

3. ———. The Rorschach Test as Applied to a Feeble-Minded Group. *Archives of Psychol.*, 1932, 136, 84.

4. BEHN-ESCHENBURG, H. *Psychische Schüleruntersuchungen mit dem Formdeutversuch.* Ernst Bircher Verlag, Bern u. Leipsig, 1931, p. 69. Also Huber, Bern.

5. ENKE, W. Die Konstituionstypen im Rorschachschen Experiment. *Zsch. f. d. Neur. u. Psychiat.*, 1927, 108, 645–674.

6. ———. Die Bedeutung des Rorschachschen Formdeutversuches für die Psychotherapie, *Sitzungsber. d. Ges. z. Beförderg. d. ges. Naturw. z. Marburg.* 1927, 62, 621–633, Berlin: O. Elsner Verlag.

7. GORDON, R. G. AND NORMAN, R. M. Some Psychological Experiments on Mental Defectives in Relation to the Perceptual Configurations Which May Underlie Speech. Part II. *Brit. J. Psychol.*, 1932, 23, 85–113.

8. HERTZ, M. R. The Rorschach Ink-blot Test. Unpublished thesis, Western Reserve University Library, Cleveland, Ohio.

9. LOOSLI-USTERI, M. Le test de Rorschach, appliqué à différents groupes d'enfants de 10–13 ans. *Archives de Psychol.*, 1929, 85, 51–106.

10. LOPFE, A. Uber Rorschachsche Formdeutversuche mit 10–13 jährigen Knaben. *Zsch. f. angew. Psychol.*, 1925, 26, 202–253.

11. MIRA, L. E. Sobre el valor del Psicodiagnostico de Rorschach. *Progressos de la Clinica*, 1925, 808–845.

12. MÜLLER, M. Der Rorschachsche Formdeutversuch, seine Schwierigkeiten und Ergebnisse. *Zsch. f. d. ges. Neur und Psychiat.*, 1929, 118, 598–620.

13. MUNZ, E. Die Reaktion des Pyknickes im Rorschachschen psychodiagnostischen Versuch. *Zsch. f. d. ges. Neur. und Psychiat.*, 1924, 91, 26–92.

14. OESER, O. A. Some Experiments on the Abstraction of Form and Color. Pt. II. Rorschach Tests. *Brit. J. Psychol.*, 1932, 22, 287–323.

15. PFAHLER, G., System der Typenlehren. Grundlegung einer pädagogischen Typenlehre, *Zsch. f. Psychol.*, 1929, Erg. Bd. 15, p. 334.

16. ROEMER, G. A. Die Innenwelt einer Persönlichkeit und das Problem ihrer wissenschaftlichen Erschliessung, Psychol. Rundschau, 1930, 2, 4–12. *Psychol. Rundschau*, 1930, 2, 33–41. *Ibid.*, 69–76; 101–109. Reprint: *Die wissenschaftliche Erschliessung der Innenwelt einer Persönlichkeit*, Basle: Birkhäuser, 1931, p. 42.

17. ———. Psychographische Tiefenanalyse einer Grossindustriellen und seiner Stabes. *Prakt. Psychol.*, 1922–3, IV, 16–28.

18. RORSCHACH, H. *Psychodiagnostik. Methodik* und Ergebnisse eines wahrnehmungsdiagnostische Experiments. Bern: Bircher, 1921, p. 42. Also enlarged, Bern: Huber, 1932, p. 227.

19. RORSCHACH, H. AND OBERHOLZER, E. Zur Auswertung des Formdeutversuche für die Psychoanalyse, *Zsch. f. d. ges. Neur. und Psychiat.*, 1923, 82, 240–273. The same, translated: The Application of the Interpretation of Form to Psychoanalysis. *J. Nerv. and Ment. Dis.* 1924, 60, 225–248; 359–379.

20. SOUKUP, F. The Study of Personality and Rorschach's Test. In Czech. *Čas. lék. česk.*, 1931, 1, 881–887. Abstract: *Zentbl. f. d. ges. Neur.*, 1932, 61, 564.

21. STRUVE, K., Typische Ablaufsformen des Deutens bie 14- bis 15- jährigen Schulkindern, *Zsch. f. angew. Psychol.*, 1930, 37, 204–274.

22. VERNON, P. E. The Rorschach Ink-blot Test. *Brit. J. Med. Psychol.*, 13, 1933, 89–114; 179–200, 271–291.

23. WEIL, H. Wahrnehmungsversuche an Integrierten und Nichtintegrierten. *Zsch. f. Psychol.*, 1929, 111, 1–50.

24. WELLS, F. L. The Systematic Description of Personality. Conference on Individual Differences in the Character and Rate of Psychological Development. Washington: National Research Council 1931, pp. 52–70.

25. WERTHAM, F. AND BLEULER, M. Inconstancy of the Formal Structure of the Personality: experimental study of the influence of mescaline on the Rorschach test. *Arch. Neur. und Psychiat.*, 1932, 28, 52–70.

Richard H. Dana

RORSCHACH SCORER

RELIABILITY[1]

Problem

OVER A thirty-year period the Rorschach technique has enjoyed an ever increasing frequency of application within a continually expanding clinical and research framework. Among the most important and least investigated aspects of Rorschach testing is the problem of reliability. There are at least two kinds of reliability germane to projective instruments including (*a*) reliability of the instrument and (*b*) reliability of the scorer. The literature contains discussions and research on reliability of the test *per se* but there are few published reports of scorer reliability (1, 6, 7). In a standard reference, this problem is only briefly mentioned: "It is desirable to make the system of classification as reliable as possible, so that different examiners will arrive at essentially similar classifications of the same sets of responses" (5, p. 19). In a recent overview, Hertz (4) does not mention reliability. Considering the importance of individual scores in the psychogram and the ratios calculated,

Reprinted from *J. Clin. Psychol.*, 1955, *11*, 401–403, by permission of the publisher and the author.

1. This investigation was supported by a research grant from the National Institute of Mental Health, of the National Institutes of Health, Public Health Service. Principal Investigators are: A. G. Ossorio and A. K. Busch. Research Associate: R. H. Dana. Acknowledgment is made to Jerome Pauker and Jack Werboff, Research Assistants, who did the reliability scoring.

the problem of scorer reliability should have received more attention in the past.

The paucity of research in this area may be due to an unverbalized awareness that conventional reliability measures may not be applicable to projective materials. A beginning has been made in discussions of reliability in TAT scoring (2), content analysis (8), and more generally, in projective techniques (3). It is sufficient to indicate here that per cent of agreement, which involves no assumptions, may have more applicability than the usual product moment or tetrachoric correlations between scores of two independent scorers.

Method

A representative sample of Rorschach records for each of eleven examiners was obtained by (*a*) following an alphabetized list of examiners, one record was pulled for each examiner from consecutively numbered files (numbered by admission date) until eleven records had been drawn; (*b*) this process was repeated six times for a total sample of sixty-six records; (*c*) this method permitted sampling from all the records in the files for a four-year period.

These records were scored independently by two scorers of approximately equal training and experience in other locales, using the Klopfer method (5). Per cent of agreement was applied as follows: (*a*) location, determinants, content, and popular main scores were treated as separate items. For example, the response W M H P would consist of four separate items; (*b*) the total N of separate items present in the six scored records for each examiner was computed; (*c*) using the N of examiner items as criterion, comparisons were made for presence or absence of identical items in the scoring of the independent scorers.

Results

Thirty-three per cents of agreement were computed (Table 1): Scorer I, Scorer II, and Scorer I with Scorer II, for each of the eleven examiners.

Discussion

There was a mean difference of 4.4 points between the agreements of Scorers I and II. This difference is attributable to *degree of care exercised*

TABLE 1

Rorschach Per Cents of Agreement Between Two Scorers and Eleven Examiners

Examiners	N Possible Agreements	*Scorers*		
		I	II	I, II
1	235	80	86	86
2	455	73	76	73
3	324	77	84	82
4	414	69	74	75
5	328	71	77	77
6	394	74	74	82
7	291	64	74	75
8	425	71	75	69
9	299	77	78	82
10	409	73	74	75
11	307	69	75	73

and use of *personalized scoring variables.* Inspection of all scores indicated that these two kinds of errors, on the part of both the original examiners and the reliability scorers, account for most of the disagreement present.

A figure of 75 per cent of agreement can be considered representative of scoring reliability in this hospital situation. The sample of Rorschach records was scored with adequate reliability to justify inclusion of the entire population of Rorschachs by these same examiners in any research requiring use of Rorschach scoring categories. It is suggested that this is an economical method of determining whether or not there exists a need for rescoring when hospital Rorschach records are used for research purposes.

This method may not have been applied previously because of the implicit assumption that there is only one *right* way of scoring each response and that equally well trained scorers will score in exactly the same manner. The eleven original examiners in this study had from one to seven years of Rorschach experience; the reliability scorers each had four years of experience. There were no significant relationships between years of experience and reliability of scoring.

The only other use of per cent of agreement for Rorschach reliability reported an over-all figure of 76 per cent using an N of 300 responses, five internationally renowned scorers, and a criterion of agreement by three scorers (7). This striking agreement between experts and the present hospital examiners suggests that increase in training and experience beyond a certain degree of competence does not appreciably affect scorer reliability. If future studies replicate a figure of approximately 75 per cent of agreement for Rorschach scoring, then the 25 per cent of disagreement may be indicative of ambiguity of the scoring categories or of personalized scoring, i.e., influences of examiner personality.

Summary and Conclusions

1. Scorer reliability for two independent scorers with each of eleven Rorschach examiners was computed by means of per cent of agreement.

2. The thirty-three agreement figures ranged from 64 per cent to 86 per cent with 75 per cent representative of this clinical situation.

3. These per cents of agreement appear sufficiently high for research purposes and the extent to which they fall short of optimal agreement may be a function of ambiguous scoring categories or personalized scoring.

4. Scorer reliability is considered an economical method of determining the need for rescoring Rorschach records to be used in research.

5. The usefulness of per cent of agreement as an index of scorer reliability appears to have been overlooked in objectification of the Rorschach and other projective instruments.

BIBLIOGRAPHY

1. AMES, L. B., LEARNED, J., METRAUX, R. W. AND WALKER, R. N. *Child Rorschach Responses.* New York: Paul B. Hoeber, Inc., 1952.

2. DANA, R. H. Clinical diagnosis and objective TAT scoring. *J. Abnorm. Soc. Psychol.,* 1955, 50, 19–25.

3. DANA, R. H. The objectification of projective techniques: Rationale. *Psychol. Rep.,* 1955, 1, 93–102.

4. HERTZ, MARGUERITE. The Rorschach: thirty years after. In Brower, D. and Abt, L. (Eds.) *Progress in Clinical Psychology.* Vol. I. New York: Grune & Stratton, 1952.

5. KLOPFER, B., AINSWORTH, MARY, KLOPFER, W. AND HOLT, R. *Developments in the Rorschach Technique.* Vol. I. Yonkers-on-Hudson: World Book Co., 1954.

6. RAMZY, I. AND PICKARD, P. M. A study in the reliability of scoring the Rorschach ink-blot test. *J. Genet. Psychol.,* 1949, 40, 3–10.

7. SICHA, K. AND SICHA, M. A step towards the standardization of the scoring of the Rorschach test. *Ror. Res. Exch.,* 1936–37, 1, 95–101.

8. SPIEGELMAN M. TERWILLIGER, C. AND FEARING, F. The reliability of agreement in content analysis. *J. Soc. Psychol.,* 1953, 37, 175–187.

Bert Kaplan

Stanley Berger

INCREMENTS AND CONSIST-

ENCY OF PERFORMANCE IN

FOUR REPEATED RORSCHACH

ADMINISTRATIONS

I N WORK with the Rorschach, interpretations are almost always based on a single test administration. The assumption is made that only in his initial and spontaneous reactions does the subject select responses which optimally reveal his personality and that these responses, with a few additions, constitute the entire universe of psychologically meaningful or interesting responses. The basis for this assumption undoubtedly lies in the theory that perception of the Rorschach blots is selective and that what is initially selected is of special significance. In the present paper, we will take the position that this selective process continues well beyond the perceptions which are ordinarily reported on a first administration of the

Reprinted from *J. Proj. Tech.*, 1956, *3*, 304–309, by permission of the publisher and the authors.

Rorschach and that the development of a technique for eliciting large numbers of additional perceptions is of psychological interest.

A number of considerations lead us to question whether it is wise to put all our eggs in the basket of a single administration of the Rorschach test. Experience in psychotherapy and in personality study indicates that very often patients are unwilling or unable to express their major concerns and preoccupations on an initial contact and only very gradually, after many sessions, do they become freely expressive. We suggest that many of the instances in which the Rorschach "does not test" as Lowell Kelly has put it, or does so in a disappointingly sparse way, are cases of this kind of initial reticence or inhibition rather than "emotional impoverishment," "shallowness," or "insufficient differentiation."

In this connection, a host of recent studies, such as those by Lord (7), Kimble (5), Klatskin (6), Eichler (1), Gibby (2) and Hutt and his colleagues (3) indicate that the circumstances surrounding the administration of the test have a considerable influence on the nature of the responses. This influence is not superficial but affects the most basic aspects of the performance. If test results derive in part from the specific situation in which the subject finds himself at a particular moment, we may draw the conclusion that any one test performance can hardly tell the whole story, since in other situations the subject might appear to be quite different.

The most convincing argument against the complete reliance of the Rorschach worker on a single performance lies in the astonishing complexity of personality. As clinicians, sensitive to this fact, we expect that even when an interview or test procedure yields apparently profound insights into personality, subsequent information will broaden the picture and modify our impressions. This process seems to go on as long as we continue to study the subject and we literally never achieve a final or true formulation. Work at the Harvard Psychological Clinic with the TAT has shown that only part of the potential of the subject is tapped by the twenty pictures in the test and that with repeated administrations of the TAT or with additional testing of the storytelling variety, important additional material can be obtained which not only expands our picture of the subject, but often sharply alters any formulation based on the first administration.

Retest studies of Rorschach performance usually reveal a great deal of similarity in responses from one administration to another. Even when there have been drastic intervening conditions, the stability of perceptions is remarkable. We believe that this stability is a function of the dominance of what has already been seen and that perceptual organizations once achieved tend, under certain conditions, to interfere with the emergence of new ones. The conditions we have in mind exist when the old perceptions are in competition with potential new ones. This is the case in the usual retest situation. If we ask why the old perceptual organizations do not interfere with new ones during the course of a single test we can say that a response which has already been given does not compete with new ones which are emerging since only the new responses satisfy the demands of the test situation. The older responses are no longer of value in terms of the immediate needs of the subject and thus lose their compelling and dominating force.

Since we were, in the present study, interested in seeing whether substantial numbers of additional responses could be produced, this analysis offered a clue to the appropriate method for eliciting them. This was simply, on the second and subsequent administrations, to ask the subject to report only new perceptions and to omit anything he had given earlier. This instruction we hoped would remove the dominating and inhibiting influence of what had already been seen.

Using the instruction to report only new and different responses, the Rorschach was administered four times. We had the following questions in mind: 1) Can subjects produce a substantial number of responses in addition to the ones given on a first performance? 2) Do these new responses, if forthcoming, add significantly to the personality picture derived from a first performance? 3) Are the new responses, if forthcoming, substantially similar to the ones given on a first performance in terms both of content and scoring categories? We believed that the answers to these questions would have certain implications for Rorschach practice and theory, for the question of the reliability of the test and would yield new insights into the correlates of Rorschach productivity, a subject dear to the heart of anyone who has given three fifteen-response Rorschachs in succession.

Procedures

The subjects in this study were twenty-eight college students who were volunteers from an introductory psychology course at the University of Kansas. The group Rorschach was administered four times, using the Harrower-Erickson slides which were projected on a screen and exposed for a minute and a half in the regular position and a minute and a half in an inverted position. On the second, third and fourth administrations, the subjects were told to give only new and different responses. The protocols were subsequently examined and a very small number of responses which we judged to be duplicates were eliminated. The time interval between the tests was four days. A special effort was made to create and maintain a friendly and relaxed atmosphere and high group morale throughout the experiment. A fifth session was held in which an inquiry was conducted, and a sixth session was held in which the subjects filled out a questionnaire asking for certain attitudes and feelings with respect to the test experience. The experiment was also explained and discussed during this session. It is of interest that all twenty-eight of the subjects who started continued in the experiment until the last session, which was optional.

Results

Table I presents the mean scores for seventeen Rorschach variables on each of the four administrations. It may be seen that productivity as measured by R fell off about a third on the second administration, but maintained itself at the same level on the third and fourth. To our question as to whether subjects can produce substantial numbers of new responses, we can answer in the affirmative since subjects who gave an average of thirty-four responses originally, produced an average of 68.6 new responses on the three later performances. These results also strongly suggest that this is not the outer limit of productivity but that a fifth and sixth administration would bring even more responses. Informal experiments with as many as nine administrations have revealed there is a gradual decrease both in number and quality.

TABLE I

Mean Score of 28 Subjects in 4 Repeated Rorschach Administrations

	Test I	Test II	Test III	Test IV
R	34.8	23.9	21.0	23.7
M	7.2	5.4	4.5	4.1
FM + m	9.1	5.9	5.1	5.1
k + K	.8	.3	.3	.4
FK	.3	.3	.2	.2
F	11.9	8.9	7.9	8.6
Fc + c	3.4	1.7	1.5	1.8
C′	1.6	1.5	.9	1.4
FC	5	3	2.9	2.5
CF + C	1.2	.9	.5	1.4
sum C	3.9	2.5	2.3	4.6
M:sum C	1.8	2.2	1.9	.9
W	17.8	9.4	7.4	12
D	14.7	12.9	9.6	8.7
d	.2	.4	.4	.4
Dd + s	2.5	2.6	3.3	2.6

Table II presents Kendall's coefficient of concordance, a non-parametric test of consistency of rank, for thirteen Rorschach variables. It may be seen that twelve are significant at the .01 level and one at the .02 level. These findings indicate that there is a significant degree of stability in the scores on the location and determinant categories over the four performances. We should mention that these scores were in the form of percentages rather than numbers of responses, so that we were working with M%, FC%, etc. This means that the fact that individuals tended to hold their ranks in all four

TABLE II

Kendall's Coefficient of Concordance, W, Showing Stability of Ranks on 13 Rorschach Variables of 28 Subjects in 4 Administrations of the Rorschach Test

Variable	"W"	p
F	.49	.01
M	.46	.01
FM + m	.48	.01
Fc + c	.50	.01
FC	.42	.01
sum C	.40	.01
M:sum C	.37	.02
W	.65	.01
D	.50	.01
Dd and S	.52	.01
Sum c*	.48	.01
M:sum C*	.42	.01
R*	.64	.01

* On the starred measures, "W" is based upon actual frequencies of responses. For those which are not starred, the scores were converted to percentages.

performances was not a function of differences in the number of responses. These findings do not, however, resolve adequately the question of whether the responses in each of the four performances are distributed in the same way among the determinant and location categories. The significant W's indicate that a similarity does indeed exist but a question remains as to the magnitude of the similarity and it is difficult to translate the size of the W's into such terms.

The product-moment correlation provides an index of similarity of relationship between sets of scores. Table III presents the correlations between Tests I and 2, 1 and 3, and 1 and 4 of scores on 13 variables. Correlations are given both for scores converted to percentages as in M% and for scores reflecting simple frequencies as in number of M responses. Of the forty-three correlations computed, seventeen are significant at the .01 level and 3 others are significant at the .05 level. R, FM, and M, and the location categories tend to show the greatest amount of consistency. The R's, taken as a group, indicate that there is a considerable amount of relationship between performance I and subsequent performances. However, the coefficients of alienation indicate that only a relatively small part of the variance is accounted for by these correlations. The highest correlation, .75 for W% between Tests 1 and 2 accounts for 52% of the variance while an R of .51 accounts for only 27% of the variance. The findings indicate therefore that there has also been a considerable amount of change. These changes were large enough so that the basic shape of the psychogram showed relatively little stability. Using only percentages of movement, form and Sum C responses it was found that when the patterns formed by these scores were compared for Tests 1 and 2, 1 and 3, and 1 and 4 for the 28 subjects separately, on only 18% of the pairs was the pattern the same so that for example, F% was still highest, M% second and Sum C% lowest.

Perhaps the most interesting data in this study have to do with the changing content of responses in the four administrations. Unfortunately space does not permit our going into this in more than a cursory way. In

TABLE III

Product-Moment Correlations of Rorschach Scores of 28 Subjects in 4 Repeated Administrations

Test	1 and 2		1 and 3		1 and 4	
	Freq.	%	Freq.	%	Freq.	%
R	.72**		.56**		.64**	
M	.07	.51**	.41*	.17	.33	.06
FM + m	.49**	.41*	.60**	.57**	.54**	.53**
F		.54**		.36		.17
FC	.30	.28	.38	.41*	.13	.37
Sum C	.16	.32	.20	.21	−.04	.20
M:Sum C	.16		.53**		.22	
W		.75**		.70**		.49**
D		.67**		.46		.62**
Dd and S		.54**		.47		.08

* Significant at the .05 level.
** Significant at the .01 level.

order that the reader get some idea of the concrete situation, however, we have presented the responses of one subject. No claim is made that she is absolutely typical or representative since reactions varied a good deal in different subjects. However we can say that this kind of sequence of responses is in no way unusual. The subject is female and age nineteen. The responses are to Card I. Inquiry is omitted.

Test 1.

   1 — Bat

   2 — Air Shield

   3 — Cliffs

v 4 — A water fountain as in a park

   5 — A Chinese tower, place for cars to drive under

Test 2.

   1 — Hands reaching out

   2 — Top—an explosion with fragments flying

v 3 — Small animals in center casting spell downward

Test 3.

   1 — Two large birds resembling people fighting

   2 — Two tiny figures like elves right in center,
       each has an arm up over his head

   3 — Egyptian or Chinese lady with full sleeves
       and tall hat in center

Test 4.

   1 — Two winged chiefs over a conference table

v 2 — Masses of molten lava

In this example new responses appear on tests two, three and four which not only lend themselves to new content interpretations but were not suggested by anything which came before. This is absolutely characteristic and occurred in every one of the twenty-eight subjects.

Discussion

What are the implications of these findings? The fact that these subjects have been able to produce large numbers of additional responses is, we believe, of considerable significance. It suggests to us that the very great individual differences in Rorschach productivity which constitute one of the most notable of Rorschach phenomena, do not stem from basic differences in capacity but are dependent instead on motivation and set and are to a considerable extent subject to manipulation. This is a very large jump from our results, especially since our subjects were college students, a group noted for its high productivity. It would therefore be very nice to have this experiment repeated with other classes of subjects, including that recalcitrant group of psychoneurotic patients who ordinarily average around twelve responses. Such experiments are planned for the near future. However, we do not feel that the correctness of our conclusion is really dependent on the results of these additional studies. Neurotic subjects in a hospital setting will undoubtedly be less responsive to our wishes than were the college students, but we would be very reluctant to believe that really basic differences exist. To get more responses from the former one would simply have to develop an appropriate test setting in which compliance with the tester's instructions satisfies the subject's needs in some genuine way. We do not mean to assert that intelligence is not related to the capacity to produce large numbers of responses but we think that subjects within the normal range have a much larger Rorschach potential than is ordinarily sampled by a first performance. Individual differences in capacity may exist at a much higher level so that some people may be able to produce as many as three or four hundred responses before quality declines and they are unable to go on while others may be able to give only seventy-five to a hundred responses. Our point is not that differences in capacity do not exist but that the number of responses given on a first performance is a poor measure of capacity.

Since a first Rorschach administration ordinarily samples a good deal less than the total Rorschach potential we may ask whether it adequately represents the larger universe of responses. Our findings are not clear on this point. On the one hand they indicate a definite similarity between the first and the second, third and fourth performances. On the other hand there is a considerable amount of change and the basic shape of the psychograms tend to be quite variable. The size of the correlations when judged by the standards against which we ordinarily measure reliability are quite low. However, there is a question as to whether these standards are appropriate in this situation.

While we entertained the possibility that the correlations might be very high and would have regarded this as convincing evidence of one aspect of the reliability of the test, namely performer consistency, our own expectations were that they would not be high since we took the position that only some aspects of the subject's personality would be expressed on a first test and that others would be expressed on subsequent performances. Our findings indicate that this expectation was correct. Nevertheless the amount of stability is considerable and may be regarded as evidence that the Rorschach test does tap some functions of personality which express themselves in a consistent way.

The demonstration that subjects can produce substantial numbers of additional responses inevitably raises the question of why they ordinarily stop so far short of their capacity. One possibility which we seriously entertained was that subjects become psychically fatigued or satiated and are actually unable to continue. Certainly some subjects act very much like brain injured patients in their inability to shift and reorganize the blot stimulus despite apparently strong efforts to do so. However, these appearances may be deceptive and further research is needed to determine whether actual incapacity or motivation and set are the crucial factors.

In conclusion, these results suggest that a certain degree of caution is appropriate in interpreting a single Rorschach performance. Such interpretations should be made in the light of the findings, presented in this study, that the responses obtained are only part of the story, and that they are tied to the peculiar circumstances under which the test was given. We interpret our data as demonstrating in conclusive fashion what many other Rorschach studies have implied; namely, that the single Rorschach performance cannot be regarded as an adequate, stable or complete representation of the personality characteristics which the Rorschach is able to describe.

REFERENCES

1. EICHLER, R. M. Experimental Stress and Alleged Rorschach Indices of Anxiety. *J. Abn. Soc. Psychol.*, 1951, *46*, 344–355.

2. GIBBY, R. S. The Stability of Certain Rorschach Variables Under Conditions of Experimentally Induced Sets: 1. The Intellectual Variables. *J. Proj. Techn.*, 1951, *15*, 3–26.

3. HUTT, M. L., GIBBY, R., MILTON, E., AND POTTHARST, K. The Effect of Varied Experimental Sets on Rorschach Test Performance. *J. Proj. Techn.*, 1950, *14*, 181–186.

4. KENDALL, M. S. *Rank Correlation Methods*. London: C. Griffin, 1948.

5. KIMBLE, G. A. Social Influences on Rorschach Records. *J. Abn. Soc. Psychol.*, 1945, *40*, 89–93.

6. KLATSKIN, E. H. An Analysis of the Effect of the Test Situation upon the Rorschach Record: Formal Scoring Characteristics. *J. Proj. Techn.*, 1952, *16*, 193–199.

7. LORD, E. Experimentally Induced Variations in Rorschach Performance. *Psychol. Monogr.*, 1950, *64*, No. 10.

VI

Current Status

L. L. Thurstone

THE RORSCHACH IN

PSYCHOLOGICAL SCIENCE*

T HE RORSCHACH test has attracted so much attention since its introduction in this country about twenty years ago that it has come to occupy a unique position among the many hundreds of tests that are being used by the psychological profession. A few years ago young psychologists studied the Binet tests in order to be able to take jobs for the purpose of assigning IQ's to people. At the present time we do not hear much about such ambitions, but we do hear often from prospective students who want to study the Rorschach test in order to be able to qualify for jobs in giving this test. Comparison of these two situations gives an opportunity to call attention to some conditions of psychological service and research that need to be improved.

When the Binet tests were most in vogue, they were regarded as some sort of base criterion for judging all other tests. The Binet tests were regarded as if they constituted something so basic that all other work had to be oriented around them. There were hundreds of studies in which the investigator was proud to report that his test agreed well with the Binet test. There is a similar attitude at the present time with regard to the Rorschach test. It is regarded as if it were something scientifically unique. Whatever it

Reprinted from *J. Abnorm. Soc. Psychol.*, 1948, *43*, 471–475, by permission of the American Psychological Association.

* This paper was presented to the Illinois Association for Applied Psychology in Chicago, November 18, 1947.

is that makes the Binet test useful or whatever it is that makes the Rorschach test useful, we can be pretty sure that the same results can be obtained with different methods and with entirely different tests. We may not know what those other methods and tests are which could be used to explore the same domain as the Rorschach test, but it seems evident enough that those who are working most enthusiastically with the Rorschach ink blots are not making much effort to discover other entirely different methods of exploring the same domain. In this respect the situation is quite different from that of the Binet test popularity some years ago. Even then, there was a good deal of experimentation with a great variety of tests and comparisons of the results in terms of various kinds of appraisal of the subjects. There was serious study of the logic of the Binet tests and there was serious effort to relate it to the psychological concepts that were current. As a result, psychologists generally took part in deliberations about the underlying theory of the Binet tests. At present we have relatively little of such effort with regard to the Rorschach tests. Such discussion seems to be confined to a cultish group that has adopted its own jargon without relation to current experimental work and theoretical work in psychological science.

It would be fortunate if the Rorschach test could be removed from its isolation from the rest of the psychological profession. This interesting test gives results that occasionally demand our attention and it is a challenging problem to discover variant methods of getting at the same types of appraisal so that the nature of the underlying processes may be better understood. That is the scientific problem in which many other psychologists could participate even if they do not belong to the select few who have qualified as full-time Rorschach examiners. The first step in removing the Rorschach test from its isolation must be in translating the specialized jargon into currently known and accepted concepts, or else in the introduction of such new psychological concepts as may be necessary and with such discussion that psychologists generally can understand the new concepts. The result may be that psychologists will come to adopt some of the Rorschach terms in their own writing just as was the case some years ago when Freudian concepts were introduced into psychological thinking. But in order to bring about such a result, it is first necessary for the Rorschach students to make themselves understood among psychologists who may see no reason why they should study the specialized jargon that has been built up around a particular set of ink blots. The first task is for the Rorschach students to put their discussion in terms that can be understood by the psychological profession. The burden of proof is on them to show that they have not only a useful trick with a particular set of ink blots but that they also have some important ideas that psychologists should learn about. It is my own judgment that the Rorschach test should be critically studied not only for the diagnostic value that it has shown in psychiatric work but also for the psychological principles and effects that are associated with projective procedures, of which the Rorschach is only one of many examples.

There is good reason why the projective methods have become very popular in psychological examining and there is also good reason for the projective methods to be incorporated more frequently into psychological experimentation. The projective method of examining consists essentially in giving to the subject an ambiguous presentation, an ambiguous task, which can be completed in many different ways. The theory of a projective test is that when the subject does respond to an ambiguous assignment, he is revealing himself in the response that he spontaneously makes. This is a fruitful device, as has been shown in a number of tests.

There is a common misunderstanding about the projective test method as regards the scoring of the performance. Many examiners seem to have the impression that a projective test cannot be objectively scored, but that is a mistake.

By way of example, I shall describe a projective test that is objectively scored. I assembled a list of about forty homonyms which had two common associations or meanings. Each one of the homonyms was so selected that one of the common meanings was human and social in significance while the other meaning was something physical or literal. The subject is asked to write as quickly as possible the meaning of each word, or an association which will indicate the meaning of the word. The responses are scored by counting the number of social associations. The individual differences are considerable and the exploratory experiments with this test indicate some relation to the temperament of the subject. Before suggesting that such a test be used for examining we would have to give it to people with known temperamental differences to determine whether it is trustworthy. My point here is merely to show one of many projective tests that can be objectively appraised if one has some psychological plan or idea in designing it.

In appraising a projective test performance, we may distinguish between two types of purposes. One purpose is to elicit from the subject some idea about his past history, the biographical detail that fits the particular case that is being examined. This can be done by free association, or by the Rorschach, or the Thematic Apperception Test, or by other projective methods. Biographical detail may be so emotionally blocked that it is more readily accessible by these indirect methods than by direct questioning. While this type of inquiry about a subject may be useful for some immediate purpose, we must remember that no amount of anecdotal or biographical detail will ever become science until someone organizes the individualistic material into some categories of fruitful classification so as to reveal the underlying parameters of the dynamical system that constitute a personality. This is the second purpose for which a projective test may be given. It should reveal, not only the biographical detail that is of interest in a particular case, but it should also reveal the subject as to the dynamical characteristics that describe his motivations and values. Even more fundamentally, it should reveal the style of his personality so that his behavior becomes at least in some sense predictable as to the style of response that he is likely to give to different types of life situations. But this cannot be accomplished as long as we stay within the narrow confines of responses to the ink blots. These must be interpreted in terms of larger classes and types of response that transcend the ink blots. If such interpretations can be made in a dependable way, then they should be described in every textbook in psychology. The student reader should be shown the experimental evidence and the psychological theorizing by which the color shock, the movement responses, the animal responses, the responses to the white spaces, become significant in the larger setting of psychological interpretation.

On many occasions I have suggested to my friends who are working with the Rorschach that they should experiment with other projective test procedures in order to throw light on the underlying mechanisms and the response types of the subject that may be of interest in understanding his temperamental characteristics. Several kinds of projective procedures should be tried with the same groups of subjects, who should be appraised as to their temperamental characteristics as well as to their preferred types of adjustment to life problems. Instead of merely suggesting that more varied forms of projective methods be tried, I shall describe a few such tests.

Recently I have discussed with some of my friends a type of projective test for appraising personality or temperament. I do not know if it will be successful but I believe that it has good possibilities. Our plan is to make a collection of prints, perhaps fifty or one hundred. These should be so varied as to type of painting that practically everybody will find some prints that he rather likes and some that he definitely dislikes. The collection should be increased until we have such diversity that everyone likes at least some of the prints. Then we want to study the clustering so that, if a subject points to a few pictures that he likes, we should be able to predict some prints that he will like and some prints that he will dislike. The art preferences may be associated with temperament. For example, it is probable that preference for highly saturated color contrasts as against low color saturations may be significant. Preference for strong action as against passive or stationary objects, preference for lots of detail as against bold outlines, fine-line work as against coarse-line work, pictures with people and those without people, photographic detail as against abstract design, and many other comparisons may be made in studying the clusters of pictures that are liked and disliked. These preferences may be related to personality. My suggestion would be to ask the subject to say nothing. I probably would ask him merely to indicate his likes and dislikes and I would have only a secondary interest in his explanations because they would probably be wrong. On the other hand, one might gain some insight from the subject's verbalizations about his preferences. One can tell by trying.

In this type of exploratory work, I should not care to have any test criteria beforehand. In this case we would depart entirely from the convention of correlating test scores with outside criteria. I would select two groups of subjects as regards their likes and dislikes, even if I had only a few people in each group. Then I would ask how these two small groups of people are different. If I could find some difference in temperament or style of personality, then I could make an hypothesis about what the difference in art preference might mean. I would proceed in the same manner for each type of preference or dislike.

The study of expressive movement is a field that should be actively cultivated experimentally by students of this problem. The early work of June Downey has been thrown into the discard by most psychologists because of criticisms about minor questions of reliability and because of validity studies, mostly with the wrong criteria. It is my judgment that she was on the right track in studying personality by objective experimental methods. The studies of Gordon Allport and others on expressive movement should be continued in the hope of finding objective experimental methods for appraising personality. One could easily list some forty or fifty experimental studies that should be made in the direction of studying personality by objective and experimental methods.

It would be fortunate if students of the Rorschach test would proceed to qualify themselves for membership in the psychological profession by insisting on experimental evidence under reasonably controlled conditions for the various interpretations that they make of the responses to a set of ink blots. There is justification for the belief that the projective test method of presenting to the subject an ambiguous task has great possibilities, and it seems plausible that a set of ink blots may be one of these fruitful test methods. Rorschach students are not making any worthwhile contribution to psychological science as long as they remain in their state of gullible and uncritical acceptance of fanciful interpretations of the responses to a single set of ink blots. If they don't have imagination to do anything more challenging, they can at least try, say, twenty different variations of the ink blots. The designs can be varied in the relative degree of freedom of perceptual closure for the subject, and in many other ways. The various types of ambiguous presentations should be studied experimentally and systematically on the same subjects in order to extract the psychological principles in this domain. When these principles begin to be understood, it will probably become apparent how the test methods may be still further improved. This progress will not be made as long as we stick to a single set of ink blots without relating them experimentally to the many variations of the projective method.

One Rorschach student has said that all he needed to know was that the psychiatrist wanted the Rorschach test. That justified the Rorschach test. There are two possible interpretations of such a remark. It may mean that the psychiatrist has so little technique himself that he grabs at anything, even a Rorschach. Another interpretation is that the psychiatrist thinks that this is all he can get out of a psychologist. Maybe he is right.

When I was asked to participate in this program, I assumed that it was not because of qualification as a Rorschach examiner. While I have included it in some of my studies, I have not been a student of the Rorschach.[1] For many years I have been associated with the development of psychological tests of considerable variety and purpose and with the development of test theory. I have been interested in the projective method which we have used in a number of experiments. My purpose in accepting participation in this program was not to elaborate on the possibilities and limitations of a particular set of ink blots. Rather, I have attempted to show why it is that the Rorschach test has not been accepted by the psychological profession, and why it is that most students of this test do not have recognition or status in psychological science. I have attempted to outline how this condition can be improved and how the students of the Rorschach might investigate their problems so that this field of inquiry can be incorporated into psychological science.

---

1. At the time when the Rorschach test was introduced to American psychologists, I discussed with Dr. David Levy the possibility of objectifying the scoring of the Rorschach test. It was my judgment that the appraisal of a Rorschach performance could not profitably be objectified without much experimental work.

Joseph Zubin

FAILURES OF THE RORSCHACH

TECHNIQUE

I F HERMAN RORSCHACH had not been carried off by the infection following a minor operation, he would have celebrated his sixty-eighth birthday last November 8. He would have looked approvingly on our efforts and would have helped make this symposium on failures a success by providing methods for their elimination in the future. For no one was more tentative in his conclusions, more demanding of continual self-survey and revision than the man who lent his name to the major projective technique. "The conclusions drawn," he says, "are to be regarded more as observations (remarks) than as theoretical deductions. The theoretical foundation for the experiment is, for the most part, still incomplete." He even went as far as hoping for ". . . control experiments taking up each symptom individually, and other psychological methods which might also be used in control research" (24).

It is both a brave and a wise move that the Society for Projective Techniques has undertaken in this symposium and it is to be congratulated on its maturity and integrity. Like the post-mortem in surgery, failures in projective techniques ought to be far more revealing and instructive than the reports of successful cases. We stand to benefit from our mistakes, find out what changes need to be introduced, what hypotheses need to be altered

Reprinted from *J. Proj. Tech.*, 1954, *3*, 303–315, by permission of the publisher and the author.

and what expectations need to be amended. Following the custom of the surgeons, only the outstanding failures of the Rorschach technique will be discussed, the outstanding successes being omitted. A cataloguing of one's failures without scanning the successes is trying to even the most mature of souls, but since it is motivated by a search for improvement we can all bear up under it. After analyzing the failures, a hypothesis to explain them will be presented, which may perhaps repay, in part, for the masochistic trend a self-analysis may engender.

One outstanding Rorschach worker has made the following surmise about Rorschach's own reaction to the current scene: "Rorschach today would still recognize the cards. Brilliant though he was, I doubt if he could find time to read the voluminous literature which is well en route to the thousand mark. I am certain that, if he could, he would be startled that from his little experiment following the 'scoring' of the responses, there emerge invaluable facts relating specifically to the way in which the patient sees his world, approaches and handles it, and of what this world consists. His anxieties and insecurities, his hurts and wishes, his fictions, his needs, his assets and liabilities, his likes and dislikes—all of these and more emerge to be viewed by the examiner. Moreover, the pattern reveals also the meaning of these things to him, the configuration of his personality which thus results, and the motivations of his behavior. It, furthermore, aids in differential diagnosis, particularly between the organic and functional types of illness, and among the affect and content disorders. The expert examiner can also obtain from the response record a practical estimation of such important personality features as intellectual efficiency, emotional maturity and balance, and degree and depth of reality acceptance. Finally, the procedure serves as a guide to therapy and an index of its success or failure" (19).

What validity do these claims have? Let us take a look at the record. The following questions need to be answered: 1) What reliability does the Rorschach technique possess? 2) What validity? 3) What relationship does it bear to the changes brought on by therapy, and 4) to the outcome of therapy, and 5) what light has recent research cast on these problems?

First, what about the reliability of scoring? This question has received but little attention and it is generally taken for granted that scoring has a high degree of reliability. Hertz (18), however, has stated on the basis of her long experience that "scoring still remains a matter of skill—art, if you will." Though this statement was made eighteen years ago, it still largely holds true today. Ramzy and Pickard (22) found that only after considerable discussion and arbitrary acceptance of certain conventions were they able to obtain consistency in their scoring. It is noteworthy that appeal to textbooks only increased their confusion. Even after this collusion, the degree of agreement was only 90 per cent for the location category. Since Beck's location tabulations were followed, it is surprising that the degree of agreement was not perfect. For determinants of Form and the Movement variety, the agreement dropped to 83 per cent, and for the Color and Shading determinants to 75 per cent. As far as content was concerned, following Beck's classifications an agreement of 99 per cent was obtained. Ames and her associates report their reliabilities in terms of product moment correlation coefficients: location categories, .92; form and movement categories, .90; color and shading, etc., .80, and content categories, .97 (1). These results are essentially in keeping with those reported by Ramzy and Pickard. Since according to Rorschach, "The actual content of the interpretations comes into consideration only secondarily" the determinants being of major importance, it is clear that the best estimate of agreement for the major scoring categories is only 80 per cent. This is a far cry from the degree of agreement expected of an individual test. The lack of objectivity in scoring is further evidenced by Baughman's experiment (5) in which fifteen Veterans Administration examiners disagreed significantly in scoring on sixteen out of twenty-two scoring categories in records based on a random selection of cases culled from their files. It is clear that failure to provide an objective scoring system is our first failure.

The reliability of the test can not be judged by split-half methods because of the heterogeneity of the blots, nor can it be judged by test-retest because of the memory factor. Alternate forms are required for this purpose. Eichler (12) reports that he tried to obtain a reliability estimate by correlating the Behn-Rorschach with the Rorschach but obtained such low reliabilities that he concluded the two forms were similar but not parallel. Thus, lack of reliability is the second failure.

The validity of the test will be analyzed from the following points of view: (1) subjective, (2) clinical, (3) statistical, and (4) experimental.

Subjective and Clinical

Subjective validation of the testimonial variety in which he who comes to scoff remains to pray, will not be commented on further. This type of evidence is so clearly discountable as utterly unscientific that it is not even to be counted among our failures.

The clinical method sometimes consists of administering and scoring the test, collecting data on the subjects' subsequent behavior and then going back to the protocol, in which are "found" signs which "unmistakably" foretell such behavior. Unless a cross validation of these signs is undertaken in another study, it is fruitless to accept them as indicative of future behavior, because with sufficient imagination and exertion of effort through trial and error, pseudosignificant signs can be found in any test. Unfortunately, such cross validation is rarely encountered.

Blind analysis is one of the spectacular aspects of the Rorschach technique and has probably been the most important factor in the acceptance of the Rorschach. One would wish that this method could be made more explicit and more public, and that the enthusiastic proponents of this method were as ready to publish their failures as their successes. Until this method becomes more open to public scrutiny, it has to be placed in the doubtful category and counted neither as a success nor as a failure.

The matching technique is another way of demonstrating validity. Unfortunately, there are many inadvertent and tangential characteristics in this method, not germane to validity, which may influence the outcome. Successful matching is frequently effected on the basis of minor details or coincidences, rather than essential equivalence. Heterogeneity of matches also makes the task too easy. Determination of the precise ground on which successful pairing is made is virtually impossible. Furthermore, most of the results indicate only that the matching is better than chance, an insufficient criterion for validity. Cronbach (9) has recently devised a trenchant methodology for freeing the matching methods from these defects, but it is quite intricate, and the one application which he made yielded no success in the matching process. Thus, the clinical evidence for validity cannot be accepted scientifically, even though it is impressive. Our failure to provide more cogent evidence for clinical validity must be regarded as our third failure.

Statistical Studies

In view of Rorschach's original purpose of devising a diagnostic test for mental disorders—especially for schizophrenia—we shall first review studies that deal with the diagnostic efficacy of the test. There are very few studies in which clinical scoring and interpretation disagree markedly with clinical diagnosis when the study is conducted in the same clinic and when the two diagnosticians have had considerable experience in working together. This is certainly highly in favor of the test, and the only question a carping critic might ask is: is there a tendency for collusion to occur in such cases, since only a few authors, such as Benjamin and Ebaugh (4), point out the care they took to avoid collusion? When we examine the relationship between the individual Rorschach scores and diagnosis, a totally different picture emerges. Guilford (16) found in three successive samples of about fifty neurotic patients, who were given the Rorschach in orthodox fashion, that no significant differences could be detected between their performance and that of a large normative group of cadets. Wittenborn and Holzberg (32) found zero correlation between Rorschach factors and diagnosis in 199 successive admissions. Cox (8) found only five scores out of a total of forty-three scores differential between normal and neurotic children, and of these five, three were in the content categories and only two in the determinant categories. These are only samples of the well-known failure of the individual Rorschach scoring categories to relate to diagnosis, which is in marked contrast to the success of the global evaluation claimed by clinical workers generally. This must be regarded as the fourth failure.

In prognosis too, the recent review by Windle (30) leaves one with very little faith in the efficacy of the prediction attributable to the Rorschach. The only successful prognostic elements seem to be based on content rather than formal factors, as shown by McCall (21). This is the fifth failure.

Since Windle's article was published, two additional bits of evidence of failure of the Rorschach in the prognostic sphere have appeared. In Barron's study (2) in which the Rorschach, together with several other tests including the MMPI were given to both patients and therapists before the beginning of therapy, while the MMPI predicted outcome significantly, the Rorschach, despite all attempts ranging from the global to the atomic, failed to do so. Rogers, Knauss, and Hammond (23) report a similar experience. As long as other tests failed to predict outcome one might have attributed the failure to the heterogeneous nature of the patient group—to an admixture of early and chronic cases, for example. When other tests succeed where the Rorschach fails, one can either conclude that the Rorschach is unsuited to prediction, or that basic personality which the Rorschach claims to measure is unrelated to the type of therapy involved.

The differentiation of organic from functional conditions has also had a checkered history of success and failure: success when viewed retrospectively but failure when the results of retrospective analysis were applied to a new sample. The latest in the series is the study by Dörken and Kral (11), who after demolishing the signs of previous workers propose a new set of their own, which will probably in turn be demolished by the next worker. The vitality of this search for signs despite so many failures can only command the awe and respect of the onlooker. Whether it will finally succeed only time can tell; meanwhile it must be placed in the doubtful category.

The success that clinicians have had in global evaluation of mental patients has not been duplicated in the global evaluations of normals. Here the series of failures is truly appalling. The story is too long to review. Some of the recent examples are—Grant, Ives, and Ranzoni (15), who found zero correlation between Rorschach evaluations and case history evaluations of adjustments in eighteen-year-old normals. The more specific adjustment signs provided by Helen Davidson (10), fared a little better, yielding correlations from .23 to .56. The failure of the Rorschach to serve as a predictor of success in the screening programs of the armed forces, in the screening of clinical psychology students and students of psychiatry, is too well known to warrant further comment. I shall quote from only one of these:

> It was regarded as very important that the Rorschach test should be given full opportunity to show what it had to offer in a personnel-selection setting. It was recognized that neither time nor personnel requirements for the routine administration and use of this test were consistent with the mass testing required. . . . Yet the test was administered experimentally to several hundred students individually according to the prescribed procedures by members of the Rorschach Institute who were serving in one of the psychological units. Two methods of group administration were also tried, the Harrower-Erickson and our own version.
>
> The results were almost entirely negative. From the individual administration of the test, neither the 25 indicators taken separately or collectively nor the intuitive prediction of the examiner based upon the data he had from the administration of the test gave significant indications of validity against the pass-fail criterion. There were two samples, one of nearly 300 and the other of nearly 200. The Harrower-Erickson group-administration form also gave no evidence of being valid for pilot selection. The AAF group-administration form when scored for the number of most popular responses showed a coefficient of .24, based upon a sample of more than 600 students (16).

The inability to differentiate between normals is the sixth failure.

Special studies aimed at evaluating intelligence by means of the Rorschach also usually come a cropper. Wittenborn (33) compared the extreme groups selected on the basis of college entrance examinations on eighteen scores of the Rorschach and failed to find any significant relationship. (This is even worse than chance, because by chance you might have expected about one of these eighteen scores to show significance on the .05 level.) The relationship of Movement to intelligence has been investigated by Tucker (28), in 100 neurotics, who found a very low correlation—.26. Wilson (31) made a more extensive study of a large college population and used Movement, Form level, Whole, Responses, Z (organization), diversity of content, and a new specially-designed-variable designated as "specification"—and found zero correlation with intelligence.

The studies in creative ability conducted in our own laboratory on creative versus non-creative writers, mathematical statisticians, and high school students have failed to reveal any differences on Rorschach performance and even tests especially designed to elicit Movement have failed (34). This is the seventh failure.

But the story of the use of the Rorschach with normals is not entirely a hopeless one. Sen (26), in England, one of Cyril Burt's students, applied the Rorschach to 100 Indian students who had lived together for at least two years. Scoring by means of Beck's scoring system, the correlations with personality evaluations by their colleagues were non-significant. However, when scored for content à la Burt, the correlations ranged from .57 to .66. When matching was resorted to, a global method, both scoring methods yielded a high degree of success: .85 for Beck's system, and even higher for Burt's system. Interestingly enough, however, when a factor analysis was performed on the Beck Scores and on the Burt Scores, the results of both analysis are equally trenchant in their relationship between the derived factor scores and personality. This is a general finding in the studies in which the raw Rorschach scores failed to relate to diagnosis or personality. When factor analysis is resorted to, a rotation of the factors usually permits certain striking correlations with behavior to emerge.

We might stop here a moment to differentiate between content analysis as used by Burt and in our own laboratory and the content category as used by Rorschach. In the Rorschach there are really three types of classifications: Location, Determinants, and Content. The Location and Determinant categories are usually spoken of as the Formal Categories, and the Content Categories are those which simply classify the percepts as animal, vegetable or mineral—so to speak—that is, the category of objects it belongs to. It might be better to contrast in the Rorschach the perceptual factors—or structural factors with the content categories. There are left reaction time, popular responses, and confabulations, contaminations, etc.—which are neither determinants nor locations and hence could be classified with content. It is the non-perceptual part of the Rorschach performance—the thought content— which we designate as the content aspects of Rorschach performance.

Examples of the scales used for content analysis of the Rorschach protocols are: 1) Formal content à la Rorschach, 2) Dynamic content—(a) degree of evaluation included in response as judged by qualifying adjectives, (b) degree of dehumanization, (c) ascendance-submission in concepts portrayed (slaves-versus-kings, for example), (d) definiteness of concept (e) abstractness (f) dynamic qualities—alive or dead, static or moving, (g) distance in time and space (h) self-reference, (i) perseveration, (j) elaboration, (k) blot versus concept dominance, (l) interpretive attitude, etc. (33). Further evidence for the success of this type of analysis is found in Elizur (13) and in Watkins and Stauffacher (29) in this country and Sandler (25) in England.

Elizur found that an analysis of content in relation to hostility yielded significant correlations with ratings of hostility. Sandler, working with Rorschach's content categories (and not with the type of content analysis being discussed here) made a factor analysis of the content scores of fifty psychiatric patients at Maudsley Hospital, ranging over eight types of mental disorder. He emerged with four factors and determined the psychological meaning of each factor by its correlation with the personality evaluation made by psychiatric interview and case history methods. These were drawn from three levels—previous personality, general background data, and present symptoms. The productivity factor, R, for example, was highly related to previous productivity in life, to chronicity of symptoms and to a schizo-affective picture at time of hospitalization. The Anatomy factor—internal anatomical objects versus external objects as another example, was related to an insecure, withdrawn, "previous" personality picture, bad physical health and an emotional deluded state for the "present symptoms." The remaining factors were analyzed in similar fashion.

Watkins and Stuffacher (29) provided a series of indexes of "deviant verbalizations" based on the content of the protocols and found that such indicators had a reliability of .77 between two raters, and that these indexes distinguished normals from neurotics and the latter from psychotics.

Factor analysis, when applied to either the orthodox scoring categories or to the content scales, emerges with factors like the following: fluency, generalizing ability, emotionality, imagination, extraversion-introversion, neurotic tendencies. Apparently, what the Rorschach expert does intuitively in evaluating the records of normals and neurotics can be obtained objectively by factor analysis. But it should be noted that direct statistical manipulation of the original Rorschach scoring categories does not lead to significant results unless they are distilled either through the mind of the expert or the hopper of factor analysis.

As for the relation of the Rorschach to changes accompanying psychotherapy, the results are in doubt. One study claims positive findings (21a) and three show negative results—Lord (20), Carr (6), and Hamlin and Albee (17). The latter found that Muench's indicators of improvement did not hold up when groups exhibiting different levels of adjustment were compared, thus negating the one positive study mentioned.

Barry, Blyth, and Albrecht (3) compared test and retest data on the Rorschach with pooled judgment of patients at a Veterans Administration Mental Hygiene Clinic. Changes in ratings of adjustment level failed to correlate with changes on the Rorschach.

The recent topectomy study (7) offered an opportunity for testing what effect the lowering of anxiety induced by the operation might have on Rorschach performance. Neither orthodox scoring nor anxiety indicators (with the single exception of reaction time) succeeded in demonstrating any changes in the Rorschach performance of the patients, although other psychological tests showed such changes. Psychometric scaling, however, did reveal certain changes and also provided a prognostic indicator. Three pairs of patients were selected, each pair consisting of one individual who decreased in anxiety and one who increased in anxiety after operation. The judgment of loss and gain in anxiety was based on psychological interviewing by means of anchored scaling devices and on the judgment of the psychiatrist. Only those patients in whom the two criteria concurred were selected. The results indicated that perception of movement of whatever variety, regardless of whether it was accompanied by empathy, correlated positively with anxiety, rising when the anxiety level rose and dropping when the anxiety level fell. The degree of tentativeness or insecurity in giving responses also correlated positively with anxiety. The following variables showed only a unilateral relationship to anxiety levels, declining with a decline in anxiety but showing no corresponding rise with rise in anxiety level: sensitivity to chiaroscuro, anatomical responses, perception of animate objects, perception of objects with texture, and degree of self-reference. The following variables also showed a unilateral but negative relationship with anxiety, showing increases as anxiety fell—accuracy of form perception and degree of congruity of the response. The statistical significance of these differences could be readily established since each patient could be analyzed as a separate sample and the significance of the difference for each patient determined. Only the variables that showed consistent changes from patient to patient were reported.

The fact that the classical Rorschach scoring is not sensitive to changes induced by somatotherapy is an old story. Lord (20) reports a similar finding in psychotherapy. Perhaps the Rorschach test reflects only basic personality structure. Someone has suggested that the goal of therapy is to arrest diseases into defects and then teach the patient to accept these defects. If therapy consists in nothing more than the acceptance of one's disabilities, no change in fundamental personality is to be expected.

Experimental Studies

Perhaps the most important question that the experimentalist would like to answer about the Rorschach technique is: what is the stimulus, what role does it play, and whether present scoring of stimulus qualities such as Color, Form, Shading and perhaps Movement have definite stimulus correlates. One way of answering this question is to alter the stimulus characteristic to see whether the responses will change correspondingly.

The most revealing study of the stimulus properties of the Rorschach is a still unpublished study by Baughman (5). He set as his goal to differentiate as far as possible between that part of the response which inheres in the stimulus and that which inheres in the responder himself. Since the characteristic of the stimulus are more readily manipulated, he devised a series of modifications of the Rorschach plates so as to reveal the potency of a given part of the stimulus for evoking characteristic responses. He started off with the standard card and eliminated first the hue factor through photographing the standard series in black and white on panchromatic film, retaining all the nuances of the shading or differences in brightness and all the other characteristics of the blot. Then, he removed the shading by making line drawings of the more striking contours within the blot and the periphery. The third modification consisted of blotting out the inside details by making the entire inside of the blot black but leaving the islands of pure white, yielding a silhouette effect. The final modification consisted simply of the periphery or outline of the blot.

While it is difficult to draw up a correspondence between the altered appearance of the card and the specific Rorschach determinant which is most prominently present or absent, the following tentative suggestions can be made. The cards in which only the periphery was present would tend to accentuate whole responses and form responses. The cards with the inside details would tend to accentuate detail responses and perhaps organization, (Beck's Z). The silhouette cards would tend to accentuate form responses and perhaps tend to suppress white space responses. The achromatic cards and the complete original set are too well known to require further discussion. The modified cards as well as the original set were administered to a group of 100 veterans, hospitalized for neuroses and character disorders. Each of the five series of blots was given to a group of twenty patients selected randomly which was equated with the other groups on IQ and educational level. Beck's scoring system was employed.

When he compared the records of the various groups, which had been administered variants of the original stimulus cards, he found, instead of the theoretically expected changes, a considerable degree of constancy in the responses. Virtually all of the significant differences were attributable to differences in stimuli which were simply objectively necessary for the occurrence of a given category of responses. For example, Detail responses were found uniformly distributed in all the variant forms of the blots except for a drop in the case of the peripheral form series, when the stimulus for D is eliminated. Apparently color and shading are not important for the Detail category. Surprisingly, the M response occurred with significantly higher frequency in the silhouette version, indicating that perception of movement is independent of shading. Categories showing but slight differences from series to series were: R, W, Form level, P, T/R, A, FM, Total time, Diversity of content, and 8–9–10%. Baughman aptly summarizes these findings: "The severest assault upon the stimulus is necessary before significant changes in resulting performances are produced."

Another analysis of the data was made by submitting the protocols, including the reaction time data and the responses, to experienced Rorschach workers to see whether color and shading shock patterns occurred only in the appropriate series. As a result of this investigation, it is reported quite conclusively that the time latency and response patterns supposedly typical of color shock occur with the same frequency whether color is present or absent. The same was found to hold true of shading and shading shock. A very substantial question is thus raised as to the wisdom of continued use of the shock indicators. Further evidence against the concept of "color shock" is provided by Siipola (27). In an especially ingenious experiment, she concluded that the affinity that color bears to emotion is based on a misunderstanding. Color shock for example is not due to color itself, but to the incongruity between the color and contour of a given blot area. The conflict engendered in the observer will take different paths depending upon the personality of the subject. While Siipola's experiment is not itself conclusive, no statistical verification being given, her explanation of color shock is ingenious, to say the least.

Many of the moot questions in scoring could be answered by Baughman's research. Thus, "Bat" to Card I practically disappears as a response when "shading" and "black" are removed, while "Butterfly" occurs equally frequently in all the modified presentations. Similarly, "Map" occurs only when shading is present. Colored areas which yield anatomy responses practically cease to do so when color is eliminated. Color is of little importance in the response "Bat" to Card II—D32, in "Monkeys" in Card III—D3 and in "Bow tie" and "Ribbon" to the same card. "Rejection" in this study was much more prominent when Color and Shading were absent, indicating that Form rather than Color or Shading is the primary source of rejection. This study needs to be repeated on groups other than the neurotic, with other scoring systems, and with other types of modification.

The second question deals with the effect of alteration of the state of the subject by means of drugs or hypnosis or shock. These experiments have not yielded very much because of the inexactness with which the psychological correlates of these induced states are known.

The third question deals with the effect of alteration of the circumstances surrounding the test. Prestige suggestions as to the importance of certain types of responses will alter the distribution of the responses in the direction of the prestige. Similarly, social situation, induced anxiety, etc., have been tried out. Some of the changes expected by Rorschach workers were validated, others not. The important conclusion to be drawn is that standard conditions are required and that Rorschach performance is not as insensitive to external conditions as some workers have claimed.

To summarize our findings thus far, the following facts are seen to emerge from our survey:

(1) Rorschach scoring and sign evaluation has an *a priori* basis which is not always validated by experimentally contrived techniques such as alteration of stimulus, alteration of state of the organism, etc.

(2) Globally, the Rorschach is an apparent success when the Rorschach diagnostician and the clinical diagnostician work closely together.

(3) Atomistically it is an apparent failure.

(4) Content evaluation whether done globally or atomistically is a success.

(5) Factor analysis of atomistic scores consisting of the usual combination of perceptual and content factors, or of content alone, correlate with personality.

What kind of a hypothesis, what kind of a model, could satisfy the above conditions? That is the scientific question before us. Before answering, let us examine Rorschach's technique as an experiment. Experiments must have as their minimal requirements—subject, experimenter, apparatus or stimulus of some kind, a well-defined task, directions for the task, acceptance by the subject of the task, a response made by the subject and recorded automatically or by the experimenter. But that is not all—the most important part is still missing—the hypothesis.

What is the hypothesis underlying the Rorschach experiment? Rorschach never stated it explicitly, but it can be stated as follows:

(1) We perceive in the artificial Rorschach space in the same way we perceive in real space.

(2) The way we perceive in real space is determined by our personality.

Both of these assumptions are impossible to test at this time because we do not know how perception takes place in real space, nor how it takes place in Rorschach space. Gibson (14) has laid the foundations for the experimental determination of these two processes but we still have a long way to go before we can experiment with them. The relation between perception and personality must await the solution of the first two problems. What can be done meantime, and how can we explain the five facts which I have listed previously?

One hypothesis that suggests itself and which I humbly think merits consideration requires a shift of emphasis from the perceptual to the content aspects of the Rorschach. It is true that Rorschach veered away from the content analysis of ink blots which was so popular with the psychologists of his day and espoused the formal aspects. He states "The content of the interpretations . . . offers little indication as to the content of the psyche." But he may have been wrong, or may have defined content too narrowly. If we define content as the essential elements of the protocol, and regard it as one would regard any other interview material, and analyze the content, the mystery is solved. Once the perceptual scoring is eliminated, and instead a content analysis of the verbal productions of the subject is made according to such categories as compulsive thinking, disorganized thinking, or creative thinking; poverty of ideas or fluency; confabulation or clarity; rigidity or flexibility; contamination or its opposite; perplexity or straightforwardness; rejection or compliance, etc., it will be discovered that such characteristics reveal themselves in the Rorschach the way they reveal themselves in the psychiatric interview. To be sure, the Rorschach interview is a standard interview and may lead to results which the free psychiatric interview can not lead to. But it is still an interview—an interview behind the veil of ink blots.

This would explain why content of Rorschach protocols is related to personality, whether evaluated globally or in isolated scales, while formal Rorschach factors fail to relate to personality. This would also explain why factor analysis of both formal as well as content factors relate to personality. In the course of the analysis, the content factors affecting the formal scores are teased out—viz.—the kind of mental content which serves to reduce R, disorganize F, disembody C or Sh, or prevent good M from arising in the mental patient and, *mutatis mutandis,* the kind of mental content which increases productivity and good responses in the normal, reveal themselves in the rotated factors. If this hypothesis be true, we should turn away from the indirect expression of mental content through determinants and location, and begin building scales for analyzing the content of the verbal productions directly. Such a beginning has been made by several workers and if we spend but 10 per cent of the harnessed energy behind the Rorschach wheel to studying the interview basis of the Rorschach, we may bring nearer the day when the contradictions that now exist within the Rorschach field are resolved.

New developments in the interview itself are fast turning it into a scientific tool, and since the interview, in the last analysis, is the basis for personality evaluation, no test today can rise above it. If we obtain objective criteria via the interview for the classification and evaluation of personality, perhaps such criteria may serve as a basis for the validation of tests.

But without an anchored interview, we float aimlessly in the sea of personality without compass or rudder.

Summary: This review of the failures of the Rorschach technique has found the following outstanding relationships:

(1) Global evaluations of the Rorschach seem to work when the Rorschach worker and the clinician work closely together.

(2) Atomistic evaluation, as well as global, of the content of the Rorschach protocols (as distinct from the perceptual scoring) seem to work.

(3) Atomistic analysis of the perceptual factors is a failure.

(4) Factor analysis of atomistic scores of both the perceptual as well as the content variety, seem to work.

The best hypothesis to explain these four facts is that the Rorschach is an interview and that its correct evaluation, like the correct evaluation of any interview, is dependent upon its content. If we provide scales for analyzing its content, we shall be well on the way toward clarifying many of the present day contradictions and obtain a better perspective on the evaluation of personality.

REFERENCES

1. AMES, L. B., LEARNED, J., METRAUX, R. W. AND WALKER, R. N., *Child Rorschach Responses.* New York: Paul B. Hoeber, Inc., 1952.

2. BARRON, F. X. Psychotherapy as a special case of personal interaction: Prediction of its course. (Doctoral Thesis, University of California, Berkeley, 1950) quoted in Sanford, N. *Psychotherapy,* Stone, C. P., Editor, *Annual Review of Psychology,* Annual Reviews, Inc. Stanford, Calif., 1953, p. 338.

3. BARRY, J. R., BLYTH, D. D. AND ALBRECHT, R. Relationship between Rorschach scores and adjustment level. *J. Consult. Psychol.,* 1952, *16,* 30–36.

4. BENJAMIN, J. D. AND EBAUGH, F. G. The diagnostic validity of the Rorschach test. *Amer. J. Psychiat.,* 1938, *94,* 1163–1178.

5. BAUGHMAN, E. E. Rorschach scores as a function of examiner difference. *J. Proj. Tech.,* 1951, *15,* 243–249.

5a. ———. *A comparative study of Rorschach forms with altered stimulus characteristics.* Ph.D. dissertation, Chicago, Illinois, March, 1951.

6. CARR, A. C. Evaluation of nine psychotherapy cases by the Rorschach. *J. Consult. Psychol.,* 1949, *13,* 196–205.

7. COLUMBIA GREYSTONE ASSOCIATES, F. A. METTLER, Editor. *Selective Partial Ablations of the Frontal Cortex,* New York: Paul B. Hoeber, 1949.

8. COX, S. M. A factorial study of the Rorschach responses of normal and maladjusted boys. *J. Genet. Psychol.* 1951, *79,* 95–115.

9. CRONBACH, L. J. A validation design for qualitative studies of personality. *J. Consult. Psychol.,* 1948, *12,* 365–374.

10. DAVIDSON, H. *Personality and economic background: a study of highly intelligent children.* New York: Kings Crown Press, 1943.

11. DÖRKEN, H. J. AND KRAL, A. The psychological differentiation of organic brain lesions and their localization by means of the Rorschach test. *Amer. J. Psychiat.,* 1952, *108,* 764–770.

12. EICHLER, R. M. A comparison of the Rorschach and Behn-Rorschach ink blot tests. *J. Consult. Psychol.,* 1951, *15,* 185–189.

13. ELIZUR, A. Content analysis of the Rorschach with regard to anxiety and hostility. *Rorschach Res. Exch.,* 1949, *13,* 274–284.

14. GIBSON, J. J. *The perception of the visual world.* Boston: Houghton Mifflin, 1950.

15. GRANT, M. Q., IVES, V. AND RANZONI, J. H. Reliability and validity of judges' ratings of adjusting on the Rorschach. *Psychol. Monogr.,* 1952, *66,* 1–20.

16. GUILFORD, J. P. Some lessons from aviation psychology. *Amer. J. Psychol.,* 1948, *3,* 3–11.

17. HAMLIN, R. M. AND ALBEE, G. W. Muench's tests before and after non-directive therapy: a control group for his subjects. *J. Consult. Psychol.,* 1948, *12,* 412–416.

18. HERTZ, M. R. The Rorschach ink blot test: historical summary. *Psychol. Bull.,* 1935, *32,* 33–56.

19. KELLEY, D. M. Clinical reality and projective techniques. *Amer. J. Psychiat.,* 1951, *107,* 753–757.

20. LORD, E. Two sets of Rorschach records obtained before and after brief psychotherapy. *J. Consult. Psychol.,* 1950, *14,* 134–139.

21. MCCALL, R. J. *Psychometric records in brain-operated patients.* Unpublished Ph.D. dissertation. Columbia University, 1950.

21a. MUENCH, G. A. An evaluation of nondirective psychotherapy by means of the Rorschach and other tests. *Appl. Psychol. Monogr.,* 1947, No. 13.

22. RAMZY, I. AND PICKARD, P. M. A study in the reliability of scoring the Rorschach ink blot test. *J. Gen. Psychol.,* 1949, *40,* 3–10.

23. ROGERS, L. S., KNAUSS, J. AND HAMMOND, K. R. Predicting continuation in the therapy by means of the Rorschach test. *J. Consult. Psychol.,* 1951, *15,* 368–371.

24. RORSCHACH, H. *Psychodiagnostics* (translation by P. Lemkau and B. Kronenburg). Berne: Verlag Hans Huber, 1942.

25. SANDLER, J. AND ACKNER, B. Rorschach content analysis: an experimental investigation. *Brit. J. Med. Psychol.,* 1951, *24,* 180–201.

26. SEN, A. A. A statistical study of the Rorschach test. *Brit. J. Psychol.,* 1950, *3,* 21–39.

27. SIIPOLA, E., KUHNS, F. AND TAYLOR, V. Measurement of the individual's reactions to color in ink blots. *J. Pers.,* 1950, *19,* 153–171.

28. TUCKER, J. E. Rorschach human movement and other movement responses in relation to intelligence. *J. Consult. Psychol.,* 1950, *14,* 283–286.

29. WATKINS, J. G. AND STAUFFACHER, J. C. An index of pathological thinking in the Rorschach. *J. Prog. Tech.*, 1952, *16*, 276–286.

30. WINDLE, C. Psychological tests in psychopathological prognosis. *Psychol. Bull.*, 1952, *49*, 461–482.

31. WILSON, G. P. *Intellectual indicators in the Rorschach test.* Unpublished Ph.D. dissertation. University of Texas, 1952.

32. WITTENBORN, J. R. AND HOLZBERG, J. D. The Rorschach and descriptive diagnosis. *J. Consult. Psychol.*, 1951, *15*, 460–463.

33. WITTENBORN, J. R. Certain Rorschach response categories and mental abilities. *J. Appl. Psychol.*, 1949, *33*, 330–338.

34. ZUBIN, J. Experimental abnormal psychology, 1953 (mimeographed edition).

Lee J. Cronbach

STATISTICAL METHODS

APPLIED TO RORSCHACH

SCORES ⸱ A Review[1]

WHILE THE Rorschach test grew out of clinical investigations, and is still primarily a method of individual diagnosis, there is increasing emphasis on statistical studies of groups of cases. On the whole, the statistical methods employed have been conventional, even though the Rorschach test departs in many ways from usual test methodology. The present review proposes to examine the methods which have been employed to deal with Rorschach data, and to evaluate the adequacy of those often used. It attempts to provide a guide to future investigations by indicating statistically correct studies which can serve as models. There is no intent here to review the generalizations about the test arising from these studies, or to call into question general research procedures, sampling, and other aspects of the studies.

This report may be considered an extension of a review by Munroe (41).

Reprinted from *Psychol. Bull.*, 1949, *46*, 393–429, by permission of the American Psychological Association and the author.

1. The writer wishes to express appreciation to Frederick Mosteller and to N. L. Gage, who read this manuscript and contributed many suggestions for its improvement.

In 1945, she considered the objectivity of previous Rorschach research. She distinguished between the goals attainable by clinical intuitive interpretation and the goals to be reached by more quantitative procedures. She traced the trend in Rorschach literature, noting the gradual decrease in studies based solely on impressionistic treatment of data or on mere counting of scores, and the introduction of significance tests, standard deviations, and other signs of adequate effort to test generalizations statistically. She also pointed out some errors in statistical thinking that lead to faulty conclusions about the Rorschach test. Munroe takes the position, and the writer fully concurs, that statistical research on the Rorschach test is not only justifiable, but indispensable. The flexibility of clinical thinking creates excellent hypotheses, but these hypotheses can be established as true only by controlled studies. Among the propositions suggested by clinical work, some are certainly untrue, due to faulty observation, inadequate sampling, and errors of thinking. Statistical controls are essential to verify theories of test interpretation, and to validate proposed applications of the test. Even though the clinician studying one person makes no use of statistics, he employs generalizations about the test which must rest on scientifically gathered evidence. Munroe demonstrated that the Rorschach test lends itself to objective studies; the writer reviews the same material more technically to evaluate the soundness of the statistical procedures on which the conclusions are based.

Clinical Treatments of Data

While this paper deals principally with statistical methods applied to *raw* Rorschach data, we shall consider briefly the statistical procedures used when clinically interpreted case records are used in a study. The Rorschach record is usually interpreted qualitatively and in a highly complex manner when the test is given in the clinic, and many studies have been based on these interpreted records. In only a few studies of this type do statistical problems arise.

Dichotomized Rorschach ratings. In one type of study, the interpreter of the records makes a final summary judgment, dividing the records into such groups as "adjusted-maladjusted" or "promising-unpromising," etc. This method is most used for validation studies, where the Rorschach judgment is compared with a criterion of performance or with a judgment from some other test. Simple statistical tests suffice to test the degree of relationship. If the criterion is expressed in two categories (as when the criterion indicates success or failure for each case), chi-square is simple and appropriate. This is exemplified in a study of success of Canadian Army officers (51), where a prediction from the Rorschach is compared with a later rating of success and failure. If the criterion is a set of scores on a continuous scale, bi-serial r is usually an adequate procedure. In bi-serial r, one assumes that the dichotomy represents a continuous trait which is normally distributed. This assumption is generally acceptable for personality traits and for ratings of success.

Rorschach ratings on continuous scale. In some studies, the Rorschach interpretation is reported in the form of a rating along a scale, rather than as a dichotomy. When the criterion is dichotomous, bi-serial r is appropriate. (E.g., a prediction of probable pilot success is so correlated with elimination-graduation from training, 21, p. 632.) For a continuous criterion, like grade-average, product-moment r is conventionally used.

These methods are not entirely satisfactory, because of a limitation of rating scales. If units on the rating scale are not psychologically equal, the correlation may not indicate the full size of the relationship. If ratings are careful, one can assume that men rated "Good" are superior to men rated "Fair," and that men rated "Excellent" are superior to both of these. But it may be unwise to assume that the jump from "Good" to "Excellent" is equal to the jump from "Fair" to "Good," as one automatically does in correlating. One solution to this difficulty is to assume that the trait rated is normally distributed in the men studied. Then we can condense the five-point scale into a dichotomy, which is the case discussed in the preceding paragraph. Alternatively, one may convert the ratings into scaled values which will yield a normal distribution (34). Bi-serial r is then appropriate, if the criterion is dichotomous. Similar reasoning applies to the correlation of a rating with a continuous criterion; one will obtain the most meaningful results by dichotomizing the rating and using bi-serial r, or by normalizing before using product-moment r. There suggestions are summarized in Table I.

Munroe (42), comparing a Rorschach adjustment rating with success in academic work, where both variables were reported on a four-category scale, used a coefficient of contingency. Where the correlation surface is nearly normal, this coefficient with proper corrections should give approximately the same result as the product-moment r for normalized data, corrected for broad categories. Yates (70) has recently offered an alternative method of adapting the contingency method to take advantage of trends in the relationship between variables expressed as ordered categories.

Matching methods. Another favorite technique for evaluating Rorschach results is blind matching, which permits a study of each case "as a whole." When a set of Rorschach records (interpreted or not) and another set of data regarding the same individuals are available, one may request

TABLE I

Preferred Methods of Comparing Rorschach Interpretations with
Criteria of Various Types

Judgment Made From Rorschach

Criterion	Dichotomy	Continuous Scale, Unequal Units
Dichotomy	χ^2	χ^2 after dichotomizing rating; r_{bis} after normalizing rating*
Continuous scale, unequal units	χ^2 after dichotomizing criterion; r_{bis} after normalizing criterion*	χ^2 after dichotomizing both variables; r_{bis} after normalizing one, dichotomizing the other; product-moment r after normalizing both
Continuous scale, equal units	r_{bis}*	r_{bis} after dichotomizing rating; product-moment r after normalizing rating

* Point bi-serial must be used if the two parts of the dichotomy cannot reasonably be considered subdivisions of a continuous scale.

judges to match the two sets in pairs. The success of matching is evaluated by a formula developed by Vernon (66). An example of its use is a study by Troup (62), in which judges tried to match two Rorschach records for each person. One hundred fourteen matches were correct out of a possible 120, judges considering five pairs at a time. By the Vernon formula, this corresponds to a contingency coefficient of .88. A coefficient of .40 was obtained when judges attempted to match the record of each case with that of his identical twin. Another excellent illustration of the method is provided by J. I. Krugman (31), who used it to establish that different evaluations of the same Rorschach protocol could be matched, and that the interpretations could be matched to the raw records and to criteria based on a case-study.

The limitations of this method are not statistical; they lie more in the human limitations of judges. A portrait based on the Rorschach may be nearly right, yet be mismatched because of minor false elements. Matching, on the other hand, might be excellent, even perfect; the study would still not guarantee that each element in each portrait was correct, especially if the subjects were quite different from each other. In fact, the portrait might be seriously wrong in some respects, without preventing matching.

A complex modification of the blind-matching method has been proposed and tried by Cronbach (9). Judges are asked to decide whether each statement on a list fits or does not fit a case described in a criterion sketch.

Since only about one-third of the statements in the list were actually made about the given case, one can test by chi-square whether the matching is better than chance. The method yields many interesting types of information: (a) an all-over estimate of the validity of predictions with relation to the criterion, (b) a separate estimate of the validity of the description for each case or for subgroups, and (c) an estimate of the validity of statements dealing with any one aspect of personality (e.g., social relations).

Errors in Statistical Studies

The majority of statistical studies with the Rorschach test have treated Rorschach scores directly, with clinical judgment eliminated. This is an important type of investigation, which presents numerous problems. Before considering general questions of procedure, however, it is necessary to deal with several errors and unsound practices found in the literature reviewed. These miscellaneous errors must be pointed out lest they be copied by later investigators, and to suggest that the studies in which the errors occurred need to be re-evaluated.

Significance tests for small samples. The critical ratio is not entirely satisfactory when applied to small samples. When there are fewer than 30 cases per group, the *t* test is preferable. This would apply, for example, in Goldfarb's (19) comparison of obsessionals with supposedly normal adolescents. His significance ratios are a bit too high, since he used the formula diff./$\sigma_{\text{diff.}}$ with groups of twenty cases. (It may be noted also that Goldfarb's study does not permit sound generalizations about obsessionals as compared to other adolescents. The obsessionals had a mean IQ of 120 compared to 97 for the normals, so that differences between the groups may be due to intelligence rather than obsessional trends.)

Chi-square is generally useful for small samples, but it is important to apply corrections when the number of cases is below fifty. This is especially important when the expected frequency in any cell of a 2×2 table is five or lower, under the null hypothesis. Many Rorschach studies fail to recognize the need for corrections, Kaback's (29, pp. 24, 38–39) being a striking example. She compares the distribution of such a score as *M* in each of two groups. To do so, she makes the distribution in a great number of intervals, with only a few cases per interval, and tests the similarity of the distributions by chi-square. In such a case, with many small cell frequencies, no significant result could be expected. Nor is it useful to inquire, as her procedure does, whether the precise distribution of *M* scores is the same for the two groups (in her case, pharmacists and accountants). Her major question was whether one group used M more than the other, and this could be answered by dichotomizing the distribution and then applying chi-square, with proper correction. In applying chi-square to the 2×2 tables, one should as a standard practice apply Yates's correction (56, p. 169). The importance of this correction will be demonstrated in Table IV. Where groups are dichotomized, it is best to make cuts toward the center, so that marginal totals will remain reasonably large. Special problems in the application of chi-square to successive tests of the same hypothesis, and to problems of goodness of fit, are discussed by Cochran (6).

Tests for significance of difference in proportions. Throughout the Rorschach literature, the formula for the significance of differences between proportions is misused. The resulting inaccuracy is slight in most problems, fortunately. This error is common in other work, and even some statistics books appear to endorse the faulty procedure. The usual formula,

$$\sigma_{p1-p2} = \sqrt{\frac{pq}{N_1} + \frac{pq}{N_2}}$$

may not be entered with p_1 and p_2, the proportions obtained in the two samples. Instead, one should substitute p_0 for p, where

$$p_0 = \frac{N_1 p_1 + N_2 p_2}{N_1 + N_2}$$

A significance test inquires whether p_1 and p_2 might arise by chance in sampling from a homogenous population in which the true proportion is p_0 (see 35, pp. 126–129). Employing p_1 and p_2, instead of entering p_0 in both terms, almost always increases the critical ratio over what it should be. Because no correct model is found in the Rorschach literature, the following example is given using Hertz' data (25).

Five boys out of forty-one, and 0 girls out of thirty-five gave zero color responses.

$$p_0 = \frac{5 + 0}{76} = .066$$

$$s.\,d._{\text{diff.}} = \sqrt{\frac{.066 \times .934}{51} + \frac{.066 \times .934}{35}} = .057$$

$$p_1 = .122;\ p_2 = .00;\ \frac{\text{diff.}}{s.d._{\text{diff.}}} = \frac{.122}{.057} = 2.14\ (P = .032)$$

This compares to the critical ratio of 2.41 $(P = .016)$ computed by the formula Hertz and other workers have inadvisedly used.

The above computation is equivalent to the determination of significance by chi-square, and yields an identical result. But in this instance the expected frequencies are so low that the correction for continuity becomes important. Applying Yates's correction, we find that P becomes .10, and the reported difference is not significant.

Several studies use the formula for proportions in independent samples when the formula for paired samples should be used. Thus Hertz (25), to compare the twelve-year-old and fifteen-year-old records of the same cases, should use a formula for correlated samples as given by Peatman (44, p. 407) or by McNemar (37; see also 13, 59). The correct formula would have yielded significant differences where Hertz found none. Other studies employing matched samples, where the significance of differences was underestimated by a formula for independent groups, are those of Hertzman and Margulies (27). Meltzer (39), M. Krugman (32), Richardson (48), and Goldfarb (20). In studies where the subjects were children varying widely in age, the proper formula would probably have yielded quite different results.

A study by Brown (4) committed this error and one even more serious. He compared records of twenty-two subjects without morphine and then with morphine. He found that fourteen increased in R and 7 decreased. He then treated these as independent proportions of the twenty-two subjects, computing the critical ratio for the difference 64% minus 32%. These are not proportions in independent samples, and Brown's statistical tests are meaningless. No manipulation of the increase-decrease frequencies is as satisfactory for this problem as the formula given by McNemar. Brown could properly have set a cutting score (e.g., 20R) and compared the percentage exceeding this level with and without morphine.

Siegel's procedure (55), in which the "percentage incidence" of a factor in one group is divided by the incidence in the second group, will be likely to produce misleading results.

An alternative formula for the significance of differences in matched groups is used by Gann (18). In applying the formula, however, a serious error was made. The formula given by Englehart which Gann adopted is

$$\sigma_{\text{diff.}}^2 = (\sigma_{M_1}^2 - \sigma_{M_2}^2)(1 - r_{if}^2)$$

r_{if} is the correlation of the matching variables with the variable in which a difference is being tested. This formula may be extended to differences in proportions, although the estimated population value (p_0) for the proportion should be substituted for M_1 and M_2, as explained above. Gann's major error was to use a value of .9741 for r_{if} in all her calculations. From the context, this seems to be a multiple correlation of all matching variables with *all* dependent variables. The proper procedure, for any single significance test such as the proportion of cases emphasizing *W,* would be to correlate the matching variables with *W*-tendency alone. This correlation would almost certainly be close to zero. By the procedure Gann used, the critical ratios are very much larger than they should be. In one comparison where Gann reported a CR of 6.02 the writer has established that the true CR cannot be greater than 2.23, and is almost certainly less.

Comparisons of total number of responses. It is thoroughly unsound to compare the total number of responses of a given type in two samples. Swift (58) tested thirty-seven boys and forty-five girls. The boys gave a total of 248 *F* responses; all girls combined gave 246. Swift used chi-square, demonstrating that these 494 responses were divided in a way which departs significantly from the theoretical ratio 37:45. But this assumes 494 independent events in her sample whereas she really had eighty-two. The *F* responses are not independent, since some were made by the same person. She might properly have used the *t*-test, applied to the means of the groups. The only correct way to use chi-square on her problem is to compare the number of cases exceeding a certain *F* score (cases, not responses, being the basis of sampling). A similar error has been made by Hertzman (26), Rickers (49, p. 231), and Werner (68).

Richardson (48) followed a different erroneous procedure. In her Table 9, she determined what proportion of all responses in each of her groups were *W* responses, and tested the difference in proportions for significance using the number of subjects in the denominator of the significance formula. The "proportion" she was studying is actually the ratio *Mean W/Mean R,* and the standard deviation of this is not correctly given by the formula $\sqrt{pq/N}$. If she must test the W/R ratio, in spite of the difficulties to be considered later, it is necessary to determine the ratio for each person separately and test differences between the groups in one of the conventional ways (e.g., chi-square, *t*-test, etc.).

Inflation of probabilities. Rorschach studies are peculiarly prone to an error which can arise in any statistical work. If a particular critical ratio or chi-square or *t*-test corresponds to a *P* of .05, we conventionally interpret that as statistically significant because "such a value would arise by chance only once in twenty times." While this usually refers to once-in-twenty samples, it may also be thought of as "once in twenty significance tests," if the several tests are independent. In some Rorschach studies, a vast number of significance tests are computed. Thus Hertz in one study reported the astonishing total of 800 significance tests (25). Many of these comparisons reach the 1 per cent level or the 5 per cent level, but even these are not all statistically significant. Quite a few of these differences did arise by chance, and unfortunately we cannot estimate how many because the tests were not experimentally independent. The proper procedure, in such a case, is to recognize that an inflation of *P* values has taken place. The analogy to monetary inflation is a fair one: The increase in the number of significance tests in circulation causes each *P* to have less worth than it would normally. We may accordingly raise our "price" arbitrarily, and insist that *P* reach a higher level than .05 before we label it "significant," and a higher level than .01 before we label it "very significant." Of the differences reported in the Rorschach literature as "significant at the 5% level," probably the majority are due to chance.

There are several ways in which significance levels may be inflated so that they become falsely encouraging. One is the common procedure of testing differences on a great many Rorschach scores. This is of course sound practice, but one must then take the total number of significance tests into account in evaluating *P*. The inflation is more subtle when the investigator rejects a large number of hypotheses by inspection without computing significance tests, and reports only a few significance tests. Thus Piotrowski and others (46) compared superior and inferior mechanical workers on "all the components used in conventional scoring as well as many others." They finally invented four composite scoring signs on which differences between the two samples were large enough to encourage a significance test. Suppose, for simplicity, that those four tests had yielded *P*'s of .02. The significance of those *P*'s must be minimized in view of the fact that four such differences were found in several hundred implied comparisons which were not actually computed, and two per hundred is chance expectation.

A comparable inflation arises when an investigator slices a distribution in order to take advantage of chance fluctuations and find some "hole" where a test will yield a low *P*. Hertz applied the formula for significance of the difference in proportions, to compare two groups on *M*% (Table II). She introduced a spurious element by slicing the *M*% distribution in so many places, and making so many significance tests. If a distribution is dichotomized in many ways, the chances of a "significant" difference rise greatly. Here only one test yielded a *P* of .05, out of nine attempted. The interpretation "It may be said with certainty, that more girls than boys at 15 years give over 11% *M*" (25, p. 180) is unjustified. In another sample this fluctuation would not occur. It is not necessary to test explicitly all possible dichotomies for this type of error to arise. If the investigator examines his distribution and makes his cut at the place where the difference is greatest, he has by implication examined and discarded all other possible hypotheses. One of the several studies where this occurs is that of Margulies, discussed later.

TABLE II

Significance Data Reported by Hertz for Differences in $M\%$ Between Fifteen-Year-Old Boys and Girls (25)

Difference Tested	Critical Ratio	P
Difference in means	1.47	.15
Difference in medians	2.32	.05
Difference in proportions		
in interval 0–1	.81	—
in interval 0–3	.81	—
in interval 0–5	1.83	.10
in interval 0–7	1.68	.10
in interval 0–9	.90	—
in interval 0–11	2.34	.05
in interval 0–13	1.24	—
in interval 0–15	1.81	.10
in interval 0–17	1.23	—

Multiple correlation procedures give rise to a similar error. Suppose ten scores are tried as predictors. These scores might be combined in a prediction formula in an infinite number of ways. When an investigator computes correlations and works out the best possible predictive combination for his particular data, he implicitly discards all the other combinations. Even though his combination gives a substantial multiple R for the original sample, it is certain to give a lower correlation in a new sample where the formula can no longer take advantage of chance fluctuations. The common practice of comparing two groups on a large number of signs and developing a checklist score in which the person is allowed one point for every sign on which the two groups differ, is open to the same objection. In a new sample many of these signs will no longer discriminate.[2] When a significance test is applied to a difference in check list scores or to a multiple correlation in the sample on which the combining formula was derived, the significance test has only negative meaning. If, even after taking advantage of chance differences, one's formula cannot discriminate, it is indeed worthless. But if the result gives a P better than .05, the formula may still be of no value. Rorschach studies which have reported "significant" differences based on an empirical formula without confirming them on fresh samples are those of Montalto (40), Harris and Christiansen (23), Hertzman, Orlansky, and Seitz (28), and Ross and Ross (52). Thompson (60) reports spurious r's but does not claim significance for them. Buhler and Lefever (5, Tables X,

2. Harris (24) claims that in his experience the Rorschach behaves differently from other tests, and that signs found to differentiate in one sample are usually confirmed in other samples. This appears improbable on logical grounds, and no evidence in the literature supports such a statement.

XX) mix new cases with the sample used in deriving scoring weights, and therefore fail to provide an adequate test of significance. Significance tests on fresh samples have been properly made by Guilford (21), Gustav (22), Margulies (38), Ross (50), and Kurtz (33). The latter gives a particularly clear discussion of the issue involved. In most studies, correlations nearly vanish when a Rorschach prediction formula is tried on a new sample.

Still another method of inflating probabilities is to recombine groups of subjects in a way to maximize differences. If one has several types of patients, all of whom earn different mean M scores, these groups may be recombined in many ways, and in one of the possible regroupings a pseudo-significant difference may be found. Rapaport and his coworkers (47) have carried inflation to bizarre levels. Not only did they consider scores in great profusion and in numerous combinations, they recombined their subjects so that the number of implicit significance tests in their volume is incalculable. They began with subjects in twenty-two subgroups. Significance tests were then made, on any score, between any pair of subgroups or combinations of them which seemed promising *after* inspection of the data. There were 231 possible pairs of subgroups, and an endless variety of combinations. Thus at times Unclassified Schizophrenics Acute were lumped with one, two, or more of the following: Paranoid Schiz. Acute, Simple Schiz., Uncl. Schiz. Chronic, Par. Schiz. Chr., Uncl. Schiz. Deteriorated; or with all the schizophrenics and preschizophrenics; or with Paranoid Condition, Coarctated Preschiz., Overideational Preschiz., and Obsessive-Compulsive Neurosis. Such willingness to test any hypothesis whatever leaves these workers open to the charge of having regrouped their cases to augment differences. They have undoubtedly reported differences which were created by artificial combinations of chance variations between groups. Every time cases are recombined for a significance test, one must recognize that a large number of implied significance tests were also made, since many other recombinations were rejected without actual computation.

Rorschach studies, because of the great number of scores and the large number of subgroups of subjects involved, are more prone to inflation than other research. The suggestions to be made for sound practice are these:

1. Compare the number of significant differences to the total number of comparisons in the study, both those computed and those rejected by implication.
2. Raise the P value required for significance as the number of comparisons increases.
3. Never accept an empirical composite score or regression formula until its discriminating power has been verified on a new sample.
4. In general, do not trust significance unless the hypothesis tested was set up independent of the fluctuations of a particular sample.

These suggestions require that the investigator have clearly in mind the number of comparisons considered. Comparisons are of three types: those rejected as improbable before the data are looked at, i.e., before the study is begun; those not computed because a cursory inspection showed no apparent difference; and those computed. Sometimes the investigator begins with, say, five groups of subjects and ten scores, and frankly wants to unearth all possible differences between types of subjects. Then there are ten ways the groups may be paired against each other, and since each pair may be compared on each score, there are a total of one hundred comparisons in the study. If, on the other hand, the investigator sets out to check only certain relationships—"Schizophrenics differ from neurotics in $F + \%$," "Manics differ from all other groups combined in $FC : CF + C$"—those limited hypotheses may be laid down in advance of the study, and only those comparisons are counted as implied significance tests. To avoid confusion, it is also well for the investigator to specify his cutting point, if a variable is to be dichotomized, before examining the differences between groups. This may be set by an arbitrary rule, for instance that each distribution is to be divided as near to its median as possible, or by an *a priori* decision to divide at some point such as $2M$. In essence, the investigator must ask himself before he gathers his data, "How many comparisons do I intend to look at, and charge myself for?" A P of .01 may be called significant if it is one of three comparisons charged for, but not if the investigator has looked at 300 comparisons in order to salvage this one impressive value.

Methods of Comparing Groups on Rorschach Scores

NECESSITY FOR CHOOSING BETWEEN STATISTICAL PROCEDURES

Because Rorschach scores are numbers which can be added, averaged, distributed, etc., most investigators have used conventional mental-test statistics without question. The most common need for statistics is to compare the test scores of groups and determine the significance of differences. The prominent methods encountered in Rorschach literature are as follows: significance of difference between means (critical ratio or t-test); analysis of variance; bi-serial r; significance of difference in proportions exceeding a particular score, or chi-square; and significance of difference between medians.

Apart from such errors as those listed in the preceding section, there is no reason for considering any of the procedures under discussion as mathematically incorrect. If a significant difference is revealed by any proper significance test, the null hypothesis must be rejected. Nevertheless, the investigator may not choose one of the techniques at random. *Different methods of analyzing the data will lead to different conclusions.* In particular, some procedures lead to a finding of no significant difference even though a true difference could be identified by another attack.

Let us illustrate first with some of Kaback's data (29). She administered the group Rorschach to men in certain occupations, and, *inter alia,* compared her groups on the number of popular responses. The means for accountants is 7.0; for accounting students, 7.3. By the *t*-test, the difference between means is not significant (*P ca.* .40). (Point bi-serial *r* applied to the same data gives the same significance level. Point bi-serial *r* and *t* are interchangeable procedures, and there is no merit in testing the hypothesis in both ways.) But if she had chosen the chi-square test, quite proper for her data, Kaback would have found a significant difference between the groups. Chi-square would be applied to compare the proportion of cases in each group having five or more popular responses. From her Table IV, this proportion is 60/75, accountants; 72/75, accounting students. The difference between accountants and accounting students is significant (*P* <.01). In this and other instances, Kaback disregarded a difference when the null hypothesis could be confidently rejected.

Further illustrative data are taken from Hertz' comparison of Rorschach scores of boys and girls. She tested each possible difference by several statistical devices, yielding results such as those for *M*% reproduced in Table II. By any of nine methods, she is informed that the two sex groups differ no more than might two chance samples. By the other computations, she is informed that the difference is significant at the 5% level. If different significance tests disagree, what one concludes depends nearly as much on what procedure one adopts as on the data themselves.

Hertz compared her boys and girls in forty-six instances. Each time, she tested the significance of differences between means and between medians. Four times the means differed significantly; five times, the medians differed significantly. But in only one out of forty-six comparisons was the difference significant by both methods. It is greatly to Hertz' credit that she saw the applicability of more than one significance test. But conclusions of research will be hopelessly confused and contradictory, unless we can find a basis for choosing between the procedures when one says " 'Tis significant" and the other says " 'Taint."

The choice between comparison of means and medians or between the *t*-test and chi-square cannot be left to the inclination of the experimenter;

the whole point of statistical method is to make an analysis freed from subjective judgment. The reason different methods yield different results is that they make different assumptions or try to disclose different aspects of the data. It is therefore important to recognize the ways in which the techniques differ. Differences which are of little concern in connection with most studies have peculiar importance in Rorschach work. The difficulties which make choice of procedures an important problem arise from three causes: the skewness of Rorschach scores, the complications introduced by ratio scores, and the dependence of Rorschach scores on the total number of responses.

CHOICE OF TECHNIQUES IN VIEW OF THE
INEQUALITY OF UNITS IN RORSCHACH SCALES

Many of the significant Rorschach scores give sharply skewed distributions for most populations. This fact is reported repeatedly (2, 25, 47). Skewness is usually found where many subjects earn 0, 1 or 2 points (i.e., *M, FM, m,* the shading scores, *CF,* and *C*), and in the location scores *W, D, Dd,* and *S.* Skewness itself is no bar to conventional significance tests. But in skew distributions the mean and median are not the same. Two distributions may have a significant difference in medians, and not in means (or vice versa) if either is skewed.[3] Furthermore, it is doubtful if a satisfactory estimate of $s.d._{mdn}$ can be obtained for a skewed distribution.

Disadvantages of the mean and related procedures. In any statistical computation based on addition of scores (mean *s.d., t,* analysis of variance), numerical distances between scores at different parts of the scale are treated as equal. Thus, since the average of 3 *W* and 7 *W* is the same as that of 1 *W* and 9 *W,* these computations assume that a shift 3 *W* to 1 *W* is equivalent to, or counterbalances, a shift 7 *W* to 9 *W.* There is no way of demonstrating equality of units unless one has some knowledge of the true distribution of the trait in question, or a definition of equality in terms of the characteristics of the property being measured. This problem is present in virtually all psychological tools, but other tests yield normal distributions which are assumed to represent the true spread of ability. On the other hand, *Rorschach interpretation based on clinical experience constantly denies the equality of units for Rorschach scores.* The average *W* score is near 6, and scores from 1 to 10 are usually considered to be within the normal range. No matter how extremely a person is lacking in *W* tendency, his score cannot go below zero. For one who overemphasizes *W,* the score may go up to 20, 30, or more. A *W* score only six points below the mean may be consid-

---

3. This argument is presented by Richardson (48). In attempting to study differences in medians, Richardson unfortunately uses an incorrect method of determining $s.d._{mdn}$.

ered clinically to be as extreme in that direction as a score fifteen points from the mean in the other direction. Munroe (42) has prepared a checklist which shows how units of certain Rorschach scores would have to be grouped in order to represent a regularly progressing scale of maladjustment. Her groupings based on clinical experience are of approximately this nature:

W (or $W\%$): 0 (or 1 poor) W response; 1–14%; 15–60%; 61–100%.

$Dd\%$:   0–9%; 10–24%; 25–49%; 50–100%.

m: 0–1; 2–3; 4–5; 6 or more.

If these units represent increasing degrees of maladjustment, the raw Rorschach scores do not form a scale of psychologically equal units. It is advisable to accept the clinical judgment on this point, especially in the absence of evidence for the assumption of equal units.

Use of median and chi-square. Unlike procedures involving the addition of scores, procedures based on counting of frequencies make no assumption about scale units. In fact, they give the same results no matter how the scale units are stretched or regrouped. The median, or the number of cases falling beyond some critical point (e.g. 10 W), depends only on the order of scores. This appears to justify the recommendation that counting procedures such as the median be given preference over additive procedures such as the mean in dealing with skew Rorschach distributions. To test the significance of a difference between two groups, the best procedure is to make a cut at some suitable score, and compare the number of cases in each group falling beyond the cut, using chi-square. This procedure is used by Rapaport (47) and Abel (1). The test of significance of differences between proportions yields the same result (see above). One virtue of cutting scores is that we may test for differences between groups both in the "high" and "low" directions. This is important, since either very high $F\%$ or very low $F\%$, for example, may have diagnostic significance. In the usual analysis based on means, deviations of the two types cancel.

In contrast to the chi-square method, many tests of significance involve computation of the standard deviation. These include the critical ratio of a difference between means or medians, analysis of variance, and the t-test. In these procedures, great weight is placed on extreme deviations from the mean. If mean W is 6, a case having 25 W increases Σd^2 (which enters the computation of the s.d.) by about 361 points; a case having 15 W increases Σd^2 by about 81 points; and 0 W, by only 36 points. In skewed Rorschach distributions, the few cases with many responses in a category have a preponderant weight in determining σ and the significance of the difference.

Whether weighting extreme cases heavily is acceptable depends on whether one considers the difference between 15 W and 25 W to be psychologically large and deserving of more emphasis than, say, the difference from 0 W to 5W. Chi-square weights equally all scores below (or above) the cutting point.

Normalizing distributions. One method used to obtain more equal units is to assume that the trait underlying the score is distributed normally in the population. Raw scores are converted to T-scores which are normally distributed (35, 67). (This procedure must be distinguished from another conversion, also called a T-score, used by Schmidt (54). Scores of the type Schmidt used are not normally distributed.) The effect of normalizing is to stretch the scale of scores as if it were made of rubber. Extreme scores below the median are weighted symmetrically to extreme scores above the median. Thus, in the conversion table prepared by Rieger and used by the writer (10), the median (6½ W) is placed at 100, and a score of 0 W is converted to 66, while 28 W becomes 134. This in effect compresses the high end of the W scale and expands the low end. This conversion does not alter any conclusion or significance test obtained by dichotomizing raw scores and applying chi-square. But the conversion alters markedly any conclusion based on variance or on comparison of means.

There is obviously much merit in using a procedure which leads to a single invariant result, independent of the assumption of the investigator about the equivalence of scores. Even if scores are normalized it is advised that the median be used to indicate central tendency, and chi-square to test significance. If, for some experimental design, the data must be treated by analysis of variance, the writer believes normalized scores will give results nearer to psychological reality than raw scores, but this judgment is entirely subjective.

Comparison of mean rank. Attention should be drawn to a new technique invented by Festinger (14) which is peculiarly suitable to the problem under discussion. This method assumes nothing about equality of units or normality of distributions, being based solely on the rank-order of individuals. To test whether two groups differ significantly in a score, one pools the two samples and determines the rank of each man in the combined group. The mean rank for each group is computed and the significance of the difference is evaluated by Festinger's tables. The method has not yet been employed in Rorschach research.

The Festinger method and chi-square are not interchangeable. Which should be used depends on the logic of a particular study. Chi-square answers such a question as "Does Group A contain more *deviates* than Group B in the score being studied?" The Festinger method gives weight to differences all along the scale, and therefore asks whether the two groups differ, all scores being considered. In one study, absence of M is quite important but differences in the middle of the range have no practical importance. In another study, differences all along the scale are worth equal attention.

The Festinger method appears to have the advantage of greater stability for small samples. Chi-square is much easier to use in samples of 30 or more per group. The Festinger method is not useful when there are numerous ties in score. Further experience with the new method may disclose other important distinctions.

SIGNIFICANCE TESTS COMPARED WITH

ESTIMATES OF RELATIONSHIP

Some investigators have perhaps not conveyed the full meaning of their findings to the reader because of a failure to distinguish between tests of the null hypothesis, and estimates of the probable degree of relationship between two variables. The former type of result is a function of the number of cases, whereas the latter is not, save that it becomes more trustworthy as more cases are included. When an investigator applies chi-square, the t-test, or the like, he determines whether his observations force him to conclude that there is a relationship between the variables compared. But if the degree of relationship is moderately low, and the number of cases small, the null hypothesis is customarily accepted even though a true relationship exists. It is proper scientific procedure to be cautious, to reject the hypothesis of relationship when the null hypothesis is adequate to account for the data. But in Rorschach studies, where sample size has often been extremely restricted, nonsignificant findings may have been reported in a way which discouraged investigators from pursuing the matter with more cases.

The study of McCandless (36) is a case in point. McCandless compared Rorschach scores with achievement in officer candidate school. In each instance save one, the t-test showed P greater than .05 that the difference would arise in chance sampling. But the samples compared contained only thirteen men per group. Under these circumstances, it would take a sharply discriminating score to yield a significant difference. If the sample size was raised to about fifty per group, and the differences between groups remained the same, twelve more of McCandless' thirty significance tests would be significant at the five percent, or even the one percent, level. When more cases are added, the differences will certainly change and most of them will be reduced in size. In fact, the writer believes, on the basis of other experience with statistical comparisons of the Rorschach with grades, that McCandless' negative findings are probably close to the results which would be found with a larger sample. But the point is that McCandless, and other investigators using small N's, have submitted the Rorschach to an extremely, perhaps unfairly, rigorous test. One way to compensate for the necessary rigor of proper significance tests is to also report the degree of relationship. A chi-square test may be supplemented by a contingency coefficient or a tetrachoric r. A t-test may be supplemented by a bi-serial r, or point bi-serial (not to determine significance, as Kaback used it, but to express the magnitude of the relationship). Sometimes reporting the means of the groups and their standard deviations, to indicate the degree of overlapping, is an adequate way to demonstrate whether the relationship looks promising enough to warrant further investigation.

To restate the problem: the investigator always implies two things in a comparison of groups: (a) that he considers the null hypothesis is definitely disproven by his data, or else that the null hypothesis is one way to account for the data, and (b) in case the null hypothesis still remains tenable, that he does or does not judge further investigation of the question to be warranted. He can never prove that there is no relationship. So, if his data report a non-significant difference, he must judge whether the difference is "promising" enough to warrant further studies. This judgment is not reducible to rules in the way the significance test is. Whether to recommend further work depends on the difficulty of the study, on the probable usefulness of the results if a low order of relationship were definitely established by further work, and in the investigator's general confidence that the postulated relationship is likely to be found.

METHODS OF PARTIALLING OUT
DIFFERENCES IN R

The usual approach when comparing groups is to test the differences in one score after another, and then to generalize that the groups differ in the traits to which the scores allegedly correspond. The various scores, however, are not experimentally independent—a man's total record is obtained at once, and his productivity influences all his scores. If two groups differ in R, they may also differ in the same direction in W (whole responses), D (usual details), and Dd (unusual details).

Thus consider the Air Force data in Table III.
The first group has more responses than the second. From the means in W and D, it would appear that the first group has more W tendency than the second, but is equal in D. But when responsiveness is controlled by converting scores to percentages, the difference in W becomes small and the second group is shown to be stronger than the first in emphasis on D.

TABLE III

Rorschach Scores Compared to Success in Pilot Training (21, p. 632)

Rorschach Score	Mean of Successful Cadets	Mean of Unsuccessful Cadets	Bi-serial r
R	18.5	15.8	.14
W	9.2	7.3	.24
D	7.1	6.7	.03
$W\%$	60.2	55.8	.08
$D\%$	31.7	37.6	−.15

The most striking illustration of this difficulty is Goldfarb's comparison of obsessionals and normals. The obsessional group averages fifty-five R; the normals, fourteen. Under the circumstances, it is not at all informative to proceed to test W, D, and Dd; all differ significantly in the same direction. One learns nothing about differences between groups in mental approach, which is the purpose of considering these three scores. Most of Goldfarb's other comparisons also merely duplicate the information given by the test in R, that is, that the obsessionals are more productive. Although the discrepancy between the groups in R is unusually striking in Goldfarb's group, it is present to a lesser but significant degree in a great number of other studies, including those of Buhler and Lefever (5), Hertzman (26), Kaback (29), Margulies (38), and Schmidt (54).

A similar problem complicated Beck's comparison of schizophrenics and normals on D. The means were 19.0 and 19.9, respectively; the σ's were 13.5 and 9.9. Beck comments as follows:

The small difference is accentuated in the very small Diff./S.D. diff. 0.34. There is, however, probably a spurious factor in this small difference. The ogives give us a hint: up to the eighty-second percentile, the curves run parallel, with that for controls where we should expect it, higher. Above this point, the schizophrenics' curve crosses over, and continues higher, and more scattering, as we should expect from the S.D. The spurious element lies undoubtedly in the fact that the schizophrenics' higher response total would necessarily increase the absolute quantity of D, since these form the largest proportion of responses in practically all records. Absolute quantity of details is then no indicator of the kind of personality we are dealing with. . . . The medians for D are 14.46, 17.2 (2, pp. 31–32).

When one makes several significance tests in which the difference in R reappears in various guises, one becomes involved in a maze of seemingly contradictory findings. And interpretation tempts one to violate the rule of parsimony, that an observed difference shall be interpreted by the fewest and simplest adequate hypotheses. To answer the question, how do obsessionals and normals differ? it is simpler to speak of the former as more productive than to discuss three hypotheses, one for each approach factor. And one may certainly criticize Hertzman and Margulies (27) for interpreting differences in D and Dd between older and younger children as showing the former's greater "cognizance of the ordinary aspects of reality" and greater concern with facts. The older group gives twice as many R's as the former, which is sufficient to account for the remaining differences.

One might argue that R is resultant rather than cause, and that the differences in W, D, Dd, etc., are basic. But the Air Force demonstration that R varies significantly from examiner to examiner (21) suggests strongly that responsiveness is a partly superficial factor which should be controlled.

Only two studies examine their data explicitly to determine if differences in other categories could be explained in terms of responsiveness alone. Werner (68) found a significant difference in $dd\%$ between brain-injured and endogenous defectives. But the latter gave significantly more R's. He therefore counted only the first three responses in each card, and arrived at new totals. With R thus held about constant, he found the dd difference still marked and could validly interpret his result as showing a difference in approach.

Freeman and others (17) found that groups who differed in glucose tolerance also differed significantly in R. After testing differences in M and *sum* C on the total sample, they discarded cases until the two subsamples were equated in R. Since differences between the groups in M and C were in the same direction even when R was held constant, they were able to conclude with greater confidence that glucose tolerance is related to M and C.

After differences in R are tested for significance, it is appropriate to ask what other hypotheses are required to account for differences in the groups. But these other hypotheses should be independent of R; otherwise one merely repeats the former significance test and obscures the issue. The usual control method is to divide scores by R, testing differences in $W\%$, $D\%$, $M\%$, $A\%$, $P\%$, etc. Such ratios present serious statistical difficulties discussed in the next section. Moreover, these formulas fail to satisfy the demand for independence from R. There may be correlation between R and $W\%$, etc. (For a sample of 268 superior adults from a study by Audrey Rieger, the writer calculates these r's: $W\% \times R$, $-.45$, $M\% \times R$, $.03$, $F\% \times R$, $.06$. In the latter two cases, there is no functional relation of the percentage with R, but the distributions are heteroskedastic. $\sigma_{W\%} = 3.30$ when R 5–19 (74 cases) but 2.09 when R 40–109 (82 cases). The corresponding sigmas for $M\%$ are 3.85 and 3.35; for $F\%$, 3.23 and 2.29. Only $M\%$ is really independent of R.)

One may control differences in R by other methods, provided many cases are available. One procedure is to divide the samples into subgroups within which *R* is nearly uniform (e.g., *R* 20–29), and make significance tests for each such set. A method which requires somewhat fewer cases is to plot the variable against *R* for the total sample or a standard sample, and draw a line fitting the medians of the columns. This may be done freehand with no serious error. Then the proportion of the cases in each group falling above the line of medians may be compared by chi-square.

DIFFICULTIES IN TREATING
RATIOS AND DIFFERENCES

More than any previous test in widespread use, the Rorschach test has employed "scores" which are arithmetic combinations of directly counted scores. One type is the ratio score, or the percentage in which the divisor is a variable score. Examples are *W:M, M:sum C, W/R (W%)*, and *F/R (F%)*. The other type of composite is the difference score, such as *FC − (CF + C)*. In clinical practice, scores of this type are used to draw attention to significant combinations of the original scores; the experienced interpreter thinks of several scores such as *FC, CF,* and *C,* at once, placing little weight on the computed ratio or difference. When these scores are used statistically, however, there is no room for the flexible operation of intelligence; the ratios are treated as precise quantities.

It may be noted in passing that a few workers (e.g., 63) appear to assume that Mean *a*/Mean *b* is the same as Mean $\frac{a}{b}$. This is of course not true; the mean of the ratios and the ratio of the means may be quite unequal. One cannot, as Kaback did (29, pp. 33, 53, 55), assume that if the ratio of the means is greater for one group than another, the groups differ in the ratio scores themselves. The reader may convince himself by computing the mean ratio for each of the following sets of data in which Mean *a*/Mean *b* is constant:

$$\frac{0}{2}, \frac{2}{4}, \frac{4}{6}, \frac{6}{8}, \frac{8}{10}; \quad \frac{0}{6}, \frac{2}{8}, \frac{4}{2}, \frac{6}{10}, \frac{8}{4}; \quad \frac{0}{10}, \frac{2}{8}, \frac{4}{6}, \frac{6}{4}, \frac{8}{2}.$$

One difficulty with ratio scores is their unreliability. Consider a case with 5 *W*, 1 *M*. The ratio *W:M* is 5. But *M* is a fallible score. On a parallel test it might shift to 0 or to 2. If so, the ratio could drop to $2\frac{1}{2}$, or zoom to infinity; such a score is too unstable to deserve precise treatment. The unreliability of another ratio is illustrated in Thornton and Guilford's data (61). The reliabilities were, in one sample, .92 for *M*, .94 for *C*, but .81 for *M/C*. In a second sample, the values were .77, .65, and .31. If unreliable ratios are added, squared, and so on, one commits no logical error, but psy-

chologically significant differences become overshadowed by errors of measurement.

Ratios based on small denominators are in general unreliable (7). $W\%$
is unreliable for a subject whose R is 12, but relatively reliable for a case
whose R is 30. In the former case, addition of one W response raises $W\%$
by 8; in the latter, by 3%. Errors of measurement always reduce the significance of differences by increasing the within-groups variance. A significant difference in $W\%$ might be found for cases where $R>25$. A difference
of the same size might not be significant for cases where $R<25$ because of
the unreliability of the ratio. If the significance test were based on all cases
combined, the difference might be obscured by the unreliability of the ratios in the latter group. One possible procedure is to drop from the computations all cases where the denominator is low. (If there is a significant difference even including the unreliable scores, this need not be done.)

The issue of skewness must again be raised. In the $M{:}sum\ C$ ratio, all
cases with excess C fall between zero and 1. Those with excess M range from
1 to ∞. The latter cases swing the mean and sigma. Following the argument
of a preceding section, it is injudicious to employ statistics based on the
mean and standard deviation, as McCandless (36) did. By such procedures,
different conclusions would often be reached if both $M{:}sum\ C$ and $sum\ C{:}M$
were tested. Procedures leading to a chi-square test are to be recommended, as
illustrated in several studies (Rapaport, 47, pp. 251; Rickers, 49; etc.) Another
solution, less generally suitable, is to convert ratio scores to logarithmic form
to obtain a symmetrical distribution (61).

A hidden assumption in ratios and differences is that patterns of scores
yielding equal ratios (or differences) are psychologically equal. Thus, in
$W\%$ the same ratio is yielded by 2 W out of 10 R, 8 W out of 40, and 20 W
in 100 R. One can always define and manipulate any arbitrary pattern of
scores without justifying it psychologically, but better conclusions are
reached if the assumption of equivalence is defensible. The regression of W
on R is definitely curved. A person with 2 W out of 10 R is low in W
tendency, since it is very easy to find two wholes in the cards. Only people
with strong tendency and ability to perceive wholes can find 20 W in the
ten cards, regardless of R. As R rises above 40, W seems to rise very little;
the additional responses come principally from D and Dd. The resulting
decline in $W\%$ reflects a drive to quantity, rather than a decreased interest
in W (cf. 47, p. 156). Put another way: a strong drive to W can easily lead
to 90 or 100% W when $R<15$; but such a ratio in a very productive person
is unheard of. If the regression of a on b is linear and a close approximation
to $(a/b) = some\ consant$, ratios may be used as a score with little hesitancy.
Otherwise the ratio is a function of the denominator.

This factor is recognized by Munroe, who indicates repeatedly in her checklist that the significance of a particular ratio depends on R. Thus 30–40% M is rated $+$ if $R = 10$, but 16–29% is rated $+$ if $R = 50$. Numerically equal Rorschach ratios, then, are not psychologically equal. Rapaport reflects the same point in testing differences between groups in W/D. Instead of applying chi-square to the proportions having the ratio 1:2 or lower, he adjusted his standard.

In records where R is too low or too high, we took cognizance of the fact that it is difficult not to get a few W's and difficult to get too many. Thus, in low R records the 1:2 norm shifted to a "nearly 1:1" while in high R records, the 1:2 norm shifted to a 1:3 ratio (47, p. 134).

This adjustment was evidently done on a somewhat subjective basis, and is therefore not the best procedure. It is unfortunate that most other workers have unquestionably assumed that a given score in $W\%$, $M\%$, or $FC - (CF + C)$ has the same meaning regardless of R.

At best, ratio- and difference-scores introduce difficulties due to unreliability and to assumptions of equivalence. There is a fairly adequate alternative which avoids statistical manipulation of ratios entirely. One need only list all significant patterns, and determine the frequency of cases having a given pattern. Thus $M:sum\ C$ can be treated in these categories: coarctated (M and C 2 or below); ambiequal, M or $C < 2$, M and C differ by 2 or less; introversive, M exceeds C by 3 or more; extratensive, C exceeds M by 3 or more. Any other psychologically reasonable division of cases may be made, and significance of differences tested by chi-square, provided that the hypothesis is not chosen to take advantage of fluctuations in a particular sample. Even this method, however, does not escape the criticism that a given pattern of two scores, such as 3 M, 3 C, has different significance in records where R differs greatly. To cope with this limitation, the pattern tabulation procedure is suggested later.

A detailed consideration of certain work by Margulies is now appropriate, since it affords an illustration of many problems presented above. Her study of the $W:M$ ratio employed a procedure almost like that just recommended, but with departures which are unsound. Margulies compared Rorschach records of adolescents having good and poor school records (38). Only her twenty-one successful boys and her thirty-two unsuccessful boys need be considered here. She was interested in comparing them on the $W:M$ pattern, in view of Klopfer's belief that this ratio indicates efficient or inefficient use of capacity. She not only tested her data in several ways, but reported the data so that other calculations can be made. Table IV reproduces a part of her data, and shows the results of seven different procedures for determining the significance of the difference.

TABLE IV

Results Obtained When a Set of Data is Treated by a Variety of Procedures
(Data from Margulies, 38, pp. 23, 26, 44)

	Distribution I			*Distribution II*				*Distribution III*	
Number of M	Successful Boys	Unsuccessful Boys	W/M Ratio	Successful Boys	Uusuccessful Boys	Pattern of W and M		Successful Boys	Unsuccessful Boys
3 or more	5	5	<1	1	1	$W<6$, M 0–1		0	10
2	9	8	1.00	0	2	$W<6$, $M>1$		8	2
1	3	11	1.1–2.9	8	5	$W>5$, M 0–1		7	9
0	4	8	3.0–4.9	5	7	W 6–10, M 2		3	7
			>4.9	3	9	W 6–10, $M>2$		1	4
			∞(W/0)	4	8	$W>10$, $M>1$		2	0

It should be noted first that Yates's correction is essential for tables with 1 d.f. and low frequencies; in each case where it is applicable, the correction lowers the significance value importantly. Second, attention may be turned to the use of chi-square to test differences between two distributions. Even if more cases were available, it would be unwise to apply chi-square to the distribution cell by cell (Procedures 2, 3), since this procedure ignores the regular trend from class-interval to class-interval. Instead, the distribution should be dichotomized. Therefore, procedure 5 is preferable to 2, and 6 is preferable to 3. It will be noted that these recommended procedures indicate higher significance than the tests in which the distributions are compared cell by cell.

TABLE IV (*continued*)

Type of Analysis	Procedure	Result	P	Results with Yates's Correction	
				χ^2	P
Central tendency	1. Significance of difference in mean M	CR= .70*	.48	..	..
Cell-by-cell comparison	2. Chi-square applied to Distribution I (3 d.f.)	$\chi^2 = 3.78***$	ca. .30	..	..
	3. Chi-square applied to Distribution II (5 d.f.)	$\chi^2 = 5.30*$	ca. .40	..	..
	4. Chi-square applied to Distribution III (5 d.f.)	$\chi^2 = 17.73*$	<.01	..	..
Dichotomy	5. Chi-square applied to number of cases with $M>1$ (Dist. I)	$\chi^2 = 3.46**$	.06	2.54**	.11
	6. Chi-square applied to number of cases with $W/M>3$ (Dist. II)	$\chi^2 = 1.86**$	.18	1.13**	.30
Frequency of selected patterns	7. Chi-square applied to frequency having $M>1$ if $W>6$ or >10; having $M>2$ if $6<W<10$ (Dist. III)	$\chi^2 = 6.58**$	.01	5.13**	.03

* Computed by Margulies.
** Computed by the writer.
*** Computed by the writer. Margulies reports 3.64.

Margulies is one of the few writers to note the unsoundness of assuming that equal ratios are equal. She pointed out that 20 W: 10 M is not psychologically similar to 2 W:1 M, and she demonstrated that the regression of M on W is significantly curvilinear. She therefore was properly critical of procedures such as 3 and 6. She next turned to the scatter diagram of M and W, and found successful boys predominating in some regions, and unsuccessful boys in others. After grouping scores into regions as shown in Distribution III, she divided the surface into two areas, one area including cases where W is 0 to 5 and M is 2 or over, plus cases where W is 6 to 10 and M is 3 or over, plus cases where W is over 10 and M is 2 or over. In other words, instead of testing whether the groups are differentiated by a cut along the straight line $M = 2$ (Procedure 5), she made her cutting line an irregular one. This hypothesis, tested in Procedure 7, gave apparently quite significant results. The results are of little value, however, since the hypothesis was "cooked up" to fit the irregularities of these specific data. In the cells where W is 6 to 10, and M is 2, there happens to be a concentration of unsuccessful boys. But to draw the cutting line irregularly to sweep in all areas where the unsuccessful predominate is a type of gerrymandering which vitiates a significance test. Hundreds of such irregular lines might be drawn. Therefore, it would be expected that in any sample some line could be found yielding a difference "significant" at the 1 per cent level. At best, the irregular line sets up a hypothesis which, if found to yield a significant difference in a new and independent sample, could be taken as possibly true.

The law of parsimony enters this problem. Wherever a set of data may be explained equally well by two hypotheses, it is sound practice to accept the simpler hypothesis. Irregular cutting lines, and explanations in terms of patterns of scores, are sometimes justified and necessary. But in this case the difference between the groups is explained as well by the hypothesis that the successful boys give more M's as by any non-spurious test of the $W:M$ relationship. Therefore, procedure 5 is the soundest expression of the significance of the Margulies data. With more cases, this difference might be found to be truly significant.

In the above analysis, we find again that different procedures, more than one of which is mathematically sound, give different conclusions. The results from chi-square are less compatible with the null hypothesis than is the critical ratio. Chi-square applied to a dichotomy gives evidence of a possible relationship whereas chi-square applied to the frequency distribution does not. Attention is again drawn to the necessity of regarding with great suspicion any significance test based on a complex hypothesis set up to take advantage of the fluctuations of frequencies in a particular sample. Finally, it is noted that explanations in terms of ratios and patterns should not be sought unless they can account for observed differences more completely than can hypotheses in terms of single scores.

Treating Patterns of Scores

Rorschach workers continually stress the importance of considering any score in relation to the unique pattern of scores for the individual. While this is done in clinical practice, there is no practical statistical procedure for studying the infinite complex interrelations of scores and indications on which the clinician relies. Instead of considering the individual patterns, the statistician can at best study certain specific patterns likely to occur in many records. A pattern can be exceedingly complex; there is no statistical reason to prevent one from studying whether (for example) more men than women show high-S-on-colored-cards-accompanied-by-emphasis-on-M-and-excess-of-CF-over-C. The only limitation the statistical approach imposes is that the same pattern of scores must be studied in all cases.

Patterns of scores may be considered by means of composite scores, by definition of significant "signs," and by the pattern-tabulation method. The composite score is simply an attempt to express, in a formula, some psychologically important relationship. Examples include the M: *sum C* ratio, and the more complex composites developed by Hertz or Rapaport. These scores may be treated satistically like any score on a single category, although most of them are ratios or differences and suffer from the limitations already discussed.

Comparing incidence of "signs." The "signs" approach has been widely used. It is simple and well-adapted to the Rorschach test. Normally, an investigator identifies some characteristic of a special group, such as neurotics, from clinical observation. Then this characteristic is defined in a sign, i.e., a rule for separating those having the characteristic. One such sign, for example, is $FM>M$. After the investigator hypothesizes that some sign is discriminative, the necessity arises for making a test of significance to see if the sign is found more often in the type of person in question. One may soundly compare a new sample of the diagnosed group with a control sample by noting the frequency of the sign in each group and applying chi-square. This procedure is illustrated in studies by Hertzman and Margulies (38), and Ross (50).

The investigator may invent his own signs, if he follows due precautions to avoid misleading inflation of probabilities. Often it is easier and equally wise to use a predetermined set of signs. The most useful set of signs available at present is the Munroe check list. She has identified numerous ratios and patterns of scores which she considers significant of disturbance in her subjects (adolescent girls). She has stated that she does not think of her method as a set of signs (41), but the difference between her list and others appears to be (a) that it provides an inclusive survey of all deviations in a record and (b) that the list is designed as a whole to minimize duplication from sign to sign. There is no reason why two groups may not be compared by applying the check list to every record, and then comparing the groups on the frequency with which they receive each of the possible checks. Chi-square is the proper significance test, as used in one of Munroe's studies (43). The Munroe signs sometimes are simply defined (e.g. $P-$ is 0 or 1 popular response), but some involve patterns of several scores (thus the sign $FM+$ is defined in terms of FM, M, and R).

Pattern tabulation. Pattern tabulation is a method devised by Cronbach for the study of relations between two or three scores (10). It has the advantage of permitting one to study the distribution of patterns in a group. To deal with any set of three scores, e.g. W, D, Dd, one normalizes the three scores for each person, and considers the resulting profile. The profile is expressed numerically in terms of the deviation of the converted scores from their average for each person. These three scores can be plotted on a plane surface, and the resulting scattergram shows the distribution of patterns in a group. If two groups are compared, any type of pattern found more commonly in one group than another can be identified, and the difference in frequency tested by chi-square. The significance level for rejecting the null hypothesis must be set conservatively, as this method involves many implied significance tests. An analysis of variance solution is also possible but not recommended in view of the fact that distributions of patterns are often non-normal.

This method cannot consider hypotheses involving more than three scores at once. It functions best when the three scores are equally reliable and equally intercorrelated. It encounters difficulty due to the fact that some Rorschach scores are unreliable, since any serious error of measurement in one score throws an error into the profile. The method does, however, appear flexible and especially useful for such meaningful patterns as W-D-Dd and M-$sumC$-F.

Another group of procedures leading to composite formulas for discriminating groups is treated in the text section.

Discrimination by Composite Scores

In many problems, it is desired to use the Rorschach to discriminate between two groups. Thus one might seek a scoring formula to predict pilot success, or a "neurotic index" to screen neurotics from a general population. The methods used to arrive at composite scores are the check list, the multiple regression equation, and the discriminant function.

Check list scores. The check list consists of a set of signs. Each person is scored on the check list and the total number of signs or checks is taken as a composite score. This method has had condsiderable success, notably in Munroe's study (42) and in the formula of Harrower-Erickson and Miale for identifying insecure persons. There are no serious statistical problems in the use of check lists. The total score can be correlated (though eta may be preferable to *r*). Differences between groups may be tested for significance, preferably by chi-square. Chi-square is advised because a difference in the non-deviate range is rarely psychologically significant; the investigator is usually concerned with the proportion of any group in the deviate range. Buhler and Lefever justifiably applied analysis of variance to their check list score, to study its ability to differentiate clinical groups (5).

Problems do arise, however, in developing check list scores. A common method is to compare two groups on one raw score after another, noting where their means differ. Each score where a difference arises is then listed as a sign, and counted positively or negatively in obtaining the check list score for each case. This method takes advantage of whatever differences between samples arise just from accidents of sampling. If sample A exceeds B in mean *M*, allowing one point in the total score for high *M* will help discriminate A's and B's. In this sample, the A's will tend to earn higher check list scores. But often in a new sample such a difference will not be confirmed, and the *M* entry in the composite will not discriminate.

One study employing the sign approach should be pointed out to Rorschach workers. Davidson (12) sought to determine the relationship between economic background and Rorschach performance in a group of highly intelligent children. Her treatment of data is noteworthy because of her procedures; statistics are applied with great intelligence, new procedures being adopted for each new type of comparison. While the reviewer disagrees with some of the judgments she made in selecting procedures, her treatment is free from overt errors and well worth study by other Rorschach investigators.

Davidson divided her 102 cases among seven economic levels. She studied the Rorschach performance in various ways. First, she made a clinical analysis of each child, and placed him in one of nine categories (introvert adjusted, childish, constricted, disturbed, etc.). The distribution which resulted is a 7×9 table. Recognizing that the expected frequency in each cell is quite small, she combined groups to form a 3×3 table before applying the chi-square test for significance. This same type of condensation would have been advisable in some other comparisons she made, such as that between personality pattern and IQ. Davidson next applied a list of signs, and obtained for each case the total number of signs of maladjustment. The number of signs was correlated with economic level, and the correlation was shown not to differ significantly from zero. She tested the significance of the difference in mean number of signs by the critical ratio. These procedures appear well suited to her data. A third attack on the data treats one Rorschach score at a time. Here Davidson placed her cases in seven categories, ranging from highest to lowest economic level. By analysis of variance, she demonstrated that differences among the seven groups were significant only for a few of the scores. The application of analysis of variance to continuous data appears to have been an unwise decision. Analysis of variance, like chi-square or eta applied to a variable divided in several categories, ignores the order of the categories. Consider the following set of means in the score $M - sumC$:

Economic level	1	2	3	4	5	6	7	Total
Mean score	1.17	1.86	1.29	0.96	−0.75	−0.13	−0.71	0.63

The downward trend from Group 1 to Group 7 gives great support to the hypothesis that this score is related to economic level. Analysis of variance estimates significance without considering this trend; the same significance estimate would be arrived at if Group 2 had had the mean of −0.13 and Group 6 the mean of 1.86. Davidson might have computed the correlation between each score and the economic level, but the skewness of some Rorschach scores weighs against this suggestion. The simplest procedure for testing this trend is to split the group into a 2×2 table by combining adjoining categories in the economic scale, and dichotomizing the Rorschach score at a convenient point. Chi-square would then give the significance estimate. Such a procedure might have yielded significant differences in several instances where Davidson found none.

In justice to Davidson, it should be repeated that her data have been singled out for critical comment because of their exactness and completeness, rather than because they were improperly handled. The foregoing suggestions point to ways in which she might have arrived at additional important findings.

The multiple regression formula. A limitation of check lists is that they are simple additive combinations of signs which individually discriminate. But in such a composite a given trait may enter several times if it is reflected in several signs, and thus have greater proportionate weight than it deserves. The check list method does not allow for the possibility that certain signs may reinforce each other to indicate more severe maladjustment than is indicated by a combination of two other non-reinforcing signs, or for the possibility that two signs which are individually unfavorable may operate to neutralize each other. Multiple regression and the discriminant function are more powerful procedures than the usual check list score, because they consider the intercorrelations of scores and weight them accordingly.

By multiple correlation, one arrives at a regression equation which assigns weights to those variables which are correlated with a criterion and relatively uncorrelated with each other. This formula may be used to predict or to discriminate between groups. One such formula is that of the Air Force, used in its attempt to predict pilot success (21):

$$2(Dd + S\%) + 6\,FM + 8\,W - 1.5\,D\% + R - (VIII - X\%).$$

Multiple correlation does not seem especially promising for Rorschach studies. Even such an elaborate formula as that above turns out to have little or no predictive value when applied to a fresh sample. Even if it were stable, any formula of this type must assume that strength in one component compensates linearly for weakness in another. In this formula, emphasis on *Dd* would cancel weakness in *FM,* in estimating a man's pilot aptitude. It is most unlikely that the factors cancel each other in the personality itself. The simple linear regression formula provides an efficient weighting if the assumption of linear compensation is valid, but interrelations between aspects of personality are probably far too complex to be adequately represented in this way. The most that can be said for a regression formula is that, when derived on large samples (and this may require 5000 cases), it is a more precise prediction formula than the simple check list score can be. It cannot hope to yield very accurate predictions if interrelations within personality are as complex as Rorschach interpreters claim.

The discriminant function is a relatively new technique giving a formula which will separate two categories of men as thoroughly as possible from a mixed sample. It would be used to develop an effective index for separating good from poor pilots (not for predicting which man will be best, as the regression formula does) or for distinguishing organics and feeble-minded. A practical procedure for dealing with multiple scores has just been published by Penrose (45), and has not been employed in the Rorschach research. It appears likely to have real value in studies comparing different types of subjects.

Like the regression formula, however, the discriminant function provides a set formula. In this formula, it is assumed that one factor compensates for or reinforces weakness in another factor. The interactions within personality are probably too complex to be fully expressed by linear or quadratic discriminant functions.

Correlation and Reliability

Correlations of scores. For one purpose or another several studies have tried to show the relationship between the several Rorschach scores or between Rorschach scores and external variables. The conventional procedure for showing that two characteristics are associated is to compute a product-moment correlation between the variables. This has been done by Kaback (29), Vaughn and Krug (64), and others.

This method is unable to show the full relationship between variables when the regression of one on the other is curvilinear. Such a regression often occurs when one variable or both have a sharply skewed distribution. In fact, Vaughn and Krug note that one of their plots is curvilinear. The extent to which association may be underestimated is suggested by the following data. The data used are taken from tests administered individually by Audrey Rieger to several hundred applicants for employment, usually for managerial or technical positions. The tests were carefully scored by the Beck method. Generalization from the data must be limited because the group is not a sample of any clearly defined population. For 268 men, the product-moment correlation between D and Dd is .735. The curvilinear correlations are η_{DdD}, .785; η_{DDd}, .823. There is significant curvilinearity. If D and Dd are normalized, the regression becomes linear except for the effect of tied scores where $Dd = 0$; for the converted scores, $r = .767$.

Brower employs rank-difference correlations in comparing certain Rorschach scores to physiological measures (3). This is a useful method for small samples and is equally sound for linear and non-linear regressions. Thus, a rank-correlation of W/M with another score is the same except for sign as the correlation for the inverted ratio M/W, but the product-moment correlations are far different.

The rank method does have the disadvantage of weighting heavily the small and unreliable differences in the shorter end of skew distributions, where many cases have the same rank. This might lower the correlations for a score like Fc, but is not a difficulty with scores distributed more symmetrically over a wide range, such as F or $VIII–X\%$. Normalizing has the same disadvantage. This is a reflection of the inability of the test to discriminate finely among cases in the modal end of a severely skewed distribution.

Reliability coefficients. Test reliability is ordinarily estimated by the retest or the split-half method. These methods are not very appropriate for the Rorschach test, the former because of memory from trial to trial, the latter because the test cannot be split into similar halves. Nevertheless, both methods have been used in the absence of better procedures.

The split-half method introduces a statistical problem which not all investigators have noted, namely, that the Spearman-Brown formula must not be applied to ratios with variable denominators such as $W\%$ and $M/sumC$. Methods for estimating the reliability of ratio scores have been treated elsewhere (7, 8), but these procedures are not useful when the denominator is relatively unreliable (as in $M/sumC$).

It is desirable to estimate reliability of scores separately for records of varying length. Vernon (65) found that Rorschach scores were much more reliable for cases where $R>30$ than when $R<30$. This implies that it is unsatisfactory to estimate just one reliability coefficient for a group with varied R. Instead, the standard error of measurement of W, or $W\%$, should be determined separately for cases where $R = 10–15$, $R = 15–25$, $R = 25–35$, or some such grouping.

The reliability of patterns of scores is a difficult problem. If both M and W were perfectly reliable, any pattern or combination based on the two scores would also be perfectly reliable. But these scores are unstable; subjects vary from trial to trial in M or W or both. Nevertheless, Rorschach users insist that the "pattern" of scores is stable. If there is any substance to this claim, it means that certain definable configurations of the scores are stable even though the separate scores are not. The configurations may be as simple as the W/M ratio or may be complex structures of several scores. One may establish the reliability of any composite score by obtaining two separate estimates from independent trials of the test.

The method of determining reliability by independent estimates has rarely been used. A study by Kelley, Margulies, and Barrera (30) is of interest, even though based on only twelve cases. The Rorschach was given twice, and between the trials a single electroshock was given, reportedly sufficient to wipe out memory of the first trial without altering the personality. In the records so obtained, R shifted as much as 50 per cent from trial to trial, and absolute values of some other scores shifted also. In several cases where scores shifted, it can be argued that the *relationship* between the scores did not shift and that the two records would lead to similar diagnoses. The authors made no attempt at statistical treatment. Probably this ingenious procedure will rarely be repeated. Useful studies could certainly be made, however, by comparing performance on two sets of ink blots without shock (cf. Swift, 57). Even if the two sets are not strictly equivalent, the data would indicate more about the stability of performance than any methods so far employed.

At first glance, it appears logical to set up composite scores, obtain two separate estimates, and correlate them. Even this is unsuitable for Rorschach problems, however. As pointed out before, a given ratio such as 20% W or W/M 2.0 has different meaning in different records, depending on the absolute value of W. The pattern might conceivably be defined by a curvilinear equation, but this becomes unmanageable, especially as several variables enter a single pattern. The problem is one of defining when two patterns are psychologically similar, and of defining the magnitude of the difference when they are not equivalent. No one would contend that the W/M balance is unchanged if a subject shifts from $12\ W : 2M$ to $60\ W : 10M$. The problem is to define and measure the balance in a numerical way. The approach pattern W-D-Dd has three dimensions. If we wish to estimate reliability by comparing two sets of these three scores we have a six-dimensional array, for which no present methods are adequate. So far, even the pattern-tabulation method reduces such data to only four dimensions, which leaves the problem still unmanageable. All that can be recommended is that additional attention be given to this challenging problem. We can now obtain adequate evidence on the stability of Rorschach patterns only by such a method as Troup's (62), discussed in the first section of this paper. It will be recalled that she had two sets of records interpreted clinically, and employed blind-matching to show that the inferences from the Rorschach remained stable.

Two unique but entirely unsound studies of Fosberg (15, 16) employed a novel procedure to estimate the reliability of the total pattern. He gave the test four times, under varied directions. He then compared the four records for each person. In one study he used chi-square to show that the psychograms for each person corresponded. But this statistical test merely showed that the D score in record 1 is nearer to D in record 2 than it is to W, C, or other scores. That is, he showed that the scores were not paired at random. But, since each score has a relatively limited range for all people—i.e., D tends to be large, m tends to be small, etc.—he would have also obtained a significantly large chi-square if he had applied the same procedure to four records from *different* persons. One may also point out that finding a P of .90 does not prove that two records do come from the same person, but only that the null hypothesis is tenable, or possibly true. Fosberg's second study, using correlation technique, is no sounder than the first. Here the two sets of scores for one person were correlated. That is, pairs of values such as $W_1 - W_2$, $D_1 - D_2$, etc. were entered in the same correlation chart. As before, the generally greater magnitude of $-D$ causes the two sets to correlate, but high correlations would have been obtained if the scores correlated came from two different subjects.

Objection must also be made to several procedures and inferences of Buhler and Lefever (5), in their attempts to demonstrate the dependability of their proposed Basic Rorschach Score. 1) They used the split-half method on the total score, by placing half the signs in one list, the other half in a second list, and scoring each person on both lists (5, p. 112). They then correlated the two halves to indicate reliability. Because the correlation was computed on cases used to determine the scoring weights for the items, the resulting correlation is spuriously high. Even if new cases were obtained, the split-half method would be incorrect because the check list items are not experimentally independent. A single type of performance enters into a great number of separately scored signs (in their check list, M affects items 1, 2, 5, 6, 7, 8, 10, 11, 12, 51, 52, 53, 86, 93, 94, 95, 96, 99, 100, 101, and 102). A "chance" variation in M would alter the score on all these categories, and would spuriously raise the correlation unless these linked categories were concentrated in the same half of the test. 2) They derived separate sets of weights from the comparison of Normals vs. Schizophrenics, Nurses vs. Schizophrenics, and other groups. The correlation between the scoring weights is high, which they take as evidence for reliability (pp. 112 ff.). At least one serious objection is that the weights were derived in part from the same cases. If, by sampling alone, FK happened to be rare among the Schizophrenic group, this would cause the sign FK to have a weight in both the Normal-Schizophrenic key and the Nurse-Schizophrenic key. The evidence is not adequate to show that the weights would be the same if the two keys were independently derived. This objection does not apply to another comparison of the same general type, where the four samples involved had no overlap. 3) Certain papers were scored repeatedly, using sets of weights derived in comparable but slightly different ways (p. 116). The correlations of the resulting sets of scores are advanced as evidence of reliability. Any correlation of separate scorings of the same set of responses is in part spurious. If responses of individual subjects were determined solely by chance, there would still be a correlation when keys having any similarity to each other were applied to the papers. The reliability of the performance of the subject, and that is what reliability coefficients are supposed to report, cannot be revealed by rescorings of the same performance.

Conclusions

The foregoing analysis and the appended bibliography are convincing evidence that Rorschach workers have sought statistical confirmation for their hypotheses. But the analysis also shows that the studies have been open to errors of two types: 1) erroneous procedures have led to claims of significance and interpretations which were unwarranted; and 2) failure to apply the most incisive statistical tests has led workers to reject significant relationships. So widespread are errors and unhappy choices of statistical procedures that few of the conclusions from statistical studies of the Rorschach test can be trusted. A few workers have been consistently sound in their statistical approach. But some of the most extensive studies and some of the most widely cited are riddled with fallacy. If these studies are to form part of the base for psychological science, the data must be reinterpreted. Perhaps 90 per cent of the conclusions so far published as a result of statistical Rorschach studies are unsubstantiated—not necessarily false, but based on unsound analysis.

Few of the errors were obvious violations of statistical rules. The Rorschach test is unlike conventional instruments and introduces problems not ordinarily encountered. Moreover, statistical methods for such tests have not been fully developed (11). It is most important that research workers using the Rorschach secure the best possible statistical guidance, and that editors and readers scrutinize studies of the test with great care. But statisticians have a responsibility too, to examine the logic of Rorschach research and the peculiar character of clinical tests, in order to sense the limitations of conventional and mathematically sound procedures.

Present statistical tools are imperfect. And no procedure is equally advisable for all studies. Within these limitations, this review has suggested the following guides to future practice.

1. Matching procedures in which a clinical synthesis of each Rorschach record is compared with a criterion are especially appropriate.

2. If ratings are to be treated statistically, it is often advisable to dichotomize the rating and apply chi-square or bi-serial r.

3. Common errors which must be avoided in significance tests are:

   a. Use of critical ratio and uncorrected chi-square for unsuitably small samples.

   b. Use of sample values in the formula for differences between proportions.

   c. Use of formulas for independent samples when matched samples are compared.

   d. Interpretation of P-values without regard for the inflation of probabilities when hundreds of significance tests are made or implicitly discarded.

   e. Acceptance of conclusions when a significant difference is found with a hypothesis based on fluctuations in a particular sample.

4. Counting procedures are in general preferable to additive methods for Rorschach data. The most widely useful procedures are chi-square and analysis of differences in mean rank. These yield results which are invariant when scores are tranformed.

5. Normalizing scores is frequently desirable before making significance tests involving variance.

6. Where groups differ in total number of responses, this factor must be held constant before other differences can be soundly interpreted. Three devices for doing this are: rescoring a fixed number of responses on all papers, constructing subgroups equated on the number of responses, and analyzing profiles of normalized scores (pattern tabulation).

7. Ratio and difference scores should rarely be used as a basis for statistical analysis. Instead, patterns should be defined and statistical comparisons made of the frequency of a certain pattern in each group. Use of chi-square with frequencies of Rorschach "signs" is recommended.

8. Multiple repression and linear discriminant functions are unlikely to reveal the relationships of Rorschach scores with other variables, since the assumption of linear compensation is contrary to the test theory.

9. Rank correlation, curvilinear correlation, or correlation of normalized scores are often more suitable than product-moment correlation.

10. No entirely suitable method for estimating Rorschach reliability now exists. Studies in the area are much needed.

There are in the Rorschach literature numerous encouraging bits of evidence. The question whether the test has any merit seems adequately answered in the affirmative by studies like those of Troup, Judith Krugman, Williams (69), and Munroe. Supplemented as these are by the testimony of intelligent clinical users of the test, there is every reason to treat the test with respect. One cannot attack the test merely because most Rorschach hypotheses are still in a pre-research stage. Some of the studies which failed to find relationships might have supported Rorschach theory if the analysis had been more nearly perfect. How accurate the test is, how particular combinations of scores are to be interpreted, and how to use Rorschach data in making predictions about groups are problems worth considerable effort. With improvements in projective tests, in personality theory, and in the statistical procedures for verifying that theory, we can look forward to impressive dividends.

BIBLIOGRAPHY

1. ABEL, T. M. Group Rorschach testing in a vocational high school. *Rorschach Res. Exch.*, 1945, 9, 178–188.
2. BECK, S. J. Personality structure in schizophrenia. *Nerv. and Ment. Dis. Monogr.*, 1938, No. 63.

3. BROWER, D. The relation between certain Rorschach factors and cardiovascular activity before and after visuo-motor conflict. *J. Gen. Psychol.*, 1947, 37, 93–95.

4. BROWN, R. R. The effect of morphine upon the Rorschach pattern in post-addicts. *Amer. J. Orthopsychiat.*, 1943, 13, 339–342.

5. BUHLER, C., BUHLER, K., & LEFEVER, D. W. *Rorschach standardization studies. Number I. development of the basic Rorschach score.* Los Angeles: C. Buhler, 1948.

6. COCHRAN, W. G. The chi-square correction for continuity. *Iowa St. Col. J. Sci.*, 1942, 16, 421–436.

7. CRONBACH, L. J. The reliability of ratio scores. *Educ. Psychol. Msmt.*, 1941, 1, 269–278.

8. CRONBACH, L. J. Note on the reliability of ratio scores. *Educ. Psychol. Msmt.*, 1943, 3, 67–70.

9. CRONBACH, L. J. A validation design for personality study. *J. Consult. Psychol.*, 1948, 12, 365–374.

10. CRONBACH, L. J. Pattern tabulation: a statistical method for treatment of limited patterns of scores with particular reference to the Rorschach test. *Educ. Psychol. Msmt.*, 1949, 9, 149–171.

11. CRONBACH, L. J. Statistical methods for multi-score tests. Paper presented before the Biometrics Section, American Statistical Association, December, 1948. *J. Clin. Psychol.*, 1950, 6, 21–25.

12. DAVIDSON, HELEN H. *Personality and economic background.* New York: King's Crown Press, 1945.

13. EDWARDS, A. L. Note on the "correction for continuity" in testing the significance of the difference between correlated proportions. *Psychometrika*, 1948, 13, 185–187.

14. FESTINGER, L. The significance of difference between means without reference to the frequency distribution function. *Psychometrika*, 1946, 11, 97–105.

15. FOSBERG, I. A. Rorschach reactions under varied instructions. *Rorschach Res. Exch.*, 1938., 3, 12–31.

16. FOSBERG, I. A. An experimental study of the reliability of the Rorschach technique. *Rorschach Res. Exch.*, 1941, 5, 72–84.

17. FREEMAN, H., RODNICK, E. H., SHAKOW, D., & LEBEAUX, T. The carbohydrate tolerance of mentally disturbed soldiers. *Psychosom. Med.*, 1944, 6, 311–317.

18. GANN, E. *Reading difficulty and personality organization.* New York: King's Crown Press, 1945.

19. GOLDFARB, W. A. A definition and validation of obsessional trends in the Rorschach examination of adolescents. *Rorschach Res. Exch.*, 1943, 7, 81–108.

20. GOLDFARB, W. Effects of early institutional care on adolescent personality. *Amer. J. Orthopsychiat.*, 1944, 14, 441–447.

21. GUILFORD, J. P. (Ed.) *Printed classification tests.* AAF Aviation Psychology Program Research Reports, No. 3. Washington: Government Printing Office, 1947.

22. GUSTAV, ALICE. Estimation of Rorschach scoring categories by means of an objective inventory. *J. Psychol.*, 1946, 22, 253–260.

23. HARRIS, R. E., & CHRISTIANSEN, C. Prediction of response to brief psychotherapy. *J. Psychol.*, 1946, 21, 269–284.

24. HARRIS, T. M. The use of projective techniques in industrial selection. In *Exploring individual differences,* American Council on Education Studies, Series 1, No. 32, 1948. Pp. 43–51.

25. HERTZ, MARGUERITE R. Personality patterns in adolescence as portrayed by the Rorschach ink-blot method: I. The movement factors. *J. Gen. Psychol.*, 1942, 27, 119–188.

26. HERTZMAN, M. A comparison of the individual and group Rorschach tests. *Rorschach Res. Exch.*, 1942, 6, 89–108.

27. HERTZMAN, M., & MARGULIES, H. Developmental changes as reflected in Rorschach test responses. *J. Genet. Psychol.*, 1943, 62, 189–215.

28. HERTZMAN, M., ORLANSKY, J., & SEITZ, C. P. Personality organization and anoxia tolerance. *Psychosom. Med.*, 1944, 6, 317–331.

29. KABACK, G. R. *Vocational personalities: an application of the Rorschach group method.* New York: Bureau of Publications, Teachers Coll., Columbia Univ., 1946.

30. KELLEY, D. M., MARGULIES, H., & BARRERA, S. A. The stability of the Rorschach method as demonstrated in electric convulsive therapy cases. *Rorschach Res. Exch.*, 5, 1941, 35–43.

31. KRUGMAN, J. I. A clinical validation of the Rorschach with problem children. *Rorschach Res. Exch.*, 1942, 6, 61–70.

32. KRUGMAN, M. Psychosomatic study of fifty stuttering children. *Amer. J. Orthopsychiat.*, 1946, 16, 127–133.

33. KURTZ, A. K. A research test of the Rorschach test. *Personnel Psychol.*, 1948, 1, 41–51.

34. LEVERETT, H. M. Table of mean deviates for various portions of the unit normal distribution. *Psychometrika*, 1947, 12, 141–152.

35. LINDQUIST, E. F. *A first course in statistics* (Revised ed.). Boston: Houghton Mifflin, 1942.

36. MCCANDLESS, B. R. The Rorschach as a predictor of academic success. *J. Appl. Psychol.*, 1949, 33, 43–50.

37. MCNEMAR, Q. Note on the sampling error of the difference between correlated proportions or percentages. *Psychometrika*, 1947, 12, 153–157.

38. MARGULIES, H. Rorschach responses of successful and unsuccessful students. *Arch. Psychol., N. Y.*, No. 271. New York, 1942.

39. MELTZER, H. Personality differences between stuttering and non-stuttering children. *J. Psychol.*, 1944, 17, 39–59.

40. MONTALTO, F. D. An application of the Group Rorschach technique to the problem of achievement in college. *J. Clin. Psychol.*, 1946, 2, 254–260.

41. MUNROE, RUTH L. Objective methods and the Rorschach blots. *Rorschach Res. Exch.*, 1945, 9, 59–73.

42. MUNROE, RUTH L. Prediction of the adjustment and academic performance of college students by a modification of the Rorschach method. *Appl. Psychol. Monogr.*, 1945, No. 7.

43. MUNROE, RUTH L. Rorschach findings on college students showing different constellations of subscores on the A.C.E. *J. Consult. Psychol.*, 1946, 10, 301–316.

44. PEATMAN, J. G. *Descriptive and sampling statistics.* New York: Harper, 1947.

45. PENROSE, L. S. Some notes on discrimination. *Ann. Eugenics*, 1947, 13, 228–237.

46. PIOTROWSKI, Z., CANDEE, B., BALINSKY, B., HOLTZBERG, S., & VON ARNOLD, B. Rorschach signs in the selection of outstanding young male mechanical workers. *J. Psychol.*, 1944, 18, 131–150.

47. RAPAPORT, D. *Diagnostic psychological testing, Vol. II.* Chicago: Year Book Publishers, 1946.

48. RICHARDSON, L. H. The personality of stutterers. *Psychol. Monogr.*, 1944, 56, No. 7.

49. RICKERS-OVSIANKINA, M. The Rorschach test as applied to normal and schizophrenic subjects. *Brit. J. Med. Psychol.*, 1938, 17, 227–257.

50. ROSS, W. D. The contribution of the Rorschach method to clinical diagnosis. *J. Ment. Sci.*, 1941, 87, 331–348.

51. ROSS, W. D., FERGUSON, G. A., & CHALKE, F. C. R. The Group Rorschach Test in officer selection. *Bull. Canad. Psychol. Assn.*, 1945, 84–86.

52. ROSS, W. D., & ROSS, S. Some Rorschach ratings of clinical value. *Rorschach Res. Exch.*, 1944, 8, 1–9.

53. SARBIN, T. R., & MADOW, L. W. Predicting the depth of hypnosis by means of the Rorschach test. *Amer. J. Orthopsychiat.*, 1942, 12, 268–271.

54. SCHMIDT, H. O. Test profiles as a diagnostic aid: the Rorschach. *J. Clin. Psychol.*, 1945, 1, 222–227.

55. SIEGEL, M. G. The diagnostic and prognostic validity of the Rorschach test in a child guidance clinic. *Amer. J. Orthopsychiat.*, 1948, 18, 119–133.

56. SNEDECOR, G. W. *Statistical methods.* Ames, Iowa: Iowa State College Press, 1940.

57. SWIFT, J. W. Reliability of Rorschach scoring categories with preschool children. *Child Develpm.*, 1944, 15, 207–216.

58. SWIFT, J. W. Rorschach responses of 82 pre-school children. *Rorschach Res. Exch.*, 1945, 9, 74–84.

59. SWINEFORD, F. A table for estimating the signature of the difference between correlated percentages. *Psychometrika*, 1948, 13, 23–25.

60. THOMPSON, G. M. College grades and the Group Rorschach. *J. Appl. Psychol.*, 1948, 32, 398–407.

61. THORNTON, G. R., & GUILFORD, J. P. The reliability and meaning of Erlebnistypus scores on the Rorschach test. *J. Abnorm. Soc. Psychol.*, 1936, 31, 324–330.

62. TROUP, E. A comparative study by means of the Rorschach method of personality development in twenty pairs of identical twins. *Genet. Psychol. Monogr.*, 1938, 20, 461–556.

63. TULCHIN, S., & LEVY, D. Rorschach test differences in a group of Spanish and English refugee children. *Amer. J. Orthopsychiat.*, 1945, 15, 361–368.

64. VAUGHN, J., & KRUG, O. The analytic character of the Rorschach inkblot test. *Amer. J. Orthopsychiat.*, 1938, 8, 220–229.

65. VERNON, P. E. The Rorschach inkblot test. *Brit. J. Med. Psychol.*, 1933, 13, 179–200.

66. VERNON, P. E. The matching method applied to investigations of personality. *Psychol. Bull.*, 1936, 33, 149–177.

67. WALKER, HELEN M. *Elementary statistical methods.* New York: Holt, 1943.

68. WERNER, H. Perceptual behavior of brain-injured, mentally defective children. *Genet. Psychol. Monogr.*, 1945, 31, 51–110.

69. WILLIAMS, M. An experimental study of intellectual control under stress and associated Rorschach factors. *J. Consult. Psychol.*, 1947, 11, 21–29.

70. YATES, F. The analysis of contingency tables with groupings based on quantitative characters. *Biometrika*, 1948, 35, 176–181.

VII

Summary

Marguerite R. Hertz

CURRENT PROBLEMS IN

RORSCHACH THEORY AND

TECHNIQUE[1]

T HE LAST fifty years have been marked by rapid developments in the field of projective techniques. Because of their early promise as tools for penetrating the total personality and understanding it in all its dynamic interrelationships, more and more clinicians have included projective methods in their examinations and growing numbers of investigators have turned their attention to research in this area. Nevertheless, projective techniques are only in the beginning stages of their development. They have yet to be established as reliable and valid techniques.

The Rorschach method, on which I would like to concentrate, is the earliest historically and the most highly developed of all the projective techniques. Yet it still lacks unqualified scientific status. Since its earliest days, we have sought to increase its objectivity and to validate its hypotheses. We have applied statistical procedures and have broadened our application.

Reprinted from *J. Proj. Tech.*, 1951, *15*, 307–338, by permission of the publisher and the author.

1. Delivered in part at the Symposium on Current Problems in the field of Projective Techniques, May 4, 1950, Midwestern Psychological Association, Detroit, Michigan.

The number of research studies published offers impressive evidence of the quickened tempo and broadened scope of Rorschach activity and gives some indication of its importance and acceptance in the fields of clinical psychology, anthropology and the social sciences. Nevertheless, many scientists (25, 33, 50, 141, 170) remain highly critical of these efforts because of limitations inherent in the method. They charge us with uncritical acceptance of data at face value, extreme subjectivity, and dependence on insights in the absence of detailed study and research. They censure what they call our disregard of the accepted rules of scientific verification, and grow impatient with our inability to show absolute and objective verification of our contentions. They are highly critical of our failure to use statistics and where we use them they point out errors in our procedures.

Whether or not these criticisms are conclusive, they suggest real and challenging problems.

Theory

We have been criticized for failure to develop a basic underlying theory for our method and for paying little attention to the theoretical and conceptual side of our problems. There can be little doubt that there is merit in these criticisms. Theoretical and systematic formulations are sadly lacking in much of our work.

As we know, Rorschach himself developed no new discipline. His thinking was influenced by the development of his time in many fields—faculty psychology, Gestalt psychology, personalistic psychology, typology, psychiatry, psychoanalysis, and psychodiagnosis. His concentration was on *method,* a method to study the personality as a functioning whole. He formulated no specific theory of personality.

Despite the fact that Rorschach's monograph appeared as early as 1921, few systematic attempts have been made to get at these fundamental considerations. We have amassed fruitful hypotheses; we have accumulated facts which we have found valuable in clinical work; but so far, we are without a well defined theory to integrate either our hypotheses or our facts or both.

Those of us in the field have not, however, worked in a vacuum. Most of us have been influenced by psychoanalytic theory and/or by the various psychological theories which emphasize a global view of personality. A review of the Rorschach literature will reveal at once many constructs included in current theories variously called functional, holistic, dynamic, organismic and the like. Thus concepts of figure and ground, the role of the part as a function of the whole, systems of stress and field formations, emphasis on the unity of personality and the dynamic interrelationships among the various components of personality, emphasis on the organized character of all responses, all appear in some form in Rorschach data, have their background in Gestalt theory, and are related to some form of field theory. Again, Lewinian concepts of degree of differentiation, rigidity, harmonious and disharmonious structure, and the like appear frequently in Rorschach work. In like manner, the psychoanalytic treatment of the determinants of mental life, the use of such concepts as mechanisms of defense, symbolism, conscious and unconscious motivation, and more, have been incorporated into Rorschach interpretation.

Thus it must be recognized that the use of psychological and psychoanalytic concepts from various schools of thought implies in a measure an acceptance on the part of Rorschach workers of the theoretical principles upon which these systems are based. To this extent, then, we have theoretical frames of reference within which we work.

In addition, in the last few years, we note serious efforts to relate the Rorschach method to underlying theory in the field of perception. Recent studies on the dynamics of the perceptual process either use the Rorschach blots directly or bear directly on the Rorschach response. Experimental work on the various factors which influence perception, studies on value and needs by Bruner and Goodman (19) and McClelland and Atkinson (105), on symbolic values by Bruner and Postman (21), on tension and tension release as organizing factors in perception by Bruner and Postman (20), and on personal values as selective factors in perception by Postman, Bruner and McGinnies (126), all help illuminate the perceptual processes in the Rorschach.

Using the Rorschach blots directly to study the temporal characteristics of perception, Weisskopf (174) investigated the influence of the time factor on Rorschach performance. More recently Stein (160) using a tachistoscopic administration of the Rorschach cards studied personality factors involved in the temporal development of Rorschach responses and made important conclusions on the adaptive functions of perception in the Rorschach.

These are of course meager beginnings in the experimental study of the perceptual process in order to formulate some theory of personality. Whether the Rorschach blots are used or not in the experimental design, it should be borne in mind that the problem of the theoretical foundation of the Rorschach method is not uniquely one for the Rorschach worker *per se*. It is much more general and awaits the development of a basic theory underlying problems of personality in general and projective methods in particular. The Rorschach worker must join with others of course in the effort to develop that theory.

Thus, while it is true that Rorschach workers borrow many theoretical formulations from widely different methodological and conceptual disciplines, it is important to recognize that they are not indifferent to fundamental theory and are not working in a vacuum. More and more they strive toward a fundamental understanding of the Rorschach response. For the time being, in the absence of generally accepted concepts, hypotheses, and specific theories, they can only repeat with Macfarlane that "the first step in projective research should be an explicit statement of concepts used and an orientation with respect to theoretical biases." (100, p. 406)

Objectivity versus Subjectivity

Turning to the perennial problem of objectivity, here too there are many dissonant notes. There can be little doubt that there has been tremendous progress in the objectification and standardization of the Rorschach method in the area of administration and scoring. Books and articles have been published with detailed instructions as to procedure [Beck (10), Bell (11), Bochner and Halpern (15), Klopfer and Kelley (89), Rapaport et al. (129)]. More uniform and efficient methods of recording and scoring responses and summarizing data have been developed [Hertz (65, 66)]. Hutt and Shor (78) have presented a systematic analysis of the probing which adds considerably to the objectivity of this phase of the administration.

There are some aspects of the procedure, however, which have been the subject of much concern. Despite considerable uniformity, there are some variations in administration which demand systematic study. These include sparse instructions versus more elaborate and detailed instructions, use of a trial blot, extensive inquiry or minimal inquiry, inquiry after each card or at the end of the test, and inquiry with or without the cards in evidence.

Several studies have discussed changes which take place in Rorschach reactions under varied instructions. Schachtel (149) has written in detail on the influence of subjective factors introduced by the Rorschach situation on Rorschach performance. The effect of social influence on Rorschach records was demonstrated by Kimble (86), on situational and attitudinal influences by Luchins (99). More recently, Gibby (46) has studied the influence of varied experimental sets upon Rorschach intellectual factors and Milton (110) on the human movement factor. In all these studies, the Rorschach test performance shows the effect of varied experimental "sets." Just so, Rorschach performance may also be affected by other more casual changes in the administration.

Differences in the nature of the inquiry conducted may likewise affect the Rorschach performance. Most examiners restrict themselves to indirect and non-committal questions, carefully avoiding all suggestions as to Rorschach factors or specific content. Yet direct questioning is used by many examiners. Rapaport recommends the procedure of asking directly for certain information. He advises, for example, that in investigating for human movement, the following questions be asked,—"Was he doing anything?" "Anything you noticed about his posture?" (129, p. 209).

Buhler, Buhler and Lefever (22) in their study of the Basic Rorschach Score have deviated from the usual procedure to such an extent that there is considerable doubt in my mind as to the validity of the application of their results to records obtained when the test is administered in the more orthodox fashion. They restrict the number of responses to "three to five," yet they permit some persons to continue and give more responses. They make specific suggestions to their subjects during the course of the test itself involving such matters as location, populars, and animal and human details. They change the inquiry by introducing the technique of alternative questioning, which is, for the most part, direct and highly suggestive questioning. Thus after an answer, "Two dogs" to Card II, they ask, "Do they seem to be standing or sitting or is it just the shape of the dogs you see?"

It may be that such deviations from the conventional procedure do not give a picture different from that which a more orthodox administrator would obtain. On the other hand, it may be that the results which they report reflect at least in part their method. Which if true, remains to be demonstrated. Until then, we are not ready to apply the Basic Scores to records administered in a more orthodox fashion. Further study to establish the validity of this application is required.

In general, systematic studies should determine the various influences or modifications in procedure on the resultant response record. Comparison of research findings is frequently impeded if not rendered impossible because of these variations in method. McFate and Orr (106), for example, point to the fact that the adolescent group in the Brush Developmental studies (59, 61, 62, 63, 71) gives much higher total numbers of responses than their group of similar make-up and age. This may well be explained in terms of differences in method of administration.

Not only the administration, but also the scoring has been developed to the point where most examiners utilize the same or approximately the same categories even though they do not always use the same symbols. This is not true of the FM (animal movement) and the m (movement in nature) which are not yet universally accepted in this country. It is of interest to note that European workers have incorporated these factors into their scoring systems

(69). Psychograms for systematic tabulations have been developed by Klopfer and Kelley (89) and Hertz (66).

Various scoring criteria have been subjected to further study. Beck (10) and Hertz (65) have introduced some changes in their respective lists of normal details and popular factors. Frequency Tables for use in scoring form level likewise have been revised by both Beck (10) and Hertz (65). These tables add considerably to the objectivity of the scoring. Recognizing the need for a more objective appraisal of the form quality, Klopfer and Davidson (88) have introduced a rating scale for study, stressing three form qualities—accuracy, specification, and organization. Beck (10) has introduced an organizational factor, "Z," Hertz (66) a similar factor, "g." Problems associated with the popular factor have been suggested by Hallowell (52), who discussed this factor in relation to the varying qualitative and quantitative criteria used for their determination in relation to age levels and different cultural backgrounds. Further consideration of these technical scoring problems will enhance the objectivity and reliability of the method.

In order to objectify the scoring even further, psychometric scales have been developed by Zubin, Chute and Veniar (191) to reduce subjectivity to a minimum and to provide for more exact quantification of the Rorschach. These scales have been further developed by Zubin and Young (192). Unfortunately, little work has been done with these scales to establish their greater merit over the traditional method of scoring.

Recently, the Rorschach method has been extended to include some type of content analysis. The suggestions of Lindner (98) and Rapaport et al. (129) as to the meanings of specific content, Goldstein and Rothmann (49) on the evaluation of physiognomic responses, and Goldfarb (47) on the significance of the animal symbol, all offer interesting leads for research. Analysis of the content of the responses of homosexuals has been presented by Bergmann (13), and Due and Wright (38) has stimulated considerable research in this area.

More systematic studies offering valuable data are reported by Wheeler (176) on the content in homosexual records and by Reitzell (130) on content in the responses of hysterics, homosexuals and alcoholics. Shaw (151) has identified "sex populars" on the basis of a study of the records of male subjects and recommends their inclusion as an extension of the probing aspect of the procedure. An elaboration of content analysis in terms of hostility and anxiety has been presented by Elizur (39). Hertzman and Pearce (75) also offer interesting leads as to the meaning of the human factor in the Rorschach response.

Continued study of the various aspects of the content of the Rorschach responses will no doubt furnish the Rorschach examiner with valuable meanings of and procedure for studying various types of responses and will add considerably to the objectivity of the method.

While the administration and the scoring of the Rorschach record has attained a measure of objectivity which promises to increase, the interpretation of the record is still a highly subjective matter. It is because of this subjectivity that we have been so frequently censured.

Most Rorschach examiners take the intuitive configurational approach when they interpret a record, studying the various Rorschach scores as interrelated and interacting configurations. There is, however, an intermediate approach less important perhaps but none the less necessary, in which the individual is studied in reference to his group. This involves norms.

Unfortunately, norms present an area in which development commensurate with our needs is still lacking. Indeed, there are many Rorschach examiners who avoid this intermediate step, stressing the greater importance of studying the individual as a unit by himself, and censuring the normative approach as quantitative, static, and sterile. Of course, consciously or unconsciously, they too employ norms, subjective norms which they have amassed as a result of their own experience. As such, however, they are unreliable because they have not been systematically subjected to verification.

Granting that an individual must be studied as a unique personality, the interpreter must have some objective and reliable frame of reference to evaluate the functioning of his subject. He cannot understand him well unless he compares him with other personalities in his group. Time and time again we see interpretations of adolescent records, for example, in which the interpreter stresses personality deviations and psychoneurotic disturbances, sometimes even more serious pathology. Yet these very matters may be seen as not abnormal when judged by the normative material available. If we know something about the general characteristics of the adolescent personality, we have a perspective in which each adolescent may be placed. This is similarly true of other age groups and other developmental periods as well as other cultural groups.

As for Rorschach normative data, we know considerably more about what to expect of the "normal" individual on a Rorschach record than we did a few years ago. Recent studies have filled the gaps for different age levels. Children's norms based on adequate samples have been reported by Davidson (36), Ford (43), Hertz and Ebert (72), Kay and Vorhaus (84), Swift (167) and Vorhaus (171); adolescent norms by Hertz (59, 61, 62), Hertz and Baker (71), Hertzman and Margulies (74), Margulies (103), and McFate and Orr (106). Rabin and Beck (128) have presented norms for schoolchildren, ages six to twelve. Normative material for adults appear in the manuals of

Beck (10), Bockner and Halpern (15), Klopfer and Kelley (89), and Rapaport et al. (129).

Despite these studies, we are not without censure because of the inadequacy of norms at many age levels and because of the inadequate samples on which so many of them are based. Again, some of the studies of children are based on scoring criteria developed with adult records (Swift [167], Ford [43], and Stavrianos [159]). Their usefulness has therefore been challenged, and correctly so.

Again, comparison of published norms of similar age groups shows some discrepancies. Further study is needed to revise them or to explain the lack of agreement. A study of the discrepancies may well contribute to a better understanding of the nature of the factors involved.

The problem is not only to amass norms appropriate to the group but also to use and to interpret them wisely. Thus, it is elementary to emphasize that normative material should be expressed in terms of a range and that deviations be identified both above and below that range. Many studies fail to take into consideration this elementary fact, causing errors in the application of normative material. Thus Muench (114) in his study on the evaluation of psychotherapy, lists several so-called adjustment patterns viewing maladjustment in terms of only one deviation. He indicates that $\%A$ for example is expected to be no greater than 50 per cent. Anything below that figure, 15 per cent for example, he terms as satisfactory adjustment. This percentage falls considerably outside the range of normality and may not reflect adjustment at all. This error is repeated several times in his study.

The interpretation of scores in reference to a normative range is likewise important. While general meanings may be ascribed to certain norms, it is generally known that the meaning of a particular score in a particular case depends upon the interrelationship of that score with various other items in the record. We are told, for example, that two to three human movement responses may be expected in the record of a "normal" individual. The interpretation of two or three movement responses in an individual record, however, depends not so much on this absolute value as on the qualitative analysis of the movement answers in terms of total output, quality, originality, popularity, in terms of their projection into abnormal areas or their restriction to parts of bodies, in terms of the specific kind of content, in relation to the total number and varieties of color responses, and finally, in terms of the total personality configuration.

This is especially true of extreme deviations from the norm. Thus a score of 15 M may reflect fine imagination, stability, and integration of the personality. On the other hand, it may reflect considerable maladjustment in the form of self-preoccupation, day-dreaming, excessive fantasy, even obsessional or delusional developments. Again, many W's in a record may show superior abilities at abstraction and generalization. Or they may suggest extreme inner pressure, overambition and compensatory behavior. A high %F+ (Ror) may reflect fine powers of intellectual control, steadiness and clear thinking. Or it may reveal rigidity of the personality, perhaps obsessive-compulsive features or depressed conditions. It is true that these are all intuitive insights but the Rorschach is an intuitive instrument.

If we keep these very elementary facts in mind, we understand that scores falling within the normal range may not indicate normality in any area in the interpretation. In like manner, scores falling outside the range of normality may or may not reflect abnormality depending upon a qualitative appraisal.

Again, when comparing the scores made by the same individual on successive tests, the numerical differences cannot be interpreted as genuine changes in personality structure without careful qualitative analysis of the rest of the record. For example, Muench's study (114), already referred to, infers change in personality structure from a 95 per cent F+ (Ror) in the pre-test to 86 per cent in the end-test, a change which means to him lack of improvement. Again, he fails to find improvement in the case where the patient gives 36 per cent in the pre-test and 43 per cent in the end-test. This is oversimplification with all its shortcomings.

In summary, norms must be utilized in the interpretation of a Rorschach record. They should be expressed in terms of range and variability of the group. It is impossible to proceed without some standards for the group with which the individual may be compared. It must be remembered, however, that norms are only rough standards and should be used only as guides. They give important information on the central tendencies of the group. When the individual record is interpreted, however, the examiner cannot restrict himself to tables of norms. The same numerical score does not mean the same thing in every record. Scores which are numerically equal are not psychologically equal. Interpretation of all scores must be made dynamically in terms of general configurations and not absolute values. Properly used and interpreted, norms furnish the interpreter with a frame of reference for the study of the individual record.

In addition to evaluation of Rorschach scores in reference to normative material and in terms of the dynamic interrelationships of patterns in the individual record, the Rorschach interpretation involves a third phase, the study of the conclusions based on Rorschach data in conjunction with case history and other test data. The information gleaned from the Rorschach analysis is projected against the family background, education, health, history, training, social relationships, and general history, past and present. Rorschach data are re-evaluated in these terms.

The interpretation of the Rorschach record depends upon what we know about the individual. The more we know, the better we can interpret and weigh the various combinations of factors appearing in the Rorschach record and the better the over-all interpretation.

This aspect of the interpretation has been emphasized and re-emphasized by Rorschach workers in the field. Yet we are challenged again and again because we rely for our findings exclusively on the reactions to ten ink blots. Thurstone (110), for example, battles a straw man when he suggests that we claim that we can understand the past history and the dynamic personality characteristics of the individual and can predict reactivity to life situations from the responses to ink blots. No such claim has ever been made.

This brings us to a related question, what should be included in a Rorschach interpretation? From the data at his disposal, the examiner gives as detailed a study as he can of the dynamics of the personality. He tries to reconstruct the personality, to understand the intellectual functioning of the subject, to probe his inner world, to evaluate his emotions in their dynamic or disintegrative activity, and to analyze the mechanisms with which he selects and organizes his life experiences in his efforts toward self-adjustment.

The examiner may detect deviations in this functioning of his subject. He may observe certain patterns which he recognizes as characteristic of certain disorders. He identifies them. If he can, he makes recommendations as to the therapy. If possible, he tries to suggest the extent of the improvement to be anticipated. This integrated picture is based on Rorschach data and all other information available.

Two problems present themselves in this connection, that of blind diagnosis and that of differential diagnosis. Blind diagnosis based exclusively on the raw Rorschach data has no place in practical Rorschach work. This has been emphasized many times but there are still many workers who attempt to use the method in this way. Many psychiatrists demand blind analyses from the psychologist. This is unfortunate practice.

Again, it is not the primary function of the Rorschach examiner to make diagnoses in terms of the traditional clinical entities. The trend today is to question the validity of these groupings, to place less stock in the old diagnostic nosology. Unfortunately, many Rorschach examiners are diagnostically oriented. They emphasize, at times, even restrict their interpretations to nosological statements. In fact, they consider their task well done if they diagnose and classify their patients with the same label as that of the psychiatrist. This, too, is unfortunate. The Rorschach can be of much greater value in other ways. Ross (138) has recently emphasized this point of view.

It must be recognized from the foregoing that the Rorschach examiner plays an important role in Rorschach testing. Indeed, the validity of the Rorschach results depends to a great measure on the ability, the clinical judgment, the competence, and the stability of the Rorschach examiner. Its efficient use requires training, not only in the Rorschach method, but in theoretical, experimental and clinical psychology, in psychopathology and in personality theory.

The Rorschach examiner must be objective. He must be competent. He must have clinical understanding of the Rorschach scores and of the processes revealed by them. He must be able and willing to utilize adequate norms as his guide. He must keep abreast of research and review carefully all evidences of validity of the hypotheses he uses. He must know what is theoretical, empirical, speculative, and proven.

The role of the examiner is just beginning to receive appropriate attention in another connection, in terms of the dynamics of the subject-examiner relationship. It has been pointed out that the examiner projects his feelings and his bias in the administration, in the inquiry, and in the suggestions he makes during the whole test situation. Further, he projects his feelings and his special bias in the interpretations. In this area there is need for carefully controlled systematic studies on subjective bias. Joel (80) has recently discussed this interpersonal equation in projective methods and has made interesting suggestions as to research. This is an unexplored field.

There is also great need for research on what is meant by clinical judgment and clinical intuition. As Cofer (29) has indicated, clinical judgments are based on specific factors in the testing situation, factors which can be identified and subjected to systematic study.

There is good reason why there has been increased recognition of the need for trained and qualified examiners throughout the world. More and more colleges and institutions of learning are providing opportunity for training and supervised practice.

Reliability

The reliability of various aspects of the Rorschach is questioned by many psychologists. Various orthodox procedures have been utilized in the attempt to establish the reliability of the method, but have been found wanting. The adequacy and correctness of these procedures have been fully discussed by Cronbach (33). While parallel series of cards of Behn-Eschenburg and more recently by Harrower-Erickson and Steiner (58) are now available, systematic studies have not been made to establish the fact that they really are parallel to the Rorschach blots. Indeed, the Behn-Eschenburg cards appear to be used at times as an additional test (Zulliger [193]).

The split-half method and the method of repeating the test have been for the most part discarded because they are inapplicable to Rorschach data and generally unsuccessful (Hertz [60, 70, 73], Cronbach [33]). Because of the global nature of the test, it is not possible to split it and work with isolated variables. Again, since conditions change from time to time, personality data cannot be reproduced exactly from one time to another as is anticipated when the method is repeated.

Swift (165) utilized a modification of repeating the test, studying the reliability of Rorschach categories using four different methods: (1) test-retest over a thirty-day interval; (2) test-retest over a fourteen-day interval with interpolation on the seventh day of a parallel series of blots; (3) test-retest on a parallel series after a seven-day interval; and (4) test-retest after a ten-month interval. While results varied with the methods used, she could offer data to show the reliability of the Rorschach as a clinical instrument.

The only successful approach to date to determine reliability is the method of matching which keeps the total Rorschach picture intact. Krugman (90), for example, demonstrated the reliability of the scoring and the interpretation of Rorschach records in a study of twenty problem children in which comparisons of interpretations were made by experienced judges and the response records and the scoring tabulations were matched with the interpretations. It is generally recognized, however, that this method has its limitations in that it can be applied only to small numbers and depends upon the skill of the judges used.

In this connection, studies utilizing test-retest procedures in convulsive therapy, hypnotic changes, and the like should be mentioned. Such studies, where the Rorschach test is repeated with conditions experimentally varied, indirectly prove the reliability of the method. Thus Kelley, Margulies, and Barrera (87) report that Rorschach records taken in a single day after initial electric shock (where the patient is amnesic to the test and hence cannot remember previous answers) are substantially the same. Systematic studies to determine reliability have not been developed, however, with this approach.

The problem of method to demonstrate the reliability of the Rorschach is real and challenging. No adequate statistical procedure has been suggested as yet to handle this problem. Nevertheless, it is generally felt that Rorschach interpretations possess a high degree of objectivity and reliability in the hands of skilled and experienced clinicians.

Validity

Another problem always with the Rorschach examiner pertains to the validity of the Rorschach method. As has been indicated (60, 70, 73), some studies attack the problem of validity directly and attempt to establish the validity of specific patterns or specific Rorschach premises. Others, utilizing the Rorschach method for other purposes, reflect upon its validity indirectly. Still others attack the problem of basic Rorschach assumptions, without however, utilizing the Rorschach blots themselves.

In the past, validity of many of the Rorschach premises has been established largely in terms of clinical studies. It is gratifying to note that an increasing number of research workers are turning their attention to direct experimentation of Rorschach hypotheses. In some instances, experimental situations have been cleverly devised to validate various aspects of the method.

Ruesch and Finesinger (142) led the way in an early study of the relation of the Rorschach color response to the use of color in drawings, attempting an experimental verification of the affective value of color in the Rorschach. More recently, Williams (179) has shown the possibilities in this approach in his experimental study demonstrating a high significant relationship between intellectual control as indicated by the form level in the Rorschach and intellectual performance under the stress of social pressure. For another factor, form-color, the relationship was low but in the expected direction. Baker and Harris (9) report similar results in their study of the recorded speech of fourteen college students under normal and stress conditions.

Validation of some Rorschach results against laboratory procedure is also reported by Brower (17) who studied the relation of specific Rorschach factors in conjunction with other test data and cardiovascular activity before and after visuomotor conflict. He could show that some of the relationships observed tended to disappear under conflict conditions.

The nature of color and color shock has been subjected to study, utilizing the galvanic skin response technique, with conflicting results. Milner and Moreault (109) show agreement between Rorschach data and galvanometric indicators. Experimental studies by Rockwell, Welch, Kubis and Fisichelli (132) also present evidence favoring the hypothesis that inhibition of associations during color shock is accompanied by an inhibition of autonomic responsiveness as measured by the changes in the palmar skin resistance. In a subsequent study (133), the effect of color upon the associative and autonomic responsiveness of normal persons is experimentally demonstrated.

Wallen (173) using the group Rorschach, studied the nature of color shock in terms of the affective reactions of stable and unstable men in service. He concluded that color produced shock, but the shock was due not to the color *per se* but to the effect of color on the perceptual process. Color increases the difficulty of perceptual integration, induces feelings of failure on the part of insecure persons, and hence causes shock.

Lazarus (96) using slides of color and non-color series with high school students could not validate the assumption that color influences performance on the Rorschach or that shock is induced by the color on the slides. He hypothesized that shock depends not on color, but rather on difficulty, shading, and/or disturbing associations.

In like manner, the validity of the relative responsiveness to Cards VIII through X as a function of color, was not established by Sappenfield and Baker (144), who used the group Rorschach. Yet, Siipola (154) in a carefully designed experiment comparing the first conceptual reactions of normal subjects to matched chromatic and achromatic blots, confirmed the fact that color in blots induces such affective phenomena as associative blocking, strong emotional reactions, and symptoms of conceptual and behavioral disorganization. She offers the hypothesis that these symptoms of affective involvement may be viewed as an indirect effect of the presence of color, that the introduction of hue creates a situation of "hue-incongruity" which initiates conceptual conflict and emotionally-toned behavior.

Reference has already been made to Stein's experimental study (160) of personality through tachistocopic exposure of Rorschach cards, which enabled him to make interesting observations not only on the understanding of personality but on the process of perception in the Rorschach situation.

Studies with the Levy movement cards (143) utilizing finger paintings with vague human figures are beginning to throw light on the meaning of the human movement response. Rust (143), using the Zubin M scales for the Levy blots, studied some correlates of the movement response in normal, schizophrenic and neurotic subjects and in patients with frontal ablations.

Experimental evidence of the validity of the Rorschach method is likewise furnished by the studies in which the test is given under experimentally altered conditions, demonstrating the extreme sensitivity of the method to changing conditions and to changing emotional states. Thus Stainbrook (157) could demonstrate progressive changes in Rorschach results on the basis of observations made at five-minute intervals following the onset of electric-shock convulsions. Again, Morris (112) reported reliable changes in pre- and post-treatment records in patients subjected to metrazol therapy.

The sensitivity of the method to mood changes and to suggestions induced under hypnosis was demonstrated by Levine, Grassi, and Gerson (97), who used the verbal graphic Rorschach methods. Bergman, Graham, and Leavitt (14) studied the Rorschach reactions in consecutive hypnotic age level regressions. Lane (94) validated interpretations of the Rorschach movement factor by inducing creativity and introversive mechanisms by hypnotic suggestion in a non-productive subject. Personality changes after the administration of drugs such as histamine were also reported by Robb, Kovitz and Rapaport (131). Wilkins and Adams (178) likewise demonstrated personality changes in patients under hypnosis and sodium amytal, on the basis of the Rorschach record.

Such experimental studies as suggested above mark only a beginning in establishing the validity of the Rorschach method. They show great promise, however. It is hoped that other aspects of the Rorschach will be subjected to this kind of experimental approach so that many of the hypotheses implied in Rorschach interpretations may be experimentally verified.

Most of the Rorschach studies on validity, however, are based on the comparisons of contrasted groups and on case studies, especially those using "blind diagnosis" and the matching method.

In the method of compared groups, the Rorschach has been shown to differentiate between individuals of varying age, intelligence, background, school achievement, of different race or nationality, of deviated personality, and between individuals suffering from various kinds of mental disorders. Many of these studies consist of analysis of the scores of extreme or contrasting groups. Others use the method of equating groups for various factors and identifying batteries of Rorschach factors which appear significantly more frequently in one group than in another. Many of these studies have been reviewed in the literature (Hertz [60, 70], Hertz and Ellis [73], and Bell [11]).

Some of the more important studies utilizing this approach include those on non-reading and clinic children by Vorhaus (172), adjusted and maladjusted children by Davidson (36), stutterers and non-stutterers by Krugman (91) and Melzer (107), and institution and foster-home adolescents by Goldfarb (48).

Important studies have been offered by Werner (175) on brain-injured and non-brain-injured mental defectives, by Sarason and Sarason on groups of high-grade familial defectives (145) and cerebral palsied defective children (146). Sloan (155) compared two groups, one who had been legally committed as subnormal but who did not appear to be psychometrically defective, and a second group with high-grade or borderline intelligence, psychometrically. He demonstrated that affective factors may interfere with the full utilization of capacities. Jolles (81, 82) likewise emphasized emotional and personality maladjustment as an important component in mental deficiency on the basis of a Rorschach study of sixty-six children who had low ratings in psychometric tests. The method of group comparison was also used by Abel (1), who studied the relationship between academic success and personality organization, by matching fifteen pairs of moron girls on the basis of IQ and chronological age, where there was a difference in school placement between the members of each pair.

Most recently, there has been an extension of this technique in the development of "signs" which occur more frequently in one group than in a controlled or contrasting group. Thus signs for evaluating good adjustment in school children have been developed by Davidson (36, 37), signs indicating mental deficiency by Sloan (155) and Jolles (81, 82), signs of adjustment in adults by Muench (114), signs to determine neurotic involvement by Miale and Harrower-Erickson (108), signs of the schizophrenic process by Klopfer and Kelley (89), signs of organic impairment by Piotrowski (118), Aita, Reitan and Ruth (2), Armitage (8), and Hughes (77). Signs have even been developed to discriminate between outstanding and non-outstanding mechanical workers by Piotrowski, Candee, Balinsky and Holtzberg (125).

Munroe's check list (115) is really a series of signs providing for the notation of deviations which are based on clinical experience. Munroe claims that the check list facilitates rapid inspection of significant aspects and interrelationships on which a general clinical judgment may be used. Using the inspection technique, she could differentiate between various degrees of adjustment of her college students.

Ross and Ross (140) developed a general "instability" and "disability" rating, consisting of combined and weighted signs occurring more often in neurotic and organic subjects than in controlled subjects, the ratings being validated against clinical findings and Binet subtests.

The signs of Buhler, Buhler and Lefever (22) which have already been referred to, probably represent the most extreme form of describing personality on a statistical basis. The authors have devised a numerical score, the Basic Rorschach Score, which evaluates personality disintegration in terms of conflict, impairment, and reality loss. According to the authors, the score differentiates the various diagnostic groups. The possibilities and limitations of this approach have been considered in a recent symposium (177) and also by Cronbach (33).

Negative results have also been reported in studies attempting to utilize signs. Kurtz (93) could find no evidence that signs are valid in the selection of personnel in the various occupations, in industrial or in military occupations. McCandless (104) failed to differentiate between two groups of officer candidates who differed widely in academic progress and achievement, using the Munroe check list. Cronbach (35) failed to confirm Munroe's findings using a similar group of college students and failed to establish her signs as predictive of academic success.

Validation of the Rorschach is also frequently made in terms of comparison with outside criteria, case records, other test data, interviews, teachers' reports, psychoanalytic data and the like. At times these comparisons are exclusively qualitative. On the other hand, frequently an adequate number of cases permits quantitative techniques to be applied. This approach is often impressive especially when blind personality analyses are made or when the matching techniques are utilized and/or when elaborate statistical procedures are employed.

Thus validation using the results of other objective personality tests have been reported by Wishner (181) who established the validity of such Rorschach factors as R, W, and Z on the basis of their relation to the Wechsler-Bellevue score with neurotic patients. He failed, however, to validate the %F+. Burnham (23) studied the degree of relationship between the % H and the Wechsler-Bellevue Picture Arrangement scores. The MMPI scores were utilized by Altus and Thompson (5), who reported a high correlation of items in the Group Rorschach and the Schizophrenic Scale scores, by Clark (28), who could validate the Rorschach color interpretations in the Group Rorschach, and by Thompson (169), who in like manner studied the MMPI correlates of two types of Rorschach movement responses in the Group Rorschach for two college groups.

Correlation of results with independent and experimentally controlled behavioral criteria has yielded conflicting results. Thus behavioral measures obtained from a teachers' rating scale and from parent interviews were employed by Swift (166) to validate Rorschach measures of insecurity in terms of ratings and "signs" but with generally negative results. When she adopted a more global approach (164), however, and matched teachers' descriptions of the personalities of her thirty preschool children with Rorschach analyses, a significantly high number of correct matchings was made.

Hertzman and Pearce (75) utilized behavior in therapy, dream interpretations, self-descriptions and descriptions of the subjects by others, in order to validate the meaning of the human figure response in the Rorschach. The judgments of therapists were utilized by Wheeler (176) in his analysis of Rorschach indices of male homosexuality. Garfield (45) took as his criteria the clinical diagnoses of a staff and demonstrated the validity of Rorschach diagnoses. Again, psychoanalytic data were utilized liberally by Schachtel in his various studies on the symbolism of form (147), movement (150), color

(148) and situational influences (149). At no time, however, does he present systematic studies of his interesting Rorschach hypotheses.

Case studies demonstrating the clinical validity of the Rorschach abound in the literature. "The case of Gregor" (12), presented at a recent symposium of the APA, which included a report of twenty-seven different projective techniques, one of which was the Rorschach, is illustrative of this approach.

Studies employing the method of correct matching have demonstrated a high degree of validity for the Rorschach interpretation. Patterson and Magaw (117) matched the Rorschach pictures of institutionalized defective boys with personality sketches written by trained observers with a significant number of correct matchings. Krugman (90) obtained a highly satisfactory result by matching Rorschach analyses with clinical case study abstracts, matching scoring tabulations with interpretations, thereby establishing a high degree of objectivity and clinical validity for the Rorschach. Reference has already been made to Swift's success in matching Rorschach analyses with teachers' descriptions (164).

Validity relying almost exclusively upon statistically designed procedures has been reported by various statisticians and research workers, interested in an ultraquantitative approach to the Rorschach method. Some have tried to intercorrelate various Rorschach factors or correlate Rorschach indices with total score and apply techniques of item analysis. Others have used factor analysis to determine which combinations carry particular loadings. Thus, using factor analysis of data provided by the Harrower-Erickson Multiple Choice Check List, Wittenborn (184) concluded that the abstract scoring procedures usually employed are of no value in attempting to appraise the behavioral significance of Rorschach responses elicited by check list procedures. A later study (183), a factor analysis of discrete responses to the Rorschach blots, again failed to support some of the common interpretations for Rorschach factors. Other studies utilizing a variety of analytical designs, tested out other Rorschach hypotheses (182, 186). He could show that Rorschach responses differ from each other with respect to the degree of perceptual control characterizing them (183, 185). He also could present evidence for the validity of scoring the human movement response as reflecting an important feature of personality not predicted from the color responses, and of combining other color responses and interpreting them differently from the total movement score. He likewise established the validity of interpreting responses separately from different areas of the card. He could not, however, justify the practice of working with the more refined scoring categories of M, C, and details.

Again, Hughes (77) proposed twenty-two different Rorschach signs for the detection of organic brain pathology, based on a factor analysis technique. Fourteen signs were established as statistically diagnostic for a group of 218 patients. Hsü (76) likewise attempted a factor analysis of Rorschach factors in order to study the reliability of the method.

Another approach utilized in the attempt to demonstrate the validity of the Rorschach method appears in those studies which demonstrate the power of the Rorschach method as an instrument of prediction. Thus Munroe (115) reported a high degree of success in predicting the adjustment of college students, academic failure, referrals to psychiatrist, and problem behavior observed by teachers from Rorschach data using the Rorschach Group Method and the Inspection Technique of scoring. Piotrowski (119, 120) had significant success in predicting the effectiveness of insulin treatment on the basis of the analysis of pretreatment Rorschach records. Similarly, prognostic patterns were identified by Halpern (54) for the prediction of response of schizophrenic patients to therapy, and by Morris (112) for the prediction of the outcome of treatment based on metrazol. Siegel (153) identified Rorschach factors associated with improvement and non-improvement and found them valid for prediction in a child guidance clinic, and Bradway (16), working with "promiscuous" girls, identified a battery of patterns which were of prognostic value in determining treatability.

Using the group Rorschach, Montalto (111) could predict achievement of women in college in terms of "signs" of adjustment. Shoemaker and Rohrer (152) predicted success of students in the study of medicine on the basis of differential Rorschach results for "over" and "under" achievers. On the basis of clusters of Rorschach patterns obtained from group Rorschach records, Thompson (168) demonstrated the value of the Rorschach in predicting success in college.

In 1942, Piotrowski (121) reviewed the progress which had been made in personality study with the Rorschach method, and emphasized especially some of the valid predictions which could be made of personality development. More recently, Morris (113) in a carefully designed study demonstrated the power of the Rorschach to predict personality attributes. Again, the prognostic possibilities of the method were demonstrated by Hertz (67) who identified ten configurations in terms of Rorschach patterns which were studied both quantitatively and qualitatively and which revealed suicidal tendencies. These configurations were further analyzed and verified in a follow-up cross-validation study (68).

It may be concluded from the above brief summary that various kinds of research designs have been utilized in continuing the attack on the problem of the reliability and validity of the Rorschach method. It would appear that many aspects of the Rorschach are impressively supported by a host of validating studies of wide variety. Nevertheless, much of the research has serious limitations; many of the findings are inconclusive. In reviewing the material, one finds that several important problems suggest themselves.

Problems

First, most of the studies have never been replicated. This is a serious omission. It is important to determine whether the results obtained in one study are peculiar to the sample used. We know, for example, that results often may be explained in terms of the statistical method which has been employed in analyzing the data. They may be explained also in terms of the experience, the clinical insight and ingenuity of the investigators. Thus Munroe's work (115) in predicting academic success would be much more valuable if it were verified. In a recent study, Cronbach (35) attempted to repeat her study on a similar college group. He could not duplicate her results. Again, Muench's study (114) validating Roger's non-directive method of therapy could not be repeated by Hamlin, Albee and Leland (55) or by Carr (24). We have many valuable studies which, if repeated, would contribute immeasurably to the scientific status of the method. They await replication.

Again, much is in use in the Rorschach which has never been validated, even clinically. Many interpretations which we give to Rorschach patterns have not been systematically validated in themselves. Some introduced tentatively as working hypotheses still retain their hypothetical status. These include the various kinds of rare-detail categories which appear in the Klopfer and Kelley manual (89), the m, the texture response, animal movement, k, Ch' (as used in Hertz scoring) or C' (as used by Klopfer), and the like. Several patterns which we use call for sytematic verification. These include W : M, P : O, the so-called circle of refinement (89), and various other combinations. In 1943, Piotrowski (122) published a stimulating paper on tentative Rorschach formulae for educational and vocational guidance in adolescence. Most of these formulae are still tentative, despite the fact they are used as established facts by many Rorschach workers.

Again, the Rorschach test is frequently employed as an instrument of research. While several aspects of the method have been sufficiently validated to permit its use for research purposes, modified procedures and tentative findings based on small scale studies and/or on isolated case studies are uncritically applied. This is especially true of many of the studies utilizing the Group Method and the Multiple-Choice Method.

In this connection, it should be emphasized again that despite the value of the method of comparing groups and of the matching technique, the individual Rorschach patterns have not been validated. In comparing groups, the Rorschach method may be shown to be valid as a differentiating instrument. The individual Rorschach pattern has not been shown to be valid, however. The factors or patterns or signs which appear with greater frequency in one group than in another may be said to be associated with the dominant personality patterns of that group and inferentially to be reflective of them. But from this we cannot conclude that each pattern is of itself valid. This is frequently forgotten.

This may likewise be said of the matching technique. Even though the method as a whole may be shown to be valid through correct matching, it must be emphasized that even in successful matching, each item in the description has not been demonstrated to be valid. In fact, although many items in themselves may be incorrectly matched, the total picture may present a correctly matched whole. This has been emphasized by many reviewers (Cronbach [33], Rotter [141]).

This poses a practical problem to those of us who work with the Rorschach as to what to utilize in the interpretation and what not to use. The examiner must have sufficient experience, knowledge and discernment to differentiate between empirical data and systematically verified data. More important, he must be on the alert to distinguish valid inferences from highly personal and sometimes fanciful interpretations.

We have already suggested a major problem in Rorschach research, a problem which has been discussed again and again but which is ever prevalent, that is, the use of Rorschach scores as separate and independent items with specific meanings, despite the recognized importance of dealing with them in their various interrelationships and in terms of the record as a whole. This point has been emphasized and re-emphasized but the procedure of using single factors in isolation persists. Recently, patterns of scores or composite scores have been recommended (Hertz [66], Rapaport [129]). Thus formulae as (FC − [CF + C] wt, (FCh − [ChF + Ch]) wt, (M + Cwt) are used in Rorschach interpretation. Even with composite scores, however, it is difficult to get meaningful results when they are used in isolation, because composite scores also depend upon other scores and the record as a whole. Hence studies which isolate composite patterns for study are not generally successful.

More recently, a configurational approach is recommended by Hertz (67) which relies upon 1) normative data for Rorschach factors and patterns which are evaluated, however, in terms of the individual record, and 2) clinical interpretation and judgment. The configurational approach combines the qualitative and quantitative evaluation and is the procedure which is usually used when interpreting a Rorschach record. The position is taken that if the configurations are carefully and explicitly described, they may be used by other clinicians with reliability, objectivity and validity, and may be subjected to experimental investigation. Thus Hertz (67) demonstrates that suicidal trends may be detected in Rorschach records on the basis of the evaluation of certain configurations which are explicitly described. She emphasizes, however, that this subjective-objective procedure must be subjected to further research to determine whether other test-interpreters will be able to make the same predictions.

Of all the methods of validation mentioned, probably the most promising is the method of prediction. Unfortunately, few of the studies using this method have been repeated. As already indicated, studies in which attempts have been made to repeat the procedure have met with little success. If this method can be systematically developed, however, so that Rorschach test interpreters with sufficient training and experience can make the same predictions on the same data, the Rorschach method will be on firm and valid ground. Of course, in this approach, it is important also that the specific patterns and their differentiating criteria, and if possible, the bases for clinical judgments be explicitly described and where possible, experimentally established.

There is an additional problem which has caused many of us much concern—that is, the validity of the procedure and the studies designed to streamline the Rorschach method. Of late there has been much concentration on shorter procedures, mass methods, rapid inspection scoring and diagnostic sign batteries in order to permit mass testing, mass diagnosis, mass production of Rorschach interpretations and even mass research.

In order to cover more subjects in faster time, the Rorschach Group Method has been used extensively despite the fact it has not been developed beyond its early experimental status. Several variations of the original method of Harrower-Erickson and Steiner (57) are used but to date no group method has been reliably established as valid; scoring norms for such factors as normal details, popular responses, form quality, and the like have not been determined; and adequate group norms have not been amassed for the age groups which are studied by means of the Group Method. It has not even been systematically established that the same principles of interpretation upon which we proceed with the individual record operate with the group record. Despite these limitations, which have been emphasized again and again in the literature (Challman [27], Hertz [64]), the Group Method has been applied extensively in clinical, educational, and industrial studies, in the armed services, and even as an instrument of research. The reviews of Munroe (116) on the use of the Rorschach in college counseling, of Harrower-Erickson (56) on the general application of the group method, of Piotrowski (123) on the use of the method in vocational selection, all emphasize the extensive use which has been made of the Group Method. More significantly, it is used extensively as an instrument of research. Roe (134–137) for example uses it as one of her techniques in her important research project on personality and vocation.

Results in studies using the Group Method are conflicting. Abt (2) reports data showing the group Rorschach as an efficient instrument for psychiatric screening of Marine Corps recruits. Harrower and Cox (162) apply the group method to various occupational groupings and find it highly valuable for selecting and placing the worker in industry. Steiner (161–162) reviews the literature and concludes that the group method is valuable in differentiating between successful and unsuccessful workers, in understanding the personality dynamics underlying occupational adjustment, and in differentiating general personality patterns for various occupational groups.

Again, Stainbrook and Siegel (158) found it valuable in making a comparative study of southern Negro and white high school and college students. Thompson (168) and Montalto (111) could differentiate between achieving and non-achieving college students by means of the Group Method. The Group Method was also utilized with apparent success by Kabach (83) who studied the relationship between personality and vocational choice, and by Brozek, Guetzkow, and Keyes (18) in their study of changes in nutritional status and personality. Anderson and Munroe (6) utilized the group procedures to study personality factors involved in student concentration on creative painting and commercial art. Reference has already been made to the extensive studies by Roe in which she utilized the Group Method among other techniques for the study of the personalities of artists (135), scientists and technicians (134) and biologists (137).

On the other hand, generally negative results are stressed by other investigators. Kurtz (93) finds the Group Method without validity in the application to industrial and personal problems. In most of the studies which he reviews, he fails to find any justification for acceptance of the group Rorschach as a valid instrument. Anderson (7) failed to confirm the study by Piotrowski et al. (125) and could not predict the efficiency ratings of machinists on the basis of group Rorschach records. Ross, Ferguson and Chalke (139) report that the group Rorschach has limited use as an aid in officer selection in the Canadian army, despite the positive results which were reported by Harrower-Erickson (56). In a more recent study, Cronbach (35) could not establish the validity of the group Rorschach in his attempt to correlate Rorschach adjustment scores with the ratings of emotional adjustment by heads of dormitories and with sociometric ratings.

In the light of the few attempts to subject the Group Method to systematic research and to establish normative data, it must be concluded that the application of the method has been indiscriminate and unwise. The studies which report positive results should be repeated, especially those which claim to be able to screen effectively and to reflect differentiating personality patterns for various vocations and arts. It is hoped that both the positive and negative results will stimulate further refinements and modifications in the group procedure and conscientious research for making it a reliable and valid instrument.

Less promising results have been reported for the Multiple Choice Test as a screening device. Harrower-Erickson (56) has used the technique with most satisfactory results. More recently, Cox (30) reports that successful sales clerks could be selected on the basis of this technique, and has devised a scoring key made up of the items which differentiated the top from the bottom quarter of a group of 108 sales clerks.

On the other hand, Challman (26) had little success with this method as a screening device. Wittson, Hunt and Older (187) concluded on the basis of a study of three groups of naval men that it is unsuitable for military selection. Jensen and Rotter (79) were unsuccessful in screening officer candidates. According to Wenfield (180) the test did not screen maladjusted from adjusted women in military service. Similarly, Springer (156) found it unsuccessful in screening naval personnel.

Again, Malamud and Malamud (101) could not use the Multiple Choice Method to discriminate between normal subjects and psychiatric cases. Engle (40) also reported that it was inadequate for differentiating between well-adjusted and maladjusted high school pupils.

In summary, it must be recognized that the validity of both the Rorschach Group Method and the Multiple Choice Test is far from established. Despite the positive results reported in some studies, both techniques require considerable experimental work in order to place them within the bounds of reliability and validity. It is possible that with further refinement and modification they will attain greater validity. One modification of the method, the Rorschach Ranking Test, has been developed by Eysenck (41, 42) who reports that this technique along with three other tests can reliably discriminate neurotic and normal subjects. Suggestions for modifications and revisions have also been made by Malamud and Malamud (102), Challman (27), and Lawshe and Forster (95). Kellman (85) is in the process of an elaborate revision of the Multiple Choice. It should be emphasized, however, that until such developments take place and objective evidence of the validity of the procedures is presented, they must be used with caution.

They should not be employed as instruments of research in their present state.

Another attempt to objectify Rorschach data and speed up the process of interpretation is the sign approach already referred to. Studies identifying signs of adjustment, neurotic trends, organic impairment, schizophrenia, and the like have been developed with more or less acceptable statistical validity. Indeed, we are told that the sign approach is simple and well adapted to the Rorschach (Cronbach [33]). Statisticians apparently like it because it represents the statistical approach to the Rorschach par excellence. While this approach may be simple, in our judgment it is not only unadapted to the Rorschach but it is incompatible with the basic principles of the method.

Clinically, the battery of signs is not valid since it fails to take into account the dynamic relationships among the various psychological processes for which the so-called signs stand. Just as with other scores, the signs depend for their real significance on other patterns and on the total record. Even for superficial evaluations, personality configurations must be studied and not independent signs.

A very serious limitation to most batteries of signs is the exclusion of patterns which by their presence suggest pathology. For example, contaminations, variations in form level, in originality and in output, position responses, color deterioration, and the like are included in few lists of signs, with the exception of the schizophrenic battery. It has been demonstrated again and again that schizophrenic records may show the necessary number of signs pointing to adjustment, for example, and yet have one or more of the above indicators which should at once withdraw the label of adjustment (55, 186).

Again, in many batteries, signs are added to obtain a composite score. Again we have the atomistic approach, do we not? We have, in fact, an appraisal of the whole in terms of the summation of individual parts. The fact that the parts are called "signs" does not change the case. Our subject has again become a collection of discrete test scores and we have again lost sight of the larger framework of relationships.

Despite the acceptance of the sign approach, study after study illustrates the difficulties of treating scores separately. Siegel (153), who developed a battery of signs reflecting adjustment in order to predict response to continued psychotherapy, cautions that the signs must be used judiciously within the essential configuration of the test pattern. Rabin (127) emphasizes the inadequacy of the sign approach for differential diagnosis. Piotrowski (124) who pioneered in the development of signs, prefers a more systematic method which he called "perceptanalysis" which emphasizes the dynamic interrelationships of the underlying forces in the personality and which is based on the %F+ as a point of reference. Examination of his method shows it to be a configurational approach and not a sign approach at all.

Munroe's check list (115) has not been widely used or successful in application. It is difficult to use even for trained examiners. In our experience in the process of rapid evaluation, many of the items are judged wrong. In a rapid over-all inspection such as is suggested, certain items serve as the basis for the decisions. Even a few errors then make considerable difference in the results.

It may be that those who are successful with the inspection technique may attribute their success to experience, insight and intuition rather than to the checks or signs per se. The inexperienced clinician cannot use the check list with any degree of validity.

The problem in the use of signs is a serious one. The sign approach is designed to permit the inexperienced worker to use—or should I say, misuse the Rorschach method. Munroe tells us:

The adjustment rating . . . is largely independent of the special skill and special experience of the individual examiner. It can be made quickly from spontaneously produced Rorschach responses according to clinical criteria familiar to examiners with even moderate Rorschach training. There is indeed some evidence to suggest that a quantitative score may be safely substituted for the examiner's rating, thus reducing the factor of personal judgment to a marked degree (115, p. 11).

Again, Davidson is happy to relate

. . . fifteen of the seventeen [signs] may be tallied by a clerk while only two (color shock and shading shock) require the judgment of an experienced Rorschach examiner (37, p. 33).

The various studies based on short cuts and sign approaches cannot be considered clinically valid or acceptable. With such approaches as described, patterns are applied mechanically and all evaluation of the dynamics of personality is excluded. This is a distortion of the Rorschach method. Clinically, results are sterile. Such attempts at oversimplification are understandable in terms of a desire to give wider utility to the method. Despite temptation, however, it is important to remember that the rule about royal roads applies to Rorschach as well as to other disciplines of learning. Those who emasculate the method with the view to giving it to clerks to handle are doing much to keep the Rorschach from attaining full scientific status.

Finally, one more problem should be considered, the extent to which statistical procedures should be applied to various kinds of Rorschach data. As already indicated, various techniques have been utilized with more or less success.

It has been amply emphasized in the literature that because of the nature of the Rorschach, most of the orthodox statistical procedures which have been used to date with Rorschach data are highly inappropriate (Cronbach [31–34], Hertz [60, 70], Frank [44], Krugman [92], and others). Many of the traditional procedures have been misapplied, often resulting in erroneous conclusions. In other cases negative results might have appeared more favorable if appropriate methods had been used. Cronbach (33) is well within the bounds of accuracy in pointing to the errors that have crept into various efforts in the field which have sought to apply orthodox statistical methods to Rorschach data.

Throughout the years, these techniques have been the subject of much concern to many of us. Investigators have shown that many of the Rorschach factors do not follow the normal distribution and hence procedures based on the assumption of normality are fallacious when applied to them. With many factors, like C. CF, m, c, cF, Do, S, s, and others, so few appear that frequently from 75 to 95 per cent of the subjects fail to score in these items. Yet means and medians for these factors are computed again and again in research.

There can be little doubt that where appropriate, the application of statistical procedures and statistical controls adds to the objectivity and validity of the method. Yet, even where appropriate statistics have been applied and results shown to be highly reliable, the interpretation of the results has often been fallacious and their application in serious error. Too often, there has been so much concentration on numbers and their statistical manipulation that meaningfulness of the data has been forgotten. While no criticism or disrespect is intended for many carefully planned statistical studies, we sometimes have the feeling that investigators have become so absorbed in their calculations and statistical formulae that important developments with the Rorschach have been impeded rather than encouraged.

Again, frequently statistical reliability gives the investigators a feeling of security, so much so that they proceed to make clinical inferences and deductions without consideration of the global nature of the instrument. No matter how proper or correct the statistical procedure, results are of little value unless they are transformed into configurational and dynamic interpretations.

In some instances, statistically reliable results based on one kind of sample are applied to other groups and to other individuals, indiscriminately. It is elementary to mention that the results of a study depend upon the nature of the sample used, age, education, kind of background, vocational experience and a host of other factors. Yet so many Rorschach examiners have applied results of published studies without investigating the nature of the sample on which they are based, or if they do investigate, they are not deterred in applying Rorschach results to their sample regardless of fit or propriety. Ford (43) develops Rorschach norms for children, yet uses the scoring criteria which are based on adolescent and adult populations. Harrower-Erickson and Miale (108) present norms based on the group Rorschach, yet express them in terms of scoring criteria developed for the individual Rorschach. Rapaport et al. (129) present elaborate statistics showing characateristic Rorschach reactions for groups of neurotic and psychotic patients, comparing them with a "normal" group, this latter composed entirely of a small group of constricted highway patrolmen. Hallowell (51) who has employed the Rorschach extensively to investigate personality and culture of non-literate groups is of the opinion that valuable insights are possible even in cases where *there are no group norms*. Indeed, in many studies on the acculturation process (53), norms and "signs" of adjustment are applied to different cultural groups, despite the fact they were developed on the basis of records of children and adults in this country.

It does not make this procedure any less reprehensible when the investigator recognizes and admits the impropriety of his procedure. The fact remains, he proceeds to use it and makes certain inferences which are not justified. It is because of this improper application of Rorschach results that so many records have been misinterpreted and so many results erroneously reported.

Summary

In summary, Rorschach workers are increasingly aware of and concerned with problems of theory, technique and methodology, problems of objectification and verification, and problems of application. Various kinds of research designs have been utilized in the attempt to meet these problems. Some progress has been made in systematizing research procedures, amassing scoring criteria and norms, using more scientific methods in handling data, examining results more critically and developing new methods for handling the complex Rorschach material.

As a result, more and more aspects of the Rorschach have been validated. Probably the studies on validation which show the greatest promise include the experimental investigations of basic Rorschach postulates and those designed to demonstrate the power of the method to predict personality development and reactions to various kinds of therapy. Clinical validation must not be discounted, however. Carefully designed clinical research has led to the establishment of the validity of many of the Rorschach findings which are accepted today.

On the other hand, there has been a serious lag in basic research. Many of our hypotheses have not been clarified or validated; many of our studies are inadequate. Studies which show promise have not been replicated. In many studies, statistical procedures have been erroneously applied. In others, statistical procedures have been correctly applied but they have been over-emphasized and/or the results have been misinterpreted. Finally, too much attention has been given to the exposition of short cuts and to their application despite the lack of evidence of reliability and validity.

There can be little doubt that there is still much to be done by way of objectification and verification of the Rorschach method. Most encouraging, there is no lack of will to do it.

It is obvious that there must be a complete re-evaluation of the research design and of the statistical procedures appropriate for the treatment of Rorschach data. Indeed, the problem goes beyond the Rorschach method. It is the problem of all techniques which attempt to describe and evaluate and "diagnose" personality. It is a problem which has been considered again and again in studies, discussions and symposia (Zubin [188–190]). It is generally emphasized that new methods must be explored which may be applied to the Rorschach method and to all other personality methods without sacrificing values of qualitative analysis. New methods must be forged which will keep the individual intact when the various aspects of his personality are subjected to scrutiny.

Allport (4) early emphasized the need for the ideographic approach to the study of personality and the systematic development of the individual case study. Perhaps this should be explored further. Other possibilities which have been suggested for use in conjuction with the Rorschach include the further development of factor analysis, the analysis of variance and co-variance, and Fisher's method of discriminant functions (Zubin [190]). The Q technique as described by Stephenson (163) may likewise be applied to Rorschach data. Another approach may be in the further development of Zubin's early rating scales for classifying Rorschach categories (191). Cronbach, too, has suggested two other statistical procedures. His method for pattern tabulation (31, 32, 34) may be of interest, although only two or three scores can be handled at a time. He also has developed a variation of the blind matching method which, though highly involved and laborious, has shown some interesting possibilities for the validation of qualitative analyses of personality structure. All of these newer statistical methods are being explored today in conjunction with Rorschach research. Statisticians are joining with Rorschach workers in this important task of developing new procedures which will permit quantitative analysis of the personality structure with appropriate cognizance of the uniqueness of the individual personality.

The problems we have discussed offer challenging opportunities for further work. Despite these problems, however, research on the Rorschach has made tremendous strides. It is fair to say that research to date provides clinical, experimental, and statistical evidence of sufficient importance to justify favorable regard for the method as a clinical instrument. Despite our limitations in theoretical explanation and in statistical verification, those of us in clinical work know that we have an instrument which works under the critical eye of the clinician. I think it fair to say that the only time it does not work is when it is dissected, distorted, modified, objectified to the point of sterility, and subjected to piecemeal and rigid statistical manipulation. Otherwise it works. The task for the Rorschach worker, for the statistician, indeed, for all who are interested in personality theory and projective methods is to find out why.

REFERENCES

1. ABEL, T. M. The relationship between academic success and personality organization among subnormal girls. *Amer. J. Ment. Def.*, 1945, *50*, 251–256.

2. ABT, LAWRENCE EDWIN. The efficiency of the Group Rorschach Test in the psychiatric screening of Marine Corps recruits. *J. Psychol.*, 1947, *23*, 205–217.

3. AITA, JOHN A., REITAN, RALPH M., AND RUTH, JANE M. Rorschach's test as a diagnostic aid in brain injury. *Amer. J. Psychiat.*, 1947, *103*, 770–779.

4. ALLPORT, GORDON W. *Personality*. New York: Henry Holt and Company, 1939.

5. ALTUS, W. D., AND THOMPSON, GRACE M., The Rorschach as a measure of intelligence. *J. Consult. Psychol.*, 1949, *13*, 341–347.

6. ANDERSON, IRMGARD, AND MUNROE, RUTH. Personality factors involved in student concentration on creative painting and commercial art. *Rorschach Res. Exch.*, 1948, *12*, 141–154.

7. ANDERSON, ROSE G. Rorschach test results and efficiency ratings of machinists. *Personnel Psychol.*, 1949, *2*, 513–524.

8. ARMITAGE, STEWART G. *An Analysis of certain psychological tests used for the evaluation of brain injury*. Psychological Monographs, *Vol. 60*, No. 1. Whole No. 277, Washington, D.C.: Amer. Psychological Association, Inc., 1946.

9. BAKER, LAWRENCE M., AND HARRIS, JANE S. The validation of Rorschach Test results against laboratory behavior. *J. Clin. Psychol.*, 1949, *5*, 161–164.

10. BECK, S. J. *Rorschach's Test*. New York: Grune & Stratton, 1949. Vol. I—Basic Processes. Vol. II—A Variety of Personality Pictures.

11. BELL, JOHN ELDERKIN. *Projective Techniques.* New York: Longman's, Green & Co., 1948.

12. BELL, JOHN ELDERKIN. The case of Gregor: psychological test data. *Rorschach Res. Exch.,* 1949, *13,* 155–205.

13. BERGMANN, MARTIN S. Homosexuality on the Rorschach Test. *Bull. of the Menninger Clinic,* 1945, *9,* 78–83.

14. BERGMANN, M. S., GRAHAM, H., AND LEAVITT, H. C. Rorschach explanation of consecutive hypnotic age level regressions. *Psychosom. Med.,* 1947, *9,* 20–28.

15. BOCHNER, R., AND HALPERN, F. *The Clinical Application of the Rorschach Test.* New York: Grune & Stratton, Inc. 1945, 2nd ed.

16. BRADWAY, K. P., LION, E. G., AND CORRIGAN, H. The use of the Rorschach in a psychiatric study of promiscuous girls. *Rorschach Res. Exch.,* 1946, *10,* 105–110.

17. BROWER, DANIEL. The relation between certain Rorschach factors and cardiovascular activity before and after visuo-motor conflict. *J. General Psychol.,* 1947, *37,* 93–95.

18. BROZEK, J., GUETZKOW, H., KEYS, A., CATTELL, R. B., HARROWER, M. R., AND HATHAWAY, S. R. A study of personality of normal young men maintained on restricted intakes of vitamins of the B complex. *Psychosom. Med.,* 1946, *8,* 98–109.

19. BRUNER, J. S., AND GOODMAN, C. C. Value and need as organizing factors in perception. *J. Abnorm. Soc. Psychol.,* 1947, *42,* 33–44.

20. BRUNER, J. S., AND POSTMAN, L. Tension and tension release as organizing factors in perception. *J. Personality,* 1947, *15,* 300–308.

21. BRUNER, J. S., AND POSTMAN, L. Symbolic values as an organizing factor in perception. *J. Soc. Psychol.,* 1948, *27,* 203–208.

22. BUHLER, CHARLOTTE, BUHLER, KARL, AND LEFEVER, WELTY D. *Development of the basic Rorschach score with manual of directions.* Los Angeles, Calif.: Rorschach Standardization Studies, No. 1, 1948, ix, 190 pp.

23. BURNHAM, CATHERINE A. A Study of the degree of relationship between Rorschach H% and Wechsler-Bellevue picture arrangement scores. *Rorschach Res. Exch.,* 1949, *13,* 206–209.

24. CARR, ARTHUR C. An Evaluation of nine non-directive psychotherapy cases by means of the Rorschach. *J. Consult. Psychol.,* 1949, *13,* 196–205.

25. CATTELL, R. B. *Description and Measurement of Personality.* New York: World Book Co., 1946.

26. CHALLMAN, R. C. The Validity of the Harrower-Erickson Multiple Choice Test as a screening device. *J. Psychol.,* 1945, *20,* 41–48.

27. CHALLMAN, ROBERT C. Book Review: Large scale Rorschach Techniques. A manual for the Group Rorschach and Multiple Test, by Harrower-Erickson, M. R., and Steiner, M. E. *Psych. Bull.,* 1946, *43,* 285–287.

28. CLARK, JERRY H. Some MMPI correlates of color responses in the group Rorschach. *J. Consult. Psychol.,* 1948, *12,* 384–386.

29. COFER, C. N. An analysis of the concept of "clinical intuition." In Kelly, G. A., *New Methods in Applied Psychology,* 1947. Pp. 219–227.

422 *Summary*

30. COX, KENNETH J. Can the Rorschach pick sales clerks? *Personnel Psychol.,* 1948, *1,* 357–363.

31. CRONBACH, LEE J. A validation design for qualitative studies of personality. *J. Consult. Psychol.,* 1948, *12,* 365–374.

32. CRONBACH, LEE J. "Pattern tabulation": a statistical method for analysis of limited patterns of scores, with particular reference to the Rorschach test. *Educ. Psychol. Measmt.,* 1949, *9,* 149–171.

33. CRONBACH, LEE J. Statistical methods applied to Rorschach scores: a review. *Psychol. Bull.,* 1949, *46,* 393–429.

34. CRONBACH, LEE J. Statistical problems in Multiscore Tests. *J. Clin. Psychol.,* 1950, *7,* 21–25.

35. CRONBACH, LEE J. Studies of the Group Rorschach in relation to success in the college of the Univ. of Chicago. *J. Educ. Psychol.,* 1950, *41,* 65–82.

36. DAVIDSON, H. H. *Personality and economic background: a study of highly intelligent children.* New York: Kings Crown Press, 1943.

37. DAVIDSON, H. A measure of adjustment obtained from the Rorschach protocol. *J. Projective Techniques,* 1950, *14,* 31–38.

38. DUE, FLOYD O., AND WRIGHT, M. ERIK. The Use of Content Analysis in Rorschach Interpretation: I. Differential Characteristics of Male Homosexuals. *Rorschach Res. Exch.,* 1945, *9,* 169–177.

39. ELIZUR, ABRAHAM. Content analysis of the Rorschach with regard to anxiety and hostility. *Rorschach Res. Exch.,* 1949, *13,* 247–284.

40. ENGLE, T. L. The use of the Harrower-Erickson Multiple Choice (Rorschach) Test in differentiating between well-adjusted and maladjusted high shool pupils. *J. Educ. Psychol.,* 1946, *37,* 550–556.

41. EYSENCK, H. J. A comparative study of four screening tests for neurotics. *Psychol. Bull.,* 1945, *42,* 659–662.

42. EYSENCK, H. J. Screening-out the neurotic. *Lancet,* 1947, *252,* 530–531.

43. FORD, M. *The application of the Rorschach Test to young children.* Univ. of Minn. Inst. Child Welf. Monog., 1946, No. 23.

44. FRANK, L. K. *Projective Methods.* Springfield, Ill.: Charles C Thomas, 1948.

45. GARFIELD, S. L. The Rorschach test in clinical diagnosis. *J. Clin. Psych.,* 1947, *3,* 375–381.

46. GIBBY, ROBETR GWYN. The influence of varied experimental sets upon certain Rorschach variables. I. Stability of the intellectual variables. Microfilm of complete manuscript, Univ. Microfilms, Ann Arbor, Mich. Publ. No. 1512.

47. GOLDFARB, WILLIAM. The animal symbol in the Rorschach test and an animal association test. *Rorschach Res. Exch.,* 1945, *9,* 8–22.

48. GOLDFARB, WILLIAM. Rorschach test differences between family-reared, institution-reared, and schizophrenic children. *Amer. J. Orthopsychiat.,* 1949, *19,* 624–633.

49. GOLDSTEIN, KURT, AND ROTHMANN, EVA. Physiognomic phenomena in Rorschach responses. *Rorschach Res. Exch.,* 1945, *9,* 1–7.

50. GOODENOUGH, FLORENCE L. The appraisal of child personality. *Psychol. Rev.,* 1949, *56,* 123–131.

51. HALLOWELL, A. I. Acculturation processes and personality changes as indicated by the Rorschach technique. *Rorschach Res. Exch.*, 1942, *6*, 42–50.

52. HALLOWELL, A. Popular reponses and cultural differences: An analysis based on frequencies in a group of American Indian subjects. *Rorschach Res. Exch.*, 1945, *9*, 153–168.

53. HALLOWELL, A. I. The Rorschach technique in the study of personality and culture. *Amer. Anthrop.*, 1945, *47*, 195–210.

54. HALPERN, F. Rorschach interpretation of the personality structure of schizophrenics who benefit from insulin therapy. *Psychiat. Quart.*, 1940, *14*, 826–833.

55. HAMLIN, R. M., ALBEE, G. W., AND LELAND, E. M. Objective Rorschach "signs" for groups of normal, maladjusted and neuropsychiatric subjects. *J. Consult. Psychol.*, 1950, *14*, 276–282.

56. HARROWER-ERICKSON, M. R. Large scale investigation with the Rorschach method. *J. Consult. Psychol.*, 1943, *7*, 120–126.

57. HARROWER–ERICKSON, M. R., AND STEINER, M. E. *Large scale Rorschach techniques; a manual for the Group Rorschach and Multiple Choice Test.* Springfield, Ill.: Charles C Thomas, 1945.

58. HARROWER, MOLLIE R., AND STEINER, MATILDA E. *Psychodiagnostic Inkblots.* New York: Grune & Stratton, Inc., 1945.

59. HERTZ, MARGUERITE R. Rorschach norms for an adolescent age group. *Child Developm.*, 1935, *6*, 69–76.

60. HERTZ, MARGUERITE R. Rorschach: twenty years after. *Psychol. Bull.*, 1942, *39*, 529–572.

61. HERTZ, MARGUERITE R. Personality patterns in adolescence as portrayed by the Rorschach ink-blot method: I. The movement factors. *J. Gen. Psychol.*, 1942, *27*, 119–188.

62. HERTZ, MARGUERITE R. Personality patterns in adolescence as portrayed by the Rorschach ink-blot method: III. The "Erlebnistypus" (a normative study). *J. Gen. Psychol.*, 1943, *28*, 225–276.

63. HERTZ, MARGUERITE R. Personality patterns in adolescence as portrayed by the Rorschach method: IV. The "Erlebnistypus" (a typological study). *J. Gen. Psychol.*, 1943, *29*, 3–45.

64. HERTZ, MARGUERITE R. Book Review: *Large scale Rorschach techniques,* by Harrower-Erickson, M. R., and Steiner, M. E. *Rorschach Res. Exch.*, 1945, *9*, 46–53.

65. HERTZ, MARGUERITE R. *Frequency tables to be used in scoring responses to the Rorschach ink-blot test.* Dept. of Psychology, Western Reserve Univ., Cleveland, O., 1946. 3rd ed.

66. HERTZ, MARGUERITE R. *The Rorschach Psychogram.* Dept. of Psychology, Western Reserve Univ., Cleveland O., 1946.

67. HERTZ, MARGUERITE R. Suicidal configurations in Rorschach records. *Rorschach Research Exch. and J. of Projective Techniques*, 1948, *12*, 3–58.

68. HERTZ, MARGUERITE R. Further study of "suicidal" configurations in Rorschach records. *Rorschach Res. Exch.*, 1949, *13*, 44–73.

69. HERTZ, MARGUERITE R. The first international Rorschach conference. *J. Projective Techniques*, 1950, *14*, 39–51.

70. HERTZ, MARGUERITE R. The Rorschach Method: science or mystery. *J. Consult. Psychol.*, 1943, *7*, 67–79.

71. HERTZ, MARGUERITE R., AND BAKER, E. Personality patterns in adolescence as portrayed by the Rorschach ink-blot method: II. The color factors. *J. Gen. Psychol.*, 1943, *28*, 3–61.

72. HERTZ, MARGUERITE R., AND EBERT, ELIZABETH H. The mental procedure of 6 and 8 year old children as revealed by the Rorschach ink-blot method. *Rorschach Res. Exch.*, 1944, *8*, 10–30.

73. HERTZ, MARGUERITE R., ELLIS, ALBERT, AND SYMONDS, PERCIVAL M. Rorschach methods and other projective techniques. *Rev. Educ. Res.*, 1947, *17*, 78–100.

74. HERTZMANN, M., AND MARGULIES, H. Developmental changes as reflected in Rorschach test responses. *J. Gen. Psychol.*, 1943, *62*, 189–215.

75. HERTZMAN, MAX, AND PEARCE, JANE. The personal meaning of the human figure in the Rorschach *Psychiatry*, 1947, *10*, 413–422.

76. HSÜ, E. H. The Rorschach responses and factor analysis. *J. Gen. Psychol.*, 1947, *37*, 129–138.

77. HUGHES, ROBERT M. Rorschach signs for the diagnosis of organic pathology. *Rorschach Res. Exch.*, 1948, *12*, 165–167.

78. HUTT, MAX L., AND SHOR, J. Rationale for routine Rorschach "Testing-the-Limits." *Rorschach Res. Exch.*, 1946, *10*, 70–76.

79. JENSEN, M. B., AND ROTTER, J. B. The validity of the multiple choice Rorschach test in officer candidate selection. *Psychol. Bull.*, 1945, *42*, 182–185.

80. JOEL, WALTHER. The interpersonal equation in projective methods. *Rorschach Res. Exch.*, 1949, *13*, 479–482.

81. JOLLES, ISAAC. A study of mental deficiency by the Rorschach technique. *Amer. J. Ment. Def.*, 1947, *52*, 37–42.

82. JOLLES, ISAAC. The diagnostic implications of Rorschach's Test in case studies of mental defectives. *Genet. Psychol. Monogr.*, 1947, *36*, 89–197.

83. KABACK, G. R. *Vocational personalities: an application of the Rorschach group method.* Teach. Coll. Contr. Educ., 1946, no. 924.

84. KAY, L. W., AND VORHAUS, P. G. Rorschach reactions in early childhood. Part II. Intellectual aspects of personality development. *Rorschach Res. Exch.*, 1943, *7*, 71–77.

85. KELLMAN, SAMUEL. A proposed revision of the multiple-choice Rorschach: theoretical and methodical problems. *Rorschach Res. Exch.*, 1949, *13*, 244.

86. KIMBLE, G. A. Social influence on Rorschach records. *J. Abnorm. Soc. Psychol.*, 1945, *40*, 89–93.

87. KELLEY, D. M., MARGULIES, H., AND BARRERA, S. E. The stability of the Rorschach method as demonstrated in electric convulsive therapy cases. *Rorschach Res. Exch.*, 1940, *5*, 35–43.

88. KLOPFER, BRUNO, AND DAVIDSON, HELEN H. *The Rorschach Technique.* 1946 Supplement, New York: World Book Co.

89. KLOPFER, B., AND KELLEY, D. M. *The Rorschach Technique.* Yonkers-on-Hudson: World Book Company, 1942.

90. KRUGMAN, J. I. A clinical validation of the Rorschach with problem children. *Rorschach Res. Exch.,* 1942, *6,* 61–70.

91. KRUGMAN, M. Psychosomatic study of fifty stuttering children. Round table. IV. Rorschach study. *Amer. J. Orthopsychiat.,* 1946, *16,* 127–133.

92. KRUGMAN, M. *The third mental measurements yearbook,* 1949, pp. 132–133. Ed: Buros, O. K. New Brunswick, N.J.: Rutgers Univ. Press.

93. KURTZ, ALBERT K. A research test of the Rorschach test. *Personnel Psychol.,* 1948, *1,* 41–51.

94. LANE, BARBARA M. A validation test of the Rorschach movement interpretation. *Amer. J. Orthopsychiat.,* 1948, *18,* 292–296.

95. LAWSHE, C. H., JR., AND FORSTER, MAX H. Studies in projective techniques: I. The reliability of a multiple choice group Rorschach test. *J. Appl. Psychol.,* 1947, *31,* 199–211.

96. LAZARUS, RICHARD S. The influence of color on the protocol of the Rorschach Test. *J. Abnorm. Soc. Psychol.,* 1949, *44,* 506–515.

97. LEVINE, K. N., GRASSI, J. R., AND GERSON, M. J. Hypnotically induced mood changes in the verbal and graphic Rorschach: a case study. Part II: The response records. *Rorschach Res. Exch.,* 1944, *8,* 104–124.

98. LINDNER, ROBERT M. Analysis of the Rorschach test by content. *J. Clin. Psychopath.,* 1947, *8,* 707–719.

99. LUCHINS, ABRAHAM S. Situational and attitudinal influences on Rorschach responses. *Amer. J. Psychiat.,* 1947, *103,* 780–784.

100. MACFARLANE, J. W. Problems of validation inherent in projective methods. *Amer. J. Orthopsychiat.,* 1942, *12,* 405–411.

101. MALAMUD, RACHEL F., AND MALAMUD, DANIEL. The validity of the Amplified Multiple Choice Rorschach as a screening device. *J. Consult. Psychol.,* 1945, *9,* 224.

102. MALAMUD, R. F., AND MALAMUD, D. I. The multiple choice Rorschach: a critical examination of its scoring system. *J. Psychol.,* 1946, *21,* 237–242.

103. MARGULIES, H. *Rorschach responses of successful and unsuccessful students.* New York: Arch. Psychol., 1942, No. 271, p. 61.

104. MCCANDLESS, BOYD R. The Rorschach as a predictor of academic success. *J. Appl. Psychol.,* 1949, *33,* 43–50.

105. MCCLELLAND, D. C., AND ATKINSON, J. W. The relation of the intensity of a need to the amount of perceptual distortion. *J. Psychol.,* 1947, *25,* 205–222.

106. MCFATE, MARGUERITE Q., AND ORR, FRANCES G. Through adolescence with the Rorschach. *Rorschach Res. Exch.,* 1949, *13,* 302–319.

107. MELTZER, H. Personality differences between stuttering and non-stuttering children as indicated by the Rorschach test. *J. Psychol.,* 1944, *17,* 39–59.

108. MIALE, F. R., AND HARROWER-ERICKSON, M. R. Personality structure in the psychoneuroses. *Rorschach Res. Exch.,* 1940, *4,* 71–74.

109. MILNER, B., AND MOREAULT, L. Etude du Test. Rorschach en relation au réflexe psychogalvanique. *Bull. Canad. Psychol. Assn.,* 1945, *5,* 80 (*abstract*).

110. MILTON, E. OHMER, JR. The influence on varied experimental sets upon certain Rorschach variables: II. Stability of the human movement variable. Microfilm Abstr., 1950, 10(1), 127–128. Ph.D. thesis, 1950, U. Michigan.

111. MONTALTO, F. D. An application of the Group Rorschach technique to the problem of achievement in college. *J. Clin. Psychol.*, 1946, *2*, 254–260.

112. MORRIS, WOODROW W. Prognostic possibilities of the Rorschach method in metrazol therapy. *Amer. J. Psychiat.*, 1943, *100*, 222–230.

113. MORRIS, WOODROW WILBERT. The prediction of personality attributes by means of the Rorschach method. Microfilm Abstr., 1950, 9(3), 176–177. Ph.D. thesis, 1949, U. Michigan.

114. MUENCH, GEORGE A. An evaluation of non-directive psychotherapy. *Appl. Psychol. Monogr.*, 1947, No. 13, 168 pp.

115. MUNROE, RUTH L. Prediction of the adjustment and academic performance of college students by a modification of the Rorschach method. *Appl. Psychol. Monographs*, 1945, No. 7.

116. MUNROE, RUTH L. The use of projective methods in group testing. *J. Consult. Psychol.*, 1948, *12*, 8–15.

117. PATTERSON, M., AND MAGAW, D. C. An investigation of the validity of the Rorschach technique as applied ot mentally defective problem children. *Proc. Amer. Ass. Ment. Def.*, 1938, *43*, 179–185.

118. PIOTROWSKI, Z. The Rorschach ink-blot method in organic disturbances of the central nervous system. *J. Nerv. Ment. Dis.*, 1937, *86*, 525–537.

119. PIOTROWSKI, Z. A simple experimental device for the prediction of outcome of insulin treatment in schizophrenia. *Psychiat. Quart.*, 1940, *14*, 267–273.

120. PIOTROWSKI, Z. A. The Rorschach method as a prognostic aid in the insulin shock treatment of schizophrenics. *Psychiat. Quart.*, 1941, *15*, 807–822.

121. PIOTROWSKI, Z. A. The modifiability of personality as revealed by the Rorschach method: methodological considerations. *Rorschach Res. Exch.*, 1942, *6*, 160–167.

122. PIOTROWSKI, Z. A. Tentative Rorschach formulae for educational and vocational guidance in adolescence. *Rorschach Res. Exch.*, 1943, *7*, 16–27.

123. PIOTROWSKI, Z. A. Use of the Rorschach in vocational selection. *J. Consult Psychol.*, 1943, *7*, 97–102.

124. PIOTROWSKI, Z. A. Experimental psychological diagnosis of mild forms of schizophrenia. *Rorschach Res. Exch.*, 1945, *9*, 189–200.

125. PIOTROWSKI, Z. A., CANDEE, B. BALINSKY, B., HOLTZBERG, S., VON ARNOLD, B. Rorschach signs in the selection of outstanding young male mechanical workers. *J. Psychol.*, 1944, *18*, 131–150.

126. POSTMAN, L., BRUNER, J. S., AND MCGINNIES, E. Personal values as selective factors in perception. *J. Abnorm. Soc. Psychol.*, 1948, *43*, 142–154.

127. RABIN, A. I. Statistical problems involved in Rorschach patterning. *J. Clin. Psychol.*, 1950, *7*, 19–21.

128. RABIN, A. I., AND BECK, S. J. Genetic aspects of some Rorschach factors. Annual meeting of Amer. Orthopsychiat. Assn., 1949.

129. RAPAPORT, D., GILL, M., AND SCHAFER, R. *Diagnostic psychological testing; the theory, statistical evaluation and diagnostic application of a battery of tests.* Vol. II. Chicago: Year Book Publishers, 1946.

130. REITZELL, JEANNE MANNHEIM. A comparative study of hysterics, homosexuals and alchoholics using content analysis of Rorschach responses. *Rorschach Res. Exch.,* 1949, *13,* 127–141.

131. ROBB, R. W., KOVITZ, B., AND RAPAPORT, D. Histamine in the treatment of psychosis; a psychiatric and objective psychological study. *Amer. J. Psychiat.,* 1940, *97,* 601–610.

132. ROCKWELL, F. V., WELCH, L., KUBIS, J., AND FISICHELLI, V. Changes in palmar skin resistance during the Rorschach test. I. Color shock and psychoneurotic reactions. *Monthly Rev. Psychiat. Neurol.,* 1947, *113,* 129–152.

133. ROCKWELL, FRED V., WELCH, LIVINGSTON; KUBIS, JOSEPH, AND FISICHELLI, VINCENT. Changes in palmar skin resistance during the Rorschach test. II. The effect of repetition with color removed. *Mschr. Psychiat. Neurol.,* 1948, *116,* 321–345.

134. ROE, ANNE, A Rorschach Study of a group of scientists and technicians. *J. Consult. Psychol.,* 1945, *14,* 317–327.

135. ROE, ANNE. Artists and their work. *J. Personality,* 1946, *15,* 1–40.

136. ROE, ANNE. Personality and vocation. *Trans. N.Y. Acad. Sci.,* 1947, *9,* 257–267.

137. ROE, ANNE. Psychological examinations of eminent biologists. *J. Consult. Psychol.,* 1949, *13,* 225–246.

138. ROSS, W. DONALD. Relation between Rorschach interpretations and clinical diagnosis. *J. Proj. Techniques,* 1950, *14,* 5–14.

139. ROSS, W. D., FERGUSON, G. A., AND CHALKE, F. C. R. The group Rorschach in officer selection. *Bull. Canad. Psychol. Ass.,* 1945, *5,* 84–86.

140. ROSS, W. D., AND ROSS, S. Some Rorschach ratings of clinical value. *Rorschach Res. Exch.,* 1944, *8,* 1–9.

141. ROTTER, JULIAN B. The present status of the Rorschach in clinical and experimental procedures. *J. Personality,* 1948, *16,* 304–311.

142. RUESCH, J., AND FINESINGER, J. E. The relation of the Rorschach color response to the use of color in drawings. *Psychosom. Med.,* 1941, *3,* 370–388.

143. RUST, RALPH MASON. Some correlates of the movement response. *J. Personality,* 1948, *16,* 369–401.

144. SAPPENFELD, BART R., AND BUKER, SAMUEL L. Validity of the Rorschach 8-9-10 per cent as an indicator of responsiveness to color. *J. Consult. Psychol.,* 1949, *13,* 268–271.

145. SARASON, SEYMOUR B., AND SARASON, ESTHER KROOP. The discriminatory value of a test pattern in the high grade familial defective. *J. Clin. Psychol.,* 1946, *2,* 38–49.

146. SARASON, SEYMOUR B., AND SARASON, ESTHER KROOP. The discriminatory value of a test pattern with cerebral palsied defective children. *J. Clin. Psychol.,* 1947, *3,* 141–146.

147. SCHACHTEL, ERNEST G. The dynamic perception and the symbolism of form. *Psychiatry,* 1941, *4,* 79–96.

148. SCHACHTEL, ERNEST G. On color and affect. *Psychiatry*, 1943, *6*, 393–409.

149. SCHACHTEL, E. G. Subjective definitions of the Rorschach test situation and their effect on test performance. Contributions to an understanding of Rorschach's test, III. *Psychiatry*, 1945, *8*, 419–448.

150. SCHACHTEL, ERNEST G. Projection and its relation to character attitudes and creativity in the kinesthetic responses. *Psychiatry*, 1950, *13*, 69–100.

151. SHAW, BARRIE. "Sex populars" in the Rorschach test. *J. Abnorm. Soc. Psychol.*, 1948, *43*, 466–470.

152. SHOEMAKER, H. A., AND ROHRER, J. H. Relationship between success in the study of medicine and certain psychological and personal data. *J. Ass. Amer. Med. Coll.*, 1948, *23*, 190–201.

153. SIEGEL, MIRIAM G. The diagnostic and prognostic validity of the Rorschach test in a child guidance clinic. *Amer. J. Orthopsychiat.*, 1948, *18*, 119–133.

154. SIIPOLA, ELSA M. The influence of color on reaction to ink-blots. *J. Personality*, 1950, *18*, 358–383.

155. SLOAN, WILLIAM. Mental deficiency as a symptom of personality disturbance. *Amer. J. Mental Def.*, 1947, *52*, 31.

156. SPRINGER, N. NORTON. The validity of the multiple choice group Rorschach test in the screening of naval personnel. *J. Gen. Psychol.*, 1946, *35*, 27–32.

157. STAINBROOK, E. The Rorschach description of immediate post-convulsive mental function. *Character and Pers.*, 1944, *12*, 302–322.

158. STAINBROOK, E., AND SIEGEL, P. S. A comparative group Rorschach study of Southern Negro and white high school and college students. *J. Psychol.*, 1944, *17*, 107–115.

159. STAVRIANOS, B. An investigation of sex differences in children as revealed by the Rorschach method. *Rorschach Res. Exch.*, 1942, *6*, 168–175.

160. STEIN, MORRIS I. Personality factors of Rorschach responses. *Rorschach Res. Exch.*, 1949, *13*, 355–413.

161. STEINER, MATILDA E. The use of the Rorschach method in industry. *Rorschach Res. Exch.*, 1947, *11*, 46–52.

162. STEINER, MATILDA E. *The psychologist in industry*. Springfield, Ill.: Charles C Thomas, 1949.

163. STEPHENSEN, WILLIAM. A statistical approach to typology. *J. Clin. Psychol.* (Monograph Supplement) No. 7, 1950, 26–38.

164. SWIFT, J. W. Matchings of teachers' descriptions and Rorschach analyses of preschool children. *Child Develpm.*, 1944, *15*, 217–224.

165. SWIFT, J. W. Reliability of Rorschach scoring categories with preschool children. *Child Develpm.*, 1944, *15*, 207–216.

166. SWIFT, J. W. Relation of behavioral and Rorschach measures of insecurity in preschool children. *J. Clin. Psychol.*, 1945, *1*, 196–205.

167. SWIFT, J. W. Rorschach responses of eighty-two preschool children. *Rorschach Res. Exch.*, 1945, *9*, 74–84.

168. THOMPSON, GRACE M. College grades and the group Rorschach *J. Appl. Psychol.*, 1948, *32*, 398–407.

169. THOMPSON, GRACE M. MMPI correlates of certain movement responses in the group Rorschach of two college samples. *J. Consult. Psychol.*, 1948, *12*, 379–383.

170. THURSTONE, L. L. The Rorschach in psychological science. *J. Abnorm. Soc. Psychol.*, 1948, *43*, 471–475.

171. VORHAUS, P. G. Rorschach reactions in early childhood. Part III. Content and details in pre-school records. *Rorschach Res. Exch.*, 1944, *8*, 71–91.

172. VORHAUS, P. G. Non-reading as an expression of resistance. *Rorschach Res. Exch.*, 1946, *10*, 60–69.

173. WALLEN, RICHARD. The nature of color shock. *J. Abnorm. Soc. Psychol.*, 1948, *43*, 346–356.

174. WEISSKOPF, E. A. The influence of the time factor on Rorschach Performance. *Rorschach Res. Exch.*, 1942, *6*, 128–136.

175. WERNER, H. Perceptual behavior of brain injured, mentally defective children: an experimental study by means of the Rorschach technique. *Genet. Psychol. Monogr.*, 1945, *31*, 51–110.

176. WHEELER, WILLIAM MARSHALL. An analysis of Rorschach indices of male homosexuality. *Rorschach Res. Exch.*, 1949, *13*, 97–126.

177. WHEELER, W., BUHLER, C., GRAYSON, H., MEYER, M., WESLEY, S., AND LEFEVER, D. Symposium on a Basic Rorschach Score. *Rorschach Res. Exch.*, 1949, *13*, 6–24.

178. WILKINS, WALTER L., AND ADAMS, AUSTIN J. The use of the Rorschach test under hypnosis and under sodium amytol in military psychiatry. *J. Gen. Psychol.*, 1947, *36*, 131–138.

179. WILLIAMS, MEYER. An experimental study of intellectual control under stress and associated Rorschach factors. *J. Consult. Pyschol.*, 1947, *11*, 21–29.

180. WINFIELD, M. C. The use of the Harrower-Erickson Multiple Choice Rorschach Test with a selected group of women in military service. *J. Appl. Psychol.*, 1946, *30*, 481–487.

181. WISHNER, JULIUS. Rorschach intellectual indicators in neurotics. *Amer. J. Orthopsychiat.*, 1948, *18*, 265–279.

182. WITTENBORN, J. R. Certain Rorschach response categories and mental abilities *J. Appl. Psychol.*, 1949, *33*, 330–338.

183. WITTENBORN, J. R. A factor analysis of discrete responses to the Rorschach ink blots. *J. Consult. Psychol.*, 1949, *13*, 335–340.

184. WITTENBORN, J. R. Statistical tests of certain Rorschach assumptions: analysis of discrete responses. *J. Consult. Psychol.*, 1949, *13*, 257–267.

185. WITTENBORN, J. R. Statistical tests of certain Rorschach assumptions: The internal consistency of scoring categories. *J. Consult. Psychol.*, 1950, *14*, 1–19.

186. WITTENBORN, J. R., AND SARASON, SEYMOUR B. Exceptions to certain Rorschach criteria of pathology. *J. Consult. Psychol.*, 1949, *13*, 21–27.

187. WITTSON, C. L., HUNT, W. A., AND OLDER, H. J. The use of the Multiple Choice Group Rorschach Test in military screening. *J. Psychol.*, 1944, *17*, 91–94.

188. ZUBIN, J. Introduction. The problems of quantification and objectification in personality: A symposium. *J. Personality*, 1948, *17*, 141–145.

189. ZUBIN, J. Personality research and psychopathology as related to clinical practice. Clinical practice and personality theory: A symposium. *J. Abnorm. and Social Psychology*, 1949, *44*, 12–21.

190. ZUBIN, J. Introduction, Symposium on statistics for the clinician. *J. Clin. Psychol.*, 1950, *6*, 1–6.

191. ZUBIN, J., CHUTE, E., AND VENIAR, S. Psychometric scales for scoring Rorschach test responses. *Character and Pers.*, 1943, *11*, 277–301.

192. ZUBIN, J., AND YOUNG, K. M. *Manual of Projective and Cognate Techniques*, Madison, Wis., College Typing Co., 1948 (mimeographed).

193. ZULLIGER, HANS. Personality dynamics as revealed in the Rorschach of a 15 year old girl. *J. Projective Techniques*, 1950, *14*, 52–60.

NAME INDEX

Abel, T. M., 48, 88, 361, 383, 406, 420
Abt, L. E., 413, 420
Ackerman, N. W., 48, 70, 73, 90
Adams, A. J., 103, 143, 231, 405, 429
Ahman, J. S., 16
Ainsworth, M., 313
Aita, J. A., 406, 420
Albee, G. W., 211, 338, 345, 410, 421
Albrecht, R., 338, 344
Allen, F. H., 90, 91
Allport, F. H., 85, 97
Allport, G. W., 31, 48, 56, 65, 79, 80, 97, 419, 420
Altus, W. D., 407, 420
Amen, E. W., 67, 94
Ames, L. B., 313, 344
Anastasi, Anne, 16, 88, 270, 289
Anderson, H. H., 48
Anderson, I., 413, 420
Anderson, J. E., 82
Anderson, R. G., 413, 420
Armitage, S. G., 406, 420
Atkinson, J. W., 393, 425

Baker, L. M., 397, 403, 420, 424
Baldwin, A. L., 66, 98
Balinsky, B., 162, 406, 426
Balken, E. R., 51, 55, 65, 81, 82, 87, 94, 98
Barker, R. G., 49
Barnhart, E. N., 88
Barrere, S., 379, 385, 402, 424
Barron, F. X., 335, 344
Barry, J. R., 338, 344
Bartlett, F. C., 61, 98
Baruch, D. W., 73, 90

Bateson, G., 33, 41
Baughman, E. E., 211, 333, 339, 344
Bechtoldt, H. P., 266, 289
Beck, E., 89
Beck, L. W., 276, 289
Beck, S. J., 49, 62, 84, 92, 142, 162, 200, 207, 211, 217, 229, 295, 308, 365, 383, 394, 396, 420
Beers, C., 66, 98
Behn-Eschenburg, H., 295, 297, 308
Bell, J. E., 394, 405, 421
Bellak, L., 73, 94, 102, 142
Bender, C., 49
Bender, Lauretta, 59, 68, 69, 70, 88, 89, 90, 95
Benedict, R., 33
Benjamin, A. C., 98
Benjamin, J. D., 92, 223, 229, 334, 344
Bennet, Georgia, 94
Berger, S., 314
Bergman, M. S., 103, 142, 220, 229, 396, 401, 421
Berkowitz, M., 211
Beyer, E., 87
Binet, A., 61, 73, 98
Blair, W. R. N., 289
Blake, R. R., 225, 229
Blanchard, P., 91
Bleuler, E., 63, 98, 231, 297, 309
Blumenthal, N. T., 43
Blyth, D. D., 338, 344
Bochner, R., 62, 92, 116, 142, 394, 398, 421
Booth, G. C., 49, 87
Bordin, R., 89
Boynton, P. L., 98
Bradway, K. P., 409, 421
Braithwaite, R. B., 276, 289

Brenman, M., 85, 92
Bridgman, P. W., 60, 98
Brittain, H. L., 98
Brosin, H. W., 216, 229
Brower, D., 16, 403, 421
Brown, E., 87
Brown, J. F., 87, 98
Brown, R. R., 353, 384
Brozek, J., 413, 421
Bruner, J. S., 393, 421
Brussel, J., 115, 142
Bucher, J., 97
Buhler, C., 73, 96, 116, 142, 356, 365, 384, 395, 421
Buhler, K., 356, 384, 421
Buker, S. L., 404, 427
Burke, C. J., 211
Burks, B. S., 31
Burnham, C. A., 407, 421
Burr, H. S., 37

Cameron, N., 49, 50
Cameron, W. M., 71, 90
Candee, B., 406, 426
Carnap, R., 276, 289
Carr, A. C., 338, 344, 410, 421
Cartwright, D., 80, 98
Cattell, R. B., 63, 421
Chalke, F. L. R., 386
Challman, R. C., 162, 264, 412, 421
Chapman, D. W., 234, 263
Chesire, L., 162
Chidester, L., 88
Child, I. L., 289
Christenson, J. A., 94
Christiansen, C., 356, 385
Chute, E., 94, 396, 430
Chyatte, C., 280, 289
Clapp, H., 93
Clark, J. H., 407, 421
Clark, L. P., 61, 98

SUBJECT INDEX

M Powers, Martha.
Bleeding heart.

$23.00

DATE			

BAKER & TAYLOR

By the same author

SUNFLOWER

A REGENCY HOLIDAY

FALSE PRETENSES

THE RUNAWAY HEART

MARTHA POWERS

BLEEDING
HEART

SIMON & SCHUSTER
NEW YORK   LONDON   TORONTO   SYDNEY   SINGAPORE

SIMON & SCHUSTER
Rockefeller Center
1230 Avenue of the Americas
New York, NY 10020

SIMON & SCHUSTER and colophon are registered trademarks of Simon & Schuster, Inc.

Designed by Deirdre C. Amthor

Manufactured in the United States of America

1   3   5   7   9   10   8   6   4   2

Library of Congress Cataloging-in-Publication Data
Powers, Martha.
Bleeding heart / Martha Powers.
p.   cm.
1. Kidnapping—Fiction.   2. Widows—Fiction.   I. Title.
PS3566.O888 B58 2000
813'.54—dc21   00-041009
ISBN 0-684-86610-2

ACKNOWLEDGMENTS

To Lynn Wolfram for being a great friend as well as the good sister who stayed awake during grammar classes. To Captain Arthur Babiak, retired, Bergen County Police Department, New Jersey, who answered endless questions on police procedure and downhill putts. To Gary Moritz for sharing his knowledge of falconry and for being patient with my ignorance. To Ruth O'Brien for forcing me to go to the next level despite my penchant for easing through the cracks. To Paul Grange for being a magician with a camera and giving immortality to my favorite dress. To Sue Sussman for enlivening meetings and conferences with her sense of humor and for remembering long-forgotten lines of poetry. Most of all to Bill Powers for the gifts of time and laughter and a sense of what's important in life.

TO
MICHAEL KORDA
AND
CHUCK ADAMS

For your support and encouragement
And for the kind of editing that makes me
a better writer

and

TO
JEAN POWERS

What a joy to watch you soar

THE SECOND COMING

Turning and turning in the widening gyre
The falcon cannot hear the falconer;
Things fall apart; the centre cannot hold;
Mere anarchy is loosed upon the world,
The blood-dimmed tide is loosed, and everywhere
The ceremony of innocence is drowned;
The best lack all conviction, while the worst
Are full of passionate intensity.

William Butler Yeats

BLEEDING
HEART

PROLOGUE

TWO-AND-A-HALF-YEAR-OLD Tyler McKenzie opened his mouth in a wide circle and blew against the front of the jewelry counter. A cloud of wet air frosted the glass, then slowly disappeared. Inside, the bright stones shimmered on the blanket of shiny gold. He liked the blue ones best. Like Mommy's eyes.

"Don't do that, sweetheart," Barbara McKenzie said, pulling him back against her side. "A couple more minutes, Tyler. Then we'll go home."

She knew he was tired. They'd been returning presents for more than an hour. He leaned against her leg. He rocked from side to side, then slid down to the floor. The tether attached to his wrist snagged on her belt loop, and he tugged to get it loose.

"Don't pull, honey. You'll tear Mommy's coat."

She unwound the coiled plastic tubing until the strap swung free, one continuous loop from Tyler's wrist to hers. She was glad that she'd remembered to bring it. Between after-Christmas sales and people returning rejected presents, the department store was dreadfully crowded. She always worried about Tyler getting lost.

From his seat on the floor, he stared up at her. His mouth stretched into a lopsided grin, but his brown eyes drooped sleepily. She ruffled the top of his blond head.

"What a love you are, Tiger," Barbara said. "Mommy's hurrying."

Tyler nuzzled her leg, purring like a cat. They'd taken him to the zoo Thanksgiving weekend. They'd made a special trip to see the lion cubs because Tyler loved the Disney movie *The Lion King*. It was the tiger, however, that had drawn his interest. Barbara had to admit it was her choice too. Tyler wasn't afraid of the huge animal. For him it was nothing more than a big cat.

She checked to see that the Velcro strap was secure around his wrist, unable to resist touching the soft skin on his cheek as she straightened up to sign the return slip. Finished, she put her wallet back in her purse, picked up the shopping bag beside Tyler and helped him to his feet.

"Only one more stop," she said as she dusted the seat of his pants with her hand.

Now that Tyler was standing, he was anxious to be on his way. His short legs moved like pistons to get ahead of her as she walked down the aisle toward the escalator.

"Wait for Mommy," she said as he strained against the tether.

She took his hand, making sure the strap that joined them wrist to wrist didn't catch on the treads moving up the escalator. Ken never used the tether when he took Tyler out. He said it reminded him of a leash for a dog. Easy for him to say, she thought. Husbands didn't have a million errands to run while trying to keep track of an active child.

"Jump jump?" Tyler said.

"Almost." She tightened her grip on his pudgy little hand, and as the escalator steps flattened out, she said, "OK, Tiger. Jump."

She raised his arm as he hurled his body forward, then steadied him as he came down in a two-footed landing at the top. He cocked his head, crowing with triumph as he smiled up at her.

"Tyler good," he said.

"Very good. That was an excellent jump," she agreed, giving his hand another squeeze before she released him.

He had just begun talking in two-word phrases. It wasn't always easy to know what he meant, but it was fun hearing the sound of his voice and anticipating what it would be like when he could verbalize more. He'd learned his colors and shapes and even learned the first part of the ABC song.

She let him pull her along as they followed the aisle around to the women's department. She opened her shopping bag and pulled out the knit tunic her brother, Grant, had given her for Christmas and placed it on the counter in front of the salesgirl.

"Last stop," she said, leaning over to kiss Tyler on the top of his head.

Making small smacking sounds, he pushed through a rack of sweaters until he reached the open space in the center. The tether stretched, and Barbara hunkered down to peer under the clothing. Tyler was sitting on the floor, his back against the center pole.

"Tyler hide," he said. He clutched the sleeve of a navy blue sweater, brushing it against his cheek as he tucked the thumb of his other hand into his mouth.

"It's a very good hideout," she said to the heavy-lidded child. "You can take a rest, and I'll be right here."

She straightened up and turned back to the salesgirl, explaining that the tunic was too long and the wrong color. She rummaged through her purse until she found the correct receipt.

The sweaters on the rack shook, and she heard Tyler cooing within his soft nest. At least he was still awake. Her parents and brother had stayed in the house over Christmas, and Tyler had overdosed on excitement and was short of sleep. She knew it was a mistake to let him nod off. He'd be crabby when she woke him.

Leaning tiredly on the counter, Barbara pulled the tether. From under the rack of sweaters, Tyler pulled back. She turned around to face the counter, waiting for the clerk to complete the transaction. The girl pressed keys on the computer, pausing after each action to stare blankly at the monitor. Finally the machine spit out several sheets of paper.

"Here you are, Mrs. McKenzie," the salesclerk said.

She set the receipt down on the counter along with a pen. Barbara signed her name, waiting as the girl stapled the two receipts together. Tucking the charge card back in her wallet, Barbara stuffed everything into her purse.

"Time to go, Tyler. Mommy's all finished."

She pulled the strap, sighing at the lack of response. He must be sound asleep. She'd have to carry him all the way to the car.

"Come on, Tyler. Wake up and we'll go home."

Settling her purse strap on her shoulder, she spread the sweaters apart, following the coiled plastic wire to the center of Tyler's hideout.

The Velcro wrist strap of the child tether was attached to the metal center pole.

Tyler was gone.

CHAPTER ONE

THE RENAISSANCE FAIRE was in full swing. Coming to Delbrook, Wisconsin, the Friday after Labor Day, it was an event of pure performance art. A whimsical imitation of a medieval market town was erected in a field above Falcon Lake. Costumed players provided a day's worth of events that ranged from plays and musical entertainments to nature exhibits and crafts to a finale of jousting, mock battles and horsemanship.

Traditionally the local schools called a day off on Friday. It gave the teachers a welcome chance to catch their breath after the hectic opening days of the school year. Now that the lake crowd had closed up their summer cottages and returned to the cities where they lived and worked, the residents of Delbrook observed the weekend of the Renaissance Faire as a time for celebration. This year the weather was unusually warm.

Nevertheless, the Warrior was cold.

Beads of sweat stood out on his forehead and slid down the side of his neck to pool at the indentation below his Adam's apple. The late afternoon heat pressed against the top of his head, but a chill, a combination of anticipation and fear, fanned out from the core of his being. His arms and legs tingled and his stomach cramped as he leaned against the railing, staring across the fairgrounds.

To the Warrior, the carnival atmosphere was alien to the serious purpose of the day's visit. The inherent danger of proximity to his home made it a daring choice. He had never worked within his own territory, and had strong misgivings. Even though the risk factor was very high, he had chosen the Faire for the apprentice's first test because it offered the greatest opportunity of success for the boy.

All week the Warrior had been restless. He had spent long nights establishing the guidelines, working out every detail to minimize the danger to both himself and the boy. The first trial in the initiation process was always the most important, setting the tone for eventual success or failure.

Despite the long training period, the boy's youth was a decided disadvantage. The test would prove whether, at four, the boy had mastered the necessary discipline to follow orders without question with all the distractions of a public place.

The Warrior had chosen his vantage point well. From the top of the hill, the outdoor patio of Ye Olde Ale House had a panoramic view of the entire fairground.

Smoke from the cooking pots and the open fires hung in a thick pall above the gaudily painted buildings of the mock town, pressed down by the humidity left behind by the recent thunderstorm. The ground was soaked and dotted with pools of standing water. In a futile effort to lessen the impact of the rain, the organizers had strewn loose straw on the main traffic areas, but despite that the ground had become a quagmire. The wet, mud-streaked crowd added a measure of veracity to the appearance and smell of the make-believe medieval fair.

The Warrior bit his lip. A sense of unease invaded his body. He hadn't counted on the rainstorm that had changed the temperament of the crowd. The sheer boisterousness worried him. In this atmosphere, anything could happen, and in an instant he could lose control of the situation.

Instinct urged him to abort the trial.

His eyes flicked across the crowd milling around the wooden benches next to the jousting field. It was easy to spot the blond boy sitting alone at the far end of the bench closest to the arena. Against the shifting movements of the excited audience, the child's immobility created an oasis of stillness.

One Who Cries was waiting for the signal. It was time for the boy to take the first step on his journey.

The Warrior could remember when he began his own training.

He had been older than One Who Cries. Twelve and lost in a world of pain and despair. He had found the answers to his search for freedom in reading about the culture of the American Indian. The tough disciplining of young boys captured his imagination, especially the tests that led to becoming a warrior. He'd steeped himself in the rituals and the customs, picking and choosing the elements he liked best and the ones he thought would enhance his own spirit.

The warrior symbolized power. And counting coup brought ultimate power.

A coup was a war honor that emphasized bravery, cunning and stealth over actual killing. It was the greatest achievement to touch an enemy with a coup stick in the heat of battle and leave him alive to wallow in shame and self-reproach. The triumphant warrior captured the enemy's spirit, which was worse than death to a man of the People.

Like a young American Indian boy, he began to train so that he would be worthy to take on the mantle of the warrior. In this he had no mentor to guide him. He would be his own teacher.

He had invented the first test when he was twelve.

During a week of planning he had fine-tuned the rules. He would select an enemy in a public place. For the coup to count, he had to touch the very center of the target's back. It must be a one-fingered touch, solid enough to elicit some reaction from the victim.

Level one had been easy to master.

Suddenly the Warrior straightened, hands tightening on the railing as he noticed the activity in the arena. Several horses had entered the jousting field.

The crowd applauded and shouted as the colorfully draped mounts with costumed knights on their backs pranced nervously around the ring. A loudspeaker bellowed over the noise of the audience, but the words were unintelligible at this distance.

Soon. It would be soon.

Eyes intent on the back of the blond head, the Warrior waited. He stood tall so that the boy would be able to see him clearly when he turned to catch the signal. The noise and commotion faded into the background as the Warrior concentrated on the child. He narrowed his focus, as if by sheer willpower he could guarantee success.

Still seated on the bench while all around him people shouted and gestured at the activity, One Who Cries looked too frail for the test ahead.

Despite appearances, the boy was in peak physical condition. He had been prepared for this moment through a strict regimen of healthy food, exercise and a highly structured schedule of activities.

The Warrior had made today's test extremely simple. It was the first time the boy had been released from confinement in a year and a half. Primarily the test was to see if the Warrior could maintain control of the four-year-old with all the distractions of the real world and an opportunity to escape.

What the boy had to do was neither demanding nor dangerous. He needed to wait for the appointed signal that initiated the coup, touch the wooden fence around the jousting field, then look to the Warrior for the signal to retreat and return to the rendezvous point. If he could, it would prove that the boy could be trusted on his own to obey his mentor's instructions.

A trumpet blew. One Who Cries rose to his feet and turned around until he was facing the Warrior. His right hand came up just below his chin and his fingers formed the sign to indicate he was ready. The Warrior raised his own hand and gave the go-ahead.

Heart racing in anticipation, the Warrior watched the boy walk with steady steps to the edge of the jousting arena. He reached out with his left hand and placed his palm flat on the wooden fencing.

Success.

One Who Cries turned around, and even at a distance, the Warrior could see the pride written clearly in the straight carriage of the boy. Now all that remained was the retreat. The Warrior raised his hand, but before he could give the signal for withdrawal, he heard a piercing cry. The boy's body jerked at the sound. His head tilted back, mouth open slightly, eyes trained upward.

A falcon soared high overhead. Even at that height, her silhouette was easily recognizable. With her strong wings, she dug into the air and climbed steeply above the arena. Wings and tail spread wide, she circled in a lazy spiral. A shiver of fear ran through the Warrior's body. This was not a part of the trial.

The falcon was a harbinger. An omen of disaster.

The Warrior started to move forward, watching the boy, who remained transfixed by the bird. The falcon slipped sideways, riding the rising currents of heat, then folded her wings against her body and dived straight down toward the earth, swooping above the crowd before she started to climb again.

One Who Cries opened his mouth in a silent scream.

Covering the top of his head with his arms, the boy raced down the aisle away from the arena. Seeing his distress, people reached out to him, but the boy dodged all attempts to hold him, ducking beneath the out-stretched arms until he was beyond the jousting field.

Free of the crowd, One Who Cries slowed. His eyes were open, but he appeared to travel blindly, mind far from the motion of his body. The mud sucked at his feet, holding him to the earth, as he staggered from side to side up the hill. The Warrior could see the heaviness that invaded the small body as exhaustion overcame his initial panic.

The Warrior drew upon his own training to guard his face from show-ing any interest or emotion, but inside he twisted with frustration.

One Who Cries had failed the test.

The Warrior pushed away from the railing, charting a path that would intersect with the boy. He held his hands, curled into fists, tightly against his sides as he strode across the crest of the hill and angled toward One Who Cries. This was the moment of maximum danger where recognition could result in the loss of the child. He tried to clear his mind of negative thoughts. His first priority was to regain control of the child.

Later there would be time for analysis. He would have to discover what flaw in the training process had resulted in another failure. At least it was not a total disaster like the last time. Bad enough, but not unalterable.

It was important to keep in mind how much time he had invested in the boy's training. Well worth finding the weakness in the program so that he could modify it for the next time. Not much time remained until the final test. It was painful to think that the boy might be a poor choice.

Like the others, however, One Who Cries was expendable.

"Look, Mom. It's Grampa's car," Jake yelled.

The car lights illuminated George Collier as Maggie pulled into her parking space behind the house. As the tall, slim figure rose from the swing on the side porch, she sighed, knowing she didn't look her best. One look in the rearview mirror confirmed the fact she couldn't look much worse.

"Hi, Grampa," Jake shouted as he got out of the car. "We just got back from my birthday party."

"It was getting late and I was beginning to worry that you'd run into trouble," George said.

"No trouble. I had to drop off the other boys," Maggie said, following more sedately as Jake bounded up the stairs to the porch. "Don't get too close, George. We're both absolutely filthy."

"Good heavens," the older man said as they came into the light. "What happened?"

"We got caught in the rain." Jake held out his dirt-streaked arms for his grandfather's approval.

"Was the party a disaster?" George asked.

"Actually, it was a great success," Maggie said. "Start taking your shoes and socks off, Jake, so you don't drag all that dirt into the house."

She brushed at the front of her once white blouse, wondering if the splatters of mud would come out in the wash. A damp strand of reddish brown hair touched the side of her cheek, and she raised her hands to anchor the curly mess behind her ears. Her sneakers made squishing sounds as she crossed the wooden floor.

She frowned at the acrid smell of smoke. She knew George's doctor had told him to give up cigars, but other than to make her father-in-law sneak his guilty pleasures, the injunction seemed to have had little effect. Oh damn! She bit her lip. No point in nagging him. He'd just shrug and ignore her, like Jake did.

"How was the carnival?" George asked.

"Super," Jake said. "Extra super. None of the boys had ever been to the Renaissance Faire. Not even Kenny Rossiter. It was awesome."

"Despite the rain?" George asked.

"Probably because of it," Maggie said. "The whole place was one huge mud hole. If you were eight years old, what could be better. The boys loved it. Believe it or not we cleaned up a bit before we came home. After a day of slogging through the muck and mire, we were a pretty nasty-looking group. And you should see the car. I'll have to have it washed, inside and out."

Jake pulled at the sleeve of George's jacket to get his grandfather's attention.

"These two guys got into a fight and they wrestled in the middle of this mud puddle. They were all covered except for their eyeballs. They looked like white marbles. And when they were all done, another guy squirted them with a hose. Oh, and Grampa, if you gave this guy a dollar, he'd eat a whole handful of mud."

"Good Lord." George turned to Maggie. "How on earth did you survive?"

"Actually, it was a lot of fun," she said. "Once I realized the boys were having a great time and there was no hope of staying clean, I just sort of relaxed. It was like being a kid again. And the big finale at the jousting arena was well worth the aggravations."

Since Jake was too excited to be very helpful, she knelt down on the porch and grabbed one foot as he braced himself with a dirty hand on her shoulder. She removed his shoes and peeled off his socks as he regaled his grandfather with the events of the day.

Male bonding, she thought wistfully as they chattered away, oblivious to her presence. That was the one thing she could never give her son. After all these many days since Mark's death and all she'd done to help him, she couldn't hold back a twinge of jealousy that George could give Jake more than she could.

"Grampa, they had these horses and these knights with poles and they'd run at each other. And smash! They'd knock each other off the horses and then finish the fight with swords. I don't think anyone got killed." There was a trace of disappointment in his voice.

"Well I should hope not." George shook his head. "I'm sorry I missed it. It must have been a real spectacle."

"Just wait'll you see. Mom bought me one of those cardboard cameras, and I took tons of pictures. I even got one of Kenny throwing up."

"A bit too much pizza and cotton candy," Maggie explained, standing up. "He was back in action almost immediately."

"Sounds like quite a day," George said, smiling down at the excited child. "I can't wait to see the pictures."

"We took them to Kruckmeyer's Pharmacy to be developed. I'll have them back tomorrow, so you can see them before we go to dinner."

In the dim porch light, Maggie noted the bright color rising high on George's cheek and guessed the reason he had been waiting for them.

"Well, you see, son," George said. "I know we talked about going to dinner and a movie tomorrow, but I've run into a problem."

Jake's eyes narrowed slightly as he stared up at his grandfather.

"I got a call this afternoon and I have to go to the country club tomorrow. There's going to be a poker game." His eyes shifted between Jake and Maggie. "We won't be able to go to a movie, but there's no reason we can't have dinner together. I thought you and your mom could have dinner at the country club and then we'd take in a movie on another night."

"That's OK, Grampa," Jake said. "Mom already planned a special dinner for tomorrow. We can go to a movie next weekend, if you want."

His voice was flat, and Maggie felt a lump in her throat at his lie. She dug the house keys out of her pocket.

"It's still pretty warm out," she said, opening the screen and unlocking the door to the second floor apartment, "but I don't want you catching cold. Give Grampa a careful hug, then run along upstairs and take a shower."

She ignored the relief on George's face as Jake hugged him then raced up the carpeted stairs. Maggie sighed as the screen door slammed.

"Is he never still?" George asked.

"Not often. Even in his sleep, he tosses and turns as if he's fighting dragons or herding cattle in some imaginary world."

"I don't recall his father being quite so physical," George said. "Mark read a lot, and at Jake's age he was content to play with his collection of action figures."

Maggie chuckled. "Jake is his own action figure."

"The boy seems to be more cheerful. Not so sad and moody as when you first moved here."

"He's better. He's made some friends in this past year, and that's helped. But if you look beneath the surface, the anger's there. Deep down, he still blames me for his father's death."

"I thought he was over that nonsense," George said. "He must know it wasn't your fault. It was a car accident, for God's sake."

Maggie shrugged. "I know that, but Jake sees it differently."

"Do you have any regrets about moving here?"

"Not when I see how well he's adjusted. Right after Mark died I thought it would be better to stay in our house in Chicago." Maggie shrugged. "I suppose part of it was an attempt to keep as much the same as I could for Jake's sake. The other part was inertia."

"I can understand that," George said. "Mark's death was a shock to us all."

He took a deep breath and blew it out as if to cut off any more discussion. Maggie knew that George had never really come to terms with his son's death. He rarely spoke about that first year, but Maggie knew from others in Delbrook that her father-in-law had lived as a recluse, only coming out when he could find a card game or when he'd run out of alcohol.

It had been a letter from Nell Gleason, her mother's friend, mentioning George's situation that convinced Maggie to move to Delbrook.

"Don't worry, George. I'm very glad we came. With you here, Jake has a real sense of family. He misses his father a lot and loves spending time with you."

"I like it too," George said. He reached out and squeezed Maggie's shoulder. He ducked his head, his words mumbled as he continued. "I know these last two years have been hard, but you've done a damn fine job with the lad."

Maggie was surprised and touched by her father-in-law's momentary softness. Normally he was not a demonstrative man. Mark had referred to his father as The Tall Silence, and the nickname fit. George was the first to admit he wasn't into that "New Age touchy-feely crap," but in the last two years Maggie had grown to love her father-in-law dearly.

"Thank you, George." She leaned forward to kiss his cheek.

"I'm sorry it didn't work out for the movie tomorrow," he mumbled. "They're counting on me to be at the poker game, and I'd hate to disappoint them."

Better to disillusion one small boy, she thought. Aloud she said, "There will be other times for a movie."

"I hate letting Jake down," George said, echoing her own thoughts.

It was difficult to be angry with George. He was far too aware of his own weaknesses. She knew he had done his best since Mark's death to be a strong male influence for his grandson. For that she would forgive a great deal.

"Why don't you come over Sunday for dinner? Jake's dying to tell you all about the birthday party."

"I'd like that," George said. "In fact, tomorrow I go right past Kruckmeyer's Pharmacy on the way to the country club. If they're ready, I'll pick up the photographs from the Renaissance Faire."

"That would save me a trip. I played hooky today, but tomorrow I'm working all day. Come about five on Sunday."

It was clear that George was pleased with the olive branch.

"Jake's a good kid, Maggie. Every day he looks more and more like his father. He'll be a real heartbreaker when he grows up. Just like his dad."

A heartbreaker just like his dad. His words kept repeating in her ears as she watched her father-in-law walk down the stairs to his car.

"A heartbreaker? Not if I can help it," Maggie muttered aloud, sitting down on the porch swing.

George's weakness was cards; Mark's had been women.

Mark with the bedroom eyes, who had attempted to sleep with every woman he met. Mark, who had ignored his marriage vows the moment the ink was dry on the wedding license. Mark, whose car had swerved off the road, killing himself along with the twenty-five-year-old woman carrying his child.

Oh yes. Mark had been a real heartbreaker.

He had broken her heart long ago. And for different reasons his death had broken the hearts of his father and his son. There were times when she wondered if any of them would ever heal.

He had been gone for two years, and yet Maggie had not been able to move beyond her anger. To George and Jake, Mark had been a wonderful son and father. Dead, he had become Saint Mark. They both assumed that she was as devastated as they were.

"Mom?"

Maggie jumped at the voice behind her. "Sorry, Jake, I was daydreaming."

"I knew you didn't hear me when I came down." He plopped down on the wooden seat beside her, leaning his head against her shoulder. "Grampa gone?"

"Yes." She put her arm around his bathrobed figure and leaned close to smell the shampoo in his hair.

"No movie. That really bites," Jake said. "Big time."

Although Maggie might have worded it more strongly, she forced out a motherly response. "Life is like that sometimes. You could see that Grampa was sorry."

"He's always sorry."

Maggie heard the hurt in his voice. "And what's this about the special dinner I had planned?"

He grimaced. "I guess I sort of lied, Mom."

"Lies stink. They always end up hurting people. Even when you're trying not to." She smiled to take the sting out of her words. "Do you know what I've been thinking about for tomorrow night's dinner?" He shook his head. "A big pepperoni pizza."

Jake's expression lightened. "DeNato's makes really great pizza."

"Excellent plan. And on the way back we'll stop at Hoffman's Video and pick up *Godzilla*. You haven't seen that in at least a week or two."

"It's my favorite."

"Don't I know it."

She pulled him to his feet. He put his arms around her waist, and when he spoke, his voice was muffled against her rib cage.

"Thanks, Mom."

It was times like this that were the toughest for Maggie. Jake was only eight, but his father's death had made him more aware of her feelings than he normally would be. He knew she was trying to make it up to him because George had bailed out of the movie. Jake's forced sensitivity to her emotions was one more thing she blamed on Mark. Tears pricked her eyelids as Jake pulled away.

"And thanks for the party. It was the best."

She grasped the chains to haul herself out of the swing. She was stiff. Jake's clean smell made her far too aware of her own odor. Definitely time for a shower.

"Race you," she said.

She released the swing chain and ran across to the open doorway. He was right behind her as she swung open the screen door. He slammed the inside door, and then, crowing with delight, he shot past her and scrambled up the narrow flight of stairs.

"What if Hoffman's doesn't have the Godzilla tape?" he called back over his shoulder.

"Then we'll rent a wonderful old musical with lots of singing, not to mention tap dancing."

"Yuck," he groaned.

With what little breath she had left, Maggie sighed. It was good to hear him laugh. For a long time after Mark's death, Jake would barely speak to her. She had thought he was asleep the night that Mark had asked her for a divorce. But Jake had been awake. He'd heard them arguing and heard his father slam out of the house in anger. The next day Mark had been killed.

Jake had blamed Maggie. If she hadn't fought with Mark, he reasoned, there wouldn't have been a car accident. Therefore it was Maggie's fault that his father was dead.

Although she had told George that Jake would eventually understand, the truth was she wondered if he ever would.

CHAPTER
TWO

THE WARRIOR OPENED the door of the locked room and stepped inside. He pressed the switch on the wall, and the string of lights, suspended close to the ceiling, illuminated the windowless room.

In the low light, he didn't see the child immediately. He wondered if he'd regressed and was sleeping in the corner under the wooden shelf as he did whenever he made a mistake. No. A lump under the blanket at the foot of the bed indicated his location. Shoes silent on the packed mud floor, the Warrior approached.

Curled in a fetal position, the boy's rounded back was pressed into the corner. His head burrowed into the pillow, arms hugging the softness against his stomach and chest. Tufts of blond hair stuck to the skin on his sweaty forehead. His eyes were closed, eyelids trembling in the depths of sleep.

The Warrior reached out his hand to stroke the cowlick rising at the front of the boy's hair. From the moment he had seen those splayed blond strands, resembling a crown of feathers, he knew the child was the chosen one. The others had been forerunners. This child was the successor.

He debated waking the child just so he could see the startled look of fear in the clear blue eyes. It happened every time the Warrior came to the boy's room. After that first awareness, the child would squeeze his lids shut, and when he opened them again, his face would be blank of all expression, his senses alert to the Warrior's every command.

One Who Cries shuddered, reacting to the dreams that populated his sleep. He rolled over onto his back, one arm flung out and hanging over the edge of the bed. The blanket bunched around his hips, revealing his naked chest and stomach.

The Warrior leaned over, staring down at the tattoo above the nipple on the left side of the boy's chest. It was small, only an inch and a half in height and width, but each color was clearly delineated.

The black line around the red heart was etched with the same meticulous care as the golden feathers on the arrow that pierced it and the teardrops of blood that rained down from the wound.

Bleeding heart.

When he had seen it in a book of graphic arts, he had taken it as his personal icon. It held no religious connotation for him. The heart shot through with an arrow symbolized his belief that a warrior could conquer any obstacle, even death. A true warrior was invincible.

The apprentice's tattoo was a duplicate of his master's.

The Warrior rubbed his fingers over the original tattoo that lay beneath the cotton shirt on his own breast. The heartbeat transferred to the tips of his fingers, moving up his arm until it reached his shoulder then spread out, running along his nerve endings to the outer reaches of his body.

The child stirred as if he felt the connection between the two of them. His eyelids fluttered, partially open, showing a thin line of white. A soft cry came from deep in his throat, but he did not wake.

The Warrior remembered how concerned he'd been when he'd made the stencil. Unlike the others he had tattooed, the boy was too young to understand the necessity to remain still, so it could not be used as a test of bravery or endurance. He worried too that One Who Cries might be traumatized by the sight of his own blood welling up around each needle prick.

Because of the placement over the breastbone and the additional pain, the Warrior had decided to take the safe route and tranquilize the boy. He'd used restraints so that even if the child roused during the procedure, his movements wouldn't affect the precision of the outlining. It wasn't so important when he did the shading. Then a slight movement wouldn't mean an unsightly mistake. He wasn't a "scratcher"; he took pride in his professional skill.

It had taken two weeks for the tattoo to heal. The scab had formed and fallen off and all had gone well until the skin dried and shed. Although the bleeding heart was perfect, the skin around the drawing had been warm to the touch and the boy had run a slight fever for two days. The Warrior kept him sedated, and on the third day the fever broke. One Who Cries woke with clear eyes and no temperature.

The tattoo was the best he'd ever done. Just the sight of it gave the Warrior a new determination to help the boy succeed.

The door closed with a click. Tyler McKenzie didn't move. He waited, listening to the silence. One time he had opened his eyes too soon. The man was still there.

A, B, C, D, E, F, G. He didn't know the rest of the alphabet song. He sang the letters in his head. One time. Two times. Three times. Sometimes he forgot the letters. He tried not to cry when that happened.

He opened his eyes slowly, searching for the single bulb shining over the door. He let go of his breath, his body shaking with the explosion of air. Every time the man left, Tyler was afraid he would turn the light out. It wasn't very bright. He couldn't see the corners of the room.

The dark was scary.

He caught his breath at the rustle from across the room. He couldn't see the mouse cage on the table. It was in the shadows. With one chubby finger he tapped three times on the wooden shelf bed with his fingernail. The sound was soft but clear in the silent room.

Scrabbling. Mouse noise.

Tyler pushed the blanket away and dropped his feet to the floor. One foot at a time. Silent on the mud floor. His chest touched the edge of the table, and he reached out to pull the mouse cage closer.

He had given a name to each of the white mice. Tiny was the smallest. Pinky's nose was always shiny. Toes had a black foot. Ears had black spots on his ears. Shorty had only half a tail. Fatso tried to eat all the food.

He peered close, searching for Mouse Ears.

The mice tumbled over each other in the cedar shavings. His heart raced when he spotted the mouse with the spotted ears. He counted the rest. Five left. Fatso was missing.

Tyler bad. Tyler sorry.

A tear inched out of the corner of his eye, and he looked over his shoulder at the door. The man didn't like it when he cried. Or talked. When he was bad the man would bring the bird.

Tyler squeezed his eyes shut to block out the picture of the bird with spread wings and hooked beak. His cheeks were sticky. He touched them, rubbing at the dried tears. He was proud that he had only cried a little when the man held up the mouse and fed it to the bird.

Not Mouse Ears.

He put his finger out and slid it between the cold metal wires. Mouse Ears bit the end of it. He let the mouse bite him one more time, then pulled his hand back. He returned to the bed, climbed up and wedged his body into the corner where the shelf attached to the wall. He wrapped the blankets around his shoulders and hugged the pillow to his face. Tucking it in the crook of his neck, he settled himself, his fist against his lips and his thumb in his mouth.

The sucking sound lulled him to sleep.

Maggie set the stack of books on the shelf behind the sales counter and brushed Styrofoam particles off the front of her skirt. She rolled her shoulders to loosen the tight muscles after a full day in the bookstore. Saturdays were always busy, and today had been no exception. A quick glance at the clock on top of the register told her Jake was due any minute and it was almost time to close.

After adding the packing slips from the boxes to the stack of them on the old-fashioned metal spindle, she looked around the bookstore to see what she had left to do before closing. Scanning the store invariably brought a smile to her face.

She had worked as a book editor in Chicago when she was married to Mark and had always fantasized about owning her own bookstore. Designing the layout and envisioning the furnishings and decorations had occupied many a coffee break and sleepless night. The reality of her dreams was even better than she'd expected.

The entry door was a sparkling pane of beveled glass, framed in solid oak with an ornately embossed brass faceplate and a matching oval doorknob. The first floor of the house had been gutted. Now instead of walls, wide archways lead from room to room, an open and airy space. Only the bathroom and the laundry room remained closed off.

Light streamed into the bookstore from the wide bay window and glass door in front and the double-hung windows on either side of the house. The contractor had told her it would be less efficient for the air-conditioning in the summer, but the sunshine-filled store was reward enough for the higher electric bill.

The contractors had suggested removing the gently curved staircase to allow for additional space within the store. With its old polished oak banister and the intricately carved newel post, Maggie wouldn't even consider it. Instead she had a door installed at the top of the stairs for security.

After straightening up the paperwork on the counter, she walked across to the café that had once been the kitchen. With thoughts of the amount of food she had consumed yesterday at the Renaissance Faire, she avoided the plate of homemade cookies that was always available for customers and staff.

"More coffee?" she asked the man seated in the cushioned wicker chair at the glass-topped table.

Brent Prentice, one of the homeowners on the south side of Falcon Lake, was a frequent visitor to the bookstore. At fifty, he was a distinguished man with dark eyes and thick black hair with patches of white at the temples and around the nape of his neck. Her father-in-law's best friend, Brent was a charmer with his gentle, almost old-fashioned manners.

"I'd love some, Maggie."

He started to get up, but she touched his shoulder to keep him in place. It amused her how he had succumbed to the comforts of the bookstore. When the renovations had been completed, Brent had been disapproving of the café atmosphere. He had warned her that books would be ruined with the addition of coffee, hot chocolate and pastries. She was convinced it was her homemade scones and raspberry preserves that had sold him on the idea.

"I see you found the new book on Florence," she said, leaning over to pour the coffee.

"My dear, it's a definite find. And very apropos. Connie and I are leaving next month for four weeks in Italy."

He picked up a paper napkin and wiped up a spot of coffee that had splashed on the table, then folded the stained napkin into a neat square and placed it beside his cup. Maggie smiled as she replaced the coffeepot.

"I'm already jealous. In four weeks you'll be able to see quite a bit."

"That's what Connie says. She's been after me for the last several years to take some time off. I would have preferred to go on a safari or trek somewhere exotic, but she only wanted Europe." He ran a well-manicured hand across the glossy page. "I suppose if I can see buildings like these, I shall be content."

"I agree. These are quite fantastic," Maggie said, leaning over to look down at the book on the table. "I was quite taken by the photography."

Brent riffled through the pages and showed her several pictures explaining the architectural importance of some of the ornamentations.

When he finished, Maggie said, "The store is closing in about ten minutes, but there's no need to rush. I have a few things to do before I lock up."

"That's quite all right," he said, closing the book. "Connie and I are going to the poker game at the country club, and I have to make some calls before we go. I'll be right along."

She knew he was waiting for her to leave so he could return the book he was reading for a fresh copy. She tried not to be annoyed, since both Brent and his wife never left the store without buying several books. Back at the front desk, she found Connie Prentice waiting for her.

"Would you be a dear, Maggie, and hang this in the window?" Connie asked, holding up a poster announcing a luncheon for the Ladies Golf League at the country club.

Although she could feel herself bristle at the patronizing tone, Maggie smiled across the counter at the woman.

In contrast to Maggie's plaid skirt, white blouse and loafers, Connie wore a lemony silk dress, matching yellow slingback pumps and was carrying a yellow-and-white clutch purse. At thirty-six, Connie was only four years older, yet she invariably made Maggie feel like an awkward schoolgirl.

"I'd be happy to," Maggie said, taking the cardboard and picking up a tape dispenser. She turned to the bay window that looked out over the park and the lake and tapped the glass panel that was about shoulder height. "How about here?"

Connie raised her hands to flip the ends of her blond hair away from the sides of her face. Her wide gold bracelet caught the late afternoon sun coming in the window, flashing brightly.

"Maybe a couple inches higher," she said. "Ah. That should be all right."

"It's a good spot. People coming along the sidewalk always peek in the window to see if the store is open."

Maggie taped it to the glass, then turned back to see Brent holding several books and standing diffidently behind his wife. Sensing a presence behind her, Connie turned, glowering at him.

"We're running late." She pushed a stack of books toward Maggie. "Pay for these, Brent, while I run to the drugstore for some aspirin. I'll meet you at the car. See you soon, Maggie."

Connie waved her hand, and with a sharp click of heels across the wooden floor, she breezed out the front door, leaving behind a tense silence and the heavy scent of her perfume.

Ignoring the woman's rudeness, Maggie rang up the charges and handed Brent the bag of books. She walked with him to the door, opening it and stepping outside.

"I need a bit of this fresh air," she said, walking down the stairs toward the park.

"It may be September, but it still feels like summer," Brent said.

Maggie lifted her head and breathed in the slightly moist air coming off Falcon Lake. The early evening was beautiful. The twilight painted the lakefront with warm reds and oranges, which added to the nostalgic appearance of the old houses that lined the park. Most of the houses in the five-block section had been converted into small stores and upscale boutiques. The street was closed off between the park and the stores. Parking was available in public lots and in the business section of town that ran on the street behind.

With the end of tourist season, a sense of peace and tranquility had settled over Delbrook. Instead of a crowd of boisterous teenagers, only some year-round residents were strolling along the shoreline of Falcon Lake or sitting on the benches around the fountain in the center of Wolfram Park.

The park had been named for one of the early traders who settled in Delbrook. Although the historical society had discovered later that Wolfram had been jailed for horse stealing, all attempts to change the name had run into stiff opposition from the locals.

Just as they reached the sidewalk she heard Jake's footsteps as he trudged around the side of the porch.

"I'm right here, Jake," she called.

Her heart sank as she saw the slumped posture and sulky expression on his face. She smiled halfheartedly at Brent and braced herself for her son's outburst.

"I hate Wisconsin," Jake said, coming to a halt directly in front of Maggie. "I wish we'd never come to live here."

His mouth was pulled into a thin line as he sloughed off his ever present backpack and dropped it on the ground beside her.

"Aren't you forgetting your manners?" she said quietly, placing a steadying hand on his shoulder and turning him to face Brent.

"Sorry, Mom," he said, the tips of his ears reddening in embarrassment. "Hi, Mr. Prentice. I didn't really mean what I said about Wisconsin."

Brent smiled indulgently at the boy. "Sometimes I wish I'd never moved here too. Looks like you've had a bad day."

"Sort of, sir," Jake said.

"What's the tragedy?" Maggie asked, smoothing his black curly hair with her hand. "When you left for Kenny's this afternoon you were looking forward to a wild romp in the woods. Didn't you have fun?"

"Kenny's dad yelled at us because we were making too much noise." Looking down at his shoes, he hesitated, then raised his head and peeked up at the adults through his dark eyelashes. "And we sort of tramped on some flowers he'd just planted."

"Ah," Maggie said.

"You have to remember," Brent said, "that Mr. Rossiter's business is landscaping, and the flowers and bushes he plants are sort of like advertisements for his business."

Jake gave a grudging nod, but his expression didn't lighten. "We told him we did it on accident, but he still made us help him do some digging." After a momentary pause, he asked, "Can I go to the playground?"

Maggie winced at the whiny tone but nodded. "Just for a few minutes while I talk to Mr. Prentice."

As if released from some invisible tow rope, Jake bounded across the grass to the small playground beside the lake. He veered toward the ladder of the slide, then circled it and instead ran up the sloping metal, reaching out to grasp the sides in order to pull himself up the last few feet. At the top he turned and sat down, pushing off from the platform, sliding smoothly to the ground. Jumping to his feet, he twirled around and started back up the slide.

"I see the painters finally completed their work," Brent said.

"They finished this morning." Maggie crossed her arms, standing beside Brent as he looked back at the house. "A few touch-ups to do, but by and large it's finished."

She stared at the house, trying to be objective. It was a small, two-story house with a wide porch across the front and around the left side. A miniature "Painted Lady." She had chosen Wedgwood blue paint for the clapboards and a rusty red trim on the slats of the porch railing, the stairs and the shutters of the house. Blue, yellow and white were the accent colors.

The bookstore took up the entire first floor, and the second floor was the apartment where she and Jake lived. On either side of the front stairs were stone planters filled with multicolored impatiens and snapdragons.

"So the bookstore has a name," Brent said, pointing to the freshly hung sign over the front door.

"Since this is the last house on the street, I decided to call it The Book End. Better than 'Bookstore,' but not altogether imaginative."

"I like it," he said. "Who made the sign?"

"Tully Jackson."

"Tully?" His tone was arch.

"I know everyone in town thinks the man is crazy."

"That's because he is," Brent said, clearly shocked. "He's not that old but he sits in a webbed lounge chair beside that old junker car at the boat landing all day. The man lives out of his car and talks to himself, for cripes' sake."

Maggie chuckled. "Don't be so stuffy, Brent. I've talked to him and I've seen the inside of the car. It's full of old clothes and odds and ends, but I really don't think he lives in it."

"How'd you find out he could carve and paint signs? He usually rants when anyone gets too close." Brent brushed the front of his suit coat as if he had come in contact with the man.

"Actually, Jake made the first approach. When we first moved here we took a picnic lunch to the park beside the boat ramp. You know Jake. He wandered over and started talking. I was a little concerned since Tully looks so peculiar."

Brent raised both eyebrows and stared down his nose at Maggie. "Peculiar nothing. He's nuts! The man wears a plastic raincoat and a white satin top hat. He looks like the Wild Man of Borneo with that long hair and beard. You've got to worry about some kind of bug infestation. Really,

Maggie, you and Jake ought to steer clear of the man. He could be psychotic."

"There doesn't seem to be anything wrong with him. He's a bit shy when you first talk to him, but he warms up after a while. Jake has sort of adopted the man. We see him once a week when we go down to the lake to feed the geese. Jake brings Tully candy bars and comic books."

"Good Lord," Brent said, shaking his head in a shuddering movement. "You shouldn't coddle the man."

At Brent's reaction, she decided not to tell him that she usually brought along homemade soup. Wanting to change the conversation, she called across to Jake who had abandoned the slide for a swing. "Time to go in."

With one last pump of his legs, Jake leaned back, pointing his feet to the sky. When the swing reached the top of the arc, he released his hands from the chains and leaped into space, landing two-footed in a spray of sandy dirt.

"I hate when he does that," she said. "It gives me a queasy feeling in the pit of my stomach."

Brent laughed. "He's all boy, that one. Well, I better get along to the car if I don't want Connie searching for me."

After his exercise in the park, Jake was in a much better humor. Back in the bookstore, he helped her straighten the books on the shelves and fill shopping bags with her regular customers' monthly book orders. When Jake's stomach began to growl, they locked up the store and went out for pizza.

Although in the beginning Jake voiced his disappointment that he wasn't going to a movie with his grandfather, the evening turned out to be fun. To keep Jake from worrying that it wouldn't be available, they'd rented *Godzilla* before going out for pizza. They'd made popcorn and sat on the couch, cheering and booing at the appropriate parts of the movie. After a long week, she was grateful to be in bed by ten-thirty.

The ringing of the telephone jolted Maggie awake. She fumbled for the receiver on the bedside table, automatically searching for the illuminated clock face in the darkened room. Her heart raced.

Two-fifteen in the morning.

She sat upright, pressing the button on the portable phone before it could ring a second time and wake Jake.

"Mrs. Mark Collier please," a young woman said.

"Speaking."

Her fingers, clammy with fear, slipped on the switch of the lamp beside the bed. She threw back the sheet and swung her feet over the side of the bed.

"This is Lechner Hospital calling. I'm sorry to tell you, but George Collier has been injured."

CHAPTER THREE

"I'M SORRY TO TELL YOU, but George Collier has been injured."

Dear God, not again. A chill ran through Maggie's body. Those were almost the same words that she had heard two years ago when Mark had been killed.

"Hello? Are you there, Mrs. Collier?"

Maggie licked her lips before she could speak.

"Yes. Go ahead."

"Mr. Collier has been brought to Lechner Hospital here in Delbrook. The doctor would like you to come."

"Please, can you tell me how badly George—eh, Mr. Collier is hurt?"

"I'm sorry, ma'am, but I don't have that information. If you come to the hospital, the doctor will be able to answer all your questions."

"Yes. I understand. I'll come right away."

Sitting numbly on the side of the bed, Maggie pressed the disconnect button. It had to be a dream. She squeezed her eyes shut, then popped them open, staring around the bedroom. Nothing had changed. She slapped the receiver against the palm of her hand. She felt the sting. Her shoulders sagged.

She could remember the same feeling when the hospital had called her about Mark's car accident. She had been afraid then to move, afraid that if she broke the circle of numbness, she would be forced to accept the painful facts.

Oh, God, let him be all right. Please, God. Jake and I love him so.

The dial tone droned, grating along her nerve endings. She returned the receiver to the cradle and tried to pull the scattered thoughts in her mind into some semblance of order. She didn't want to wake Jake until she had established his grandfather's condition. He had already been through one trauma when his father had died. She didn't know how he'd react to another.

She opened the bedroom door and slipped across the hall to Jake's room, peering in to see if he was still asleep. In the light from her bedroom she could see his dark curly hair sharply outlined against the white pillowcase. His eyes were shut and his breathing deep and even.

Closing the door, she walked down the hall to the living room. Aside from the stream of light from her bedroom, the apartment was dark. The floor creaked under her bare feet, and she shivered at the sound. She hated this time of the morning before the sun rose. She remembered after Mark died when she couldn't sleep and she had paced the floor, feeling alone and frightened in the big house in Chicago.

In the living room she looked out the side window and felt instant relief as she spotted the lighted pane in Nell Gleason's studio.

Nell was a night owl, especially when she was working on a new painting. Grateful that she wouldn't be waking the older woman, Maggie dialed, rocking back and forth on her heels until Nell answered. Maggie quickly explained the situation and asked if she could come over and stay with Jake. At her friend's immediate acceptance, the knot of tension between her shoulders loosened.

Hanging up, Maggie went into the kitchen, turned on the light in the stairwell and ran down the stairs to unlock the outside door.

Upstairs again, she washed quickly and brushed her hair, fastening it with a wide, tortoise-shell barrette to keep it off her face. The mirror reflected her inner turmoil. Against her reddish brown hair, her skin appeared whiter than usual, and she grabbed a lipstick, adding a bright slash of color to her lips. She exchanged her nightgown for jeans, sneakers and a blue-and-white gingham blouse.

Back in the kitchen, she ran water into the coffeepot, measuring the grounds hurriedly before she turned it on. The normality of the action was somehow comforting. The pungent aroma of fresh brewed coffee began to filter into the air as she heard the downstairs door open and Nell Gleason appeared at the top of the stairwell.

The older woman wore a navy blue sweatshirt and navy pants, both of which were liberally covered with splotches of paint. A line of colored stripes marched up her left sleeve where she had wiped her paintbrush. Maggie could see flecks of paint in her flyaway hair, which was dyed a peculiar color of salmon pink. A streak of magenta ran from the corner of her right eye into the hair at her temple.

"Oh, I'm so sorry about George," the older woman said, breathing heavily from the climb. She enveloped Maggie in an embrace redolent of turpentine and paint, patting her back as if she were only five and had wakened from a bad dream.

The hug made Maggie feel less isolated. Nell had grown up in Delbrook with Maggie's mother, standing as godmother when Maggie was born. Despite the thirty years difference in their ages, she and Nell were the closest of friends.

"I made some coffee for you, and Jake is still asleep," Maggie said. "Sorry I had to take you away from your painting."

Nell waved her hand. "The piece is almost done, so it's not a problem to leave it. Have you heard anything more?"

"Nothing since that first call."

"An automobile accident?" Nell asked.

"That's what I'm assuming. I hope to God no one else was injured." Maggie's lips quivered as images recalled from Mark's fatal crash flooded her mind.

"Amen to that. Well, there's no point in our imagining the worst. You better get along now and see what the doctor has to say," Nell said. "Are you all right to drive? You look a little white around the gills."

"I'm OK." She scooped up her purse and reached for her keys hanging on the hook beside the door. "The phone call spooked me. Sort of catapulted me back to Mark's death."

"Of course it did. Think positive thoughts and don't worry. You'd better take a jacket. It's chilly out." Nell stood with Maggie at the top of the stairs. "I'll be here with Jake as long as you need me."

"Bless you. I'll call you as soon as I know anything."

Maggie grabbed her windbreaker from the line of clothes hooks in the stairwell and hurried down the steps. Outside she pulled on the jacket as she walked along the side porch to the back stairs where her car was parked.

Let him be all right, she chanted as she drove through the empty streets to the hospital. She prayed Jake wouldn't wake up while she was gone. He would know there was something wrong if she wasn't there.

Her mind on automatic pilot, she parked the car and hurried in through the emergency room entrance.

The receptionist asked her to wait while she called for information, then motioned to a security guard who led Maggie through a maze of corridors to a door marked PASTORAL CARE and opened the door.

"Mrs. Collier?" A gray-haired woman rose from her chair, coming forward to take Maggie's hand. "I'm Ann Bhat, the pastoral counselor."

"Please, call me Maggie." Strange how the normal courtesies of life continued, she thought. "I've come about George."

Ann led her to a leather chair in front of the desk and, instead of returning to the far side, sat down in the chair opposite.

"Mr. Collier is your father?"

"No. My father-in-law. George's son, my husband, died two years ago."

Maggie could feel her heart beating in her ears. George must be hurt worse than she had first thought, otherwise she would have been taken to his room. Her body began to tremble, a slight vibration like a running motor.

"How difficult for you." Ann folded her hands in her lap and leaned toward Maggie. "Mr. Collier was brought to the hospital, but the doctors were not able to save him. I'm sorry to tell you, but your father-in-law passed away a short time ago."

"Oh, God, no!" Maggie reached up and covered her ears as if she could block the words. "It can't happen again. He can't be dead."

Dropping her hands in her lap, she closed her eyes, swallowing the lump in her throat. Pictures of George flashed behind her eyelids, a kaleidoscope of memories. George holding Jake at his christening, the older man's face stern as he tried to hold back tears of joy. Jake holding up a string of fish for his grandfather's approval. George holding her as she and Jake stood beside Mark's casket.

She was too stunned to cry. How can I tell Jake about George's death? First his father and now his grandfather. It wasn't fair. How could this happen again?

It was so much like her experiences when Mark died that it was almost past bearing. A nightmarish déjà vu. She could remember bargaining with God, begging Him to keep Mark alive for Jake's sake. She had promised she would give up her editing job and devote her life to making Mark happy.

Her fingernails bit into the palms of her hands as she fought the rising tide of anger that threatened to choke her. God hadn't listened then, and now He'd let it happen again.

"Maggie? Are you all right?"

The grief counselor's voice came from a distance. Maggie opened her eyes, taking in the concern on the woman's face. She was softly pretty and elegant in dress and mannerisms. She looked familiar. Possibly she'd come into the bookstore or Maggie had seen her around town.

"I'm all right," Maggie said, wishing that the numbness she had felt earlier would return to replace the gnawing ache of loss. She tried to pull herself together. "It's a shock, but I suppose not unexpected."

"Not unexpected?" Ann's brows furrowed in confusion.

"I always worried when George was out late with his cronies. I know he drank at the card games, and I never approved of him driving home even if it wasn't very far. Was anyone else involved in the accident?"

The counselor's mouth opened and closed but no sound came out. She shook her head slightly and leaned toward Maggie, once more taking her hand.

"Did someone tell you that it was an auto accident?"

"No. I just assumed it was. If it wasn't a car accident, what happened?"

The phone rang, the sound cutting through the tension in the room. Ann reached across the desk and picked up the receiver.

"Pastoral Care. Ann Bhat speaking." She listened for a moment, nodding her head. "Yes. Mrs. Collier is here now."

At mention of her name, Maggie sat up straighter. What could have happened to George? A heart attack? A stroke? A dozen possibilities whirled around in her head, and she found herself impatient for answers.

"All right. I'll wait until you get here." Ann hung up and turned back to Maggie. "That was Police Chief Blessington. He's at the front desk and is coming back to talk to you. He'll be able to explain everything."

What does Charley have to explain? Maggie thought, shifting in her seat, unable to sit still. With the police chief involved, it must be more serious than she had anticipated.

"What happened to George? What aren't you telling me?"

Without answering Maggie's questions, Ann rose to her feet and went to the coffeepot on a table in the corner of the room and poured coffee into a dark blue stoneware mug with the hospital logo emblazoned in yellow.

"I think some coffee might help," she said. "Sugar or cream?"

Maggie shook her head. She could see by the closed expression on the older woman's face that she would have to wait for answers. Taking the coffee, she cupped both hands around the mug, drawing comfort from the warmth. She breathed in the aroma slowly to block out the antiseptic hospital smell that she would always associate with death. She looked up at the clock on the wall. Three o'clock. It seemed impossible that so much had changed in just forty-five minutes.

She touched her hand to her forehead. It was hot and sweaty in the still air. She stood up and unzipped her windbreaker. Taking the keys out of the pocket, she shoved them into the pocket of her jeans and pulled off the coat. She bundled it up and set it on her purse.

"Would you like a bag for your things?" Ann said.

The woman seemed grateful that she could be of some help. She bustled over with a bright yellow plastic bag with the logo of the hospital printed on the side. Maggie's hands shook as she took the bag, jammed her windbreaker inside and dropped it beside her chair.

The door into the hall opened, and Charley Blessington filled the doorway.

"Aw, damn it, Maggie. I'm so sorry about George," he said, his voice ricocheting off the walls in the small office.

Charley was a big man, tall with wide shoulders and a solid, muscular body. His thick blond hair stood on end as if he'd been running his fingers through it. Eyebrows, an explosion of blond hair above his silvery blue eyes, dominated his face. At forty-five he had been almost twenty years younger than Maggie's father-in-law, but she knew they had been good friends.

He crossed the room in long strides as Maggie set her mug on the desk and struggled to her feet. He put his arms around her and gave her a quick bracing hug. Then, hands on her shoulders, he pushed her away and looked down, his blond eyebrows bunched over his eyes. I'll get a crick in my neck if I continue to stare up at him, she thought. She smiled at the sheer inanity of the thought.

"That's the girl," he said, squeezing her shoulders. "You got to keep a stiff upper lip when times are tough."

"What happened to George?" she asked.

"Now I know you're anxious to get to the bottom of this, but let me grab some coffee before we get started."

Without waiting for her answer, Charley strode over to the table, reaching out for the mug that Ann Bhat held out to him.

"I'll get some of the paperwork started," Ann said as she headed for the door.

Charley crossed the room and sat down behind the desk. He took several sips of the coffee and then set the mug carefully on the blotter. He leaned forward onto his elbows, staring at her over tented fingers. Despite the smile on his face, Maggie could feel a certain intensity to his look.

"What happened to George?" she asked. "I assumed he'd been in an automobile accident, but when I mentioned it, Ann looked surprised."

"Didn't anyone tell you what happened?"

"No. I just got a call that he was here. I didn't even know he was dead until Ann told me."

"When did you last see George?" he asked.

"Friday night. He came over to find out how Jake's birthday party went. We talked on the porch, but it was late, so he didn't stay long. Then he called today just before he left for the country club."

"Did he seem out of sorts? Tense?"

"What the hell is going on, Charley? George is dead, and no one will tell me anything." Her hands shook with the effort it took to keep her body still. She gripped the arms of her chair and glared across the desk at the police chief.

He held up his hands, palms toward her in a placating gesture. "Be patient a few minutes longer and then I'll explain everything. Did he have anything important to say when you talked to him?"

"He wanted to know what time he should come for dinner."

Maggie came to a halt, shaking her head. She'd talked to him less than twelve hours ago. Last night she'd made a pineapple upside-down cake, and just before she went to bed she'd taken pork chops out of the freezer to make George's favorite recipe.

"I can't believe he's gone," she said. Her eyes stung with unshed tears, and she blinked rapidly to hold them back.

"I feel the same way, Maggie. Doris and I ate at the club last night. I stayed to play poker. We finished up around midnight, and your father-in-law was gloating over the fact that he had won on the last hand. George would have loved going out a winner."

Maggie sniffed and nodded her head.

"Did George call from the country club?" he asked.

"No."

"Did you hear from anyone before the hospital called?"

"I don't like the tone of these questions, Charley," she said, "and I think I'm finished giving answers."

Charley accepted her antagonism with good nature.

"Well now, Maggie, this is going to come as a shock," he said. "Your father-in-law wasn't in an accident. Someone attacked him. We'll have to do an autopsy before we know for certain, but it appears that someone stabbed George."

Maggie pressed against the back of the chair, wanting to put some distance between herself and Charley's words.

"Stabbed? I don't understand," she said. "You mean like in a fight?"

"Well, we don't know if it was a fight. It looks like it might have been some sort of botched robbery."

"A robbery. Oh, dear God. Where was he when this happened?"

"He was still at the country club. On the eighteenth tee."

Charley's reply was so unexpected that Maggie felt totally disoriented. She pressed her fingers against her shaking lips and tried to catch her breath.

"A robbery?" She felt stupid repeating his words. It was like some idiotic comedy sketch. "What happened?"

Charley stared hard at her. She suspected he was waiting to see if she was going to break down. When she managed to pull herself together, he flopped back in the desk chair, his mouth pulled into a grimace of anger.

"At this point we don't know much," he said. "At one-oh-two, we got a nine-one-one call to send an ambulance to the country club. One of the cleaning crew found George. The kid didn't know what had happened, but he saw the blood. He said it looked like George's heart was bleeding. He came racing back to the club for help. The paramedics got there within five minutes, but it was already too late."

"Why was George out on the golf course?"

"It looks like he mighta walked out along the eighteenth fairway to have a cigar." Charley shook his head, rubbing one hand over his hair. "The poker game was over, and I thought he'd gone home like everyone else. When I got back to the club, his car was still in the parking lot."

"You said robbery. Was the car broken into?"

"No. It was locked and undisturbed. We're thinking robbery, because George's wallet is missing and his watch is gone."

"I can't believe it."

"Damn it, I can't either." Charley pushed himself to his feet, angry color rising to his cheeks. "Delbrook is hardly a high-crime area. Sure, we've had little penny-ante shit. But nothing violent since I've been chief of police."

"Didn't anyone see anything or hear anything?"

"Well, honey, we don't know. The numbnuts who was first on the scene didn't think to hold the guy who found the body." He saw her wince and came around the desk and put his hand on her shoulder. "I'm sorry, Maggie. This is all pretty grim, and for the moment we don't know much. But believe me, we'll find out who did this."

Maggie swallowed hard. "What do I do now?"

"Ann is going to help you take care of things. Because of the nature of George's death, an autopsy is required."

"Oh, God, I forgot about that," she said.

She pressed the palms of her hands together to hold back a shudder of distaste. Death was difficult to handle in any case, but the details surrounding a violent death made everything much worse. She knew. It had been like that when Mark died.

Charley continued. "We won't be able to release the body to the funeral home right away, but I'll make sure everything gets expedited as quickly as possible. Where's Jake?"

"I called Nell Gleason to stay with him."

"Good. I'll take you to Ann, and she'll try to cut through the formalities and get you home before your son is awake. I know this is going to be tough for him, coming so soon after his father's death. You might want to talk to Ann about that."

"I will. And you'll keep me posted?"

"You have my word on that. We'll find out who did this. No matter how long it takes."

Maggie picked up her purse and the yellow hospital bag and followed the police chief through the hospital corridors until they reached the emergency room. To her surprise, she found Brent Prentice waiting for her.

"Nell called to tell us about George. Connie and I didn't want you to be alone," he said by way of explanation. "I should have known Charley'd be here to take care of you."

Maggie was touched that Brent had come. She could see in his eyes his own sadness at the death of his friend, and despite her own sense of loss, she wanted to console him. He opened his arms, and Maggie naturally stepped into the circle, kissing him on the cheek. "I'm glad you came."

He smelled of soap and starch, she thought as she accepted his comforting embrace. It was the perfect combination for him. His fussiness and his old-fashioned mannerisms always reminded Maggie of a time gentler than the fast-paced rudeness of modern life.

"It's unbelievable," Brent said. "Connie and I were with him tonight at the country club along with Charley and the rest of the crew."

Maggie was unable to speak around the lump in her throat. Brent sensed her distress and turned toward Charley. Without removing his arm from around her shoulder, Brent held out his hand to the police chief. Joined in their mutual mourning for a lost friend, the two men shook hands gravely.

"As I was driving over here I was trying to remember when I first met George." Brent shook his head. "Since I grew up in Delbrook, I think I've always known him. Once I came back from college, though, is when we really became friends."

His bottom lip trembled, and he swallowed before he could continue. "He taught me how to fish."

Maggie smiled. "George said you hated it."

Brent sniffed, and his mouth twitched with humor. "I did. Those slimy worms and bleeding fish. Good Lord, how repulsive. He said my face turned green as the grass around the lake. The thing was that he never looked down on me for disliking it. He said a man ought to know how to do things even if he never did them again."

"That sounds like George. He had a succinct way of putting things," Charley said.

"Nell said George had some kind of accident. Automobile?"

Maggie opened her mouth, but before she could respond, Ann Bhat opened a glass door in the hall and smiled at the threesome.

"I told you Charley would bring her here," she said to Brent. "While you gentlemen talk, I need Maggie for a few minutes."

"Go on along," Brent said, giving her shoulder a reassuring pat. "I'll talk to Charley."

Too tired to argue, Maggie followed Ann into the office. The grief counselor helped her through the paperwork, explaining everything as they went along. Thank God Charley had already identified the body. When Mark died, she had been the one to make the identification, and she'd had nightmares for several months afterward.

"I think that's it," Ann said. "Let me give you my business card."

She placed a white card in a slit on the front of the bright yellow folder that contained copies of all the paperwork. Maggie's eyes burned, and she rubbed them. She felt drained. Ann picked up the folder and opened the door into the corridor. The police chief was gone, but Brent waited for her, his mouth set in a grim line.

"Dear Lord, Maggie, what kind of world is this where a man can be killed for his money and a watch?"

"I know. It doesn't make sense. Not here in Delbrook," Maggie said. "Let's get out of here."

"Where are you parked?" Brent asked.

"In the back lot. The emergency spots were all filled."

"I'm in front. Wait for me and I'll follow you home."

"I'm really fine, you know."

He held up one well-manicured hand. "Please. I have orders from Connie and Nell."

Maggie smiled as he strode briskly toward the lobby, then turned back to Ann.

"I don't feel right leaving George here. I haven't even seen him. I haven't said my goodbyes," Maggie said with a catch in her voice.

"There will be time for that later, my dear." Ann patted her arm. "Right now the police work must take precedence. For the moment you can catch your breath, see to your son and think about making arrangements."

"You're right. I can't thank you enough for your help."

"That's what I'm here for. I'll be your liaison for anything that has to do with George. If you have any questions in the next day or two, call me."

"It really hasn't hit me yet. I know in my head that George is gone, but it doesn't have much meaning right now."

"Part of it is the shock of how he died. I know you have many questions, but just take it slowly. Chief Blessington will do his job. Do what you can to keep your strength up. Your toughest job will be to keep a buffer zone between all of this and your son."

Maggie shook the woman's hand as she took the yellow folder and tucked it into the plastic bag along with several brochures that Ann thought might be helpful when talking to Jake. She gave a quick wave of her hand and headed down the corridor, sighing as she saw the ladies' room next to the emergency room door.

The fluorescent ceiling lights added to the ghostly reflection above the sink. She washed her hands, staring at the dark circles under her eyes. Leaning over, she scooped up some cold water and splashed it against her face. It helped a little, she thought as she rubbed some color into her cheeks with a paper towel. She rested the palms of her hands on the edge of the sink and leaned forward, staring at her face in the mirror.

I can't do it again. I can't.

How was she going to tell Jake about his grandfather? Tears rose to her eyes, and she squeezed them shut, fighting for control. She rested her forehead against the cool surface of the mirror and tried to breathe slowly. When her heart beat more evenly, she opened her eyes. For a long moment she stared at her mirror image, searching for strength in the pale-faced woman in the glass.

I have to do it. I have to do it for Jake, she thought.

Leaning over, she picked up the yellow plastic bag and settled the strap of her purse over her shoulder. With one more glance at her reflection, she raised her chin, straightened her back and left the washroom.

The hospital doors slid open automatically. Outside, the crisp breeze felt good after the overheated air in the hospital. Sniffing in the freshness, she walked down the empty sidewalk to the parking lot. She was surprised by the number of cars that remained even at four in the morning.

She wasn't used to being out at this time of the morning. Although the sky was not as dark as when she had first arrived, shadows clung to the edges of buildings and created odd shapes where the streetlights didn't reach. She stopped at the edge of the parking lot, shivering.

She'd been in such a hurry to get to the hospital that she hadn't noticed where she'd parked. The lights in the parking lot threw shadows on the ground, and she could feel her heart beating as she walked down the aisle between the cars. The scrape of gravel made her jerk around, but she could see no movement.

"Nerves," she muttered in disgust. She tried to relax the tension between her shoulder blades with little success. The call from the hospital had frightened her, and now, with George's violent death, the perceived safety of Delbrook was shattered. She thought she'd left the stabbings and robberies behind in Chicago. Alone in the parking lot, she was afraid.

Near the end of the line of cars she spotted her blue Corolla. She increased her speed until she was almost running. Panic had taken over, and she breathed in shallow gasps. Shifting the hospital bag to her left hand, she dug in the pocket of her jeans for the car keys.

She could have cried in relief when she reached the car and hurried into the space beside the door. Keys in her hand, she fumbled for the lock. She couldn't hear anything over the sound of her own breathing and a loud roaring in her ears, but she had an impression of movement behind her. Something hard slammed into her back.

She fell sideways. Her head and shoulder crashed against the car, and she bounced off, sliding toward the ground. She threw out her hands to break her fall. The rough asphalt surface scraped the palms of her hands as she landed in a heap beside the car.

Lights flashed before her eyes, and she blinked to drive away the nausea that engulfed her. A dark figure blocked out the light, and darkness invaded her senses.

CHAPTER
FOUR

"MAGGIE? Are you all right?"

She could hear the voice close to her ear calling her name. Lethargy held her in a gentle embrace, and she clung to the floating sensation. Even if she had wanted to answer, her mouth was dry, and when she tried to speak, no sound came out. A sharp pain lanced through her shoulder when she moved, bringing back the terror that had possessed her before she passed out. She squeezed her eyes shut and ignored the voice.

"Maggie." Strong hands shook her. "Maggie."

Despite her fear, she responded to the urgency in the man's voice and opened her eyes. Darkness. She couldn't see anything. Panicked by her blindness, she struggled against the hands on her shoulders.

"It's all right, Maggie. It's Brent."

Recognizing his voice, she sagged in relief. Now that her eyes had become accustomed to the dark, she could see she was lying on the ground between two cars. Brent knelt beside her, the white hair at his temples gleaming in the darkness.

"Can you sit up?"

"I think so. I hit my head."

She raised a hand and touched the bump on her head. No dampness, so at least she wasn't bleeding, but she winced at the tenderness. She took inventory of the rest of her body. Her shoulder and the palms of her hands had taken the brunt of the damage.

"Maybe you should lie there, and I'll go for help."

Frightened to be left alone, Maggie grabbed the sleeve of Brent's jacket to hold him in place.

"I'm all right," she said. "Just help me up."

Brent shifted his hands and lifted her to her feet, holding her until she could get strength back in her legs. The ground shifted, and she closed her eyes, letting her head rest against his chest.

"Maybe we should go back into the hospital so you can see a doctor."

She couldn't see his face, but she could hear the concern in his voice. "No. I'm all right. Just dizzy."

"I should never have let you come out here alone." He patted her back. Awkward thumps that he probably thought were encouraging but only made her head ache. "Just wait until Connie hears about this."

Realizing his concern for her was slightly outweighed by his fear of Connie's recriminations, Maggie felt better, not quite so light-headed. She took a deep gulp of air, and he released her.

"That's it. Big breaths. Then you won't pass out again."

"I didn't faint. Someone hit me."

"What?" Brent grabbed her, and she flinched at the pain as his fingers bit into her left arm. She pulled away, flexing her shoulder.

"Someone hit me," she repeated.

"What are you talking about? I didn't see anyone." His voice was sharp, and he glanced around as if to prove his point. "I drove up and found you lying on the ground."

Brent's car was still running, parked in the center of the aisle with the door open as if he had leaped out when he saw her. She leaned unsteadily on the trunk of the parked car and looked around the parking lot. No sign of anyone and no motion near any of the cars.

"I'm not making this up, Brent. Someone was here."

"Are you sure you aren't a little giddy? When I drove up, the only one I saw was you."

Maggie shook her head, regretting the motion as pain pounded in her temple. "Someone hit me and then stole my purse."

"Stole your purse?"

Her words shocked him. He stared down at her, searching her face before nodding.

"Stay here."

He hurried over to the open door of his silver Lexus, reached under the seat and pulled out a flashlight. He struggled with the switch, smacking the flashlight against the palm of his hand until a weak beam flickered on the ground. He swept it back and forth as he came toward her, then crouched over as he searched between the cars.

"I've found your purse, Maggie. And your car keys." He stood up, brushing at the knees of his pants, then came toward her, the purse held out in front of him like a trophy. "It must have rolled under the car when you passed out."

She gritted her teeth as he handed it to her. "I didn't pass out. Someone tried to take my purse. Oh rats! Where's the hospital bag?"

"Hospital bag?"

"It's bright yellow plastic. I had it when I left the hospital."

She bent over searching the ground for the bag. Brent halfheartedly flashed the light around, but it was nowhere in sight.

"Are you sure you didn't leave it in the hospital?"

Maggie put a hand up to her throbbing forehead. For a second she wondered if she might have left it in the bathroom. Brent stood patiently beside her, waiting for her to make a decision. It was clear that he didn't believe that she had been attacked, so how would she convince anyone else?

Her head hurt. Her bones ached. She had a few bruises, but she hadn't lost anything of value. There was nothing in the bag but her jacket and the folder that the grief counselor had given her.

"I'll call the hospital later," she said. "All I want to do right now is go home."

"I'll drive you. I don't think you should risk—"

He stopped short as she held up her hand.

"Damn it, Brent! I am not prone to fits of the vapors. I'm perfectly fine to drive. My palms are stinging and my shoulder and head hurt, but I'm fine. Nothing a hot bath won't cure."

Brent rocked back and forth, defensive in the face of her anger. Seeing his distress, Maggie took a deep, steadying breath.

"Please forgive me, Brent. You've been wonderful coming to the hospital, and here I am snarling at you."

"My dear, you've had a dreadful shock. It's no wonder you're upset."

His deep voice soothed Maggie's jagged nerve endings, and she didn't object when he handed her into the car, waiting beside the door until she buckled her seat belt. With almost a courtly bow, he held out her car keys.

"Now don't make a fuss, because I intend to follow you until you're safely home. Then I'm going to stop by the police station. We've never had much crime in Delbrook. Now all of a sudden it's a war zone. Charley Blessington should know about this. After all, if you thought you saw a purse snatcher, it could have been the same man who robbed George."

"If Grampa had gone to the movie with me last night, he wouldn't be dead."

Jake's whispered comment made Maggie wince. She reached out to him, but he backed up against the living room archway, his body rigid. Slow tears slid down his cheeks, and he brushed them away with the back of his hand.

"Grampa promised he would take me. When I say I'm gonna do something, you always make me keep my promise," Jake cried. "Why didn't you make him go to the movie?"

Even though it was an unreasonable question, Maggie couldn't find any defense against his charge. She knew Jake's anger was only a reaction to the news of his grandfather's death. Still, it hurt.

"I know this doesn't make sense," she said, "but it could as easily have happened if he went to the movie with you. It could have happened any-where."

"Oh, Mom, it's just not fair. I don't want him to be dead."

The words seemed torn out of his shaking body. Maggie crossed the room and put her arms around him. He resisted her touch, his back and arms stiff and unbending. She held him firmly, rocking him as she had done when he was younger. She'd missed cuddling him. These last two years since Mark's death, Jake had kept her at a distance.

Fighting to keep her own tears at bay, Maggie stared dully at the clock on the wall.

Eight o'clock in the morning. Less than four hours of sleep.

When she returned from the hospital, she sat with Nell, talking and making lists of things she would need to do. She was too keyed up to eat, but Nell stayed to give Maggie a chance for a quick nap. It seemed as if she'd only closed her eyes when Nell shook her to tell her that Jake was awake and that she was going home.

The sobs that shook Jake lessened, and his body began to relax. She felt his arms wrap around her waist, and this time he returned her embrace. With that she couldn't hold back her own tears. She wasn't sure whether she was crying for George's loss, Jake's grief or her own feeling of abandonment.

When Mark died, her anguish had been part regret and part guilt. Their marriage had begun with such promise. How could she have let their life together deteriorate until there was nothing left to be salvaged? It was all her fault. She'd failed to keep her marriage alive, and because of that, Mark was gone and Jake was being torn apart by sorrow and pain.

A hiccuping sob brought her back to the present and the devastated child pressed against her. She reached into the pocket of her skirt and pulled out a wad of Kleenex. She smiled as they shared the tissues.

"Come on out to the kitchen, honey. We'll feel better after we've had something to eat."

"I'm not hungry."

"Well, you can sit with me at least. I'm starving."

She pushed him ahead of her across the hall to the kitchen and pulled out a chair at the small table by the window. She ignored him as she brought over silverware and plates. Pouring two glasses of orange juice, she set one down in front of him and carried her own over to the stove.

The phone rang, and the answering machine automatically picked it up. It had been ringing ever since word of George's death got out. Earlier Nell had answered the phone, but when a reporter called, she had turned on the machine.

The room filled with the aroma of scrambled eggs and toast. She set everything on the table, sat down and helped herself to a plateful. Jake drank his juice, and she made no comment when he filled his own plate and started to eat.

"Where's Grampa now?" he said around a mouthful of toast.

Though startled by the abrupt question, she assumed he wanted practical details not a religious discussion.

"He's at the hospital. The doctor will examine him to find out what made him die."

"Will they look for clues?"

"Yes. Then he'll be taken to the funeral home. Just like with Dad."

Jake didn't look at her, continuing to stare at his plate as if choosing a question from a list written on the surface.

"Is he all cut up?"

"Oh, no, honey. This is way different than a car crash. I think Grampa will look like he's sleeping."

"That's what you said about Daddy."

She had been so numbed by Mark's death that she hadn't fully taken into account how frightened Jake would be when he saw his father at the funeral home. The auto accident had been devastating, and although the funeral director had done what he could, the face Jake saw lying in the casket did not exactly look like his father's.

"I'm sorry about that, Jake." Her shoulders sagged at the sudden flash of memory. "Your dad had been hurt really bad. I tell you what. I'll take the first look at Grampa, and if he looks yucky, I'll tell you, and you can decide if you want to look. Deal?"

After a pause, Jake nodded.

Maggie stared at him, debating the next step. He needed to ask questions, and she didn't know what answers were appropriate for his age. She let him finish eating and then she said, "Can I ask you something?"

He raised his head, eyes narrowed and his expression wary. "Sure."

"When your father died you were only six. That's pretty young to deal with death. When someone dies, there are a lot of details to take care of and a lot of questions to be answered. You're eight now and you understand more, so I don't know if you want to know about some of these things or if you just want me to go off and take care of them."

His eyes moved back and forth as if he were reading her face. She remained still, giving him time to think.

"I want to go with you, Mom. I'm not a kid anymore. I guess I need to know about all this stuff."

His response broke her heart. Innocence lost. Welcome to adulthood. She stood up, gathering the dishes and putting them in the sink so that she could keep her face averted. She swallowed back her tears, and when she could speak without her voice giving her away, she continued.

"I'd like you with me, too. I don't think it's going to be awful, Jake. It'll be sad because we'll be missing Grampa, but we can help each other."

The telephone rang. She jumped at the sound but was grateful for the interruption.

"Let's go down to the bookstore and get away from the phone," she said. She reached for her keys on the hook beside the door. "Can you unlock the door?"

"Sure," Jake said.

He grabbed the keys and raced down the hallway. By the time Maggie arrived, he had the door open and had flipped on the lights at the top of the stairs leading down to the bookstore. Jake hopped down the stairs, his shoes clattering on the oak treads. Since it was Sunday and the store wasn't open, she left the door to the apartment open.

Light poured into the first floor from the bay window, and she was glad they'd come downstairs. The bookstore had been her refuge ever since it first began to take shape. She had invested a lot of thought into the layout, and it had taken on her personality. She was more comfortable here among the books than she was in her own living room. The warmth of the room surrounded her, and since George had been so much a part of the renovation, she felt his presence in a comforting way.

She rooted in the cupboards for a bag of French vanilla coffee. It was George's favorite, and she had always loved the smell, just a hint of vanilla, not too overpowering. She stood beside the coffeemaker, breathing deeply as the aroma began to fill the room.

"Look, Mom," Jake said. "Kenny and his dad are here."

He raced across the wooden floor to the front door. Maggie reached up for coffee mugs, listening to Hugh Rossiter's deep voice as he talked to Jake. She should have known he would come. Hugh had been a good friend since she moved to Delbrook. A single parent himself, he understood much of what she had gone through after Mark's death and had offered her friendship and a lot of support with Jake.

She chided herself for a moment of vanity as she pushed her fingers through her unbrushed hair. Too bad she hadn't had time for a quick shower when she got up. It might have made her eyes less red and puffy.

"I hope it's not too early to come over," Hugh said as he came toward her.

"Not at all."

She met him halfway and smiled at Hugh's son, Kenny, as he followed Jake into the café area.

"We've finished breakfast, but there's some doughnuts and coffee cake in the refrigerator," she said.

"I think Kenny's hungry," Jake said, hauling the boy across the room by pulling on the sleeve of his striped shirt.

The two heads were close together, talking in conspiratorial whispers. Kenny was as fair as Jake was dark. He was a fragile-looking child with small bones and a soft whispery voice. Jake and Kenny had become friends in the years when they visited George in Delbrook. The move to Delbrook had solidified the friendship, and now the boys were inseparable.

Although Jake acted as spokesman and had a tendency to be annoyingly bossy, Kenny didn't seem to mind it. He would never be an aggressive child, preferring to have Jake plan and lead the action. Letting the boys fend for themselves, Maggie turned back to Hugh.

"Thanks for coming over."

"Sorry about George," he said.

He put his arms around her. He was six foot tall, so her head rested easily in the center of his chest, and for a moment she relaxed, feeling safe and secure. Catching the nudge between the two boys, she stepped away from Hugh's embrace.

"Can Kenny and I take the doughnuts and some milk into the children's room and watch TV?"

"Yes," she said, grateful to see that the arrival of his friend had done much to lighten the serious expression he'd worn since learning of his grandfather's death.

After the boys were settled and the TV was a low rumble in the background, she poured coffee for Hugh and they sat down at one of the glass-topped tables.

"Brent called to tell me about George," Hugh said. "A robbery! I still can't believe it."

"They're calling it a robbery at this point."

"What else could it be?"

Bewildered at the sharpness of his reply, she shook her head. "I don't know. I only meant that George's watch was an old Timex. Hardly worth enough to interest anyone. And he never carried much cash."

"A robber wouldn't know that." Hugh drank some coffee, his voice sounding hollow behind the mug.

Maggie nodded her head in agreement. She didn't know why the whole idea of a robbery seemed wrong. Maybe because Delbrook was such a quiet town, or maybe because she'd never known anyone who'd been killed during a robbery.

"How are you holding up?" he asked.

"I guess I'm still pretty numb. So many things to consider. Thank the Lord it's Sunday and the store's closed. I don't want to think about this week. There's a big shipment coming in, and I've got to box up the returns and get them out of here. There's so much to think about, and I've got so many questions."

Maggie heard the frantic tone in her voice and closed her mouth on the last words. She felt like a child, wanting to shout, "It's not fair!" When she looked across at Hugh, she could see the compassion in his eyes, and his quiet presence warmed her.

"You want me to take Jake over to my house for the day?" he asked. "Kenny and I are going to take Morgana for a hunt this afternoon. It'd get Jake outside. Fresh air's always healing."

Hugh was the master falconer of the Delbrook Falconry Club. Several times Jake had accompanied Kenny and Hugh on a hunt or a training exercise, and he'd loved the experience. Maggie had seen Morgana, Hugh's hawk, and other birds at local events and had gone with the boys to the falconry exhibit at the Renaissance Faire.

Granted the birds were fascinating and beautiful, but Maggie was still ambivalent whether she wanted Jake to get too involved. He had enough death to deal with, and the wild savagery of the kill frightened her. Naturally the more resistant she was, the more interested Jake was.

"Thanks for the offer, Hugh." She reached across the table and patted his hand. "I know Jake will be sorry to miss a chance to see the bird in action, but I think for right now we need to stick together. I talked to Jake just before you got here, and he wants to go with me when I make the arrangements. He's got a lot of questions, and I'm not up to finding the right answers."

"Kenny and I could go along." He put his other hand on top of hers, dwarfing her hand with his large ones. "You should have someone with you."

Once more Maggie could feel herself succumbing to the pull of Hugh's comfort and offer of protection.

Thanks to the prosperous landscaping business he owned, Hugh was considered, at thirty-eight, the most eligible divorced male in Delbrook and, according to Nell, in most of Wisconsin. An ex-marine, he was ruggedly handsome with the tanned muscular body of an outdoorsman.

They had been dating casually in the last several months. It had begun as outings with the boys, then Hugh had taken her to a couple of movies and a dinner. Maggie enjoyed his company, enjoyed having another adult to talk to, but resisted further involvement.

Although not particularly verbal, Hugh had given the impression recently that he would like her to consider a more serious relationship. He'd been a solid presence in her life since she moved to Delbrook, and she loved his son, Kenny. He would make a good husband and father except for one problem. She wasn't in love with him.

She extricated her hand from his grasp and got up to get more coffee. "Thanks for the offer, Hugh, but I think this is something that Jake and I need to do alone."

"What about dinner? You'll have to eat sometime. Why don't you and Jake come over when you're done?"

"Right now that sounds good, but let me see how the day goes." Wanting to change the subject, she asked, "Were you at the poker game last night?"

"Yes. It wasn't a scheduled game. Connie and Brent were supposed to be out of town. I was going to a seminar on composting over at the college. It was rescheduled."

A diverse group made up the weekly poker games, a blend of different personalities united by their common enjoyment of poker. Not everyone played each time. It depended on who was available and who was eager to play. Several women played, but it was primarily a men's group.

"Charley told me that George was the winner," she said.

"Yes. Going away."

"I'm glad. Was he all right?" She waved her hand back and forth, not sure what she wanted to know. "Was the dinner OK?"

Hugh looked at her as if he didn't understand why she would ask the question. "The dinner was good. He had prime rib. Rare, the way he liked it. We sat at that big round table overlooking the eighteenth green."

Although the details were sparse, just hearing about George's evening eased some of the heaviness in her heart.

"He passed around some pictures of Jake's birthday party over at the Renaissance Faire," Hugh said as if he sensed she wanted to hear more.

"I forgot he was going to pick them up," Maggie said.

"You must have taken the first couple pictures. The others were strange-angled shots, so my guess is that Jake had the camera at that point." He grinned when Maggie nodded. "The best shot of all was the one of Kenny throwing up. Perfectly centered. Unfortunately well-focused. It got a general hoot of approval from the group."

Maggie chuckled. "It sounds like George's evening was just the kind he would have wanted."

"Agreed," Hugh said. "Including the fact he won the biggest jackpot of the night on the last hand with only two pair. A poker player can die happy after that."

Maggie sat at the desk in the bookstore, staring out at the empty park beyond the bay window. The afternoon had turned gray with lowering skies, leaden clouds reflecting in the smooth surface of Falcon Lake. She found it difficult to keep her attention on work as the realization that George was gone sank into her consciousness.

Damn it, George! If you'd done a better job of raising Mark, maybe I wouldn't be sitting alone at this desk surrounded by bills and order forms and publishers' catalogs. I don't know how to go on. I'm afraid for Jake and I'm so alone. I hate it! First Mark leaves and now you. I hate you *both!*

Appalled by her thoughts, she caught back a sob and squeezed her eyes tight, rocking back and forth in an agony of anger and fear.

Since she'd moved to Delbrook, George had been a major part of her life. Someone she could go to for companionship, conversation and a sense of belonging. Already she could feel an empty spot opening in her heart, a void, part anger for his abandonment and part sorrow for the future that would never be.

Can Jake handle this latest tragedy?

She could only hope that in the last year he'd seen the pride and joy in George's eyes and understood the unconditional love that his grandfather felt for him. She had left Chicago so that Jake would have the stability that comes with belonging to a family. Was a year enough time for Jake to feel secure?

The bookstore was Maggie's sanctuary, but was it for Jake?

The house had originally belonged to Abigail and Tina Kitchie, old friends of Maggie's mother. Abby was a tall, long-faced woman somewhere in her mid-seventies, while her sister, closer to eighty, was short and stocky with a bawdy sense of humor and barking laugh. Twenty years earlier Abby and Tina had renovated the house into a bookstore and moved into the apartment on the second floor.

During the time of her mother's final illness, Maggie had seen a great deal of the sisters. The bookstore became an emotional refuge for her and a much needed break from her hours at the hospital. After her mother died, Maggie always stopped by to see Abby and Tina when she, Mark and Jake came to visit George.

It was during one of her visits after Mark's death that Maggie mentioned she was considering moving to Delbrook so that she and Jake could be close to George. Tina had died a year earlier, and Abby mentioned that she wanted to move closer to her daughter in California. Or as Abby put it, she could harass her daughter more easily if she was in the same state. She asked Maggie if she'd be interested in buying the bookstore.

"Mom?"

Jake's call broke into Maggie's thoughts, and she raised her eyes to the gently curving staircase that led from the apartment upstairs to the first floor of the bookstore.

"I'm down here, honey," she replied.

Jake leaned his stomach on the banister and half slid, half hopped down the stairs. Holding on to the rounded newel post, he jumped the last three steps, landing in a heap. The video cassette clutched in his hand flew out and skittered across the wooden floor until it bumped against one of the bookcases in the center of the room.

"Sorry, Mom," he said, scrambling to his feet and racing across to pick up the black vinyl box.

"Did it break?"

"Naw," he said, wiping it off on the seat of his pants. "It's in the case. Can I watch it again?"

"*Godzilla?*"

"Yes. We don't have to take it back until tomorrow."

Jake really needed some down time, Maggie thought. His face was pale and there was a tightness around his mouth that indicated how strung out he was. If he relaxed with the comfort of his favorite video, he might fall asleep. The days ahead would be difficult enough, and some extra sleep would boost his energy levels to get him through.

"Why don't you watch it down here and keep me company?" she said.

"OK. I can set it up."

He zigzagged back and forth between the bookcases, running his fingertips across the backs of the books as he headed for the archway into the children's room. He opened the doors of a low cabinet which housed a TV-VCR combination. He pried up the top of the vinyl box and inserted the tape. Remote control in his hand, he turned on the TV.

His eyes fastened to the screen, he walked backward, hitting the buttons on the remote to start the tape. Then with a quick glance over his shoulders, he flopped down among the pillows and set the remote control on his chest. As the sound boomed out, Maggie jumped.

"Can you turn it down a little?"

For answer, the volume decreased until it was only a gentle background murmur. She smiled as she watched Jake's instant absorption in the video. Other movies had appealed to him, but nothing came close to his fascination with what she considered, despite its production costs, to be nothing more than a low-budget sci-fi film. Jake's eyes drooped, unfazed by the carnage on the screen, and she had high hopes he'd just drift into a reviving sleep.

Perhaps Jake felt the same sense of safety and security that she had felt the first time she entered the bookstore.

When Abby suggested buying the store, Maggie had jumped at the chance. It was the perfect solution. Maggie would be able to earn a living that would still keep her free to spend time with Jake after school and when he was on vacation. She met with Abby's "man of business," Gerry Goldey, and the financial arrangements were made in record time. They were able to move to Delbrook during the summer, with time enough to get established before Jake had to start school.

For Maggie it was a new beginning. A home and a business untainted by memories of infidelities or unhappiness.

A light tap on the window beside her desk brought Maggie back to the realities of the present with a resounding jolt. Her head jerked around to see Charley Blessington standing outside on the front porch of the bookstore.

She had been so absorbed in her thoughts that she hadn't seen or heard him walking across the porch. His blue-uniformed figure filled the center pane of glass and blocked out the late afternoon sun. When he realized he had her attention, he pointed to the front door.

"I'm sorry, Charley. I didn't see you," she said, unlocking the heavy oak door. "Come on in."

"This is really some place, Maggie," he said, looking around. "I hate to admit I feel rather out of my element. Most I ever have time to read is Wanted posters and financial reports from the mayor telling me about budget cuts."

Maggie had always wondered if the chief of police had really been born in the south or had only assumed the drawling way of speaking to put people at ease. With his folksy chatter it would be easy to underestimate Blessington. George had always maintained that Charley was one of the best card players in the group, able to read the unconscious mannerisms of the others to his own advantage.

He hooked his thumbs into his belt and strolled around, stopping occasionally to look at something that caught his interest. As she might have expected, he was drawn to the true crime and men's adventure section. He peeked into the children's room, smiling as he spotted the sleeping Jake breathing in rhythm with the soft murmur of the TV. He moved quietly after that, making a full circle of the store.

"Poor kid," he said. "He's really had a rough couple years."

He kept his voice low, but even with all the books to absorb the sound, it echoed around the room. Maggie indicated the wing-backed chair she'd pulled up close to the desk. She sat back down in her own chair and waited as he took a seat and shifted his beeper, a cell phone and the revolver on his hip to a more comfortable position.

"How are you and Jake holding up?" he asked.

His expression was earnest, but she had the feeling the question was more a formality than anything else.

"We're doing all right. Shocked, of course."

"Aren't we all?" He raised his leg, resting the ankle on the knee of his other leg, smoothing the uniform material with the palm of his hand. "Dagnabbit, Maggie. We're going to get to the bottom of this. It looks like pretty quickly, too."

"Have you discovered who attacked George?"

"That's why I stopped by, so I could fill you in on what's happened since I talked to you this morning. First off, I want to tell you that someone turned in that hospital bag you lost last night."

"I didn't lose it, Charley." She tried to keep the annoyance out of her voice, but she could feel a flush of heat rise to her cheeks. "I thought Brent explained what happened."

"Well, he did and he didn't." The chief of police appeared ill at ease in the face of her indignation. "Now don't get all riled up. He said you thought someone had attacked you, but in his opinion you'd had some kind of a 'spell,' and when you woke up, the bag was missing."

"Oh for God's sake, Charley!" Maggie snapped. "I'm not some simpering drama queen. I ought to know the difference between a near mugging and a dumb-ass swoon."

"I'm sure you do," he said. "On the other hand, you'd just had a violent shock to your system."

"Bullshit! Someone assaulted me in the parking lot, and it's your job to find out what happened."

Tears of frustration filled her eyes, confirming Charley's opinion of her emotional instability. Biting back any further arguments, she changed the subject.

"How is the investigation going?" she asked.

"We finally interviewed the worker from the country club who discovered George. His name's Dennis Nyland."

"I don't know him," she said.

"You'd recognize him if you saw him. Mid-twenties. Pierced ears and a nose ring. Ponytail and tattoos all over his body." From the tone of his voice, it was hard to tell which Charley disapproved of most.

"Now I know who you mean."

"He cleans the locker rooms at night to pick up some extra cash. Lives at home with his mother and runs a graphic arts business out of the garage."

"Dennis found George?" she asked. "Did he see what happened?"

Charley shrugged, grimacing for an answer. "He says he didn't. His story is that all the guests were gone by twelve-fifteen and he was finishing mopping the floor of the ladies' locker room. It was hot downstairs, and at twelve forty-five, he ducked outside to have a . . . cigarette."

Maggie heard in the careful hesitation that Charley wondered exactly what Dennis had been smoking. She didn't care. All she wanted to know was what had happened to George.

"Nyland didn't want to get caught smoking, so he ducked into the trees and walked along the eighteenth hole toward the tee. He heard a noise up ahead and snuck out toward the fairway until he had a clear view. He saw a man bending over something on the surface of the tee."

Maggie could feel a slight tremor inside her body and wrapped her arms across her stomach.

"Apparently he made some sound, because the man whirled around, and when he saw Nyland, he went streaking off into the trees. Dennis heard the chain-link fence rattle as the guy climbed over into the parking lot of the boat ramp."

"Did he recognize the man?"

"Yes, he did. The moon was as bright as a spotlight. He got a clear view of the attacker." Anger made his voice louder. "The man who stabbed your father-in-law was that homeless nutcase who lives out of his car. Tully Jackson killed George."

CHAPTER
FIVE

"TULLY JACKSON WOULD NEVER HURT GRAMPA."

At the sound of the high-pitched voice, Maggie and Charley jerked around to see Jake standing rigid in the archway. He had the dazed look in his eyes of one who had just wakened from a sound sleep.

"Now, son," Charley temporized, rising to his feet.

Jake bristled at the placating tone. Maggie beckoned him forward.

He came across the floor slowly, giving a wide berth to the chief of police. He sidled up to Maggie's chair, and she put her arm around his waist, pulling him close to her side.

"Mom, you know Tully wouldn't hurt anyone," Jake said before she could say anything. "He wouldn't."

"I don't know how much you heard, honey, but I think we need to listen to Chief Blessington before we jump to any conclusions. Maybe he can clarify things for both of us."

Charley sat back down on his chair, perching on the edge of the seat, clearly uncomfortable with Jake's presence.

"Did you hear me tell your mom that Dennis Nyland was outside and saw someone up beside your grandfather?"

"Yes, sir. But Tully wouldn't hurt Grampa. Tully's my friend."

"That may well be, Jake. But sometimes things happen that no one intends to happen." He raised his eyes to Maggie as if asking her how to proceed.

"Dennis was positive that it was Tully?" she asked.

"Yes. He said he saw the white satin top hat clear as a beacon, and when the man ran off, that plastic raincoat Tully wears was streaming out behind him like a cape."

"But Dennis didn't see him attacking George?" she asked, wanting to be perfectly certain she understood.

"No," Charley admitted. "He just saw him bending over the body."

Maggie felt Jake's shudder at the chief's words and her arm tightened around him. She wanted to shelter him from hearing any of the details of the attack, but she had learned from Mark's death that it was better to know the real facts than to make up a fantasy to fill the gaps. She could see on Blessington's face his resistance to talking in front of Jake, but she knew it would be easier this way.

"Then what happened?" she prompted.

Charley seemed to realize that she wasn't going to let him off the hook. With a heavy disapproving sigh, he flopped against the back of his chair.

"Nyland ran up to the tee and discovered that it was George."

"Was he dead?" Jake asked.

Maggie flinched at the stark question. She wasn't surprised, since the thought had been uppermost in her thoughts too.

"Yes, Jake. Your grandfather was already gone. According to the report from the doctor, there was only the one wound in his chest. He was stabbed with a thin-bladed knife. I don't think your grandfather ever really knew what happened. It was very fast."

Jake exhaled a soft breath of air. Obviously he had been worrying, thinking his grandfather had been in pain.

"Then Nyland ran back to the clubhouse and an ambulance was called. The paramedics pronounced him dead at the scene."

Charley waited, as if to give them time to absorb the details before he continued. "I'm sorry I couldn't get this information to you sooner. It took us a while to find Nyland. He was so upset about finding George that when the police released him he went to his girlfriend's house, and they both got drunk. His mother didn't think to tell us about the girlfriend until late this morning. I sent a car over there to bring him in."

"Have you talked to Tully? What does he say about all this?" Maggie asked.

"The bastard's run away." He shot an embarrassed glance at Jake and rubbed a hand over his face. "Sorry, Maggie, it's been a tough day."

Jake's body trembled, but when Maggie looked at him, she could read nothing in the blank expression on his face. She remembered that look from after Mark's death, and she bit her lip in concern. She didn't know if she was doing the right thing by letting him hear all the details. Time would tell.

"We've put out a bulletin on Tully, but so far we haven't found him." Head cocked to the side, Charley eyed Jake. "We've had a car watching for him at the boat ramp, but there's been no sign of him. You wouldn't happen to know where Tully goes when he's not sitting beside his car, do you, son?"

Jake shook his head. "No, sir."

The chief stared at him for a few minutes, as if weighing the truthfulness of the answer. Jake remained perfectly still under the scrutiny, but Maggie could feel the rapid beat of his heart where his body pressed against her side.

"What if he didn't do it?" Jake asked.

Charley was rising from the chair but sat back down at the boy's question. He pursed his lips as if trying to decide what to say.

"If he didn't do it, then we'll get to the bottom of this, son. I know you call Tully your friend, but there's something you should know. I don't want you to think we're picking on him just because he's—eh—different. Police work isn't done that way. It's not like TV, you know."

"Just 'cause he was there," Jake said, "doesn't mean he hurt anyone."

Charley nodded. "You're right about that. When we work on our investigation, we have to take a lot of things into account that might prove whether someone's guilty. So after we heard about Tully, we got a search warrant and went over to the boat ramp and had a look through his car."

Jake's eyes opened wide. "Did you find any clues?"

"Yes, son, we did." The chief leaned forward so that his face was on the same level as Jake's. He waited until the boy's eyes lifted to his before he spoke. "I think your mom told you that some things were taken when your grampa was killed. On the floor of Tully's car we found your grandfather's watch."

The Warrior's arms and legs tingled and his stomach cramped as he leaned against the railing staring down at the people on the lower level of the mall.

He pressed the knife at his side.

Excitement raced through him as he felt the metal hidden beneath his clothes. It was too bad that he couldn't wear it on his belt, visible to everyone's eyes. The small dagger was beautiful, crafted with aesthetic as well as practical considerations. He could recall the shiver of joy as the antique dealer placed it across the palm of his hand and he stared down at the exquisite workmanship.

The blade was five inches of thin, pointed steel, sharpened on both edges. The shiny brass cross guard, or quillon, extended only an inch beyond the blade. The hilt was braided silver wire that spiraled to a rounded knob, on top of which was a raised heart.

A *misericorde.*

To him, it meant "heart of mercy." In medieval times, a warrior used the knife to kill a friend or an enemy who was terminally injured but not dead. The coup de grâce. The symbolism appealed to him.

He'd bought the *misericorde* ten years ago and had worn it as often as he could without risking disclosure.

The antique dealer had recommended a leathersmith who fashioned a sheath of deerskin with thin flat straps for attaching it to his body. Resting along his left side beneath his upper arm, it was invisible. No one knew it was there, but he was conscious of it every time he pressed his arm against it.

Despite his disappointment that he needed to keep the knife hidden, there was something sensual about wearing it against his skin.

He was restless. Badly shaken by the events of the last several days. He needed a chance to rebuild his confidence. Drawing a deep breath, he searched the Sunday shoppers for a worthy opponent for a feathering coup.

He could recall how once he had mastered the touching coup, he had invented the next level of tests. As before, he would chose a target in a public place. This time, instead of merely touching the enemy, he had to place a feather on the enemy's person and walk away without detection.

He had chosen falcon feathers, collected in the woods during the spring and summer molt. In the beginning he used body feathers, but as his skills increased, he began to use the more highly prized flight feathers: primaries, secondaries and tail feathers.

If the occasion was special enough, he tagged with eagle feathers, but that decision had to be considered on a case-by-case basis in order to preserve his limited supply.

He began by slipping the feathers into pockets and bags but eventually gained such dexterity that he was able to insert them beneath layers of clothing, next to the victim's skin. The kick of adrenaline as he watched the unsuspecting "feathered" victim walk away was worth the occasional dark or suspicious look he received when he followed a subject too closely.

His one-day record was an even dozen.

He still found the most pleasure in feathering. Perhaps it was the knowledge that the victims would find the feather when they were alone and know someone had been near enough to touch their private places.

Whenever he felt the restlessness coming over him, he could hold it within controllable limits by searching out risky targets and earning a feathering coup.

He straightened up, hands gripping the railing as he spotted the dark-haired child in the center of the milling crowd below. The boy's head was tilted back, his eyes following the flight of a small bird that had become trapped inside the shopping mall. Silhouetted against the skylight, the sparrow fluttered against the glass, searching for escape.

It was a sign.

He moved to the escalator, eyes intent on the child. A young woman in a clinging jersey dress reached for the boy and led him along one of the corridors of the shopping mall. Impatient for the escalator to descend, he pushed ahead and, when he reached the first level, hurried along the tiled floor in the direction the boy had taken.

Eyes sweeping across the crowd, he spotted them at the entrance to the department store. He quickened his pace, careful not to jostle anyone and draw attention to himself. He wove in and out of the crowd until he spotted the boy and his mother and could slow his pace to follow the twosome.

Suddenly, as if she sensed a threat, the young mother cocked her head and turned to scan the crowded aisles of the department store.

He had seen that look before. A mother protecting her chick. Some psychic signal had warned her of danger, and from now on she would be on the alert. It was basic and it defeated him.

No coup today.

• • •

Tyler was hungry.

The man wouldn't come until his tummy made noises. When he was bad he only got one dish of food. It was a big dish, but it was just once. He could tell because of the lights.

When the first dish came, the man left the lights on all around the room. When the second dish came, only the light above the door stayed on.

He slept then.

He didn't like the dark. He was afraid the bird would come back in the dark and bite him.

When all the lights were on and the man was gone, he marched around the room. He liked the sound of stamping feet. He was punished if he talked, so he made noises. He could blow air and make a funny sound when his lips moved. One time a sound came from his mouth. It was so loud and strong it jerked his chest. It came again and again and then it went away.

Across the room he heard the mice rustling. He slid to the ground and ducked under the shelf. He brushed his hand along the back wall until he found the crust of bread left over from the last dish. Crawling out, he clicked his fingers as he carried the prize to the table.

He pulled the mouse cage to the edge. Mouse Ears was still there. Toes was gone. Four. Just four now. There used to be so many. More than he could count.

He broke off a piece of bread and pushed it through the wires. Before his friend could reach it, the other mice gobbled it up. He broke off two small pieces. He picked them up and tapped on the cage with his finger and rubbed the bread against the wire.

Holding the second piece of bread above Mouse Ears, he stuffed the first piece inside the cage. When the three mice ran over to it, he dropped the other piece in front of Mouse Ears.

Tyler good job. He clapped his hands, jerking his head around when he thought he heard a sound outside the door. He pushed more bread into the cage and propped his chin on the table so he could watch the mice eat it.

His tummy growled. He picked up the remainder of the bread and returned to the shelf bed. Snuggling into the corner, he held the bread under his nose. He closed his eyes and smelled it. The mom lady appeared in his head and he smiled.

The moon was high in the sky by the time Maggie drove past the stone lions that guarded the entrance to McGuire's Irish Estates. Despite the grandiose name, the forty houses that made up the tight-knit community were crammed together on a low bluff at the west end of Falcon Lake. She wound through the narrow streets until she came to George's house and pulled into the parking space at the back.

Like all of the houses in the Estates, George's house had begun life as a summer cottage. Some had been renovated so completely that little remained of the original structure, but her father-in-law had kept the framework, adding modern conveniences and insulation to make it a year-round home without losing the simplicity of design.

Turning off the headlights, she sat still, waiting for her eyes to adjust to the dark. As the night settled in around her, her muscles relaxed and the tiredness she had kept at bay seeped into her body in waves of lethargy. God, it was wonderful to just sit quietly. She'd been running all day, doing the best she could to deal with the practical and emotional demands of the day.

Wes Upton, the funeral director, had understood Jake's need to ask questions and had responded matter-of-factly. Later, at St. Bernard's Church, Father Cusick made suggestions for the funeral service that gave both Maggie and Jake a degree of comfort amid their sadness.

Back at the apartment there had been phone calls and visits by friends, and by the end of the day she had been grateful to Hugh for his offer of dinner. Afterward, she called Nell to stay with Jake so she could pick up clothes for George and take them to the funeral home.

She had been getting ready to leave when Jake flew into a temper tantrum. He had handled the grim details of the day with such emotional control that she had been stunned by his agitation.

"Don't go, Mom," he wailed. "Please don't leave me."

She reached out to hug him, but he fought her, his arms pounding against her back and shoulders as she pressed him against her chest.

Tears rolled down her cheeks, mingling in the dark curly hair of the distraught child.

Please, God, help me. Don't let me lose him, too.

Eventually Jake quieted, and she helped him get washed and into bed, sitting on the edge and patting his back until he drifted off to sleep. When Nell arrived, he didn't rouse, and despite her own exhaustion and despite the fact it was already ten o'clock, Maggie hurried down the stairs for the drive to George's house.

She turned off the motor, rubbed her tired eyes and stared through the windshield at the house. A light mist hung in the air, painting the clapboards a ghostly white.

The house looked forlorn. Her impression was fueled by the sad knowledge that George would never return to stand on the redwood deck overlooking the lake.

She opened the car door and shut it carefully. In the quiet of the night all sound was magnified. Most of the houses were still summer homes, closed up until next year. Only a few older people, like George, lived in the Estates full-time. These were the hardy golfing and fishing set who rose at the first hint of light and faded with the setting of the sun.

She looked up at the treehouse that hung partially over the parking area. It had been Mark's when he was a boy, and was now a clubhouse for Jake and Kenny.

The single room, balanced between two thick limbs of the maple tree, was accessible by a wooden ladder, nailed to the massive trunk, that led to the trap door in the wooden floor. George had built the original, and Mark had added to it until it was truly palatial. The large room had windows with movable shutters and a tar paper roof that, according to Jake, made the treehouse watertight even during a thunderstorm.

The knotted rope that Jake used for a swing was coiled into a circle and fastened to the trunk of the tree above the platform. She remembered holding her breath as Mark showed Jake how to shinny up the rope. His hands had seemed too small to grasp the thick rope. Both George and Mark had been impatient with her gasps of fear and sent her off to sit on the deck overlooking the lake so that Jake would not be influenced by his mother's qualms.

Maggie blinked rapidly to disperse the tears that filled her eyes. Her emotions were too close to the surface to risk getting caught up in memories. If she got moving, she'd only be here a short time.

Her sneakers crunched on the gravel path that wound down to the back door, sounding overly loud in the oppressive silence. The lilac bushes scraped against the side of the house, a rhythmic complement to the chirp of the crickets. The wind had picked up and clouds drifted across the face of the moon, blotting out the light. She stood still, afraid of tripping on the uneven ground.

As the light returned, she could see the dark shape of the canoe, propped upside down on sawhorses against the back of the house. Originally belonging to Mark, George and Jake were refinishing it.

Maggie set her purse on the top step of the back porch and walked over to the canoe. In the shadow of the house, she could only see the outline, not the natural grain of the wood. She ran her hand along the side, feeling the patches where the wood had been sanded smooth and others where it was still rough to the touch.

Will it ever be finished? Her hand dropped down to the canoe paddle, leaning against the leg of the sawhorse. Fingers tightening on the shaft, she picked it up, setting it on her shoulder and leaning her cheek against the smooth blade of the paddle.

There was no one to take over the project, and Jake was too young to work on it alone. She glared at the canoe. It symbolized all the schemes and activities that would never come to pass now that George was gone.

A burning anger raced through her body, and she raised the paddle from her shoulder, wanting to smash the canoe just as George's murder had shattered their lives.

Another cloud covered the moon, blotting out the light and leaving her in darkness. Deprived of sight, her ears picked up the sound of furtive movements as someone approached the side of the house. She froze at the sound, straining to hear.

The scrape of a shoe on the gravel, the rustle of bushes as someone brushed past and then nothing. Only the silence of an unknown trespasser lurking beside the house.

Oh God, someone was here!

CHAPTER SIX

SOMEONE WAS TRYING to break into George's house!

Maggie knew that someone had attacked her in the hospital parking lot. Maybe it was him! This time she wouldn't let him get away. Her hands squeezed the wooden canoe paddle as the tide of anger rose to block out any thought except a need to act.

Soundlessly, she slid her feet across the grass, hugging the back of the house until she reached the corner and could see around the side of the house. Between the bushes, she could see the outline of a man silhouetted against the lighter shades of the clapboards. The window in front of him was open, and it looked as if he was preparing to climb inside.

A burglar! How dare he break into George's house!

Infuriated, Maggie sprinted forward, raising the canoe paddle over her head. The man must have heard her charge, because he jerked around to face her before she could bring the paddle down full force. At the last minute he thrust an arm out. The paddle hit his arm, bouncing once before it struck him in the head.

The man dropped to his knees, and Maggie pulled back, raising the paddle for another strike. She was in mid-swing when the man raised his head and shouted.

"Don't hit me. I'm a lawyer."

The sheer absurdity of the words brought Maggie to her senses, and she tried to stop the arc of the canoe paddle. It was too late. The flat blade slammed into his shoulder and knocked him over. In the dim light she stared down at the man lying on his back, his body motionless.

Oh God, don't let me have killed him.

As if in partial answer to her prayer, the clouds parted and moonlight set the scene aglow. The sprawled figure was illuminated, and she could only gasp in surprise.

She had been expecting an ill-kempt second-story man and instead got a yuppie in a dark suit, button-down shirt and a royal blue tie. Even the blood threading down the side of his face didn't change the fact that her attacker looked as if he'd just come from a board meeting not a prison cell. As if to emphasize that fact, a thin leather briefcase lay in the grass at his side.

Maggie threw down the canoe paddle and dropped to the ground beside the man. She put a hand on his chest and sighed in gratitude as she felt the steady beat beneath her palm. She tipped her head back in silent prayer, then as her eyes touched the open window, her heart jolted at the reminder that the unconscious figure had been attempting to climb in the window.

Wanting answers, she poked his shoulder, but he didn't rouse. Safe enough for the moment, she thought. Gingerly she unbuttoned his suit jacket and reached into the pocket inside. She withdrew a thin leather wallet. With shaking hands, she opened it and flipped through the credit cards until she found his driver's license.

Illinois license. What was he doing in Wisconsin? He didn't look like a man on vacation.

Holding the license close to his head, she compared the photo to the man on the ground. In the harsh moonlight, there were pockets of shadow on his face. With his even features, hawklike nose and strong chin he might have been considered a handsome man except for the jagged scar that was now visible, running along the left edge of his jawline from his ear to his chin. The right side of his face, although streaked with blood from a cut on the side of his head, was unmarked.

She took out a business card and tilted it to catch the light so she could read the raised print. His name was Grant Holbrook. He worked for Etzel, Doyle, Glynn & Williams in Chicago, Illinois. In a flash, the words the man had shouted just as she hit him registered in her mind.

"Don't hit me. I'm a lawyer."

In any other situation that statement would have elicited the automatic response of: "All the more reason to hit you." In this case she suspected she'd made a dreadful mistake. No matter what Grant Holbrook is doing outside George's house, if he doesn't die, he'll sue me, she thought in rising hysteria. Better call 911.

She started to rise when she felt the first movement of the man on the ground. Her glance rose to his face, and she caught her breath at the flash of angry brown eyes that glared up at her. Before she could act, his arm shot around her, pinning her to his chest as he brought her face down to within inches of his own.

"Who are you?" Holbrook demanded in a thin whisper that was in sharp contrast to the power in his arm. "Why did you hit me?"

"Oh thank God, you're alive," she said, ignoring his questions. "I thought you were breaking into the house."

"I'm here to see Collier." He shook his head to give emphasis to the denial, then groaned in pain.

At the mention of her father-in-law, Maggie felt even more guilty. "Don't move," she said. "I was just going to call the paramedics."

"No." The word was feeble but definite. "Help me up."

He pushed himself to a sitting position, remaining hunched over his knees while his breathing shuddered in and out of his chest. Guiltily Maggie stared down at the wallet in her hands. She reached out for the briefcase and jammed the wallet and the loose cards into it and tucked it under her arm. Standing up, she leaned over and put an arm under the man's elbow as he struggled to his feet.

"Can you walk?"

"Give me a minute," he said, his voice raspy. "OK."

He towered over her, but in his weakened condition he didn't intimidate her. She led him along the side of the house to the redwood deck that jutted out over the bluff. She took most of his weight as he used the railing to pull himself up the three steps. She eased him down on one of the green plastic chairs and set his briefcase on the picnic table.

"Sit here," she said. "I need my keys."

She ran to the back porch where she'd left her purse, and as she came back toward the deck, she spotted the canoe paddle. She was so appalled by her earlier attack that she picked up the paddle and shoved it under the bushes out of sight.

Back on the deck, she searched for George's spare key that she carried in the zippered pocket of her purse.

The old-fashioned house key turned easily in the lock, and she opened the door into George's living room. She pressed the light switch on the wall, and the center fixture came on. Maggie let out a low cry.

The room was in chaos. The contents of the desk drawers had been dumped in a heap on the floor and all the storage areas had been emptied and lay scattered around the room.

She whirled around, snarling at the injured man in the deck chair. "What were you searching for in the house?"

"I wasn't in the house," he said in an abused voice. "I was looking in the window."

Rising anger gave strength to his voice. It sounded less thready than at first. Maggie bit her lip, wondering if he was telling the truth.

"Why were you looking in the window?"

"Why should I tell you? Who are you?"

In the light from the living room, she could see him raise a shaking hand to his forehead. The feeble gesture filled her with guilt, and she responded automatically.

"Maggie. Maggie Collier," she blurted out.

"George Collier's daughter-in-law?"

"Yes," she said. "Who are you and what are you doing here?"

"My name is . . ." Holbrook reached inside his suit coat, feeling around for his wallet.

"It's in your briefcase on the table," she said in a choked voice. "I already looked through it when you were unconscious."

"Well, damn!" he muttered.

She was embarrassed but still uncertain about who the man was. "Were you climbing in the window or climbing out?"

"Neither, damn it," he snapped. "I need to talk to Collier. I knocked on the back door, but there was no answer. I walked around the side of the house and found the open window. The next thing I knew you were attacking me."

When he finished speaking he sagged in his chair as if the long answer had drained him. What to do? Despite the villainous scar on his jaw, he had made no aggressive moves toward her and seemed genuinely incensed that she had hit him.

"Let's get inside where I can take a look at that cut on your head," she said.

She helped him to his feet, handed him his briefcase and nudged him over to the door. He held on to the door frame as he scanned the disorder in the room. He looked back at her, reacting to the scowling censure in her eyes.

"I did not do this, Ms. Collier!" he snapped. "I may have scared off whoever was in here when I knocked on the back door."

"Maybe," she said, refusing to absolve him until she was convinced of his innocence.

Despite his bedraggled appearance, Grant Holbrook had a presence as he drew himself up to his full height. He wasn't a big man, but somehow the living room seemed smaller than normal. Watching as he scanned the room, Maggie sensed that little escaped the notice of his flashing dark eyes.

She walked ahead of him, turned on the light in the kitchen and found the same disorder. Cupboard doors were open and drawers were pulled out, their contents littering the surface of the kitchen table and the floor. Picking up a pile of papers from the oak table, she dumped it on the countertop beside the sink and pulled out one of the chairs.

"Sit," she said.

Without a word, Holbrook lowered himself to the seat, wincing as he propped the briefcase against the chair leg. In the glare from the overhead light, he looked as if he'd been in a dreadful accident.

Dried blood streaks coated the right side of his face and stained the beige shirt and royal blue tie with dark red ribbons. One of the buttons on his suit coat hung by a thread, drawing her eye as it swung back and forth with every breath he took. There was a streak of mud on the knee of his pants, and the high polish on one of his shoes was dulled by a wide scrape on the toe.

"Dear Lord, you look awful," Maggie said, covering her mouth with a cupped hand.

"I don't feel all that terrific either," he said. "Do you have any liquor?"

Appalled at what she'd done to the man, Maggie reached into the cabinet beside the stove and pulled out a bottle of brandy. She took out a glass, then reconsidered and took out a second one, filling them with ice. She poured the alcohol into the glasses and carried them over to the table. She stood beside the man, wondering if he should drink with the cut on his head.

"Do you think you have a concussion?" she asked.

"I don't care. Give me the damn glass," he said ungraciously.

She handed it to him and watched as he took a tentative sip.

"What is this?" he said, licking his lips in confusion.

"Ginger brandy. You're in Wisconsin, Holbrook. Only California consumes more brandy than Wisconsin, and it has five times the population."

"Thanks for the news flash," he said.

He took another sip, closed his eyes, breathed deeply and then swallowed. Two more swallows and he set the glass down on the table. She could see his cheeks take on a healthy flush, and a hint of red crept back into his colorless lips.

"Do you need a doctor or should I tell the police to bring an ambulance?"

His eyelids flew open, and he stared up at her. "You can't call the police."

"Why not?"

"They'll take one look and charge me with breaking and entering, and then I'll have to charge you with assault and battery."

"You wouldn't," she said; but one look at the tightness around his mouth and she guessed that he would. She sagged against the counter.

"Where's George Collier?" he asked. "Where's your father-in-law?"

At the mention of George's name, Maggie's hands began to shake, the ice in her drink clinking against the side of the glass. She sat down in the chair on the other side of the table, took a quick sip and grimaced at the sharp bite of the alcohol. Setting the glass down, she stared across at Holbrook.

This is not the man who robbed and killed George, she thought with a sinking feeling. His question gave some verification to that fact.

"Who are you?" she said.

"I told you before," he said. "Grant Holbrook. I'm thirty-seven, have a law degree from Case Western Reserve University and currently work at a law firm in Chicago. There's a number on my business card that you could call for confirmation from one of the partners. I drove up here to talk to George Collier."

"Where's your car?" Maggie said. "Why didn't you park it out back?"

"I parked it up along the edge of the park." For an instant the corners of his eyes crinkled as if he could read the suspicion in her mind. "I know, it looks bad, but I didn't know exactly which house was your father-in-law's and I wanted to have a chance to look over the place before I announced my arrival."

"Why?"

"I'd never met or talked to Mr. Collier." He shrugged. "I'm the cautious type. No point in rushing in before I'd had an opportunity to check things out."

"You sound like a lawyer," she said.

"I *am* a lawyer, Ms. Collier, and as such I'm trained to be both cynical and skeptical."

"Sorry for the cheap shot. It's been a long day."

She took a sip of her drink, staring at him over the rim of her glass. With his straight, dark brown hair and tanned features, he had a GQ look, marred only by the scar on his jaw. The ugly raised ridge added a hint of character to an otherwise too-handsome appearance.

"What time did you get here?"

He looked at the clock on the wall. "It's ten-thirty. I got here around ten. It took me a couple minutes to park the car and walk down here. I'd guess you attacked me around ten after ten."

He bit off the words. Maggie got to her feet, uncomfortable with his anger, even if it was justified.

"I want to look at that cut before I decide what to do."

Holbrook shrugged. He took another sip of his drink and watched as she moved around the kitchen. She rooted through the disorder until she found several terry cloth towels, a basin for water and a small first-aid kit. Steam rose from the water as she set the basin on the table. She dropped one of the towels in the water.

"You should take off your jacket and tie," she said.

He reached up and loosened the knot at his neck, pulling the tie out of his collar.

"Oh shit! That's my Hermés tie," he said, staring in disbelief at the bloodstained silk. "Damn thing cost a fortune."

"Maybe I can get the blood out."

He snatched it out of her reach, folded it carefully and slid it into the pocket of his suit coat. "You've already done enough."

Ignoring his comment, she stepped behind his chair and helped him remove his coat. She could see his mouth tighten as he saw the dangling button. His hand shot out and he grasped the button, snapping the thread, and slapped it into her outstretched hand.

She jumped at the abrupt movement, frightened by what he might do next. Her hand shook as she shoved the button into the pocket with his tie and hung the coat on the back of his chair. She moved back to the basin of water and wrung out the wet cloth. When she turned back to face him, the sight of the blood on his shirt banished her fear.

No wonder he was so bad-tempered. He'd lost a great deal of blood. Gently, she pressed the wet cloth to the side of his face. She could feel his jaw clench as she wiped the blood away from his cheek.

The cut was just inside the hair line above his right temple. He sucked air into his lungs and pulled away as she touched the tender area.

"Hold still," she said.

"Watch what you're doing. It hurts."

"Don't be such a baby, Holbrook."

She refused to let him know how the sight of the gash on his head made her almost physically sick. If she'd hit him a little lower on the temple, the injury might have been far more serious.

"What did you hit me with?" he asked.

"A canoe paddle."

"It felt more like a sledgehammer."

He relaxed under the soothing strokes of the wet cloth. When his face was free of the dried blood, he looked considerably more civilized. Despite the scar, he was a handsome man, and she could see why he'd be so full of himself. He would have a devastating effect on susceptible young women. Luckily she was neither an ingenue nor a young innocent.

"It doesn't look as if you need stitches," she said. "It's stopped bleeding."

She picked up the wet cloths and the basin of bloody water and took them over to the sink. She washed everything and wrung out the towels, hanging them over the arm of the faucet to dry. Finished, she returned to the table and sat down.

"At the risk of sounding redundant, Ms. Collier, where is your father-in-law?" He cleared his throat and leaned toward her. "I have to talk to him. It's very important."

Searching for words, she shook her head, but before she could say anything he hurried on.

"I've come a long way in order to speak to him."

"Please, Mr. Holbrook," Maggie said. "I'm not trying to prevent you from talking to him. I'm trying to tell you that it's just not possible. George Collier is dead."

"He can't be!"

Holbrook slammed his fist on the table with such force that Maggie jumped, pressing against the back of her chair. The color leached out of his face as the action jarred his already injured body. The muscles in his face and neck rippled as he fought to control his fury. He stared at her, sucking in his breath as he read the truth in her expression. He had half risen out of his chair and just as suddenly collapsed back onto the seat.

"Another wild-goose chase." He muttered the words, more to himself than to her.

For some reason the news of George's death was a devastating blow. Defeat was written in the sag of his body, the emotions so genuine that Maggie felt sorry for him. Curious to find out the connection between this stranger and her father-in-law, she sat quietly.

"I'm sorry for your loss," he said in a voice devoid of inflection. "I hope he wasn't sick long."

The words were a conditioned response to her grief. He didn't look at her, staring down at the surface of the table instead.

"He wasn't sick," she said. "He was killed in a robbery."

It took a moment for the words to penetrate. He raised his head, eyebrows furrowed on his forehead. He was like an animal on a scent, nostrils flared and every sense alert.

"When did this happen, Ms. Collier?"

"I'm not sure it's any of your business, Mr. Holbrook."

At her words, his expression became even more intense.

"I'm not asking out of idle curiosity. I assure you it's very important."

"Did you know my father-in-law?"

He shook his head. "I was given George's name by a friend of his in Chicago. Hamilton Rice."

The mention of George's friend caught Maggie by surprise. She wasn't prepared for the emotion that swamped her as she thought of their long-term friendship.

"Oh rats," she said. "I'll have to call Ham and tell him what's happened."

Knowing how close the two men had been, she could almost picture Ham's reaction. Her mouth trembled, and she pressed her fingers against her lips until she was more in control. She cleared her throat before she could speak.

"Ham and George have known each other for years," she explained.

"I gathered from what Hamilton said that they were fishing buddies."

"Yes. Ham used to live here in Delbrook, but he moved to Chicago years ago."

Maggie wasn't sure why the mention of a mutual friend should go such a long way toward giving credibility to the stranger, but it did. Although she didn't trust him completely, she felt less on guard than she had been.

"I know you don't know me and have little or no reason to trust me," he said. "I drove all the way here from Chicago to talk to your father-in-law on a very serious matter. I didn't know he was dead. It would be very helpful if you could tell me what happened to him."

She took a sip of her drink, letting the liquor roll over her tongue before she swallowed it. She could feel it spreading through her body and took another long swallow. Back against the chair, she rested the cool glass against her cheek and raised her eyes.

"I don't know a lot about what happened to George," she began.

It was strange retelling how she'd been called to the hospital and learned of George's death. She had repeated the story so often during the day that the sentences had taken on a certain structure and rhythm that imparted an element of news reporting to the process. There was safety in the rote recital. She could keep her emotions in check and free her mind to concentrate on other things.

His eyes never left her face, and for a moment she felt self-conscious. His entire attention was concentrated on her as if he was analyzing her words, her voice and her expressions to gain a complete picture of the events.

He probably is, she thought. After all he is a lawyer, used to observing and judging. She wondered what kind of law he practiced and if he was any good at it.

"You said George won the poker game last night?" he asked when she finished. "Was the betting particularly heavy so that someone at the country club might have been tempted to rob him?"

Maggie shook her head. "No. The winning was all on paper. At the end of the evening, the chips are counted and added to the running tally that's kept at the club. At the end of the year the players settle up. Money isn't the reason for the poker games. It's the joy of the competition."

"Did George normally carry a lot of cash?"

Maggie smiled. "No. He was extremely frugal."

"Do the police have any idea who did it?"

"According to Charley—that's Chief of Police Blessington—the person they think attacked George is Tully Jackson. A very peculiar man who sort of lives at the boat ramp parking lot that abuts the golf course. He was seen bending over George, and then took off when a worker from the country club spotted him."

"You sound as if you don't think he did it."

"I honestly don't know." She shook her head at the continued confusion in her mind. "Tully is one of those people that just doesn't fit into society. I think he might be homeless, but I don't even know that for sure."

"Is he crazy? Psychotic?"

"This sounds stupid, but I don't know. Lost. Troubled. Shy. All of those are just words that apply to him but don't describe him adequately. I lived in Chicago and I've seen people like Tully pushing grocery carts containing all of their possessions. Long scraggly hair. Unkempt beard. Talking to themselves. Panhandling."

"I know the kind you mean. A lot of them are war veterans who just can't deal with society. Many of them are suffering from post-traumatic stress syndrome. Does he look like a vet?"

She snorted. "What does a vet look like? Tully is somewhere in his forties. I don't think he's mentally handicapped, but he has a very childlike quality about him. I realized early on that he was more comfortable talking to my son, Jake, than he was to me."

"Have the police taken him into custody or charged him?"

"They would if they could find him."

"He's run off? Sounds like a pretty strong admission of guilt."

Maggie shook her head. "If Tully didn't do it, my guess is he's hiding out somewhere."

"You don't think he's left the area?"

"I don't think he'd leave without his car. It's filled with his belongings. I saw Tully a couple of weeks ago. He has an old lounge chair that he sits in. I gave him a new beach towel because the one on his chair was looking pretty threadbare."

Maggie could remember the shy smile he'd given her when Jake presented the towel along with two Snickers bars.

"He held it up to admire the huge sunflowers on the towel. He said he was afraid it might rain later in the afternoon, so he'd save it for the next day. 'In the meantime,' he said, 'I'll keep it with my treasures.' He folded it up carefully and placed it on top of a pile of things in the back-seat of the car."

"Where's the car now?"

"I think the police have it." When his expression intensified, she gri-maced. "I forgot to mention that they found George's watch in Tully's car."

He blinked once. "And that doesn't convince you that he killed your father-in-law?"

She shrugged. "They didn't find George's wallet."

"Do you think Tully might have been the one who searched the house?" Holbrook asked.

"Tully strikes me as a person who has an old-fashioned idea about ter-ritory and privacy," she said. "I don't think he'd come into George's house uninvited."

She noticed that as her story unfolded and he began to ask questions, his energy level increased until he appeared strong and well focused. She wondered if his earlier frailties were an act to garner sympathy. If so, she'd just run out of patience.

"All right, Mr. Holbrook," she said. "Let's hear *your* story."

Mired in her own suspicions, she spoke more harshly than she in-tended. Other than a raised eyebrow, the man showed little reaction. He was silent for a moment, rubbing one shoulder and rolling it forward as if it was stiff. It was probably bruised from the second time she'd hit him, and she felt a twinge of guilt when he caught her eye and then leaned for-ward onto his elbows. When he spoke, his voice was soft, but each word was enunciated clearly.

"Two Christmases ago, Tyler McKenzie, a two-and-a-half-year-old boy, was kidnapped from a shopping mall in Cleveland, Ohio."

Maggie shuddered at the bald statement. If he'd hoped to capture her attention, he'd calculated right.

"Dear God in heaven," she said. "Have they found him? Is he safe?"

"No, they haven't found him. And I try not to think about whether he's safe or not. He disappeared as completely as if he'd been beamed up by aliens."

"I remember once when my son, Jake, wandered away while I was trying on some shoes. I couldn't have taken my eyes off him for more than a minute." Her voice thickened as she remembered the fear when she'd looked up and found him missing. "I doubt if I've ever been more frightened in my life. I pity this boy's parents. I can't imagine how one survives the loss of a child."

"The parents are coping as best they can. In the beginning I think they existed in a kind of limbo." Holbrook's tone was thoughtful. "Listening every day for a phone call. Watching the door and the street for a glimpse of a small blond boy running toward them."

He coughed to cover the emotion that had crept into his voice.

"Were there any witnesses? Suspects?"

"No witnesses ever turned up, and the police have exhausted every lead without coming up with any suspects. They couldn't find a trace of Tyler. As a final desperate measure, the parents announced a reward for information leading to the safe return of the boy. Flyers were made up and distributed throughout the Midwest. It's been posted on the Internet. Message boards, an e-mail campaign, that sort of thing. Since the amount of the reward was sizable, the police were flooded with calls."

"How much was it?"

"One hundred thousand dollars. The money has been deposited with my law firm in Chicago, and people who don't want to go to the police can contact us directly."

He turned around to reach the jacket on his chair and pulled out a square of paper. He unfolded it, pressing it out flat before he handed it across to her.

At the top of the page in bold type were the words: "Have you seen Tyler?" Beneath the headline was a color picture of a little boy wearing a Christmas sweater. His blond hair stuck out beneath a stocking cap, and a stuffed tiger was cradled in his arms.

Maggie stared down at the flyer and the sweet innocent face of the missing child. Instantly her mind conjured up pictures of Jake at two, and she could feel the muscles across her stomach contract at the possibility that something could happen to her son.

She looked carefully at the picture, but there was nothing familiar about the boy. She wanted to recognize him, but to the best of her knowledge she'd never seen the child before.

Her throat tightened and she had difficulty swallowing back the bitter taste of fear as she read the paragraph about the child's disappearance. Below that there was another line of bold type specifying the reward. At the bottom of the page, also in bold type, was an e-mail address: FindTyler@aol.com. Beneath that, the telephone number of the police and another number to contact the law firm handling the reward were listed.

Her hands shook as she handed back the paper. "This is truly a horrific situation, and I pray to God you find the boy. But what does any of this have to do with George?" she asked.

Holbrook didn't answer immediately. He folded the paper carefully and put it back inside his jacket. When he faced her, his eyes were hard, the scar standing out along his clenched jaw.

"After Tyler had been missing a full year, the case was pretty much closed. The investigation was no longer active, although interest was generated occasionally by a phone call or some other possible lead."

"And the parents?" Maggie asked.

"Although they never stopped wishing and hoping, they became resolved to the fact that they would never see Tyler again. Some of the people involved in the investigation believe that Tyler is dead." He paused, swallowing several times before he continued. "Maybe it's easier thinking that he's dead than that he's being hurt or abused. In any case, that's where the case stood until yesterday."

"Tyler was found?"

"No. Nothing that spectacular," he said. "This morning I talked to Hamilton Rice, a friend of your father-in-law. Mr. Rice wanted to know if there was still a reward for the missing boy. I said only if the child was recovered alive. He said good because George Collier knew where to find Tyler."

CHAPTER
SEVEN

"YOU'RE CRAZY," Maggie said, slapping her brandy glass down so hard on the table she was surprised when it didn't break. "How would George know where to find Tyler?"

Her fingers tightened around the glass, and she had to restrain herself from throwing it at him.

"That's what I came up here to find out," he said.

"And that's why you were skulking around George's house? You thought he might be holding this child for the purpose of collecting the reward."

Her comment was not a statement; it was an accusation. Grant held up his hands, palms toward her in a defensive position. He couldn't hold back a wince as he moved his shoulder, but she ignored any attempt to elicit sympathy.

"I'm not saying your father-in-law was in any way involved," he said. "I may have taken time to look around the property, but I approached with no prejudice. I knocked on the back door."

"I should have hit you harder," she said, her eyes flashing with her anger. "George Collier was an honest, caring person. The idea that he would be involved in a kidnapping is not only insulting, it's downright libelous."

"I'm not accusing your father-in-law of anything, Ms. Collier. All I'm telling you is what George's friend told me."

Maggie's mouth pulled tight. "When did you talk to Hamilton Rice?" she asked.

"This morning. Around ten o'clock."

"Look, Holbrook, the whole story about the little boy is appalling, but I think there's a huge mix-up here. At the time you talked to Ham, George was already dead."

Too restless to remain seated, Grant pushed his chair back and stood up. He held on to the back of his chair as he waited for the light-headedness to pass.

"Do your ministrations run to a couple of aspirins?" he asked.

Her eyes narrowed at his sarcasm, but the reminder of his injuries left her off balance. He'd have to remember that. He needed all the leverage he could get. He had to have her help. Everything depended on it. With a sigh she stood up and reached into the cabinet above the sink and handed him a bottle of painkillers.

"Should you take them when you're drinking?" she asked.

"Probably not," he said.

He pried open the top of the bottle, poured two tablets into his hand and swallowed them down with the last of his drink. He added more brandy to his glass. When he held the bottle up, she shook her head.

"I want to repeat that I'm not accusing George Collier of anything," he said, "but the mere fact that your father-in-law has been murdered at this particular time seems highly suspect. Will you let me explain why I came to talk to George?"

"All right, Holbrook," she said. "Make your case."

She sat back down, staring up at him, her chin raised in returning antagonism. She appeared tough, but the dark circles under her eyes indicated that the circumstances of George's death had taken a physical as well as an emotional toll on her resources.

Taking a long pull of his drink, he studied her. Despite the fact that her reddish brown hair was disheveled and she wasn't wearing any makeup, she had a soft Irish beauty with her pale skin and crystalline blue eyes. She was a little younger than he—at a guess, early thirties—with a petite but nicely rounded figure.

Working as a criminal defense lawyer in Chicago had jaded Grant. He trusted few people in his life, and yet even after their inauspicious meeting, he liked what he saw in George Collier's daughter-in-law. She wasn't easily intimidated. She'd shown courage in attacking him. Ms. Collier would make a formidable ally. Although she didn't know it, he needed her more than she needed him. God willing, they might be able to help each other.

"Your father-in-law's friend Hamilton Rice called last night, but I was out and didn't get the message until this morning. He told me that George had telephoned him yesterday, Saturday evening, from the Falcon Lake Country Club."

"That's where the game was."

Her surprise at his mention of the name of the country club helped get him on a credible footing. Grant rested his hip against the kitchen counter. The booze and the aspirin were helping to ease some of the aches in his body. Now all he had to do was stay sober long enough to convince Ms. Collier to help him.

"George asked Hamilton if he remembered the little boy who was kidnapped in Cleveland. Apparently they had been stuck in the Cleveland airport for about five hours right after Christmas. Not last Christmas but the year before."

"Every year George and Ham go to Florida for a week of fishing." She spoke slowly, as if she were reaching back for the memories in order to confirm or deny his words. "Two Christmases ago they flew to Cleveland to pick up John Pfeifer and Ralph Glaser for the flight to Miami. A blizzard hit the Midwest, and the four of them were snowed in at the Cleveland airport for five or six hours."

"I know it's a long time ago, but do you remember what day it was?"

"Yes. The reason I remember is that they were worried that they wouldn't make it to Miami for New Year's Eve. They had planned to celebrate in style and had wanted to get down a day earlier. They were stuck in Cleveland on December thirtieth."

"Tyler disappeared on December twenty-eighth. The reward was announced on the thirtieth. If they were in Cleveland, anywhere near a television or a radio, they would have seen the news stories."

Maggie took a sip of her drink, then pushed the glass away as if it were distasteful.

"Look, the phone call may be true, but the rest of it has to be some sort of fantasy on Ham's part. Something that George said might have gotten scrambled."

"From what Hamilton said, your father-in-law sounded pretty excited. Hamilton couldn't hear him very well because there was background noise, but George indicated that he'd just come across some information that might help locate Tyler."

"Look, Holbrook, George and I were very close. I talked to him just before he left for the country club, and there was nothing in his attitude or behavior that indicated he possessed information of this magnitude." She shook her head to add weight to her words. "Believe me, I would have known."

"What if he discovered the information once he was at the country club? Wouldn't it be possible that he'd call Hamilton right away?"

"I suppose he might have."

Her tone was grudging. She shrugged. Wincing, she reached up, massaging her shoulder with her fingers.

"I've been obsessed with my own injuries, but I suppose I should have asked if you'd been hurt in our 'introduction' outside," he said.

"Thanks for caring. In this case you're off the hook," she said. "Someone tried to steal my purse, and I think I've pulled a muscle in my shoulder."

"Someone tried to rob you?" he asked. "When?"

"Last night. Well, actually it was early this morning when I was coming out of the hospital."

"After you were called about George?"

She nodded.

"What happened?"

"I don't really know. Someone shoved me and grabbed for my purse as I fell. I hit my head and wrenched my shoulder on the way down. Luckily a friend of mine came along and scared off whoever did it."

"And your purse was gone?"

"No. I had a pretty good grip on it. Whoever it was ended up with a plastic hospital bag full of paperwork and my old windbreaker."

Grant forced his body to remain still while his mind whirled with conjecture.

"What did the police say?" Grant asked.

"Not much. They're pretty busy with the investigation into George's death."

"Couldn't this have some bearing on the case?"

"No one believed that I'd been attacked." A flush of indignation rose to her cheeks. "The general opinion was that I'd had some sort of panic attack, passed out and made up the story out of embarrassment."

"Did you?"

She shot him a dark look.

"No. I was uneasy from the moment I stepped outside the hospital. You know how you have the feeling someone is around and watching you. An itch in the center of your back. I never saw anyone. Just had a feeling of movement, a hard shove on my back and then I was falling."

"So only the hospital bag was missing?"

"Yes," she admitted. "Someone found it in the parking lot during the day and took it into the hospital. The assumption is that when I fell, the wind inflated the bag and sent it sailing out of reach."

"I'd like you to think about something, Ms. Collier," he said. "Doesn't it seem strange that in less than twenty-four hours Delbrook, Wisconsin, has become a dangerous place to live? One stabbing and two robberies?" He waved his hand toward the mess in the kitchen. "And by the looks of it, you can count this as number three."

Maggie ducked her head, but not before he spotted the flash of fear in her eyes. He could tell that her father-in-law's violent death had shaken her badly. If her reactions were like most people in a case of random violence, she would be ignoring the inconsistencies and trying to convince herself that George had been killed by a passing stranger who had committed the crime and fled. With a young child, the thought that a killer was still in the area would be frightening to contemplate.

"What you're suggesting is that whoever killed George also tried to take my purse and then came over here to burglarize the house?"

Her brows were bunched up as she waited for him to deny it.

"That would be my guess. I suppose you could make a case for someone knowing that George was dead and using the opportunity to rob the house, but somehow I don't think that's what happened. It looks to me like someone was searching for something."

"Why? Why is this happening?"

Grant came back over to the table and sat down across from her.

"Let's say that George is at dinner and discovers some information about Tyler. He's not sure about it and he calls Hamilton to check if the boy is still missing. Does that seem reasonable so far?"

Eyes steady on his face, Maggie nodded.

"In the meantime, someone realizes that George has this information and confronts him. There's a fight, and George is stabbed."

"Do you mean Tully?"

"Let's call him X. This is all hypothetical anyway, so just go with me for a moment."

He was comfortable going over the elements of a case, weaving the various strands of the puzzle in hopes that they'd form some kind of pattern. All he could do was try to connect what they knew with what might reasonably be assumed to have happened.

"For the sake of an argument we'll say that X didn't mean to kill George. When it happens, he panics. He tries to make it look like a robbery. You said yourself that George's wallet and his watch were stolen."

"If he tried to make it look like a robbery, why would he attack me and then come here?"

"Say there's a piece of evidence that George has that the murderer wants. Maybe he doesn't find it when he searches the body. So X goes to the hospital and waits around until he sees you coming out with a hospital bag. He could have assumed that you had George's personal effects and decided to make a grab for it."

"But there was nothing in the bag," she said.

"He wouldn't know that."

"And when he didn't find what he wanted in the bag, he came here to look?"

Holbrook nodded.

"What's he looking for?" she asked.

"I wish I could tell you." He didn't intend for his tone to come out so strident, but he was frustrated that he didn't know.

"Didn't Ham give you any kind of a clue?" she asked. "What exactly did he tell you?"

Grant rubbed his hands over his face, the beard stubble rasping against his palms. God, he ached. The pounding in his head had lessened, but it was hard to concentrate. He wished he knew how far he could trust her and how much information he could safely give her without putting her in danger.

His first consideration had to be Tyler's safety. According to Hamilton, George must have discovered something relatively solid or he never would have made the call. And the fact that George might have been killed because of that knowledge made it all the more important that Grant keep his own counsel.

"What did Ham say?"

Her repeated question brought him back to the present.

"Nothing really. He told me that it was George's story to tell. He was only making the initial contact. I didn't press him because I assumed I'd be able to get the information directly from your father-in-law. I called George, but there was no answer. I tried off and on today, but by five, when I still hadn't reached him, I decided to drive up here."

He took a quick glance at the clock above the stove. Eleven-thirty.

"It's not too late to call, if that's what you're thinking. But I'm the one who has to make the call," Maggie said. "Ham needs to hear what happened from me. Besides, he'll be more likely to tell me exactly what George said."

Grant reached down for the leather briefcase beside his chair. His mouth tightened at the sight of his wallet, license and business card lying loose inside. He looked across at her, and she raised her chin in defiance.

He took the business card and set it on the table as close to her as he could reach. She turned her face away as if she hadn't seen the gesture. Flipping open the wallet he replaced the license, then reached inside the flap for the piece of paper where he'd written Hamilton Rice's phone number. He pulled out his cell phone, dialed the number and handed the phone to her.

As she began to speak haltingly about George's death, Grant stood up and walked into the living room to give her some privacy. Although moving made his teeth ache, he knew he needed to keep his muscles from stiffening.

Avoiding the cluttered areas where the burglar had dumped things, Grant wandered around the first floor, trying to draw a sense of George from his environment. The main room led out to the deck and off a short hall to two small bedrooms and a bath. The first bedroom was George's. It was spartan and neat except where the intruder had dragged things out of the closets and drawers. The walls were covered by family pictures, and Grant leaned close to examine them.

After he'd gotten the call from Hamilton Rice, he did as much as he could to check into the background of George Collier and his family. Before he arrived in Delbrook, he already knew about Maggie, Jake and the death of George's only child, Mark.

Pictures of George and his grandson generally included a string of fish. Jake looked very much like his father, a handsome dark-haired man who dominated the photos, white teeth flashing in a tanned face.

Maggie photographed well, her Irish coloring enhanced by the outdoor settings. Feisty as she was, Grant was beginning to think of her as Maggie. She was less formal than he was, and neither the title of Mrs. nor Ms. fit her. Looking at the pictures, he was intrigued by the look of vulnerability in her eyes.

"Keep your head in the game," he said aloud.

The second bedroom was set up partially as an office. As he took in the outdoor prints and the meticulously cared-for fishing equipment, he became more and more convinced that George was not involved in the kidnapping but had stumbled onto something that resulted in his death.

Thoughtfully he walked back to the kitchen, stopping in the doorway. Maggie sat at the table, the cell phone still in her hand. Hearing him enter, she stood up, and he could see the sheen of tears that filmed her eyes.

In death it was always the little things that caught at the heart, he thought. He could bet that she was thinking of her father-in-law's long friendship with Hamilton Rice and that she was hurting with the knowledge.

She closed her eyes and took a long, sniffling breath. When she opened them again, she had regained some control.

"Ham is driving up tomorrow afternoon. I told him that there would be a wake for George in the evening and a memorial service on Tuesday." She held out Grant's cell phone. "Thank you. Ham said he thought someone should stay in the house until he gets here. I said I would ask if you would do that."

Stunned by the vote of confidence, Grant said, "Hamilton must have done a whale of a sell job."

"Apparently you have mutual friends," she said.

He caught a hint of a smile in her eyes, and gave a nod of his head in acknowledgment. Her partial acceptance of him released some of the tension that had knotted his stomach. It was provisional, so he'd still have to tread carefully. He'd do whatever it took to get the information he needed.

"What did George tell him?" he asked, putting the phone in his briefcase.

"Ham said George called from the country club around eight-thirty Saturday night." Her eyes opened wide, and she shook her head. "I can't believe that's only yesterday. I feel as if this all happened days ago."

"It's a lot to absorb. Any death is traumatic, but violent death takes a stronger psychological toll, Maggie," he said.

It was the first time he'd used her first name. Aside from one startled glance from beneath her lashes, she made no comment.

"At any rate," she continued, "dinner was over and they were taking a break before the card game. Ham said George wouldn't say much. He was talking from a pay phone just outside the bar. The upshot of the conversation was that he asked Ham to find out if Tyler was still missing."

"Did he mention Tyler by name?"

"No. He referred to him as the child kidnapped in Cleveland. Ham knew immediately who George meant. I don't know if Ham told you that he went to the Internet, checked various sites until he found one of those flyers you showed me. That's how he got your name and your phone number. George told Ham not to contact the police directly."

"Did George say that he'd seen the kidnapped boy?" Grant asked.

"No. He said he'd seen a picture of him. At least he thought it was the missing child, but he wasn't sure."

"A picture? You mean a photograph? How would he get a photo of Tyler?"

Grant heard her sharp inhalation of breath. It didn't seem possible that she could get any whiter, but her skin took on a translucent appearance as if she'd received a massive shock.

"The pictures," she said.

A jolt of excitement zinged along Grant's nerve endings. "What pictures?"

"My son, Jake, just turned eight. I bought him a camera for his birthday party on Friday, and he took pictures all day long. A friend of mine, Hugh Rossiter, was at the country club the night George was killed. He was telling me about the evening, and he said that George passed the pictures around the table during dinner."

Grant prowled around the edges of the kitchen, too restless to remain still. "Do you remember what was in any of the pictures?"

"No. I haven't seen them. George said he'd pick them up and bring them over today when he came for dinner."

Her chin quivered, and he knew she was thinking that there would be no more family dinners with her father-in-law. Just as he thought she might burst into tears, her eyes opened wide and she stared across at him.

"Do you think it's possible that George saw Tyler in one of the pictures?"

Since that was exactly what Grant thought, he tried to keep his expression from giving his own thoughts away. In the twenty months since Tyler had disappeared, there had been so many false leads that he knew better than to jump to conclusions. Even so, his heartbeat accelerated and his depression lifted a fraction.

"It's possible. Or at least someone who looked like Tyler," he cautioned. "It was just one roll of film?"

"Yes. I got him one of those cardboard cameras that you use once and then throw away. I can't even recall how many exposures there were."

"Did your son use all of the film?"

"Yes. I took a few pictures when the boys first arrived. Jake had invited four of his friends from school."

"Were you here at George's house?"

"No. At my house. If you came via the expressway, you drove through the center of town. My house is at the end of the historic area, facing the lake and Wolfram Park. The boys all met in the park, and then I drove them to the Renaissance Faire."

"The Renaissance Faire? The festival across the lake at Camp Delbrook?" Grant asked.

He tried to keep any show of excitement out of his voice. He'd come across Camp Delbrook in another context, and it might prove to be the connection that he was looking for.

"Yes," she said. "Delbrook Community College owns the land and supplies counselors and other volunteers to run a camp for inner-city kids from Milwaukee during the summer. The camp closes on Labor Day, and the Faire opens the following Friday."

"So the majority of pictures were shot by your son at this Renaissance thing?"

"Yes. I may have snapped a couple pictures while the boys were eating, but for the most part, Jake took the rest."

"Do you know where the pictures are now, Maggie?"

"No. I didn't know George had them until Hugh told me, and with everything that's happened, I haven't really given them a thought."

Grant stopped pacing and leaned against the countertop, facing her. He ran a hand over the back of his head and massaged the tension at the base of his neck The pounding had lessened to a low-grade headache that should be gone by morning.

"If George had the pictures at the club," he said, "they should have been on his body. Unless whoever killed him took them."

Maggie shuddered. "If that's true, then why would the murderer search the house or steal the hospital bag?"

"I don't know."

"How old was Tyler when he disappeared?"

"Two and a half."

"So he'd be four now," Maggie said. "When he disappeared he was just a baby, chubby face, stocky body. By now he would have turned into a boy, lengthened out, his face leaner with more individual traits apparent. He would have changed so much that I can't believe George would have been able to recognize him."

"I thought of that the moment you told me about the photos. I know it sounds crazy, but all I can think of is all the people who have recognized other children from the fuzzy photos on the side of milk cartons. It gives me hope."

She bit her lip, her expression hesitant. "Look, Holbrook, instead of talking to me about all this, you should be talking to Charley Blessington, the chief of police."

"You're the only one I can talk to at this point." When she opened her mouth to object, he raised a hand, palm toward her. "Hear me out. If by the wildest chance any of my premise is true, there's a good chance that Tyler is in the vicinity. What do you think would happen to the boy if whoever was holding him got wind of the fact that I was here searching for him?"

Maggie's hands flew up to cover her mouth. Her haunted expression indicated her understanding of the situation.

"If your father-in-law was killed because he discovered something about Tyler, then anyone who was at the country club has to be considered a suspect. And you said yourself that Chief Blessington was at the dinner and stayed for the poker game."

"But Charley was George's friend. Everyone at the game knew him and liked him. These are all good people."

He couldn't hold back a sharp bark of laughter. He almost resented her naïveté.

"I was born a cynic, Maggie, and dealing with the law over these years has given me a jaundiced view of mankind. For what it's worth, good people can do bad things. They're not perfect. They have all the faults and frailties that are a part of our humanity."

"So what you're telling me," she said, her voice soft and expressionless, "is that I can't trust anyone?"

"That's exactly what I'm saying," he said, and she winced at the acid in his tone.

"How do I know I can trust you?" she asked.

"Believe me, Maggie, despite what happened earlier between us, you have absolutely no reason to distrust me. In fact, I'm the one person you can have complete confidence in, because I have the most at stake."

"For a moment I forgot you were a lawyer, Holbrook." There was a definite bite to her voice. She needed to strike out at him. "I should have remembered you have a major stake in the hundred-thousand-dollar reward. So you're just in it for the money?"

"No, not the money," he said. "I put up fifty thousand dollars of the reward myself. All I want to do is to locate the boy. Tyler McKenzie is my nephew."

CHAPTER
EIGHT

"ALMOST BACK TO NORMAL, George," Maggie said, wiping a dusting cloth across the surface of the desk. "Just your bedroom to finish."

Maggie was grateful that there was no one in the house to hear her running dialogue with her father-in-law. She'd spent the morning removing the evidence of the break-in, and to keep the pain of her loss from overwhelming her, she'd talked to George as if he were watching her every move. She hoped he was. Touching his things had made him seem very close.

With a final brush of her hand across the back of George's desk chair, she hurried across the living room, opened the door onto the deck and stepped outside.

The day was cool with a hint of the crisp fall days ahead. Leaves were beginning to fall, covering the ground with a carpet of mottled colors. Reds, oranges and luminous yellows overlaid the grass. The soft throb of a motor on the far side of the lake floated up to her. The beauty of the moment juxtaposed with George's murder made a shocking contrast.

Murder. Robbery. Kidnapping.

The words seemed alien to the shimmering water and the brilliant fall coloring. How could evil exist in such a setting? Only two days since George had been killed, and still there were so many questions.

When she arrived at the house after dropping Jake off at school, Grant Holbrook had been gone. On the kitchen table was a note saying the police had OK'd the cleanup of the house and that he had gone to town to run some errands and pick up food for lunch. She had to admit she was nervous about seeing him again, because she had begun to question the agreement they had made the night before.

"Have I made a pact with the devil?" she wondered aloud.

Even though Ham Rice had told her that she could trust Grant, she had wanted to go to the police and tell Charley Blessington the whole story about Tyler and the photographs. Only when Grant indicated that George's involvement might be questioned did she agree to keep everything from Charley.

She'd told Grant that she wouldn't speak to the police until she was convinced that George wouldn't be accused of anything, but she didn't tell him the real reason for her acquiescence.

She couldn't let Jake question his grandfather's character.

After two years Jake finally had begun to recover from his father's death. She had talked about Mark's virtues and his faults so that Jake would not grow up believing his father was perfect. She had never lied to him, but since she was the only one who knew that Mark had been unfaithful, she had felt no need to explain that part of Mark's character.

The sudden death of his grandfather threatened Jake's psychological well-being. She could see it in his volatile emotional outbursts. He was dealing with anger, abandonment and sorrow. Once again she felt the need to protect Jake from anything that would taint his memories of George. What would happen to Jake's equilibrium if his grandfather was suspected of being involved in a kidnapping?

Anyone knowing George would realize the whole idea was ludicrous, but she wasn't willing to take a chance that, in the frenzy to find answers, George's call about the kidnapping could be misconstrued.

"Back to work," she said aloud as she pushed herself to her feet. "Just time before lunch to finish your bedroom, George."

Putting fresh linens on the bed, Maggie fluffed up the pillows, smoothing a hand over the appliquéd black-and-white loon in the center of the quilted comforter. Turning her head, she checked to make sure that everything was in order.

She stood at the door of the closet and brushed her fingers across the soft leather elbow patch on the sleeve of George's black-and-white tweed sport jacket. She'd given it to him for Christmas soon after she'd married Mark, and it had always been his favorite. She raised the cuff, touched it to her cheek, then dropped it back into place.

She pressed her hands against the small of her back, stretching backward to ease her tight muscles. The physical labor had been a godsend to keep her from thinking about the confusion in her own mind, but now that she'd completed her chores, her mind was flooded with the pain of reality.

She stood still, her eyes closed against the threat of tears. She was alone again. She didn't know if she had the strength to start over and shore up the protective barricades she'd built after Mark's death.

"Maggie?" Connie Prentice's voice sounded from the back door.

"Come on in," she called, jolted back to the present.

"There you are, my dear. I saw your car parked out back," Connie said. "Brent and I just had to stop in to see how you were doing."

She crossed the living room, her high heels clicking against the floorboards, and put her arms around Maggie, kissing the air in the general vicinity of her right ear.

Flowery perfume swirled around Maggie, and she stepped away from the cloying scent. Connie's eyes dropped, a quick scan from Maggie's hastily bound-up ponytail to the soles of her ancient loafers. She didn't exactly sneer, but it was close to being offensive.

"Thanks for stopping by," Maggie said, holding on to her temper. "Where's Brent?"

As if on cue, the back door opened. "Maggie? Connie?"

"In the living room," Connie called out.

Heavy footsteps crossed the kitchen floor, and Brent Prentice appeared in the doorway. His expression was grave as he crossed over to kiss Maggie's cheek. The lines in his face seemed to be more deeply etched than when she'd seen him at the hospital.

"How are you holding up?" he asked.

"Pretty good. Jake and I are both tired but doing OK."

"I can't believe he's gone. George was always such a vital man. A real presence." Brent's eyes teared up. He sniffed several times, then reached in his pocket and pulled out a freshly ironed handkerchief. Turning away, he blew his nose, walking over to stare out at the lake.

"Mr. Sentimental," Connie said, flipping her hair away from her face. Her tone was caustic, and she smiled to take the sting out of it. She sat down on the couch, settling her skirt becomingly before she patted the cushion beside her. "Now, Maggie, come and sit down and tell us what you know."

Wavering between amusement and annoyance at Connie's usurping the role of hostess, Maggie remained where she was on the far side of the glass-topped coffee table.

"Would you like some coffee or tea?" Maggie asked.

Although Connie opened her mouth to speak, Brent's reply came first.

"No thanks, Maggie. We just finished lunch at the country club," he said. With one final blow of his nose, he tucked the handkerchief back in his pocket.

"Everyone was talking about George. I still can't believe it happened after the poker game," Connie said. "Both Brent and I were there of course. George was still at the club when we left."

"The word is that Tully Jackson's involved." Brent's mouth was pursed with distaste.

"I wouldn't be at all surprised. That man always gave me the creeps." Connie shuddered. Her painted nails clicked nervously on her wide gold bracelet, her personal trademark. "He never said anything to me, but he was always staring. All that hair and those probing eyes. I always thought he was dangerous."

"You never know with those types. Probably mental," Brent concluded. He brushed some invisible specks of dust off the sleeve of his navy pinstripe suit. "I understand that there'll be a wake tonight for George."

"Yes," Maggie said. "Charley Blessington called this morning to say George had been taken over to Upton's Funeral Home."

"Is there anything we can do?" Connie asked.

Her eyes flicked around the room as if to suggest a major cleanup was needed. Maggie was grateful that she hadn't stopped by several hours earlier to see the aftermath of the break-in.

"I appreciate your asking, but everything is pretty much taken care of."

She glanced at the clock on the wall and realized that Grant would be back soon. Hoping to get Brent and Connie out of the house before she was required to make any introductions, Maggie stood up.

"If you think of anything, you just have to call," Brent said.

He reached out to help Connie to her feet. For a moment she hesitated as if she wanted to stay, but then shrugged, batting his hand away as she rose to her feet. He took Maggie's hand and slipped her arm into the crook of his. He patted her hand as they walked out to the kitchen.

"I'd be happy to stay and give you a hand," Connie said. "I hate to think of you dealing with this all alone."

"How sweet you are to offer," Maggie said, opening the back door, "but I'm just taking everything one day at a time."

With another flowery embrace from Connie and Brent's formal kiss on the cheek, the couple left. Maggie closed the door, leaning against it as she watched them walk along the path to their car. Just as she took a deep sigh of relief, she saw Grant turn into the street and pull into the parking spot next to Brent's car.

Maggie's stomach gave a free-fall lurch. She had agreed that Grant could pose as Mark's cousin, but she wasn't comfortable with the deception. Since it was Grant's idea, she would leave the introductions to him. Turning on her heel, she walked out on the deck to straighten the patio furniture. Only when she heard the back door open again did she return to the kitchen.

Grant was standing beside the sink, a bemused expression on his face, a grocery bag cradled in his arm. His suit and shirt, covered in a plastic bag from Sylvester's Dry Cleaning, hung from the back of a kitchen chair, and a bag from Copeland Haberdashery was on the seat.

"I don't know who that woman was, but she asked enough questions to give my law partners a run for their money in the investigation of witnesses," he said by way of greeting.

"Connie's a real estate agent," Maggie said, "who, along with her husband, was one of the poker players the night George died."

"I liked him, but she gave me a hellava grilling. I thought at one point she was going to ask for my fingerprints and a copy of my stock portfolio."

"Did she believe your story?" she said, feeling the buildup of tension across her shoulders and her neck.

"I think I passed. She and Brent looked surprised when I said I was Mark's cousin, but neither of them really questioned it. I explained that you'd asked me to stay here so the house wouldn't be empty."

"What if they check up on you?"

"Then they'll find I'm exactly who I said I was. A lawyer from Chicago who's come for George's funeral."

He set the bag of groceries on the counter, then turned to give her his full attention. He could see she was shaken by his first encounter with someone from Delbrook.

"Look, Maggie," he said. "I know you're afraid that I'll be denounced as some sort of impostor. Keep in mind that even if that happens, it won't impact on you. Your story is that I introduced myself as Mark's cousin and you had no reason to disbelieve me. Since you didn't know I even existed, you can claim total ignorance if someone questions you."

"I know. It's just that I hate lying." She bit her lip as if her honesty were some kind of character flaw.

"You don't have to lie. I'm the one that has to, and believe me, I'm very good at it. Some people say that's how I make my living."

He could see that she wanted to make a sarcastic retort, but her eyes flicked to the cut on the side of his face and she swallowed the comment. She might not like subterfuge, but she had strong reasons for going along with it.

"The key to lying is to stick as close to the truth as possible. I had a long talk with Hamilton Rice this morning. I told him everything I told you, just like we agreed. He's willing to claim that he knew me through George and had called to tell me about his death." He grimaced, pulling at the lobe of his ear. "Actually, he said he would once he'd laid his baby blues on me and checked my bona fides."

"Ham's the cautious type," Maggie said.

"Will he be able to hold up his end?"

"Among his many jobs, Ham was a private detective for years. He earned most of his money as a skip chaser."

"I think I'm going to like this guy." He smiled with genuine amusement at this latest news. "Hamilton says it's safest to say I was related to George's late wife, Edna. She wasn't from Delbrook. Someplace in Minnesota. I've decided that if anyone asks, I'll say my mother and Mark's mother were cousins. If pressed for details, I'll describe my favorite aunt, Hadie Yates. I won't have to make up any strange stories. She was a real corker."

He could see her eyes soften under his light banter. How nice it must be to never have a need to lie, Grant thought. To live life openly and honestly without hiding your feelings or playing mind games. For a moment he resented her uncomplicated life.

"I'm sorry," she said as if she could read his mind. "I understand why this is necessary. I'm just having a hard time with it. I'll get better."

"You don't have to get better. The important thing to remember is that as far as you know, George was killed in a robbery. Pretend I really am a relative, come to give you moral support."

"All right. I can do that."

"Good girl," he said, hoping he didn't sound condescending. "Let me put this stuff away, and then I'll fix us some lunch."

While he took his suit and the bag of clothes into the other room, Maggie put the groceries on the counter and set the table. When he returned, he began to arrange the ham and cheese on a platter, moving around the kitchen as if he was long familiar with it.

Despite the fact she didn't trust him and wasn't sure she liked him, she was surprised at how comfortable she was in his company.

He was wearing new blue jeans, a tweedy brown knit shirt and a pair of Docksides. Except for a slight stiffness when he moved, he was none the worse for his contact with the canoe paddle.

"What did the police say about the break-in?" she asked.

"No fingerprints," Grant said in disgust. "I suppose anyone who watches TV nowadays knows how to avoid them. The police officer dusted around the window and a few other places, but it was apparent right away that Officer Chung was getting nothing but smudges."

"Did you tell her that it looked more like a search than a robbery?"

"She thought someone was looking for cash. She filled out the paperwork and said that because of George's death, she'd give the report directly to Charley Blessington. Said to tell you she was sorry about George and she'd talk to you at the October meeting of something."

"Sophia and I belong to the same church guild. She's doing a program on her trip to Seattle where she helped the police set up a soup kitchen like one our guild established in Milwaukee."

He got out a jar of mayonnaise, uncapped it and set it on the table.

"Did you take your son to school this morning?"

"Yes. I decided to close the bookstore until after the funeral, which freed me up to talk to Jake's principal this morning. She said the structure of the school day would give him a feeling of security and he'd have less time to think about his loss. The teachers were prepared to discuss George's murder in class today, and Jake will have a chance to talk about his grandfather's death with his peers."

"Sounds like a good school."

"They've been very supportive. Both now and when we first moved up here."

"Your boy's had a tough couple of years," he said.

He didn't ask her how she was coping with this second tragedy. The sadness in her eyes and the droop of her body when she didn't know he was looking gave ample evidence of her grief.

"On the way over here I stopped at Kruckmeyer's to ask about the photographs," Maggie said.

She got out plates and napkins and poured a glass of milk, then, without asking, opened a cold bottle of beer and placed it on the counter beside him.

"The pharmacy doesn't keep any copies of the pictures."

"That doesn't come as a great surprise." Grant took a quick swallow of beer. "The camera?"

"That's destroyed, and everything goes into the incinerator." Maggie sighed as she pulled out a chair and sat down. "Unless George left them someplace in the country club, someone has already taken them. If that's true, what are they searching for?"

"I wish I could tell you," Grant said.

He placed the platter of ham and cheese on the table and opened the plastic wrapping on a loaf of rye bread. While she made a sandwich, he brought over a bag of potato chips and a jar of pickles.

"Is this enough food?"

"Perfect," she said, taking a bite of her sandwich.

"Why don't you give me a little background on that couple I just met while we eat," he said as he dropped down on the chair across from her.

She raised the red-and-white checkered napkin, and for a moment her chin quivered as if she'd suddenly been reminded of George. She wiped her mouth slowly, and when she dropped the napkin, he could see she was back in control.

"Connie Prentice is the granddaughter of the town founder, Delbrook Falcone," she said.

"Falcon Lake was named after him?"

"No. The similarity is just a coincidence. Delbrook was a major contributor to the Audubon Society. He named the lake for the birds in the area and the town for himself."

"It's got to be a great ego trip to have a town named after you," Grant said.

"My mother used to tell me stories about old Delbrook," Maggie said. "He'd been a big hunter in his youth. Always in the woods with a gun, until one day he got a little careless and winged one of his neighbors.

Gave up hunting for conservation and wrote treatises on the habitats of local birds. A bit odd, but otherwise a pretty interesting old coot."

"How about Brent? He looks a lot older than Connie. Love match or the making of a dynasty?"

"I'd say the latter. Connie's thirty-six, and Brent just had his fiftieth birthday in June. According to local gossip, Connie's father, Edmund Falcone, was Brent's godfather and paid for his education. He's an architect. Edmund hired him to draw up plans to renovate the original Falcone house on the south side of the lake. An old rambling place, added onto over the years."

"Is it still there?"

"No. It burned to the ground. It happened about a year after Connie and Brent were married."

"Is Edmund still alive?"

Maggie shook her head. "There's some kind of mystery surrounding his death and the fire. He'd had a stroke and was confined to bed. I don't know if he died in the fire or shortly after."

She watched as Grant carefully spread mayonnaise on his bread, working it precisely to the edges before layering on the slices of ham. She had to laugh when he measured the dimensions of the bread and cut a single piece of Swiss cheese to fit exactly. He spoke without looking up.

"Go ahead and snicker," he said. "I can't help it that I'm set in my ways. I like things very precise. It comes from being a bachelor for thirty-seven years."

"Anti woman or just anti marriage?"

"A little of both." He cut the sandwich into two equal rectangles, wiped the knife and set it beside his plate. He took a good bite out of one of the halves and chewed reflectively before he spoke again. "I came pretty close a couple years ago. Her name was Veronica. She was the daughter of one of the partners in the law firm where I worked at the time."

"Sounds like an upwardly mobile move."

"I thought so too." He saluted her with the beer bottle. "It was a pretty heady situation. I got so caught up in the social whirl that I lost my focus for a while. Veronica wanted me to run for political office. As she and her father always said, Chicago needs good Republican candidates."

"Can a Republican win an election in Chicago?" she asked in amusement.

"Not that I'm aware of." He finished off his sandwich and applied himself to the potato chips. "There's something very seductive about being wooed by some of the biggest moneymen in Chicago. Celebrity is very sexy. People ask your opinion and may even listen to your answers. You're invited to all the 'in' black-tie affairs, and everyone tells you that you're just what the party has been waiting for."

At some point he'd forgotten that he was talking to her. It was as if he were giving a monologue on the drawbacks to stardom. She was surprised by the note of bitterness in his voice and wondered what had caused it.

"Did Veronica break it off or did you?"

"Mutual consent. I had an accident, and it was as if this"—he tapped the scar on the side of his jaw—"were the outward sign of a character flaw. It marred the perfect profile of the man she'd hoped to mold into a handsome, debonair political animal."

"She can't have been that shallow," Maggie said.

He stared across the table, his face turned up to the light so that she could see the scar. She wondered if he was expecting her to recoil in horror. When it was new, it might have been ugly. Red and swollen, the edges jagged. Once healed it was noticeable but hardly disfiguring.

"Maybe not. Veronica always sat or walked on my right side. If she couldn't see the scar, she could forget that it was there. She wanted me to have plastic surgery, but I'd grown used to it." He ran his thumb along the ridge. "Each day the scar became less obvious, but in Veronica's mind it grew bigger and uglier until she could no longer stand to look at me."

"Was it a car accident?"

She could see the muscles beneath the scar ripple at her question. She should have remembered she was a stranger not a friend.

"I apologize for asking such a personal question," she said.

"Since I've dropped into your life without asking permission, I'd say you have a right to satisfy your curiosity as to the kind of person I am."

He finished off his beer, setting the bottle precisely in the center of the table. His head was bent, so Maggie couldn't see the expression on his face, only hear the condemnation in his voice.

"The early part of last year, I spent a great deal of time trying to drink Chicago dry. Although I only have a hazy memory of this edifying period of my life, my friends are happy to point out that it was not a pretty sight." He reached for the beer bottle, switching it from hand to hand as he spoke. "I wasn't a happy drunk. I was a mean, pissed-off bastard, looking for a fight. Naturally I discovered several bar patrons happy to oblige."

"You got the scar in a bar fight?"

He raised his head, his mouth twisting into a cynical smile.

"For a moment you sounded just like Veronica. Technically it wasn't a bar fight. Two guys jumped me as I was leaving the Silver Stallion, a bar in a particularly seedy section of Chicago. They robbed me, stripped me naked and were considering cutting my throat when the cops arrived. Saved by Chicago's finest."

Maggie caught the bitterness in his voice and wondered what had brought on the binge drinking. Then she knew.

"This was after Tyler disappeared."

Wanting to spare him, she made it a statement, not a question. He blew out a sigh of relief that he hadn't had to spell it out for her. His body sagged against the back of the chair. Maggie remained still, letting him set the pace.

"Two Christmases ago I went to visit my sister, Barbara, in Cleveland. I'd been much too busy with my campaigning that year to do much traveling even though she'd asked me to come several times. My nephew, Tyler, was growing so fast, and she didn't want me to miss seeing him."

He didn't look at her. His eyes were focused on the empty beer bottle as he rolled it back and forth between the palms of his hands. The words came out slowly, as if it were the first time he'd spoken them aloud. Maybe it was, Maggie thought.

"Veronica was incensed with my decision. Christmas was a prime time for fund-raising parties, and she was furious when I told her I was going. My decision was made primarily to prove to Veronica that she couldn't dictate to me. When I got to Barbara's I was bored."

"Too much domesticity for you?" Maggie asked.

"I was plunged into toddler hell," he said, the corner of his mouth curling in self-mockery. "I'd never been around children for any length of time. Tyler was cute but much too young to hold my interest for more than a few minutes. He had a dog, and the two of them climbed all over me whenever I sat down. The dog was a mutt with bulging eyes in a gooney-looking face. His name was Barney. Did you ever hear that old song 'Barney Google with the goo goo googly eyes'?"

Maggie chuckled. "Small world. George used to sing it to Jake when he was little. Jake loved it."

"So did Tyler," Grant said. "For a year after he disappeared, I used to wake up in a cold sweat with that song playing over and over in my head."

The muscles in his jaw bunched, and Maggie heard the pain behind his words.

"Barbara's husband, Ken, is an oncologist with the Cleveland Clinic. I like and respect the man, and he was kind enough not to kick me in the ass for my behavior. We managed to survive Christmas. Forty-eight hours after I arrived, I announced I had to return to Chicago for some important meetings."

He set the beer bottle down, steadying it with his fingers, then rose to his feet. He began to pace, moving restlessly back and forth between the refrigerator and the sink.

"Veronica was delighted, seeing my early return as a capitulation to her demands. Barbara was less thrilled. She and Ken had just discovered that she was pregnant with their second child. She had been having bouts of morning sickness and was hoping that I'd help her with Tyler because Ken had an emergency call to the hospital. I was firm in explaining that I couldn't stay. I was too busy. I had important people to meet."

Maggie could feel the buildup to his story in the way he bit off each word, speaking in short angry sentences.

"Barbara had asked me if I could watch Tyler while she ran errands, but I'd managed to get an early flight out. She drove me to the airport, and since she had no one to baby-sit with Tyler, she took him with her to the mall. She was making Christmas returns." He took a deep breath, swallowing once before he continued speaking. "She was returning the present I'd given her when Tyler was kidnapped."

CHAPTER NINE

PLUSH MAROON VELVET DRAPERIES and silky sheers hung at the windows, breaking up the long wall of gold embossed wallpaper that lined one side of the room. The furniture, wood surfaces rubbed to a burnished sheen, represented no specific period. The chairs and couches were upholstered in rich tapestried material illustrated with quaint medieval hunting scenes. Underfoot the thick patterned carpet leached sound from the room and suggested a place for quiet contemplation.

The Warrior stood inside the doorway, letting his senses absorb the emanations of death that permeated every corner of the funeral home.

He had decided to come at the last minute. If he didn't make an appearance, it would be noted and an explanation would be required. Now that he was here he realized that it was going to take all his control to act appropriately and not draw attention to himself.

His mind conjured up a medicinal odor, but any hint of antiseptic would have been overridden by the cloying scent of flowers that were scattered around the room in vases and baskets and wire stands flanking the mahogany casket.

Flowers. Flowers in myriad shapes and colors. Live flowers, not silk. Dying from the moment they were cut.

Maggie stood beside Jake at the front of the room. He approved of her mourning clothes, a light blue silk dress with a pleated skirt and white collar and cuffs. The simple lines gave height to her petite figure, and the soft color enhanced her lightly tanned skin with a touch of golden highlights.

Jake looked very grown up in his navy suit and white shirt. He rocked from foot to foot as if he hadn't fully broken in the new shoes he wore. Aside from that, he didn't fidget but remained attentively next to his mother. Occasionally he leaned his dark curly head against her arm or touched her with his hand as if to reassure himself that she was still there.

The Warrior made suitable gestures of sympathy. Maggie's responses were warm, her voice tinged with the pain of loss. Despite an outward appearance of fragility, she was a strong woman. He could see in her steady gaze the ribbon of courage that started in the core of her body and infiltrated her entire being. Her crystalline blue eyes startled him. They contained the concentration and focus of a warrior.

The observation startled him, and he moved away to speak to the boy. Jake, like many only children, was comfortable with adults, talking with ease and a degree of interest that was unusual for a boy of eight.

Maggie had done an excellent job in training Jake.

Much to think about, the Warrior thought, as he stepped away so others could offer their condolences.

Between the family group and the casket was a brass metal easel that held a rectangular posterboard covered with pictures. He drew closer, his eyes skimming across the photographs, seeing George's face in most of the pictures. He wished he could remain in front of the collage, but he knew he would have to approach the coffin.

Viewing the body. The concept was alien to his beliefs.

The body was only a shell that housed the spirit. The wake was an anachronism, an ancient tradition that glorified the corporal aspect of life over the spiritual.

He stood about a foot away from the ornate kneeler placed at the front of the casket. The maroon velvet coverings on the hand rest and knee pad were clean and free of stains, but the nap was slightly worn from use. He preferred to stand.

He would miss George.

Who could have guessed that such diverse events would come together, converging on that night, as if it were fated? Nothing had prepared the Warrior for it. No tingle of apprehension had shivered up his spine Saturday night when the poker game was over and George said he wanted to talk.

They walked along the fairway, and George told him about being in Cleveland and seeing the media frenzy about a missing child. Then in a voice filled with exhilaration, George had told him he'd recognized the kidnapped boy in the pictures taken by his grandson at the Renaissance Faire.

In a movie, the Warrior would have rejected the coincidence, and even now he had difficulty believing that something so random could nullify the meticulous planning he'd done to ensure safety from discovery.

George had no concept of the Warrior's involvement. He was too full of excitement that he'd recognized the child and was eager to present the evidence. The Warrior could still recall how his heart had hammered in his chest when the stack of photographs from the Renaissance Faire was passed to him and his fingers touched the slick surface of the first picture.

The poorly focused faces of three grinning boys filled the majority of the frame of the photo. George's teeth flashed in a wolfish smile as he tapped the picture, pointing to a small blond child in the background. Seated on the wooden bench beside the jousting arena was One Who Cries.

The Warrior's fingers stiffened, and he almost dropped the pack of photos. Until George pointed it out, the Warrior hadn't even noticed the child on the bench. One Who Cries was easily recognizable.

Impatiently George showed him the next picture. Again, the half-turned face of One Who Cries could be seen in the background.

What an improbable twist of fate. Sweat beaded on his forehead and his skin was moist as he handed the photos back to George. The Warrior knew without question that he would have to destroy the evidence.

It would be simple enough. George had slipped the bunch of pictures inside the carrying folder. The negatives would be in the short half-pocket of the folder.

They had walked along companionably, George excited and talkative as he smoked a cigar and discussed the significance of the pictures. He spoke with the ease of friendship, and by the time they reached the eighteenth-tee box, the sense of betrayal was so strong that the Warrior was primed for an explosion. The sight of the folder of incriminating pictures triggered the attack.

George stood motionless, holding the photographs, his eyes wide in question as the Warrior opened his shirt and pulled out the knife. The Warrior thrust it home with his right hand, the palm of his left braced on the raised heart at the top of the dagger.

Misericorde. Heart of Mercy.

George never saw the knife. The tattoo of the bleeding heart on his friend's chest held him transfixed.

"Tattoo."

He uttered the single word before he pitched forward onto the surface of the tee.

The Warrior stared down at the body. Moonlight reflected off the blade of the knife, a flicker of gold combining with the dark red of blood.

The folder of pictures lay on the grass under George's hand. He knelt down beside the body and pulled the folder out, encountering no resistance from the limp fingers. The reality of what he'd done began to seep into his consciousness, and he glanced at George's face, wanting to deny the truth of his actions.

A shout made him glance up, and he saw the ghostly figure of Tully Jackson appear out of the darkness.

He didn't turn around. He knew his presence had been discovered, and every instinct told him that he had only moments to escape before he was recognized. Moving quickly, he reached inside George's jacket for his wallet, then tore the watch off his wrist. He ran to the back of the tee, ducked between two weeping cherry trees and skirted along the edge of the next fairway until he reached the heavier brush along the fence separating the golf course from the parking lot at the boat landing.

Jamming the pictures and the wallet in his pocket, he slipped the knife back into the sheath at his side and rebuttoned his shirt. He reached the chain-link fence, racing along beside it until he spotted a low-hanging tree limb. Sprinting toward it, he reached up and grabbed the limb, using his momentum to lift him as he vaulted over the fence and landed in a heap on the other side.

Tully's car was only five feet away. He crept past it and spotted the partially open window. Careful not to touch the car, he rubbed the fingerprints off George's watch and stuffed it through the opening.

He didn't waste any more time. Keeping to the shadows, he ran along the fence to the far end of the parking lot where he had left his car after the poker game, tucked tightly against a thicket where it was almost invisible. Keys in hand, he climbed into the car, started it and drove quickly out of the parking lot.

Reliving the night of George's death, the Warrior's breathing grew ragged. He could close his eyes and feel the rapid beat of his pulse, a remembered combination of exhilaration in the act of killing and fear of discovery and punishment.

It had always been that way. An intermingling of pleasure and pain. Counting coup. He had always thought of killings as death coups. Just another variation on the tests.

A cough reminded him that he was not alone in the funeral home. He needed to stay in the moment.

He took a step forward and placed his hand on George's shoulder. The suit material was smooth against his fingers. He would have liked to touch his friend's chest, to see if the wound would emit any vibrations, but knew that action would spell disaster.

"Goodbye, George," he said and silently turned away.

The food was getting cold. Tyler hadn't touched it since the man left it. It was the second dish. He should eat and go to sleep. His tummy hurt. His nose was stuffy and his eyes itched. That always happened when he cried. Even so he didn't make any sound.

He heard the scrabble of the mice and pulled a corner of the blanket over his head. He lay on his side on the bed shelf, his ears covered, and stared at the food.

It was the brown meat. He liked it because it was easy to chew. The white meat was always cut in little squares, but it wasn't juicy. The tiny green trees were good, but he was glad the dish had lots of the orange sticks. They made a snapping sound when he chewed them.

Was Mouse Ears gone?

A tear slid from the corner of his eye and landed on the back of his hand. He had dropped the feather. He didn't want to squish it tight, so when he tried to put it where the man told him, it fell on the ground. When they got back to the room, the man took another mouse. Tyler kept his head up like he was told, but he made his eyes see funny so he wouldn't be able to tell which mouse was gone.

Scritch. Scritch.

Even with the blanket over his ears he heard the sound. He hammered his heels against the shelf bed. The dish bounced. His stomach would keep hurting until he counted the mice. He pushed the blanket away.

He reached out and grasped the top of the mouse cage. Resting his chin on the table, he closed his eyes and pulled the cage closer until the cold wires touched his forehead. Slowly he opened his eyes.

Shorty. Tiny. And the last mouse was under the shavings. Tyler poked a finger inside the cage. Nose twitching, Mouse Ears peeked up at him.

Tyler smiled.

"That's quite an outfit Mrs. Gleason is wearing," Grant said, his eyes intent on Nell as she stood talking to Walter Kondrat, another one of the poker players, on the far side of the bookstore. "I suppose it's suitable for a memorial dinner in Wisconsin."

"Your trouble, Holbrook, is that you've been hanging out too long with the trendy set. You're an arrogant snob." Maggie's voice was sharp, offended by his caustic remark.

Unlike Nell's usual attire of sweat suits, liberally dabbed with paint, or something from her vast collection of denim, she was wearing a black cotton ensemble consisting of a batwinged blouse with lace inserts, a mid-calf, tiered lace skirt and black open-toed wedgies, bound to her feet by black hemplike ropes that snaked around her legs in a spiral. A small black bow was tucked into the salmon-tinted curls just above her ear.

Despite the gravity of the occasion, Maggie had to chuckle, tipping her head slightly to get the full effect. "The outfit suits Nell," she said. "She's an artist."

"Landscapes or poodles?" Grant asked.

"Lawyers are always quick to judge. You should keep a more open mind, Holbrook," Maggie said. "Nell is a splash painter."

"A what?"

"You know. Like Jackson Pollock."

"You're kidding."

He stared across the room, and she could see he was having trouble coming to grips with this revised vision of the woman he had taken to be an eccentric.

"I've only been in her studio a few times," Maggie said. "It's an experience. The floors are covered with several layers of old sailcloth she uses as tarpaulins. After she's prepped a canvas, she lays it in the center of the floor. She works on large surfaces. Usually six feet by eight feet. Then when she's all ready, she puts on some classic CDs. Her favorite is Pink Floyd's *The Wall.*"

"Now I know you're kidding."

"The different paints are mixed in old coffee cans until they're just the right consistency. Then, with the music blaring, she moves around the canvas, hurling paint with long-handled brushes until she's satisfied."

Grant's eyes had a glazed look as she finished. "Is it a hobby or does she sell them?"

"She sold the last one for twenty thousand to a woman in Beaver Dam who wanted what she called a 'sofa-sized' painting to draw together all the colors in her living room."

"Good God Almighty!"

Grant stared at Maggie as if trying to decide if she was making the whole story up. When he saw she was serious, he bowed his head, placing a hand over his heart.

"My apologies to Mrs. Gleason and the entire state of Wisconsin for my earlier cutting remarks," he said. "If Hamilton hadn't warned me to stay away from her, I'd go over and apologize."

"Ham's right," Maggie said, placing her hand on his arm. "Nell's as sharp as they come. She'd be the first one to suspect you aren't who you say you are."

"I'll remember that," he said. As he saw Doris Blessington heading in their direction, he wandered away.

Maggie followed him with her eyes. She'd been very aware of him over the last two days. He'd handled himself well at the wake yesterday, the memorial Mass this afternoon, and now the dinner at the bookstore. He'd kept a low profile, not intruding on the other mourners but speaking to them easily when they approached him.

She had worried initially that his intensity and the fact he was a stranger to the people in Delbrook would make him the focus of undue attention, but he blended in so easily that his presence barely raised a ripple of conjecture.

"I think George would be pleased," Doris Blessington said as she kissed Maggie's cheek and looked around the room. "The memorial Mass was very touching, and I'm sure he would have been delighted with the dinner here at the bookstore."

"I thought Jake would feel more comfortable here," Maggie said. "I can't take credit for the other arrangements. George had already done that."

"You don't say."

Doris leaned closer to Maggie, eyes glinting at the possibility of some tidbit of gossip. Her behavior didn't ruffle Maggie. The police chief's wife was known for her personality rather than her intelligence. An adorable child, a beautiful teenager and a handsome married woman, she had been flattered, pampered and protected all her life.

Since Doris was never required to be anything but decorative or entertaining, she found her calling in providing the latest in local news and rumor, reporting it without passing judgment or reveling in the transgressions of others. She didn't hesitate to disclose her own family's affairs, so people seldom took offense. On the other hand, they rarely shared secrets with her.

"After Mark died, George made all the decisions for his own funeral," Maggie said. "He told Father Cusick that he wanted a simple service and gave him a list of songs for the Mass. He'd arranged and paid for everything at the funeral home."

"How extraordinary," Doris said. "He must not have wanted you to have to deal with things after what you went through with Mark."

"A perfect example of George's thoughtfulness," Maggie said. "It really helped Jake to know that his grandfather had planned things and that we were carrying out his wishes."

The older woman's eyes filled with tears. "He was so very proud of Jake. This last year with you and the boy here in Delbrook made a great difference in George's life."

"I hope so," Maggie said, reaching in her pocket for a tissue, which she pressed into Doris's hand. "I wouldn't trade a moment of our time with him. For Jake's sake, as well as my own, I wish it hadn't come to such an abrupt ending."

She looked over at the children's room where Jake and Kenny Rossiter had their heads together in a whispered conversation.

Oh damn! They're up to something, Maggie thought.

Under normal circumstances, she would have been quick to investigate, but after the last several days, she was expecting some rebellion or at least an emotional outburst to counter the somber atmosphere that had surrounded the boys.

The wake and the memorial Mass had been difficult for Jake, but now that the reality of his grandfather's death was beginning to sink in, he was accepting it better than she'd expected. Not that he hadn't loved George, but his grandfather's death was far less gut-wrenching than the major trauma of his father's death.

"I can see that Jake and the Rossiter boy are still thick as thieves."

"An apt comment, Doris. I was thinking much the same thing."

"The friendship has been good for both of them. Jake has brought Kenny out of his shell. When his mother left three years ago, Kenny was so withdrawn that it was worrisome."

"Does Kenny see his mother at all?" Maggie asked.

"No. No one knows where she went. She was here in Delbrook one day and then the next it was as if she'd been erased from the face of the earth. I never asked Hugh. I don't think anyone did."

"She was a local girl?"

"Yes. Her family lived just north of town. Julie Caldwell was a pretty young thing. Unfortunately she had such round heels I doubt if she could stand on the side of hill without falling on her back. Everyone suspected she was carrying on behind Hugh's back. My guess is that she found someone who was better in bed."

"That must have been awful for Kenny."

"Hugh took Kenny to work with him. His landscaping business wasn't as successful then as it is now, so he had more time for the boy. Hugh said he hoped the physical chores around the nursery would keep Kenny busy and too tired to dwell on his loneliness. He'd been a solitary child, content to play by himself. Hugh provided the structure and the companionship when he needed it most."

Maggie scanned the room, spotting Hugh's curly head rising above the knot of men talking beside the bar set up in the café area. It was strange that she didn't really know more about him. He wasn't one to talk about his life. He was a physical man, comfortable doing things rather than discussing them. If she ever hoped to have any kind of continuing relationship, she'd have to get him to open up.

Suddenly Hugh looked up, catching her watching him. He didn't smile, but there was an intensity to his glance that warmed her. Then he turned back to Charley Blessington, who was speaking. By the gravity of the expressions, she suspected George's death was the subject of the conversation.

"Tully Jackson is still missing," Doris said.

The non sequitur threw Maggie for a moment. "I wondered if he'd turned up. Do you really think he would attack George?"

Doris shrugged. "Charley always thought he was a public nuisance. The man's been a thorn in his side for years. Said it didn't look good having someone like Tully hanging around town. Unfortunately he couldn't think of any legal way to get rid of him."

"How are you doing, Maggie?" Nell asked.

Maggie had been so absorbed in Doris's conversation that she hadn't seen Nell's approach, and her heart leaped at the voice so close to her ear.

"Don't sneak up on me like that," she said, patting her chest for emphasis. "You could give me a heart attack."

"You know, Nell," Doris said, "on anyone else that outfit might look a dash outré. On you, it has genuine flair."

"Being an artist of mature years has certain advantages," Nell said, patting her salmon curls. "I can wear what I damn well please, and people consider it eccentric rather than just plain peculiar."

"George would have appreciated your dressing up for the occasion," Maggie said. "Those shoes are definitely a work of art. How are your feet doing?"

"Not good." She made a face. "You know sneakers are more my speed. Unfortunately they didn't look right."

"Well, ladies, Charley's giving me the signal, so I better take my leave. Let me know, dear, if there's anything I can do."

Doris kissed Maggie on the cheek and walked over to join the men.

Nell leaned closer to whisper, "Did she have anything new to report?"

"No. Only that Charley and George had had what she called 'words' about a month ago and haven't been speaking. She didn't know what had caused the rift, but she said that luckily they had resolved it after dinner Saturday night, so that by the time the poker game started, they were back on friendly footing."

"Walter Kondrat was there, so I'll have to ask him if he knows what the fight was about," Nell said. "Typically male, however, he either won't have noticed or he'll tell me it was just a misunderstanding."

"Where is Walter?" Maggie asked. She glanced around the room, spotting the big man talking to Hamilton Rice on the far side of the dining room.

"I should have known he'd be with Ham," Nell said. "Rice doesn't look sixty-five. He was a good friend of my husband, you know. Once Ham moved down to Chicago, we didn't see that much of him. I always liked him. He's got a wicked sense of humor."

"Don't I know it," Maggie said. "I met him when I was first dating Mark, and he loved to tease me. We saw a lot of him when we lived in Chicago. Since Mark's death, only a couple times."

With his permanent tan and thatch of white hair, Ham was a good-looking man. He wasn't a great deal taller than Maggie was, but she thought of him as a big man with his broad shoulders, barrel chest and short but powerful legs. He moved with deliberation, walking with a rolling gait that got him to his destination without any appearance of haste.

His blue eyes twinkled out at the world from a nest of wrinkles. He had been George's oldest friend, and she was grateful that he had come to Delbrook to lend his support.

Nell's eyes narrowed as Grant Holbrook joined the other two men. Her gaze was intense as she stared at Grant, who was bracketed by the two older men.

"I didn't get a chance to talk to that young man either yesterday or earlier in the evening," Nell said. "Walter just told me he's Mark's cousin. And he came all the way to Wisconsin for the funeral?"

"Yes." Maggie licked her dry lips. "He's related to George's wife."

"Edna?"

"Ham said he doesn't bear much of a family resemblance to Edna. She was not a handsome woman, I gather. Ham said Mark got his good looks from George's side of the family. I never knew Edna. She died when Mark was in his teens."

Maggie knew she was babbling, and she pressed her lips together to keep from blurting out any additional information.

"Yes," Nell said, her voice thoughtful. "One of those really nasty cancers. She was in a lot of pain for about a year. I used to stop by for a visit a couple times a week. To help her pass the time, I taught her to tat."

At Maggie's blank look, Nell rolled her eyes.

"It was a different age when I was growing up. Needlework, knitting, sewing were all considered necessary accomplishments for a young woman. Tatting, you ignorant child, is a form of lace making. You use a hand shuttle to weave delicate patterns that you can add as edging on a handkerchief or a tablecloth."

"I think I saw that demonstrated once on a PBS special."

Maggie tried to keep a straight face, but Nell caught the amusement in her voice and smacked her on the wrist. "You need to show a little more respect for your elders."

Maggie grinned an apology. "Mark never talked much about his mother. For that matter, neither did George."

"To be honest, Edna was only a presence in the household. She cooked, cleaned and sewed, making as little fuss as possible. I doubt if George ever paid her much mind. He was never unkind; he just never seemed to notice her. As far as he was concerned, her only real achievement was in giving birth to Mark."

"How sad," Maggie said.

"She was an unhappy and lonely woman. We really only got to know each other in that last year before she died. Not friends. Just two women talking."

Nell turned away from Maggie, her eyes resting on Grant. Maggie could feel the tension building up in the muscles across her back. She didn't know what was coming, but she didn't think she was going to like it.

"I don't know if you knew that Edna was from a little farming town in Minnesota." Nell's voice was soft but clear. "The summer she turned twenty, a tornado ripped through the town. It wiped out everything in its path."

"How awful," Maggie said.

"In those days there were no early warning signals, so the death toll was high." Nell stared at Grant, a calculating expression on her face. "The tornado killed everyone in Edna's family. When she came to Delbrook she was alone. She had no relatives. No family at all."

Maggie sucked in her breath at Nell's words.

"I know you're stunned," Nell said, bending close to Maggie so she could whisper in her ear, "but the man is clearly an impostor."

"An impostor?"

"Don't be frightened, dear." Nell took hold of Maggie's elbow. "We'll work our way over to Charley Blessington. He'll know what to do about this. For all we know, Grant Holbrook could be the man responsible for George's death."

CHAPTER
TEN

"GRANT HOLBROOK might not have killed George," Nell said, "but he is an impostor."

Maggie could not have spoken if her life depended on it. It was the very thing she had feared when Grant first concocted the charade. She could feel the rush of heat rising to paint her cheeks with guilty color under the intense scrutiny of the older woman.

"You're a party to this deception, Maggie?" Nell's grip tightened on her arm as she stared at Maggie in rising bewilderment.

"Yes. But. I-I . . ."

Before she could do more than stammer out a few words, Grant was beside her. He held out his hand as if he knew she was in need of support, and she grasped it with a sigh of relief at his rescue.

"George's wife Edna had no living relatives," she said, by way of explanation.

He faced Nell without flinching, one eyebrow lifted in amusement. "Then I assume you have already figured out that I am not one of Edna's shirttail relatives," he said.

"I see nothing funny about this subterfuge, Mr. Holbrook." She straightened her spine, lips pressed together in disapproval. "I don't want to create a scene, but I intend to speak to Chief Blessington about this situation."

"Don't get on your high horse, Nell." Hamilton Rice stepped into the space between Nell and Grant. "Not until you know more."

Ham's watery blue eyes crinkled in a tanned and leathery face. His voice wasn't deep but had a shivery warmth that made listeners believers. He opened his mouth as if he wanted to reassure her and was only waiting for her permission. Nell was unmoved by his charm.

"Don't con me, you old reprobate," she snapped. "Can any of you give me one good reason why I shouldn't denounce Mr. Holbrook?"

"I can," Grant said. He kept his voice low, words enunciated clearly. "I think George Collier was murdered and it was made to look like a robbery."

Nell's body jerked as if she'd taken a blow. Ham put his hand beneath her elbow and Maggie moved closer to steady her. Grant was all too aware of the people milling around the bookstore and knew that at any moment someone might realize that some drama was being played out in their midst. Despite that, he remained still, letting her focus her attention on him.

"I apologize for upsetting you," he said. "Both Maggie and Ham have had time to get used to this idea. I swear to you my impersonation is for a very good reason. I know it's a lot to ask, but do you suppose you could trust the three of us—all right, the two of them—until we have an opportunity to explain?"

"Please, Nell," Maggie said. "It's very important."

Grant wasn't sure what the older woman's decision would have been had Jake not chosen that particular moment to join the group. Nell's eyes softened as the young boy slipped his hand into his mother's and leaned his head against her arm.

"Kenny's going home, Mom."

Grant could see that the general exodus was beginning. Nell grimaced in indecision, but with one more glance at Jake, she sighed in obvious surrender.

"While your mom says goodbye to your grandfather's friends, Jake, why don't you and I keep Mr. Holbrook company?"

Grant could only smile as the older woman took hold of his arm and Jake's hand and led them, rather like recalcitrant children, to a circle of chairs in the teen section beneath the staircase. With a worried look over her shoulder, Maggie followed Ham Rice over to the people at the door.

Maggie's feet hurt from standing so long on the hardwood floors: Her mind was on rote as she bid people goodbye and thanked them for coming. As things slowed down, she looked around for Kim Shearman, who had been in charge of the buffet table. The heavyset woman was carrying a cardboard box into the laundry room.

"Kim?" Maggie called, following the woman inside.

"Everything's all cleaned up, Maggie. Did everything go all right?"

"Wonderfully well. I just came back to thank you for helping out here tonight. George always said you did a fine job when you served them on poker nights."

A wide smile stretched Kim's mouth even as her eyes filled with tears. She set the box down on the top of the dryer, brushing at her eyes with a corner of her apron.

"They've been meeting at the club for the last twenty years. Ever since I was married. Your father-in-law was such a nice man," she said. "I still can't believe Tully Jackson stabbed him."

"The police don't know that for sure, Kim."

"Everyone was talking about it at the country club. It's real creepy that Tully ran off. He could be hiding anywhere around here. I'm that scared about going out to the parking lot at night. My husband drove me over here tonight and he's waitin' outside till I'm done."

"That's a good idea. No point in taking any chances until they find out what happened."

"Delbrook was always safe as a church picnic," Kim said. "It's like bizarre."

"I know what you mean," Maggie said. "Violent attacks happen in big cities, not in towns like this."

" 'Sides, Saturday night the card game was real quiet. Not like some weeks. Sometimes they'd fight all during the game and one of the players would just get so disgusted they'd throw stuff. You know, cards or chips. Nothing big."

"George said it could be a pretty noisy group."

"He should know. A couple a years ago, he was the worst of the lot." Kim snorted. "It was after your husband died. If you pardon my saying, George was drinkin' quite a bit in them days."

"That's what I heard. He didn't have much to drink on Saturday, did he?"

"No. He had a manhattan before dinner, but he didn't even finish it. Walter Kondrat was doin' the honors, if you know what I mean." Kim shook her head in disgust. "Between you and me, Mrs. Collier, Walter was really carrying a load."

Walter was a big man with a bushy mustache. He'd always reminded Maggie of a walrus, and she couldn't picture him staggering around drunk. Her amusement must have been apparent, because Kim lowered her voice, partially covering her mouth with the corner of her apron so her words wouldn't carry out to the bookstore.

"It ain't a pretty sight," she said. "Walter gets real feisty. Him and George had a nasty go-round after dinner."

"A fight?"

"Just words. Walter was real hot like. It happened right outside the ladies' room. That's how I heard it. Walter said it wasn't any of George's business."

"What wasn't?"

"I don't know. I missed that part," Kim said. "All I know is it was somethin' that George thought Walter should quit doing. He said it wasn't fair to anyone. Walter told George he better keep his mouth shut or he'd be asking for trouble. George said it was too late, she already knew."

"She?" Maggie asked, totally mystified.

Kim shrugged her shoulders. "I didn't hear anyone's name. Walter was getting madder and madder, and I got a little worried. I was just sure he was going to have a stroke and keel over. So I went back and flushed the toilet again just to let 'em know I was in the john. By the time I come out they was gone. I was that relieved."

"How strange. Walter never mentioned anything to me. Were they still fighting during the poker game?"

Kim shook her head. "When I got back to the dining room, George was pumpin' coffee into Walter, and by the time the cards were dealt, the booze had worn off a bit. It was a real quiet game. I was glad when George won the last pot."

"It was a grand way to end the day." Maggie patted Kim on the shoulder. "I'm sure you're tired and want to finish and go home. I appreciate your sharing your thoughts tonight. You've been very kind."

Kim picked up the box full of food trays and carried it over to the back door where she already had a stack of things.

"Let me help you," Maggie said.

She opened the back door and waved to Kim's husband, who was leaning on the side of his truck talking to Frank Woodman, the manager of the country club, who'd arranged everything for the buffet supper. The men hurried over and piled the bags and boxes into the pickup, and Kim and her husband drove away.

"You look tired, Maggie," Frank said. "Everything all right?"

"I'm pretty beat, but I'm glad I found you. I wanted to say thanks for making this such a lovely evening."

"It's the least I can do. You know how sorry I am about George." He took her hand and, after a moment of hesitation, leaned over and kissed her cheek. "You warm enough?"

Maggie nodded. It was a beautiful September night. Indian summer–like with a clear, almost cloudless sky.

"Who would have thought we'd have to be afraid in Delbrook?" Frank said.

"A sign of the times. Every time I turn on the news I get more frightened for Jake's safety. Gang attacks. Home invasions. School shootings." Even the words frightened her. Shivering, she took a deep breath of the fresh air. "It's hard to even think of violence on a night like this."

"Too true. " Frank smoothed a hand over the top of his graying hair. "I just wish I knew what happened. I've gone over and over everything with Charley, and I'm just utterly mystified."

Maggie didn't know Frank well. She'd seen him around town and when she'd gone to the country club. Tall, somewhat gaunt with even features, but nothing that set him apart. George had described him as competent and efficient. The kind of man who could be counted on to do his work with little complaint and retire after years of service without leaving much of a legacy behind.

"Did you play poker Saturday night?" she asked.

"Just for a little while. Brent Prentice was stuck at home, waiting for a long-distance call. Connie asked if I'd sit in until he arrived." Frank stared up at the sky, his voice contemplative. "By the time Brent got there at nine I was looking for any excuse to get out of the game."

"Losing your shirt?"

"No. Everyone seemed out of sorts. Walter was sulking for some reason, and Hugh Rossiter and Charley Blessington got into an argument over Camp Delbrook."

"The camp?" Maggie asked.

"I don't know if you're aware that there's going to be a massive rehab of the camp this year. Right after the fall cleanup. They're going to modernize a lot of the cottages and the main buildings. The mews is one of the buildings up for rehabbing. Hugh was furious that he hadn't been consulted, because the birds get upset pretty easily and there was barely enough time to move them to temporary quarters."

"Why wasn't Hugh told earlier?" Maggie asked.

"Well according to Hugh, Charley Blessington is on the board of directors and deliberately kept him in the dark so that one of Charley's cronies would get the contract, which included new landscaping. Saturday night, Hugh made a couple of comments about political influence, and Charley got on his high horse." Frank chuckled. "Hugh has lived in Delbrook all his life, and of course the chief's friend moved here from Illinois last year. You know how the folks around here feel about that."

"I was lucky when I moved from Chicago. Since my mother had lived here and George was a resident, I wasn't considered a carpetbagger."

"Illinois residents get blamed for a lot of the tourist troubles. The locals think they come to Wisconsin and use up the natural resources and screw up the environment. In truth, the nonresidents put millions of dollars into the economy that helps us maintain our parks and tourist attractions."

"You should run for mayor," Maggie said.

He reddened slightly. "Connie Prentice is talking to the Lakeshore party about drafting me for the next election. She's trying to convince me to accept."

"I think you'd be an excellent mayor. You certainly do a fine job running the country club, so how much different could it be to run the town?"

Maybe Frank wasn't flashy, but he would certainly be an asset to the town council. The people who worked at the club appeared contented with his leadership, and he dealt with the guests graciously without being dogmatic or obsequious.

"If Connie's in favor of it, you know Brent will back you," Maggie said.

"He owes me big time for the night of the poker game. He missed dinner, but I had the kitchen hold a plate for him. You know how fussy he is about his schedule. Once he'd eaten he was in better spirits, but by that time he'd ticked off Connie and she'd left in a huff."

"These poker players must be a cantankerous lot. Although I heard it was a quiet game until George won the final jackpot."

"The group gets a little ornery sometimes, but they manage to work it out." Frank chuckled. "I'm glad George won, but even that was strange. He rarely bluffs, so when he just kept betting, everyone dropped out. In my opinion, George wasn't bluffing, he was distracted and forgot he was holding only two pair."

"Why was George distracted?"

"I'm not sure. He'd been upbeat, showing off those photos of Jake's birthday party. He passed them around the table, and we all had a good laugh. There was a lot of reminiscing about kids and parties during dinner and even in the early part of the poker game. I was sitting across from George when I noticed how still he was."

Maggie leaned against the door frame as she listened to Frank.

"His face was pale and his mouth was pulled tight as if he were in pain. I thought he was having a heart attack. Suddenly he pulls the pile of pictures out and stares at the top one as if something has struck him. He looks up and catches my eye. Shaking his head, he stuffs the photos into his jacket and picks up the newly dealt poker hand."

"Those were the birthday pictures?"

"Yes," Frank said. "He plays several more hands, and he appears to have shaken off what was troubling him. I was still concerned, so I kept an eye on him, although this time I didn't let him catch me at it. About ten minutes later, George pulls the photos out of his pocket again, stares at the top one and then slowly flips through the rest. He stops once more about halfway through, then shuffles them together and puts them back in his pocket."

Maggie's nerves hummed with excitement. What had George seen in the pictures? Was it possible that Grant's premise was correct and that George had seen Tyler in one of the pictures?

"Did George say anything?"

"He said he needed to make a phone call. The group was ready for a break at that point, so there was a lot of milling around. When the game started again, he seemed in better spirits but was quieter than usual," Frank said. "I wondered if the earlier reminiscing had gotten him thinking about Mark. I couldn't help but notice, when I was looking at the photos, how much Jake resembles his father. My thought was that George was feeling Mark's loss and that was why he was so distracted during the card game."

"It's possible, I suppose," Maggie said. "I wish I'd seen the pictures."

"Don't you have them?"

"No. All of George's things were sent to the police lab. Charley gave me a list of what they had, but the photographs weren't on it. I've asked around, but nobody seems to know what happened to them. I don't suppose George left them at the club."

"Not that I'm aware of. I'll check with the dining room staff, but if anyone found them, they'd turn them in to me." Frank patted her arm. "They've probably just been misplaced. They'll probably turn up once things settle down."

Maggie wasn't convinced of that. If what Grant had suggested was true, Maggie suspected the photographs had already been destroyed.

"Would you like something to drink, Mrs. Gleason?" Grant asked. "I think Ham has the front door covered, and Maggie's got the back."

He caught a flash of amusement in Nell's eyes and felt some encouragement. She hadn't denounced him when she first discovered the deception, but he didn't fool himself that the main crisis had been averted. She was a smooth old gal. It had only been postponed.

"Could I have a Coke, Aunt Nell?" Jake asked. "Kenny and I only had one before dinner."

"You can think of this as a test," Grant said.

Nell sniffed. "One Coke for Jake. Make mine brandy. A double."

Grant poured the drinks, handed them out and sat down again. Although the older woman's attention was focused on Jake, he knew she was aware of his every move, assessing him as he talked to the boy.

"Your mother says you like to fish. Did you do any fishing when you lived in Chicago?"

"A couple times my dad took me. We didn't catch anything. I kept getting my hook stuck." He took several long sips of his Coke, then carefully set the glass on one of the tables from the café area. "Mom packed us a big lunch, and we sat on these huge rocks and watched the boats go in and out of the harbor."

"I know where you were. That's one of my favorite spots for boat watching. Which do you like better? Sailboats or motorboats?"

"Motorboats." He blew through his lips, a sputtering engine sound. "The sailboats are way too slow. The best part was when a monster sailboat almost smashed on the rocks. That would have been cool. But it didn't."

"Now I see why reality TV shows are so popular with the young male set," Nell said. "The more carnage, the better the ratings."

"Think it's the testosterone?" Grant asked.

Despite herself, Nell chuckled. "That and shit for brains," she said under her breath.

At the unexpected comment, Grant inhaled part of his drink. He coughed several times to catch his breath, but when Maggie and Ham arrived, his eyes were tearing and he was still sucking in air.

"Really, Nell, you don't have to kill the man," Ham said with a quick glance at the amusement on the older woman's face.

"I'm OK," Grant managed to gasp out. "Everyone gone?"

"Yes," Ham said. "I hope you don't mind, Nell, but I told Walter I'd take you home later since I haven't had a chance to talk to you."

"How about a nightcap?" Maggie said. "It's getting late and Jake is itching to get out of his dress-up clothes."

"Mom made me wear my new school shoes," he said, raising his legs straight out so they could inspect his shoes.

"Very good looking," Ham said in admiration. "That's a dynamite shine."

"Grampa helped me pick them out." Jake's lip quivered.

"Time for bed, honey," Maggie said, walking over to the counter where she'd left her purse. It wasn't on the shelf. She looked around in growing bewilderment.

"Problem, kiddo?" Ham said.

"I can't find my purse," she said.

"Are you sure you left it here?"

"Yes," she answered shortly.

"What's it look like?" Grant said, joining them along with Nell and Jake.

"It's navy blue with three gold X's."

The group fanned out, searching the bookstore.

"I found it," Jake yelled from the bathroom.

Maggie hurried over to find him picking up the items that were spread out on the floor beside the washbasin.

"You probably left it on the sink and someone knocked it off," Nell said.

"Nice work, Jake," Maggie said. She took the purse and kissed him on top of the head. "Now say your goodnights and I'll tuck you in."

Upstairs, she helped Jake get into his pajamas and then sent him in to wash. Picking up her purse from the nightstand, she carried it out to the kitchen. She hadn't wanted to make an issue of it, but she knew with a certainty that she had left her purse on the shelf under the counter not in the bathroom.

Opening the clasp, she checked to see if her wallet was inside. It was there and so was the fifty dollars she had placed in the bill compartment. Lipstick, comb, handkerchief and other odds and ends.

At the funeral home she had placed the sympathy cards in her purse as she left. She pulled them out and noticed that each of the envelopes had been opened. The list of George's effects that had been given to her at the hospital had been taken out of the zippered pocket where she'd placed it.

Someone had taken her purse into the bathroom to search it.

Her hands shook as she put everything back inside. It gave her a sick feeling knowing that someone had touched her things. Who had taken her purse, and more importantly, what were they looking for?

"What you're asking me to believe," Nell Gleason said, "is that George's death was actually a premeditated murder committed by someone who was at the country club on Saturday night?"

"That's exactly what we're trying to explain to you," Ham said.

The voices drifted up the curved staircase from the bookstore as Maggie stood in the doorway to the second-floor apartment. Sliding her hand along the smooth oak banister, she walked partway down, then sat on the steps. Resting her forehead against one of the stair posts, she looked between the spindles at the group seated at the round mahogany table in the main room of the bookstore.

Grant leaned back in the captain's chair across from Nell, with Ham between them facing an empty chair.

Grant raised his head, the only one aware of her presence. His eyes were steady on hers, but she could read nothing in the dark brown gaze.

"If you believe that the killer was not a passing stranger, but someone in Delbrook, why haven't you gone to the police?" Nell's voice was shrill with indignation. "Why in God's name are you keeping this secret?"

"For the simple reason, Nell, that we don't know who committed the murder." Grant turned his full attention on the older woman, but Maggie realized much of what he said was for her benefit. "For all we know, someone on the police force may be the person who attacked George."

"You don't mean someone," Nell said. "You mean Charley Blessington."

Her words were met by silence. Nell's mouth pulled into a tight line of alarm as she swung her gaze between the two men. Maggie must have made some sound, because her friend turned her head and saw her sitting on the stairs.

"Dear God, Maggie, is this what you believe too?"

"I don't know what I believe." She rose to her feet and continued down the stairs to join the group. "It's only just dawned on me that this whole situation is so far out of my understanding that I feel as if I've just fallen down the rabbit hole. And I'm very frightened."

Ham stood up and came around the table to meet her at the bottom of the steps. He opened his arms, and she stepped into his embrace, feeling an immediate easing of the fear and confusion that had surrounded her since George's death. She felt as if the cavalry had arrived.

"I've barely had a chance to say hello to you," Maggie said, kissing his tanned cheek. "I'm so glad you're here. This is a god-awful mess."

Ham gave her a reassuring hug, then released her. "Jake's asleep?" he asked, jerking his head toward the second floor.

"Yes. I sat with him for a while after he dozed off to make sure. I don't want him hearing any of this. He's got enough to manage just dealing with George's death."

"Agreed."

Maggie stepped closer and spoke for Ham's ears only. "Can we believe this man?"

He looked over her shoulder, his eyes assessing Grant, then returning to Maggie.

"Yes," he said. "Grant and I have mutual friends who vouch for him. He may be a bit uptight and anal, but he's got a reputation for being honest and ethical."

"That's high praise for a lawyer," she said. "He has his moments of charm, but I don't think he trusts me any more than I trust him."

"If you'd hit me in the head with a canoe paddle, I might be a bit standoffish, too," Ham said, a wide smile accompanying the raising of his eyebrows.

"That was before I even knew him," she said. "I've been tempted to hit him again every time he brings it up. He's a bully. He's got his own agenda, and he's trying to guilt me into following it."

Ham's eyes were serious as he stared across the room at Grant. "He's hurting, kiddo. Like you and Jake, he's sustained a hellava loss."

Maggie sighed. "I hate it that you're right, Ham. I'll try to be less hostile and hope he's worthy of the consideration."

"Since I got here yesterday, we've talked a fair amount, and I'm getting a feel for who he is. He's the kind of man who doesn't like to delegate. If he had his way, he would have come up and nosed around on his own. Instead, you and I know who he is and what he's looking for, and now Nell is questioning him. It shook him up that she uncovered his charade so easily. He believes you and I have motivation for covering for him, but he doesn't know about her."

She turned her body until she had a good view of Grant. He was listening to Nell, his expression fixed in what Maggie thought of as his lawyer look. His expression was attentive, his brown eyes absorbed in observing every movement, yet despite his stillness, she suspected his mind was buzzing with decisions to be made.

It was interesting to watch him without being the object of his scrutiny. Despite his scar, Grant was a handsome man.

After years of dealing with Mark's infidelities, Maggie was less susceptible than most to the automatic confidence engendered by a good-looking face. Mark had used his appearance to manipulate and persuade. With a calculated look, he tried, usually successfully, to burrow deep into her emotions to get what he wanted. Worst of all, he had been able to lie with an ease that left her shaken in her own ability to judge character.

"What was your gut reaction when you first heard his story?" Ham asked. "Did you believe him?"

"Not at first," she said. "Even now, I don't want to believe him, but the more I hear the more I'm beginning to think his premise is correct. He's very compelling. When I listen to him I'm convinced that the story is true. It's only when I get away from him that it seems too bizarre. What do you think?"

Ham looked thoughtful.

"I have absolutely no doubt that he believes what he's telling us. The question that comes to mind is why he's so convinced that Tyler could be in Delbrook. I think we need to examine the entire picture so we know exactly which pieces are missing."

Maggie followed him back to the table, sitting in the empty chair beside Nell. The older woman reached out and squeezed her hand.

"I don't know what to make of all this, dear," she said. "So much to take in."

While Maggie had been upstairs with Jake, Grant and Ham had told Nell about Tyler's disappearance and the call from George that had brought Grant to Delbrook. It was clear that Nell was upset by the awful revelations, but she appeared to be taking the whole thing in stride. Whether it was her age or her personality, Nell had a capacity to listen without making judgments, keeping her mind open to even the most outrageous of theories.

"There's something that has been bothering me, Grant," Ham said as he sat down. "After George called me asking about the missing child, I did a bit of checking into the case. I went online and downloaded a lot of the articles in the Cleveland papers about Tyler's disappearance. It was grim but fascinating reading. What I'm wondering is why you haven't mentioned the other kidnappings."

"Other kidnappings?" Maggie asked.

The jagged scar stood out as the muscles rippled along Grant's jaw. From the glare he shot Ham, it was obvious that he wanted to discuss only George's death and his nephew's kidnapping.

"Well, Mr. Holbrook," Nell said. "If you expect us to give you any further help, you need to come clean."

Grant's head was bowed, his face in shadow. It intrigued Maggie that he had an ability to sit motionless without the usual nervous twitches others had when they were in a quandary. As a lawyer he would have learned to take a quick assessment of his options and then choose the one most suited to the situation.

"You're right," he said. He raised his head, his lips pursed as if his decision to speak had left a bad taste in his mouth. "When Tyler was taken we assumed it was by some kind of sexual predator."

Maggie shivered at the words. She wondered if she'd ever again look at the world the same. Delbrook had been a safe haven, but in the last twenty-four hours an evil presence had invaded the town. Like a child, she wanted to cover her ears but forced herself to listen to Grant's words.

"My sister and brother-in-law thought it was some local molester," he continued, "and that if we found him, Tyler would be returned. As a lawyer I've seen too much to be that sanguine. I was aware that after four or five days the chances of a quick solution to any case are poor. It was only later in the investigation that we discovered what we were up against."

Grant paused.

"The kidnapping fit a very specific pattern. It had happened before. In another city. In another state. Two other children had been taken in circumstances similar to Tyler's."

"Were the children found?" Nell asked the question that Maggie was too afraid to ask.

Grant didn't speak for a moment, and when he did, it was apparent he was upset.

"The boy was located and returned to his parents. The girl was found, but it was too late. She was dead."

CHAPTER
ELEVEN

"ONE OF THE CHILDREN DIED? Murdered?" Nell's question was a horrified whisper.

"The girl was dead, but there was no hard evidence to prove it was murder." Grant bit off the words.

In his own mind, he had always considered it murder. If the child hadn't been kidnapped, she wouldn't have died.

"Why the hell didn't you tell me about the other children when you first told me about Tyler?" Maggie asked.

Maggie's face was flushed with anger and her hands were clenched on the edge of the table.

"I wanted to keep it simple," he said.

"You thought if I was sympathetic to your story about your nephew, I wouldn't go to the police," Maggie said.

Grant shrugged at her accusation. He could feel the stillness of Hamilton and Nell but ignored them, focusing all his attention on Maggie.

"Tyler is my first priority. I will do whatever I can. Use any trick, any subterfuge to get the information I need to find him."

His temper threatened to overpower his common sense. He inhaled slowly through his nose to get his breathing back under control.

"Consider my position, for God's sake! When I left Chicago, I didn't know if George had kidnapped Tyler. I'd briefly checked on both George and Hamilton, but I still didn't know if either of them were law-abiding citizens. It occurred to me that they might be working some kind of scam to get the reward. Hell, for all I knew, they could have been the kidnappers."

"Once you understood that George wasn't involved," she said, "you could have told me."

"I'm a lawyer. I don't trust anyone. Once it became clear that you knew nothing about George's phone call to Hamilton, I felt reasonably comfortable telling you about Tyler's disappearance."

"But not everything," she said, her mouth thinned into a bitter line.

"Be fair, Maggie." He spoke directly to her, his voice soft. "Would you have held something back?"

She refused to meet his eyes, her head bent and her gaze fixed on the surface of the table.

"Yes," came the grudging reply.

Silence filled the room, but this time the edge of tension had dissipated slightly.

"All right, children," Ham said, "if you're done spitting, maybe we could move on. If we're going to get anywhere, we need, as the Gen Xers say, to be on the same page. Why don't I tell you what I've been able to find out, and Grant can fill in the blanks?"

Grant was grateful to be out of the spotlight. He was too close to the story. For twenty months he'd lived with the guilt that Tyler's disappearance was his fault. The boy was never out of his thoughts. In the daytime he could bury his emotions in work, but when he slept, his nightmares were filled with every kind of psychological and physical abuse of the boy.

Ham pulled a small notebook out of his pocket and flipped through several pages.

"Four years ago, a child disappeared from a movie theater in Detroit. His name was Eddie Harland, and he was five years old," he said. "No witnesses to a struggle. No ransom note. The kid's folks didn't have a lot of dough. They both worked to support Eddie and his two younger brothers. It was assumed that the boy had been kidnapped by a child molester."

"Eddie was at a movie? By himself?" Maggie asked. "Didn't anyone see anything?"

"No," Grant interrupted. "He was with his mother and his brothers. It happened when the show ended. The lights in the theater were still low. His mother was carrying the youngest and holding the hand of the middle child. Eddie was holding his brother's hand. When they got outside the theater and his mother discovered Eddie was missing, she went back inside to see if she could find him. It couldn't have been more than five minutes before she panicked and called for security. Just five minutes, but Eddie was gone."

Maggie's hand flew up to cover her mouth, and then she looked across the table at Grant. He could feel her reaction as if it were a physical thing.

"It makes me almost sick to my stomach to hear this," she said. "Every mother has probably had one of those moments when she loses contact with her child. First you can't believe it, and then, when you do, you're so shocked that you're almost paralyzed. After that, the panic sets in."

"That's exactly what my sister said when Tyler was taken," Grant said. "Barbara was so careful, and yet in the blink of an eye he was gone. Even when she started to search, she thought he had wandered away. Or was hiding."

Originally, when he'd told Maggie the story of Tyler's kidnapping, fear and horror had been her basic reactions. Once he explained his theory about George's murder, he could feel her resistance and resentment.

When he and Hamilton had arrived yesterday at the funeral home for the wake, Grant had caught the hint of hostility that accompanied Maggie's greeting. His presence in Delbrook frightened her. Without his story of kidnapping and murder, she would have accepted the fact that George had been accidentally killed in a botched robbery.

Grant felt some sympathy for Maggie's preferring to cast a blind eye to the presence of evil in her life. From what little he knew of her, until the tragic death of her husband, she had probably led the relatively uncomplicated life of a suburban wife and mother in Chicago. She was unprepared for the world of deception and danger that she found herself in.

Despite their mutual antipathy, he had been drawn to her from the beginning. He needed to fight any involvement. She represented a distraction to the focus and detachment required if he hoped to get to the bottom of this latest twist in Tyler's disappearance.

Only Tyler matters. He repeated the phrase in his mind, then turned his thoughts back to the discussion.

"The police investigated Eddie's disappearance thoroughly," Ham said, "but couldn't find a trace of the boy or any viable suspects."

"You said they found the first child. That was Eddie?" Nell asked Grant.

"Yes. Exactly one year from the day he was kidnapped in Detroit, Eddie was discovered in a Cineplex in Toledo, Ohio. The show was over, and the cleanup crew found him sitting all alone in the empty theater."

"Was he hurt?" Maggie asked.

Grant wasn't sure how to answer the question.

"According to what I read in the newspaper archives," Ham interjected, "Eddie was in excellent health. He was clean, physically fit and looked to have been well cared for during the year he was missing."

"One of the details omitted from most reports," Grant said, "was that Eddie was dressed in brand-new clothes: shirt, pants, underwear, shoes and socks. The movie theater was in a mall, and the clothes had been purchased that day. The police found the labels in a trash container in the men's room closest to the lobby of the theater."

"Fingerprints?" Nell asked.

Grant shook his head.

"The child was five when he was taken and was kept for a year?" Maggie asked.

"Yes. Exactly a year," Grant said.

"At six," she continued, "he would have been able to tell the police what happened to him, and despite the fact he was taken from Detroit and returned in Toledo, he should have been able to give the police enough information to conceivably pinpoint where he had been held. Maybe even who had kidnapped him."

When neither Ham nor Grant made any comment, she raised her head, glancing from one to the other, her eyebrows drawn together in question.

"When Eddie was found he couldn't speak," Grant said.

"Couldn't?" Nell leaned forward, her eyes intent. "Couldn't or wouldn't?"

"According to the doctors it's a matter of semantics." Grant clipped his words to hold back the emotion that swamped him when he thought about what trauma might have caused the child to go mute. "Nothing was wrong with the boy. Everything necessary for speech was intact. They examined him extensively and could find no physical reason for his inability to speak. Psychologically was another case altogether."

"When they examined him, did they find any indications of abuse?" Maggie bit her lip, waiting for the answer.

Grant spoke directly to her. "No. No bruises, broken bones, scars or any sign that he had been sexually abused. Aside from the fact that the boy was speechless, Eddie Harland was in better shape than when he disappeared."

Ham shifted restlessly in his chair.

"Eddie was returned three years ago. He's nine now," he said. "I picked up much of the basic story in a fast search on the Internet, but the one thing I didn't find was what the boy had to say when he finally broke his silence."

"Nothing," Grant said.

There was pain in the single word, Maggie thought as she looked at the man who until two days ago she'd never met. Grant took several deep breaths, as if to cover the break in his control.

"The parents refused to let the police see the boy after he was returned," Grant said. "They were grateful that he'd been returned to them, as they put it, 'undamaged.' They refused to let the police interview him. Then or later. Even after the second child was taken and the connection was made between the two cases, the parents denied all requests. And after Tyler, they refused again."

"Did Eddie ever speak?" Maggie asked.

Grant shook his head. "He began to talk shortly after he was returned. I got that information through a contact with the school Eddie attended. The principal obviously couldn't give me access to the child. All she would say was that, as far as she knew, he had never spoken about the year that he was missing."

Maggie pushed back from the table, her mind full of compassion for the child and his parents. Chilled, she rubbed her hands over her arms.

"I know how I'd feel if Jake was kidnapped. I'd feel enormous guilt that I had failed to protect him. Then the only thing that would matter would be to help him return to a normal life. I wouldn't let anyone near him to stir up memories of pain or fear." As she noticed the others looking at her, she shrugged. "Sure, I know it's big-time denial. But I wouldn't care. Only Jake would matter."

"I understand what you're saying, Maggie," Nell said, "but there's bound to be some payback for the psychological damage. Maybe not now, but what will happen in the coming years? I think Eddie's parents are making a major mistake."

"I do too," Maggie said, "but in a case like this, what does anyone know? Just in dealing with Jake after his father's death, I felt out of my depth, knowing when to push and when to back off. God knows what kind of resources Eddie's parents have to help them cope."

She stood up, too restless to remain seated. Walking around the bookstore, she touched the backs of the books, needing the tactile sensation of familiar and nonthreatening objects. Just talking about Jake had brought her fear for him close. She wanted to distance herself from the intensity of the emotions around the table. She reached out a hand to the poster that had been brought over from the funeral home and was now suspended on an easel beside the front door.

Jake had made the poster from pictures they had gathered the day after George died. Maggie and Nell had helped him make a collage. He had laboriously cut and pasted the photos onto the thick posterboard until he was satisfied that it gave a good representation of his grandfather's life and interests.

The center picture had been taken the year before Mark died. The perfect family, she thought, staring at the smiling foursome. George was in the middle, holding Jake, while Mark and Maggie stood on either side, separated by only a few feet and yet worlds apart.

Her lips quivered as she fought back tears. Two of the four are gone. Please, God, keep Jake safe.

"Tell us about the second child," Maggie said, without turning around.

"The next child was from Minneapolis," Ham said, picking up the story. "Her name was Noreen Flood. She was four years old. She disappeared from the Minnesota Zoo almost three years ago."

"How soon after the boy was found?" Nell asked.

"A month later," Ham said. "Eddie was returned in October, and Noreen was taken in November." He closed the notebook and continued. "One year from the day she was kidnapped, Noreen's body was discovered at the Milwaukee County Zoo in the moat around Monkey Island."

"Did she fall in? Did anyone see her?" Nell's questions ripped out in her impatience for answers.

"Her body was discovered by a security guard," Ham said. "It was late at night, and the zoo was closed. Despite extensive publicity, no one came forward to say they had seen or heard anything."

Maggie could hear Ham flip the pages of the notebook and waited for him to continue.

"According to the coroner's report, Noreen Flood died after midnight. The cause of death was listed as accidental drowning. There was evidence that she had climbed over the bar and across the grass which left stains on the knees of her blue jeans."

"No signs of abuse?" Nell asked.

Grant shook his head. "None. Like Eddie, the girl was extraordinarily healthy and unmarked by abuse either physical or sexual."

"Her clothes?" Ham asked. "New?"

"Yes. Once again they found the packaging, labels and tags in the men's room near the monkey exhibit."

"Men's room would indicate that whoever took the kids was male," Ham said.

"Most probably," Grant said. "Noreen's hair was cut short like a boy. These days fathers are so involved with their children it's not unusual for a man to take a small girl into the men's room. It would be far less noticeable than if he tried to accompany her into the ladies' room."

Maggie touched one of the pictures on the poster, her finger sliding across the slick surface. George was pushing Jake on the swing in Wolfram Park. Behind them were the faces of other children, playing happily on the other playground equipment. How far away it seemed from the subject under discussion.

"Noreen died in November, and Tyler was taken in December," Grant said. "Once we knew about the other two cases, we began to hope that he would be returned at the end of the year. The anniversary day came and went with no sign of Tyler. In the opinion of the police, the fact that he was not returned suggested that he might be dead."

"Did you believe that?" Ham asked.

"I couldn't accept it. Neither my sister, Barbara, nor her husband believe it either. We don't talk about it now, but until we have hard evidence, we keep the hope alive."

Maggie remained beside the poster but angled her body until she could see all three of the people around the table. Grant's head was bent, his body sunk against the back of his chair. His hands gripped the wooden arms, and even at a distance she could see the white skin across his knuckles.

Except for an occasional slip, Grant kept his emotions under control, but she could hear the underlying pain in his tone of voice. His attempt to cover his agony caught at her heart. How often had he paced the floor at night? Awakened in a sweat? Visualized the circumstances in which his nephew existed?

Grant coughed, releasing his hold on the arms of the chair.

"You can imagine how I felt when I first got Hamilton's phone call. If there was even the slightest chance that George knew where Tyler was, I had to find out."

"What I still don't understand is how you know it's the same person who is taking the children?" Maggie asked.

"According to the police reports," Grant said, "there are enough similarities between the three cases that they believe it's the work of one man."

"That might be true of the first two cases, but not in Tyler's disappearance." Ham's voice was sharp as he confronted Grant. "In your nephew's case, a child is missing. Thousands of children are missing every year. Since you have such total confidence that it's the work of one man, you've got to be holding out a significant piece of evidence. What connects Tyler to the other two?"

For several seconds, Grant didn't move, then he sighed and released a slow stream of air. With a shudder, he pushed himself upright, propping his elbows on the table, his fingers tented beneath his chin. He gave Hamilton and Nell a quick glance and raised his head to look across the room at Maggie. Even though his eyes were in shadow, she could read the decision in his face. He had decided to tell them whatever it was that he'd been holding back.

"After Eddie Harland was taken, the police searched the movie theater. Aside from the usual trash, they found only one thing out of the ordinary. An eagle feather."

"An eagle feather? Now that's something I didn't hear about," Ham said. "And the girl? Noreen?"

"Noreen's parents were divorced. She was at the Minnesota Zoo with her father. It was the day after Thanksgiving, so the place was crowded. Noreen and her father were in the main Asian Tropics building. In the nocturnal tunnel the Asian animals are in lighted habitats behind glass windows set into the wall. The viewing room is illuminated along the floor."

Maggie had taken Jake to the Brookfield Zoo and the Lincoln Park Zoo in Chicago, so she was familiar with comparable layouts and could picture the scenario.

"Noreen and her father were about halfway into the exhibit when someone screamed. A white mouse was loose and scuttling along the floor, sending the people scrambling to get out of the way. In the general stampede, Noreen was separated from her father. Security was called, but she was nowhere to be found."

"Judas!" Ham smacked the arm of his chair with a tight fist. "This sick bastard has big brass ones to take such a chance."

"According to the police, the higher the risk, the more the kidnapper gets off on it if he succeeds." Grant's mouth was a grim line. "The police searched the exhibit and found a few things of possible interest, but then they hit the jackpot."

"Let me guess," Ham said. "An eagle feather?"

"On the nose. It might have gone unnoticed except for a very sharp-eyed detective who had a friend working the task force in Detroit. She had told him about Eddie's kidnapping and shared more than she should have. Although she knew they were keeping certain information out of the newspapers, she told him about the eagle feather."

Maggie felt the rise of tension in the room and knew exactly what Grant was going to tell them. He looked across at her and gave a single nod, his mouth curved into a smile that had little to do with humor.

"And yes, you've guessed correctly," he said. "When Tyler was taken from the department store, on the floor beneath the clothing rack he'd been hiding in, the police found an eagle feather."

Even though she'd been expecting Grant's words, Maggie felt goose bumps rise across her skin. Nell sagged back in her chair, and Ham let out a slow stream of air as if he'd been holding his breath.

"I think we could use a break," Grant said.

Nell reached for the pitcher of water in the center of the table and re-filled the glasses, raising her own and drinking thirstily. Ham took the op-portunity to locate the bathroom. Grant pushed his chair back, the legs scraping on the hardwood floor. He stood up, rolling his shoulders to loosen the tension in his back and neck, then picked up one of the water glasses and brought it over to Maggie.

"I like the pictures," he said, nodding his head toward the poster.

"Jake put it together. I think it gave him an outlet for his grief to be able to focus on the good times."

"I didn't get a chance to look at it during the wake." Grant leaned closer, his eyes scanning the pictures. "Your father-in-law had a lot of interests. Family. Fishing with Hamilton. The poker group. What's this?"

The photograph was one of George holding a hawk on his gloved hand. Maggie smiled at the wary expression on her father-in-law's face.

"That was taken last fall when he went with Hugh Rossiter on a hunt sponsored by the falconry club. He told me later that he refused to make eye contact with the bird because he was convinced it would take it as a signal to attack him and peck his eyes out."

"A falconry club?" Grant asked. "Here in Delbrook?"

"Yes. George wasn't a member, but some of his friends were. There's a picture of the group somewhere on here." Maggie scanned the poster, finding the photo close to the bottom. "For a small town it's a good-sized club. Six members. Charley Blessington and Connie are pretty active in the club, and Hugh Rossiter is the master falconer."

"Half of the poker group," Grant said.

Maggie started in surprise and took a closer look at the photo.

"Where do they meet?" he asked.

"Over at Hugh's place on the south side of the lake. At least that's where they keep some of the birds. Hugh converted one of the buildings into a mews and a clinic."

"With a veterinarian?"

"No. Most vets don't work on wild birds. Falconers for the most part take care of their own birds. It's a pretty intense sport."

"Is Walter Kondrat a member?" Grant asked.

Maggie glanced quickly at Nell, but the older woman was holding a low-voiced conversation with Ham on the far side of the room.

"No. Walter's only interests, outside of work, are poker and Nell. Not always in that order. Nobody knows how Nell feels."

"Who are the other three in the picture?"

"Lorraine Pickard is the woman on the left. Last year she moved to an Indian reservation in Minnesota to work on an agricultural project. I know it sounds loony, but it was something about birth control for chickens. Next to her is Mike Offenlach. He owns a body shop over on Cumberland." She tapped the face of the last man in the picture. "You might have met Brian Harper at the wake last night. He's into computers and kids. He's got six children already, and he said once that he's hoping to field an entire baseball team."

Grant studied the picture as she identified each person, then scanned the rest of the photos on the posterboard.

"Your father-in-law seems to have led a very full life. I'm sorry I never met him. His friends had a lot of nice things to say about him at the wake and earlier tonight at the dinner."

"He's definitely left a void in our lives." Maggie raised her eyes to the staircase. "Jake and I will miss him."

"That's what Hamilton says. I gather he and George had a lot of great times together."

"They were good friends. By the way, I invited Ham to stay at George's place with you."

"To keep an eye on me?"

She ignored the question. "You two seem to have hit it off."

"You don't sound as if you approve." Grant stared across the room, where Hamilton was still talking to Nell. "Hamilton arrived at George's after lunch yesterday, and we had a lot of time to talk before the wake. If you're interested, I'm sure he'd let you see a copy of my references."

"Personal or professional?"

It startled her that she felt so comfortable in his presence that she could joke.

"Do I actually see a possibility that you're beginning to have a little faith in me?" he asked.

"Don't get your hopes up, Holbrook. I'm not the trusting type."

"Funnily enough, I think you are."

"Break time is over, you two," Ham said, pulling out Nell's chair for her. "Nell and I have been talking, and there are a couple questions we'd like to ask."

Grant touched Maggie's elbow, and she walked over to join the group. She set her glass back on the tray and took a can of pop, opening the top and swallowing, hoping the caffeine would give her a boost of energy. She shook off the feeling of lethargy that threatened to envelop her and waited for Ham to begin.

"I understand why you're convinced that the kidnappings are the work of the same person or persons," Ham said. "But what I don't see is why you're so convinced that George's death is the result of his recognizing Tyler in the pictures from Jake's birthday party. There must have been hundreds of calls from people convinced they'd seen Tyler. Why are you so positive that George did see Tyler?"

Grant must have been expecting the question, Maggie thought. He looked relieved that someone had asked it.

"When Tyler disappeared I spent as much time with my sister and her husband in Cleveland as I could. I went with them to the police station and I sat in on all the meetings. Once the actual investigation was in full swing I was at loose ends. I'd been asked to let the professionals take over."

The muscles in his jaw rippled. That request had clearly rankled him. As Ham had said earlier, Grant was not the sort of man to step back, leaving the decisions to others.

"Although I knew I was not at liberty to talk about the eagle feather, I asked if anyone had considered contacting law enforcement officials in the Midwest who might have come across some reference to eagle feathers. No one was particularly receptive to the idea."

"I thought the police or FBI had some sort of data bank that would have that information," Nell said.

"They have various data files, but the way it works is that the feather would only be noted if it was connected to the commission of a crime. If there was no crime, it wouldn't be in the data. My thought was that someone might have come across feathers in another context."

"So the police suggested that you do the research?" Maggie asked. "It would give you something to do and keep you out of their hair."

Grant looked across at her and smiled as if she were a particularly bright pupil. Maggie was surprised at the pleasure his approval gave her.

"You guessed correctly," he said. "Frankly, it didn't matter to me why they gave the project to me. I needed to be doing something."

"I'd feel the same way," Ham said.

"From the moment Tyler was taken I used all the resources at my disposal to get information. I'd never defended anyone charged with any kind of sexual deviancy. I found it personally repugnant. So I needed to start from ground zero."

Grant reached out and opened a can of beer, tipping his head to drink thirstily before he continued.

"I talked to experts. Read books and articles on sexual predators. Interviewed psychiatrists. Monsters like this usually have a long history of antisocial behaviors. My hope was that the eagle feathers might be the beginning of a trail I could follow."

He shrugged.

"I went online looking for organizations for retired police officers and other law enforcement professionals. My prime focus was the Midwest since that was where the three kidnappings had taken place. I kept my postings simple. I asked if anyone had run across a reference to eagle feathers in the commission of a crime or even the suspicion of a crime. Then I waited."

"Pretty good idea," Ham said. "Did you get any hits?"

"Unfortunately, more than I'd hoped for. It started out slowly, but eventually the response was overwhelming. Hundreds of e-mails. Each one had to be read and evaluated. A majority could be ruled out immediately. Kooks and crazies. People wanting to sell me eagle feathers. People telling me the dire consequences of selling and/or buying eagle feathers. Lonely people who just wanted to make a contact. It was about two months into the project that I finally got a break.

"I got an e-mail from a retired cop who said that for several years he'd had complaints from people about finding eagle feathers. No crime was committed, so it never made it into the books, but he remembered it because it was so unusual."

"What do you mean?" Nell asked. "How did they find the feathers?"

"According to this guy, people found feathers in their purses, in their houses and inside their clothing."

Maggie shivered. "I don't like that."

"Neither did the people who found them," Grant said. "The only feather this cop had actually seen was turned in to him at a carnival here in Wisconsin. A young woman found the feather inside her blouse when she went to change into her bathing suit. The only reason the cop knew about it was that he was in charge of giving out the prizes for the games that were played all through the day. The woman presented the feather, thinking it entitled her to one of the prizes."

"When was this?" Maggie asked.

"Twenty years ago."

"Twenty years ago? What possible bearing could that have on this case, Grant?" Maggie said, letting the irritation show in her voice.

"I know it's a long time ago, but hear me out," Grant said.

Ham cocked his head on the side, eyeing Grant through narrowed eyes. "You said the feather turned up at a carnival in Wisconsin?"

He nodded. "The carnival has been held for the past twenty-five years starting the Friday after Labor Day. It used to be sponsored by the

Four-H Club in conjunction with the Chamber of Commerce. Lots of crafts and baking contests and even an auction of farm animals."

"You mean it's still being held?" Nell asked.

"Yes. An outside company runs the event, but it's still in the same venue. It used to be called the Falcon Festival, but the name's been changed," Grant said. "It's called the Renaissance Faire."

CHAPTER
TWELVE

"THE FESTIVAL where the feather was found," Grant said, "is called the Renaissance Faire."

"No shit, Sherlock!" Ham slapped the table with the palm of his hand. "So the Renaissance Faire is your connection between Tyler and the feather and George and the birthday pictures."

"Exactly," Grant said. "I'm cognizant of the fact that they could be unrelated events. In real life, however, bizarre coincidences do happen. Think about it. Twenty years ago the kidnapper could have been fairly young. Maybe not old enough for a driver's license or with no opportunity to travel anywhere. So it's plausible that when he acted out, he'd have done it in his home territory."

"So the first eagle feather was found in Delbrook," Ham repeated.

"The first feather we *know* about," came Nell's dampening comment.

"It's a weak case," Grant conceded, "but it's the only one I have."

He glanced across at Maggie. Her expression was somber, and except for a startled look when he mentioned the Renaissance Faire, she'd remained motionless. Her eyes were focused on a spot somewhere over his left shoulder, and even when he shifted around to draw her attention, she didn't respond. Her detachment worried him, but Ham spoke before Grant could draw her into the conversation.

"You said a cop e-mailed you about the eagle feather. Did you talk to him?"

"Yes. At length."

"I was still living in Delbrook," Ham said, "twenty years ago. If the cop worked here then, I probably knew him. Who was it?"

"Artie Babiak," Grant said. "He said he had a place on the south side of the lake."

"I do know him. And so does Nell," Ham said. He looked at her, and she nodded her head. "He's been off the job about fifteen years. Pretty active around Delbrook. He ran the annual golf tournament at the country club. His wife, Arline, was the ladies' golf champ for about three years running. His kids are all in New York State, so when he retired he moved up around Lake George."

"That's the guy," Grant said. "Artie's got a great memory for detail. He says after that first feather got turned in, he heard rumors of others. Nothing concrete. No crime. Nothing on the books. Those were the days when people didn't sue for every real or imagined injury. Artie said they never identified the 'Eagle.' He always thought the guy would do something to get himself in real trouble, but it didn't happen on his watch."

"Too bad about that," Ham said.

"So basically you've got two threads that connect Delbrook to Tyler," Nell said. "The eagle feather that turned up twenty years ago at the festival at Camp Delbrook and your assumption that George saw a picture of Tyler at the same festival which is now called the Renaissance Faire. It's pretty thin, Mr. Holbrook."

"Agreed." Grant released a heavy sigh. "It would never get to the grand jury. I should state here that my hypothesis has met with little enthusiasm from the police. Before I came up here to Delbrook, I called Joe Moore, the detective in charge of the investigation in Cleveland. When I first came across the information on the eagle feathers, I contacted him. He didn't laugh, but it was obvious that he didn't think much of my conclusions. At least not enough to warrant a deeper investigation."

"I would have thought the police would jump at any lead," Nell said.

"You have to understand that they've had hundreds of leads. Elvis has been sighted fewer times than Tyler. Calls from people accusing relatives and friends, either for the reward or just out of spite. The usual village-idiot calls. My eagle feather theory ranks up there with the latter bunch."

"A child is missing. Every lead should be followed." Nell pursed her lips.

"I agree. Unfortunately I'm not running the investigation," Grant said. "So I called Joe Moore and told him that George might have seen a picture of Tyler. He wasn't impressed. He suggested I contact George directly to see if I could get a positive ID."

"If only we had the photographs," Ham said, "at least we'd have some hard evidence to take to the police."

"Then I could prove that whoever has Tyler lives somewhere in the vicinity," Grant said, "and that whoever killed George was at the country club that night. Someone he knew."

"That's not possible," Maggie snapped. "It can't be true."

"Why not?" Grant countered. "Because you don't want it to be true?"

Maggie jerked back in her chair. Tears rose to her eyes as she struggled for words to refute his charge. She opened her mouth to speak, but closed it again because she knew that what he said was true. She didn't want to believe it.

She didn't want to accept the fact that someone in Delbrook had kidnapped a child and had deliberately murdered George. She had known ever since talking to Frank Woodman that Grant's theory was probably correct. If she told him what she knew, he would dig into every corner of Delbrook to find answers. Grant's investigation would put them all at risk.

The threat of exposure could drive the killer to desperate measures. He would attack again, and this time Jake could be in jeopardy. All she could think of was that she might be risking Jake's life.

"Easy does it, son," Ham said. "Maggie doesn't live in your kind of world. She's only just now trying to get a handle on something that's been gnawing your ass for two years. In fact, we all are."

Grant's face turned a fiery red, all except for the scar on his jaw, which stood out like a white-hot brand.

"I don't mean to be rude, but I'm running out of time. I need to find out what George knew about Tyler and how the photographs connect up. No matter what it takes, I'm going to find out what I need to know. If that offends you, I'm sorry."

Maggie shook her head, and the tears that hung on her lids overflowed, falling unnoticed on her cheeks.

"It doesn't offend me. It terrifies me. You're right. I don't want it to be true. I'm coward enough to want it to go away. I want to turn the clock back and pretend you never came to Delbrook. George is dead, and every instinct in my body tells me that Jake is in danger."

Ever since George's death, she'd felt she had to control her emotions for Jake's sake. Now she'd lost the battle. She cupped her hands over her mouth to muffle the sobs that ripped through her body.

Feeling Nell's arms encircle her, Maggie clung to her friend, letting her tears wash away some of the fear and loss she'd bottled up. Reeling from one new revelation to the next, she was exhausted, and every detail added to the nightmare quality that surrounded her.

Slowly the sobs lessened until only an occasional shudder shook her body. A handkerchief was tucked into her hand, and she took a deep breath and raised her head from Nell's shoulder. Too embarrassed to meet anyone's eyes, she kept her head bent and blew her nose. Her cheeks itched from the salt residue of her tears, and she rubbed the hand-kerchief over her face.

"You missed a spot," Ham said.

Letting out a watery sniff, she raised her head to glare at him. "No wonder you never married. Nobody would have you."

Ham chuckled. "In actual fact, the woman of my dreams was already married, but I take your point."

Maggie hated the fact she'd lost control in front of a stranger, but she finally found enough courage to look across at Grant. For once, his hard, brown eyes were filled with warmth and compassion, and his expression held nothing back, letting her see that he understood her fears.

"I'm fine," she said in answer to his unspoken question. "Apparently I needed to let off a bit of steam."

He nodded once, swallowing back whatever words he might have spoken.

"I'd say you were entitled to a breakdown, dear," Nell said. "Now that you've released all that pent-up emotion, I expect you'll feel a lot better. We're all here to support you. You don't have to carry such a heavy load by yourself." Suddenly she yawned. "Lordy, Lordy, I'm fading. Is there any coffee left?"

"Yes. Kim made a fresh pot before she left. Get some, and I'll run up and check on Jake," Maggie said.

She was grateful to be able to escape in order to regain her compo-sure. She had left the door at the top of the staircase ajar, and now she pushed it open, walking along the hall to Jake's room. She eased open the bedroom door, and a wedge of light from the hall streamed across the floor.

The bedroom was stuffy, but she'd noticed a chill in the air as they came home, so she didn't want to open his windows. Being short of sleep, his resistance would be down, and she didn't want him to catch a cold. She tiptoed across to the bed.

Looking down at the sleeping boy, she flashed on the picture of the missing child. Dear God, how does a mother survive? she thought. Just the suggestion that something could happen to Jake made it difficult for her to breathe. She leaned over and brushed her lips against the soft skin at Jake's temple. Heat rose from his body, bringing the earthy smell of an active boy to her nostrils.

It was an odor she associated with summer and children. A lump formed in her throat, and she swallowed painfully as she thought of the three mothers who had lost their children to some psychopath. She couldn't conceive of the pain. Jake was her whole life.

She stood at the top of the stairs to the bookstore, holding the railing, wondering what she should do. She knew that when she returned to the meeting downstairs, she had to be prepared to participate fully. No half measures would do.

Grant intended to investigate George's murder in order to find Tyler. She had two choices. She could either join the clandestine investigation or she could go to Charley Blessington and tell him everything she knew.

Could her involvement hurt Jake?

If the investigation heated up and the killer panicked, Jake could be at risk. Knowing that was a possibility, she would need to prepare for such an eventuality in order to safeguard her son. If the murderer wasn't caught, Jake and others could be in real danger. So, as far as she could see, her help in the investigation would ultimately bring safety to him.

She needed to consider his mental health as well as his physical. Jake partially blamed her for Mark's death, and she suspected he had transferred that blame to include some responsibility for George's death.

It was partially her fault that her relationship with Mark had deteriorated. Perhaps she had failed Jake by refusing to fight harder to keep the marriage alive. She wouldn't fail him again.

In her heart she knew something wasn't right with George's death, and she needed to find out what was wrong. She owed that to George as well as to Jake.

It appeared that the decision was easier to make than she had first suspected. She would do whatever she could to help find the person who had killed her father-in-law.

Walking back down the stairs to the bookstore, she felt more centered. Since George's death she had done what was required for basic survival. Like an old-fashioned pulp fiction heroine, she had let events dictate her actions rather than making her own decisions.

It was time to take control of her life.

The reviving aroma of freshly brewed coffee added to her sense of determination as she returned to the bookstore. Nell had set out a plate of crackers and cheese, and Maggie was surprised to find she was hungry. Ham was pouring coffee, and Grant was holding a basket of grapes.

"Just wait until Beth comes to work tomorrow," Maggie said. "She'll wonder who's been raiding the refrigerator."

"Who's Beth?" Grant asked, eyeing the grapes with dismay. "Are these hers?"

"No. They're mine. I buy them for Beth Witecki, who runs the bookstore. She's a thin wisp of a girl with a passion for grapes. She used to work for one of the bookstore chains in Milwaukee, but when she got married she moved to Delbrook. I was out of my depth when I first bought the store. Beth took pity on me and came to work here."

"You spoil her rotten," Nell said.

"Please. I'll do anything to keep her from quitting. I was really naive when I got into this business. I thought all you needed to run a bookstore was a love of books. I was an editor. I knew when to dot *i*'s and cross *t*'s, but I hadn't a clue how to read a balance sheet or an order form. The reality is that bookselling is a killer of a business. To be a successful bookstore owner you have to know all aspects of running a business and then layer on a wealth of knowledge about the publishing world."

"And this woman can do that?" Grant asked.

"Beth gets high creating graphs and designing budgets. She handles accounting, orders stock, takes care of returns and baby-sits the occasional author who wanders into town for a book signing. All in all, she's responsible for the day-to-day functioning of the store."

Grant chuckled. "If Beth quits, you'll sue me for cause. First thing in the morning I'll buy some grapes and bring them over. She will have no grounds for resigning."

Maggie picked off several of the grapes, popped one in her mouth and sighed at the rush of sweet juice. Pulling out a chair, she sat down at the table, nodding her thanks to Nell for the coffee.

"Before we continue I need to tell you what I learned tonight from

Frank Woodman, the manager of the country club," Maggie said. "I think it goes a long way to proving your theory about the pictures, Holbrook."

She grimaced under the intensity of his look. She could almost read his accusation at her delay in bringing up the subject.

"Don't bother to ask," she said. "You know how resistant I've been to your theory. I didn't want to believe any of it. Tonight I needed to listen to everything before I could actually accept it all."

She told them what Frank had told her about George's reaction to the pictures, his preoccupation and his abrupt leaving to make the phone call, which she assumed was to Ham. It all fit together to make a complete picture of the evening.

"Someone could have overheard the conversation," Ham suggested. "George said he was calling from the pay phone in the hall. He was pretty cagey, but if someone was listening, they might have gotten the gist of the call, which was that George had seen the pictures of Tyler."

"That would explain why the killer struck when he did," Grant said. "He couldn't afford to let George leave the country club with the pictures. In fact, he couldn't let George leave at all."

Silence followed Grant's words. Maggie swallowed to get the dryness out of her throat.

"There's something else you need to know," she said. "My purse was searched tonight. I did not take it into the bathroom where Jake found it."

"Are you sure, kiddo?" Ham asked.

"Positive. I didn't have any proof that someone tried to steal my purse outside the hospital, but I do here. It wasn't a robbery. My money and credit cards weren't taken, but all of the sympathy card envelopes had been opened and the list of George's effects that were sent to the police lab was taken out of the zippered compartment where I'd put it."

Grant could feel his heart jerk at the revelation, and he could see that Nell and Hamilton were shocked.

"Shouldn't you tell the police?" Nell asked. "There's bound to be fingerprints."

"My guess is that it would be pointless," Maggie said. "Jake put all of the things back into the purse when he found it and then I handled everything when I looked through it."

Nell shivered, and Maggie reached over and squeezed her hand to reassure her.

"First the hospital, then George's house and now my purse," Maggie continued. "Someone is very definitely searching for something. We assume he has the photographs, and if that's the case, what is he looking for?"

Grant had been wondering that ever since he'd found the break-in at George's place. "Whatever it is," he said, "must not have been found yet. Maybe the conclusion is that there's nothing to be found."

"I certainly hope so," Nell said, "but until we're sure of that, keep your doors locked, Maggie."

"Luckily, George made sure the apartment was well supplied with dead bolts," Maggie said. "It would take a swat team to get inside."

She set her hand on the table, index finger extended, the tip of her nail tapping the table as if she were preparing to speak. She exhaled sharply and looked at each of the faces around the table.

"Much as I've denied this since you mentioned it, Grant, George had to have been killed by someone who lives in Delbrook. Someone who knew him and was at the country club the night he died."

"What brought this on?" he asked.

"The missing pictures were shot primarily at the Renaissance Faire. If it was Tyler, he wasn't at the Faire alone," Maggie said. "Someone had to bring him there and take him away. This is a local fair. It doesn't pull in people from great distances."

"That's true," Ham said.

"I took the boys to see the falconry exhibit. Connie Prentice had both her birds there and demonstrated various aspects of the sport. She released one of the falcons and brought it back with a swing lure. It was a real crowd pleaser."

"I assume Brent wasn't too far away," Nell said.

"No. He was there, and so was Hugh Rossiter. Probably the rest of the falconry club, too. George told me Charley Blessington was there most of the day, but I didn't see him."

"I was there for a short time but went home before the rain," Nell said. "I met Walter for lunch, and he was still there when I left."

"That's pretty much the whole poker group with the exception of Frank Woodman," Ham said.

"I don't think we can count him out. He could have been there even though no one saw him," Maggie said. "So basically what I'm saying is that it could be anyone in town. We'll have to be careful who we talk to."

"I agree," Grant said. "Safety has to take precedence. This investigation has to be low-key. The killer is going to be feeling pressure from the police. We don't want to increase that level so that he panics and tries to cut and run."

"You think that's a possibility?" Ham asked.

"I don't know, but it's something I don't want to risk for Tyler's sake," Grant said. He faced Maggie squarely. "I'm not diminishing the importance of your father-in-law's death, but if my nephew is still alive, my first priority is to locate him. Hamilton and I have marked out some areas that we can concentrate on."

"I understand that," Maggie said. "George would want us to focus on Tyler. What can Nell and I do to help?"

"For the moment just go along with the fiction that I'm your mother-in-law's relative come to offer support. Naturally, it would be better if no one knew about George's call to Hamilton," Grant said, nodding toward the older man.

"So you're saying we should just sit tight?" Maggie persisted.

"Exactly. Don't talk to Charley Blessington," Grant continued. "I can't stress enough that we don't know who can be trusted. We have to assume that anyone who was at the country club the night George was killed is a possible suspect. That includes Charley."

Maggie could feel the blood pounding in her ears as it dawned on her that Grant had no intention of letting her get involved in his investigation. One look at Nell told her that she had come to the same conclusion. The older woman rolled her fingertips on the top of the table in a steady tattoo, a visible sign of her agitation.

"I don't want to rain on your parade, Mr. Holbrook, but there's something going on here that leaves me feeling that Maggie and I are out of the loop. You and Ham have the look of Peck's bad boys." She grimaced, sniffing the air. "I raised three children, and I could always tell when one of them had smuggled a frog into the house and was planning to release it during the night."

Maggie caught the look of guilt that passed between the two men. The compatible interaction hadn't been particularly noticeable before, but now that she thought about it, they had told the story of the crimes as if they were working together as a team. How had they managed to bridge the thirty-year difference in their ages and become allies?

"It's nothing you have to worry about, Nell," Ham said.

"Oh please," she said. "The next thing you'll do is pat us on our heads and tell us this is man's work."

He closed his mouth in a firm line and shot a quick glance at Grant.

"Since Hamilton's been up here, we've talked about the case and come to some conclusions." Grant had the grace to look slightly self-conscious. "We think it would be safest if you and Maggie distanced yourselves from any involvement in the investigation."

"And you expect us to go along with that decision?" Nell asked.

Maggie knew the older woman well enough to recognize the disdainful tone, but Grant was oblivious. Ham opened his mouth as if to offer a warning, but one look at Nell and he pressed his lips together.

"I was hoping you would," Grant said.

"Then you're an idiot," Nell said. "I'm not sure what sort of women you're used to dealing with, Mr. Holbrook, but you're off the mark here. If you expect either Maggie or myself to keep our mouths shut, we want a full partnership in whatever scheme you two have in mind."

"It's not that simple . . ." Grant started.

Ham covered his eyes and sank lower in his chair.

"And the horse you rode in on," Nell barked. "You have forgotten something very important here. George was Maggie's father-in-law and my friend. If we are to believe your story, then it was a premeditated murder, and we have a duty to join in any effort to discover the perpetrator."

"You can't shut us out, Holbrook," Maggie said. Her tone had a finality to it. "We're not discussing a business decision, nor are we dealing with a local voting issue. We're talking murder and kidnapping. You don't have any choice but to include us."

"Judas Priest!" Grant said. He flopped against the back of his chair and glared at Ham. "You should have warned me."

"You wouldn't have believed me."

"Well, Mr. Holbrook? What's it to be?" Nell asked.

Grant threw up his hands in surrender. In any other context the situation would have been comical. He could see in the somber expressions on each face an awareness of the risks involved.

"All right, ladies, you're in," he said.

Grant had found a yellow legal pad on a shelf in the kitchen and now he pulled it toward him and wrote the date and the time in bold letters across the top of the first page. When he looked up, he could see that this simple action had put an official stamp on the meeting.

"Two things I want to make very clear," he said. "First, my intention is not to set up an investigation that will lead to vigilante justice. What we're looking for is evidence leading to George's murderer or Tyler's presence that we can take to the police. Agreed?"

His glance moved around the table as each of the others nodded in agreement.

"The second thing to keep in mind is that if at any time I feel things are getting out of control, I'll pull the plug on the investigation and we'll take what info we have to the police."

"Absolutely," Ham said.

"I can live with that," Nell said.

Maggie's eyes were wide, and Grant could detect a hint of fear in the blue depths, but she met his gaze without flinching and nodded her head. He smoothed a hand across the yellow pad of paper.

"I've never run an investigation into murder," he said, "but I don't think it's much different than building a court case. I'd like to suggest we dig into the background of people involved and pool as much information as we can access in hopes that we'll see a pattern or find some evidence. That being the case, our first consideration must be Tully Jackson. Do any of you believe that he killed George?"

"He makes an easy choice," Ham said. "But from what I know and have observed, I don't think he did it. I've talked to him when I've been up here fishing with George. He'd have no reason to rob anyone. As far as I can see, his needs and wants are very small."

"I don't think Tully's stupid," Nell added, "but he's not a candidate for *Jeopardy*. If the person who killed George is the mastermind behind the kidnapping, then Tully is definitely out."

"I agree," Maggie said. "I'm really worried about him. This is a man who's fragile. My guess is that he's gone into hiding because he's frightened. He might have seen whoever killed George, and that information would put him in dreadful danger."

"Do any of you have any idea how we can contact him?" Grant asked.

"No." Maggie shook her head. "It's possible that he might contact someone if he needs help."

"We have to pray that Tully doesn't pick the wrong person," Grant said. "It could be his death warrant."

CHAPTER THIRTEEN

"IT'S NOT THAT EASY to get eagle feathers, you know."

Nell's comment came out of the blue, breaking through the tension that filled the room after the discussion about Tully. Her eyes were focused on the black bow she'd pulled out of her hair. She untied the ribbon and straightened it out, sliding it back and forth through her fingers.

"When I was first starting out as an artist," she said, "I decided that the way to fame and riches was to come up with some gimmick that would generate publicity. The theory was that once the art world became aware of my creativity and artistic genius, I'd become a media darling, travel throughout the United States and become filthy rich."

"Let me guess," Ham said. His blue eyes glinted with amusement. "You were twelve at the time?"

Nell pursed her lips and shook her head. "I was a very sheltered child. A late bloomer. Not a loose cannon, like some I could mention." She drew herself up, her ample bosom more prominent than usual. "I was sixteen. The age of optimum wisdom."

"Ah, I remember those days." Ham nodded. "Dare I ask if your gimmick had anything to do with painting naked while wearing a headdress of eagle feathers?"

Grant tried to hide his grin, but Nell's gaze swung to him, and she snorted in disgust.

"Men have no imagination beyond the sexual plane," she announced.

"Bless the little darlings," Maggie said.

"My gimmick, you old roué," she said to Ham, "was to paint with eagle feathers."

"A sixteen-year-old has few really creative ideas," Ham said. "I suppose that might have been considered avant-garde in those days."

"Don't make it sound like it was before fire, Ham," Nell drawled. "You were probably out of school and in the working world at the time."

Ham clapped a hand over his heart as if mortally wounded. The banter between the older couple added a much-needed lightness to the atmosphere.

"As you might have guessed, the project wasn't a wholehearted triumph." Her tone was rueful. "I couldn't paint worth a damn with the feathers. I actually might have had more chance of success had I painted naked. Several years ago, I decided to resurrect the project, and much to my dismay, I discovered that there were enormous penalties for owning or using eagle feathers."

"You're kidding," Ham said. "You mean fines?"

"Yes. They can be as high as ten thousand dollars for having a feather in your possession."

"Did you know about this?" he asked Grant.

"I didn't until I started researching the eagle feathers. The laws were set up on the theory that if you protect the feathers, you protect the birds. I think the only people allowed to own and work with eagle feathers are Native Americans, who can use them in art and in cultural rituals."

"It's curious that when the feathers turned up after the kidnapping, they were eagle feathers," Nell continued. "It might be worthwhile to call Artie back to see whether they were all eagle feathers and just which feathers they were. Wing, body or tail feathers."

"Let me call him," Ham said to Grant. "He knows me and will be more likely to talk to me."

Grant jotted down several notes. He'd call Herb Stebbins, a friend of his with the U.S. Fish and Wildlife Service, to get a refresher course on the regulations surrounding eagle feathers.

Nell bit into a cracker, sending a shower of crumbs down onto the top of her dress. She automatically brushed them away as she reached for another cracker.

"Shouldn't we be setting up a list of suspects?" she asked.

"Yes, and I think unless we find evidence to the contrary, we must consider the poker players to be our prime suspects." Grant could see by

their expressions that they didn't like that thought. "I understand your re-
luctance to address this situation, but it's more likely that George was
killed by someone he knew than by a complete stranger."

"It's tough for us," Ham said. "We know these people. They're friends
of ours."

"I understand that," Grant said. "These people were with George
during the evening and would have known if he had discovered any information about Tyler. Just because the people at the club are your friends
doesn't make them above suspicion."

"I hate it that you're right, Holbrook," Maggie said, heaving a sigh.
"Frank told me something else when I talked with him earlier. When
Connie and Brent stopped by George's house to give me their condolences on Monday, Connie said George was still at the club when they
left."

"So that gives them both an alibi," Nell said.

"That's what I thought," Maggie said. "However, when I talked to
Frank Woodman tonight, he said that Connie was at the club for dinner
but Brent didn't arrive until after dinner was over."

"That means two cars," Ham said. "I suppose they followed each
other home."

Maggie shook her head. "According to Frank, Connie was angry with
Brent and went home early."

"Why would she lie about it?" Nell asked.

"A very good question," Grant said, making a note. "Anyone want to
do a bit of background research on Connie and Brent?"

"I can do that," Nell said. "I'm having lunch with Doris Blessington
this week. I'll do a little pumping. Doris always knows where the bodies
are buried."

Grant spoke quickly, before anyone registered the unfortunate wording. "I'd like to go over to Camp Delbrook and look around. I need to see
where the Renaissance Faire was held. I understand the camp is closed."

"It's not like you're dealing with Camp David," Nell said. "There's no
way to keep anyone out. The camp takes up about two hundred acres on
the west end of the lake. Most of the cabins and outbuildings are located
on a hill leading down to the south shore."

"There's a security guard just inside the main entrance to monitor
who goes in and out, and there's another one down by the boat landing,"
Maggie added. "The place is closed, but there's always a lot of people

around. The community college uses several of the buildings for administrative offices, so you can stop there if you have any questions."

"Between the woods and the lake, anyone could get into the camp without being seen?" Grant asked. The others nodded.

"In addition to that," Ham said, "Hugh Rossiter's landscape company is located next to the camp. His father started the business, and when he died Hugh took it over. He owns a piece of adjoining property, which he uses for direct access so he doesn't have to go in and out through the main entrance. His company takes care of the grounds maintenance for the camp, and he lives and has offices in a house on the shore."

"If you want to get a look at the camp, you can come with me tomorrow," Maggie said. "I told Hugh I'd pick up Kenny after school and drop him off at the landscape office."

"That would be great," Grant said. "It'll give me a quick overview so I'll have some idea what to check out at a later visit."

"You thinking your nephew might be held at Camp Delbrook?" Ham asked. He leaned forward, his eyes flashing. "It would be risky, but there'd be plenty of places to hide one small boy."

Grant nodded. "That's my thought. Maggie was telling me a little about the falconry club, and I'd especially like to get a look at the mews."

"When we're over at the camp tomorrow, if Hugh doesn't offer to take you to see the birds, I'll ask him."

"What exactly are we looking for?" Nell asked.

"Whoever has taken the children has to have a place to keep them," Grant said. "I can't believe they're passed off as family members. It'd be much too dangerous. Someone could recognize them or just question their presence. So I think we have to consider an alternate place. Someplace a child could be confined."

Even though the sound was barely audible, Grant heard Maggie's cry of distress. Color had drained out of her already pale face.

"You must think I'm incredibly stupid," she said. "I've heard all the same things that Ham and Nell have, but it's as if I'm working out some intellectual puzzle. Then all of a sudden you'll say something and it hits me on an emotional level."

"Remember, Maggie," Grant said. "I've been living with this for twenty months."

"I know that, but just now all I could picture was a child caged up in some sort of cell. Eddie and the little girl, Noreen, were imprisoned for a year. And now Tyler. Dear God! Those poor babies." She was close to tears. "It's monstrous. Who could do such a thing?"

Grant reached out a hand and placed it on top of hers. Her fingers were entwined as if in prayer, and he could feel a slight tremor beneath the surface of her skin. He kept his touch impersonal, a reminder of a comforting presence.

"Don't be so hard on yourself, kiddo," Ham said. "Nell and I have seen a lot more of life than you have. Besides, we haven't taken quite the series of shocks you have in the past two days. You must be a bit punchy at this point."

"I'm not sure that's a really good excuse." She gave him a watery smile. "I have to admit that I've avoided thinking about the ugly and sordid crimes in the news. I know they exist, but I've made a conscious effort to filter out the details."

"Most of us do," Grant said. He gave her hands a pat of reassurance and then withdrew his own. "Only when something happens that hits close to home do we really look into the face of evil. Circumstances force us to examine it."

Maggie took a deep breath, sitting up straighter in her chair. "If we're thinking of places where Tyler could be held," she said, "we need to consider the Falcon Lake Country Club. The clubhouse is old and rambling. Frank Woodman told me once that some of the rooms upstairs are kept permanently closed off to keep the heating and air conditioning costs lower."

"And don't forget the maintenance sheds and equipment buildings that are possible places to keep a child." Ham tapped his fingers in a nervous beat on the top of the table. "Dave Gerbitz is a pilot and a photographer. He takes shots of farms and other properties in the area. Sort of a strange cuss. He flies with a golden lab named Boo who sits up in the copilot's seat as if he's ready to take over the controls. I'll ask Dave if he's got some photos of the golf course so we'll know how many buildings there are and can check them off after we've judged them empty."

"Good idea," Grant said. He made a note to ask Hamilton to see if he could get other photos, especially of Camp Delbrook.

"How about Walter Kondrat?"

"Walter lives in McGuire's Irish Estates about a block away from George's house," Nell said. "He did a major renovation a year ago and knocked down the internal walls on the first floor so it's a totally open plan. Upstairs there are two bedrooms and a bath. No third floor or attic space and no basement. No place inside the house to hide a child."

"Does he own any other property?"

"Not that I'm aware of," Nell said. "His father had a house in town, but it was sold when he died ten years ago. Walter's wife died young. Do you remember when, Ham?"

"Maybe thirty years ago. No kids. I don't think Walter wanted any. He was always tied up with his insurance business. Going to make a million."

"And so he did, and now he's got no one to leave it to," Nell said, mouth pursed in disapproval. "His sister will have the last laugh yet."

"He has a sister here in Delbrook?" Grant asked.

"No. She moved to Colorado about twenty years ago. I went to school with Crystal. She married her high school sweetheart. B. D. Wintrick. Word was that the initials stood for big and dumb." Nell laughed. "But Lordy, Lordy, he was beautiful. At any rate, Walter didn't approve. He said B. D. had no business sense, and when they ran into financial trouble, Walter refused to lend them any money."

"Are they still in Colorado?" Grant asked.

"Last I heard. Crystal said that Walter would end up rich and alone. Looks like that's what's going to happen, except when he dies, his sister will get all the money. If Walter'd been the victim instead of George, Crystal would be the prime suspect."

"I always thought you'd eventually marry Walter," Maggie said.

"That's what everyone thinks," Nell said.

"Well?" Ham asked, his eyes sparking with curiosity.

"I'll be sure to let you know if I have any announcements," she said dismissively. "Let's move on, shall we?"

From the sound of it, Grant didn't think that Walter would pan out as a suspect in this case, but he'd have to wait and see if anything turned up. He looked down at the pad of paper. That left the Blessingtons. He'd make Charley his project, he thought, circling the name.

"We should probably have a list of the other people who were at the club but not in the poker game," Maggie suggested. "I can get that from Frank Woodman. I talked to him tonight to see if anyone had found the photographs from Jake's party. I can tell him I need the names so I can ask around about the pictures."

"I can't urge you strongly enough to be very careful," Grant said. "Someone in Delbrook is living a double life and will do whatever it takes to protect any disclosure. If we're right in our assumptions, George was killed out of fear of exposure."

"I agree," Ham said. "I know you want to help, Maggie, but if it looks like you're digging around for information, you could put yourself at risk."

Maggie's mouth was drawn into a grim line. "I understand the danger," she said. "Doing nothing won't keep me or Jake safe. Finding George's murderer will."

"I don't want to frighten you any more than you already are," Grant said, "but the killer will be watching you. He has no idea whether George told you about the photographs. Since you've mentioned nothing so far, he might be reasonably assured that you don't know anything, but he'll be on the lookout for any unusual activity on your part."

"I'll be careful," Maggie said.

"That goes for all of us," Grant said. "If the murderer gets the idea that our investigation is getting close, he'll strike out. He's murdered at least once. He won't hesitate to kill again."

The Warrior stomped along the path through the woods above the lake. The moon was so bright he could see his way clearly, and he could smell the rain in the air. The imminence of a storm always made him restless.

It had rained when he took his first trophy.

He'd taken the child to prove he had reached the highest level of counting coup. Completing the act, he was overwhelmed with exhilaration. He had the power of life and death over the boy.

As an excuse to keep First Child in his possession, he decided to train him as a warrior. The training period, although experimental, had gone well, and the Warrior decided if the boy could accomplish one coup, he would be released.

Since he had taken First Child from a multiscreen theater, the Warrior selected a similar setting for the test. It would be easy enough to blend into the crowd as children and adults mingled in the lobby. The risk factors were minimal.

As soon as they entered the theater, the Warrior knew he had miscalculated. A new animated film had opened the day before, and the Saturday afternoon crowd was enormous. He decided to abort the test just as a harried mother pushed forward followed by a stream of children wearing party hats.

First Child was swept away in the crowd.

The Warrior could see the panic on the boy's face just before he was lost to sight. It was pointless to search. His only hope was that once free of the throng, the boy would return to the lobby. Locating a vantage point where he could see all entrances, he waited. When the police car pulled up in front of the theater, he knew the boy had been taken from him.

The Warrior climbed the trail to his favorite spot overlooking Lake Falcon. He came through the trees on the top of a flat rock bluff, and in the moonlight the view opened up around him.

The Aerie. He had come to this particular spot for years. It was his sanctuary, a refuge where the sights and sounds worked into his soul, chasing out the fears and doubts that possessed him. He sat down on the natural rock ledge and stared down at the shadowed panorama of sky, trees and water.

A month after the debacle at the theater, he had taken a child at the zoo near Minneapolis.

Wearing a baseball cap, jeans and a Minnesota Vikings jacket, there had been no indication that the four-year-old wasn't a boy. When he discovered the mix-up, his first thought was to jettison the girl. She stared at him with wide eyes, blank of all expression. Her stoicism convinced him that she had the soul of a warrior.

A year later he discovered he had misread the signs.

Since he had found her at a zoo, he had set her test at the Milwaukee County Zoo.

The moment they entered the zoo, Girl had been drawn to Monkey Island as if it were a magnet. She stood at the metal guardrail, looking across the grassy expanse at the monkeys beyond the moat. Wanting to work with her strengths, he had chosen Monkey Island as the rendezvous point.

Aware of the human element that had resulted in the loss of First Child, he had found a place for them to hide until the zoo was closed.

The November night was cold. It was close to midnight when the trial began. When he gave the first in a series of three bird calls, Girl appeared, walking steadily toward the enclosure for the Kodiak bears. She leaned over and stuck a feather in the ground in front of the iron fence.

She stood for a moment staring at the sidewalk as if she couldn't remember what to do next.

The Warrior held his breath. She looked around, her eyes catching the moonlight for an instant, then she started off down the path that led to the seals and polar bears. Pleased with her success, he let her get ahead of him.

She was not waiting for him at the rendezvous point. He wandered around the paths, searching for her, keeping to the shadows and listening for the sound of the security personnel. It wasn't until morning that he learned about the child who'd ducked under the guardrail at Monkey Island and drowned when she fell into the moat. In life, Girl had been drawn to the monkeys, and her curiosity to get closer to them had caused her death.

Above him, an owl cried out, and the Warrior felt his body tense.

Time was running out. The risk of discovery was always present during fall cleanup at Camp Delbrook, but in one month the place would be swarming with workers as each of the buildings was inspected to determine the amount of renovation needed to bring them up to code. He'd only just heard of the violations, so at least he had time to plan what to do about One Who Cries.

He should have released the boy at his year anniversary. His attachment to the child had put him at risk. When he had disposed of George, he thought the situation was under control. Now there was Maggie. She wasn't content to let her father-in-law rest in peace. He'd covered his tracks, but there were still some loose ends to tie up. Once that was done, he'd have to deal with her.

Maggie, along with One Who Cries, would have to be eliminated.

The man was angry. When he left, he banged the door.

Tyler peered out from beneath the shelf bed. He had heard banging outside the room and climbed under the shelf, pulling the blanket with him to hide behind. If the man brought the second dish, he didn't want to be seen.

Huddling under the blanket, his teeth chattered and his bottom was cold. He stuck one hand out and touched the mud floor. It was damp.

The man had yelled at him when he couldn't get the feather into his pocket. It was a big feather, not the little fluffy ones he was used to. He tried it three times. He could see the red on the man's cheek. When he missed the last time, he thought the man would get the bird.

Instead, he used the knife.

Tyler pulled his knees up to his chest. He bowed his head until his forehead touched the blanket. Tears tickled the inside of his nose, but they didn't come out of his eyes. His throat hurt, and he tried to swallow, but it was hard.

Was Mouse Ears dead?

The man had held his knife over the top of the mouse cage. He stabbed it through the wires. One. Two. Three times. He squeezed his eyes shut. He could hear the knife go right through the cage and hit the table.

The man laughed.

When Tyler opened his eyes, he saw the blood on the back of the mouse. The man held it up by the tail. He took it with him when he left.

Tyler tapped his finger on the bottom of the shelf bed. He listened. No mouse sounds. He tapped again. When he heard nothing, he pulled the blanket over his head and closed his eyes to sleep.

CHAPTER FOURTEEN

"WAITIN' ON JAKE?"

Maggie jumped at the sound of Charley Blessington's voice beside the open window of her car.

"Dear Lord, Charley, you just about gave me a heart attack."

"Sorry about that," he said. "I was passing when I saw your car and thought I'd stop and chat a spell."

Charley was so big that she felt at a decided disadvantage inside the car. She got out and leaned against the door, head back to look up at the chief of police. The afternoon sun was behind him, so his face was in shadow and Maggie had to squint.

"I'm picking up Jake and Kenny Rossiter," she said with a quick glance at the empty stairs leading up to St. Bernard's School. Just a few more minutes and the whole area would be swarming with screaming and shoving children. "Since Mark's cousin has never been up to Delbrook, we're going to take him for a drive around the area."

Still apprehensive about Grant's impersonation, she blurted out the information. She bit her lip to keep from further disclosures.

"Grant Holbrook," Charley said, his voice questioning. "He seems a nice enough fella for a lawyer. Surprised I never heard George talk about him."

"I don't think they ever saw much of each other. Ham knew him because they both live in Chicago."

"Chicago's a pretty big place," Charley drawled. "You didn't know Grant when you lived there?"

"No. Mark may have," Maggie said, grateful to come up with at least one answer that Charley couldn't verify. "Ham called Grant to tell him that George had died. It was very kind of him to come all the way up here."

"I understand he's going to stay around and give you a hand with George's affairs. Can't believe that Hugh Rossiter will cotton to having competition for the title of most eligible bachelor in Delbrook."

Talking to Charley about Grant was difficult for Maggie. She hoped he would take the heat rising to her face for a blush rather than an indication she was lying.

"By the way, Charley, do you know what happened to the photographs of Jake's party that George was passing around the night he died?" she asked, anxious to change the subject.

"Don't you have them?"

"No. They weren't listed among George's effects," she said.

"Well, that's funny." Charley tugged at his earlobe. "You're right though. I made the list out myself, and I don't recall seeing the photographs. We were looking at them during dinner, so if they weren't among George's things, they may be in his car."

"His car!" Maggie caught her breath. "Oh, my God, Charley, I totally forgot about it."

"You've had plenty to think about," Charley said. "We had it towed over to the motor pool, and the lab tech went over it. No sign that anyone had been in the car besides George. Why don't I have one of the uniforms drive it over later?"

"I'd really appreciate that, if you can spare someone."

"I'll have Wayne Brody run it over."

"You better have him bring the car to the bookstore. Parking is tight with both Ham and Grant over at George's place. Tell Wayne to call and let me know when he's coming so I can drive him back to the station house."

"Let him walk back," Charley said. "He's on my 'S' list. Called in sick last week, and I found out he was up at the Fernley Casino. Got an addiction to the one-armed bandits."

Maggie laughed. "I know Wayne and always thought his weakness was bridge."

"Since his divorce he's picked up a lot of new vices."

The dismissal bell rang, and almost in the same instant the doors of St. Bernard's sprang open and children exploded from every exit.

"Anything new on the investigation?" she asked.

"Nothing very promising." Charley raked his fingers through his hair. "We've interviewed everyone who was at the country club that night, and as you might figure, no one saw anything."

"Dennis Nyland was the only one who saw Tully Jackson?"

"Yep. Wish he'd seen the actual attack. I'd like to be able to take a strong case to the grand jury."

Maggie waved as she spotted Jake coming out the door of the school. He raced down the concrete stairs, leaping the last three steps and landing in a heap on the sidewalk. His bulging backpack cushioned his fall, and he scrambled to his feet.

"Hi, Mom. Kenny'll be right out." He threw his arms around Maggie's waist, and she leaned over to give him a kiss. "Hi, Chief Blessington."

"Looks like you got a ton a homework in that backpack," Charley said. "What all you got in there?"

"Just books and stuff." Jake flushed under the police chief's scrutiny. "We're learning about Egypt. The pyramids and those funny-looking statues without noses."

"Sphinxes?" Charley asked.

"That's it," Jake said.

"I can see you're learning a lot of important things. You musta had a good day at school?"

"All except for lunch. It was puny," Jake complained. "And I'm starving. Can we stop on the way to Kenny's for some fast food, Mom?"

"No. Mr. Rossiter said he'd have something for you when we got there," Maggie said, looking around for Jake's shadow. "Where is Kenny?"

"He'll be right out. He had to finish a paper."

"Why don't you change out of your school shoes and keep an eye out for him while I finish talking to the chief?"

Jake opened the back door of the car and climbed inside. He rolled down the window, watching for his friend as he pulled off his shoes. Charley leaned a hip against the fender of the car.

"You still haven't found Tully Jackson?" Maggie asked.

"Not a sign. I swear to God, that man has lit out of town. I've had every officer on the police force looking for him. We've combed all his usual haunts and haven't picked up so much as a scent of him."

"Does he have a permanent place here in Delbrook?" Maggie asked.

"Beats the hell out of me."

Charley's voice was harsh with frustration. His eyes were focused on a spot behind Maggie, and she finally realized he was staring at Jake. He lowered his voice.

"Sometime when I'm not around, you might ask Jake and Kenny if they know where Tully lives. I have the distinct feeling that they know more than they're telling. They always spent a lot of time hanging around the boat ramp, and they may be the only ones who know how to get in contact with Tully."

"I'll ask," she said, "but I'm sure if Jake knew, he would have told you when you asked him before."

Maggie really wasn't so sure of that. Jake counted the eccentric loner as his friend and wasn't particularly fond of the chief of police. If Jake thought Charley was unfairly pursuing Tully, he'd balk at telling him anything.

"Tully's been a thorn in my side for ages. I've tried to get rid of him for years, and now my failure to do that has cost George his life."

"You don't know for certain that Tully killed George," she said, all too aware of Jake's listening ears.

"It's just the sort of thing people who are living on the fringe of society are capable of. They're so alienated from the rest of us that when something happens to set them off, they just go berserk."

Charley pushed away from the car and paced a few feet away as if he was too wound up to remain still. His face was flushed, and his hands were squeezed into fists.

"I feel so damn bad about George, Maggie," he said, facing her. "Doris has been pushing me to run for mayor in the next election, but I haven't been all that keen on it. But I tell you true. If I can nail Tully and wind this case up, I believe I will do just that."

"Mom says it's going to rain tonight," Jake said.

The rest of his words were inaudible as he leaned over to whisper in Kenny's ear. There was something furtive about the gesture that gave Maggie the uneasy feeling the boys were hatching something. She wished she'd talked to them before she picked up Grant. It was too late now. Camp Delbrook was just ahead.

"Try to stay out of trouble while we're at the camp," she said over her shoulder to the boys in the backseat.

"We will, Mom," Jake said much too quickly. "Do you think Mr. Rossiter will take him to see the birds?"

Maggie eyed Jake in the rearview mirror, but his head was bent, so she couldn't see his face. Unwilling to lie to him, she had let Grant introduce himself as Edna's nephew from Chicago. For some reason, Jake refused to address Grant directly. She had suggested "Mr. Holbrook," "Cousin Grant" or simply "Grant," but Jake didn't seem comfortable with any of the names.

"That depends on his schedule and the birds," Maggie said.

"I don't think I've ever seen a hawk up close," Grant said. "Are there a lot of birds, Jake?"

After a short silence, Jake replied, his tone grudging. "No. Just four."

"In one big cage?" Grant asked.

"No, separate. It's hard to explain."

Maggie cleared her throat, and Jake saw her watching him in the mirror. He ducked his head, but not before she'd seen his awareness of his rudeness.

"Mr. Rossiter has two birds that he keeps in the mews," he said. "The other two birds belong to Mrs. Prentice."

"That's Connie," Maggie said to help Grant keep the names straight.

She turned in between the square stone pillars at the entrance to Camp Delbrook and pulled up alongside the gatehouse. She rolled down the window as Joyce Albrecht looked up from the book she was reading. As near as Maggie could tell, the uniformed guard read only World War II novels, preferring the ones with garish swastikas on the cover. Joyce set the book down and walked outside the security office, smiling as she recognized Maggie.

"I heard about your father-in-law and I was sorry," she said. "George was an upright man. I'll miss seeing him around here."

"We all will, Joyce. Thanks for your kind thoughts." Maggie indicated Grant in the passenger seat. "This is Grant Holbrook."

"Ah, Edna's nephew. The lawyer from Chicago." Joyce leaned over, hands on her thighs so she could look in the window. "Glad to meet you. I

heard you were living at George's house with Ham Rice. Will you be staying long?"

"I'm not sure," Grant said. "I'm giving Maggie a hand settling
George's affairs."

"Hi, boys," Joyce said, her gaze shifting to the backseat. "If you're
running around in the camp, stay away from the dining hall. A ton of volunteers are arriving today to help with the fall cleanup this week."

"Kenny's dad already warned him," Jake, the spokesman, said.

"They're creating a temporary dormitory out of half the dining hall,
and they don't need any distractions from you two," she said, standing upright, her eyes frosty as she stared at the boys. With a nod, she stepped
away from the car and waved them through.

"Word is out," Maggie said with a sideways glance at Grant. "It's a
small town. Everyone knows everyone's business."

"So I gather." Grant grinned. "Do you suppose for the rest of my life
people will refer to me as Edna's nephew?"

"For as long as you're here," Maggie said. She pointed to the empty
flat land along the top of the ridge. "This is where the Renaissance Faire
is held. Nothing much to see now. The village houses are just stage sets,
and they're folded up and stored until next year. Just over the hill beyond
this flat area are the stables. Bleacher seats are put up around the exercise
ring to create the jousting arena."

"It's sad when they take everything down." Jake stared morosely out
the window. "It was cool when all the banners were up and you could
walk around the village and see the jugglers and magicians. Now it's just
trees and dirt and the old buildings."

"Make-believe can be much more exciting than real life," Grant said,
clearly in sympathy with the boy.

"Maybe so, but this view is hard to beat," Maggie said, bringing the
car to a halt as they rounded a bend and came to the top of the steep hill
leading down to the lake.

The dirt and gravel road wound past, dark red- and green-sided
buildings nestled among the foliage on the hillside. The green shingle
roofs blended into the landscape, and even the white trim on doorways,
porches and windows didn't look out of place. At the base of the hill, flickering through the leaves like an aquamarine, was Falcon Lake.

Maggie drove slowly, pointing out the administration building, the dining hall, the outdoor theater and some of the cottages, feeling self-conscious between Grant's intense scrutiny and her awareness of the boys in the backseat, listening to every word.

"In case you're housebound," she said, "this is a great place to get some exercise. If you stop by the administration office tomorrow, you can get a map of Camp Delbrook. Along with indicating the roads and hiking trails, it shows a layout of the whole campground."

Grant nodded absently as if his mind were already making an inventory of the structures and the terrain beyond the windshield. Maggie knew she'd never view the camp the same again. She stared at each building, wondering what secrets were held behind the walls.

Driving through the camp on the way to Hugh's, Maggie could feel a rising tension. Suggesting that Grant come with her today had been easy enough to propose, but now that they were here, she felt a vague sense of betrayal.

How could she even consider that Hugh could be involved in George's death or the kidnapping of a child? She knew Hugh. He was a friend. Could she be such a bad judge of character that she wouldn't recognize a truly evil person?

Her mind buzzed with questions as she thought back over all the conversations she'd had with Hugh, searching for clues to his moral center. It was frightening that she couldn't say with any certainty that Hugh was innocent.

If she couldn't exonerate Hugh, how on earth would she be able to evaluate the rest of the people on the list of suspects?

At the bottom of the winding road, she drove along the lakefront, passing the swimming beach and the boat docks until she reached an L-shaped turn that meandered back up to the entrance to the camp. Beyond the turn was a parking lot that led into Hugh Rossiter's landscaping business.

She pulled into a parking space in front of the two-story house with the white porch that faced out onto the lake. Jake and Kenny bolted out of the car, bounding up the porch stairs to disappear inside as the screen door slammed behind them.

"Not a bad view," Grant said, getting out of the car to stare at the lake. "I've never been up to Falcon Lake before, and I can't imagine why. Not only is it beautiful, but it's incredibly peaceful."

Maggie laughed. "You ought to see it before Labor Day. The people who live along the shore put up with the chaos just for days like this after the summer crowd goes home."

The screen door squeaked, and Maggie turned to see Hugh Rossiter framed in the doorway.

"Is it OK for Jake to have something to eat? Kenny said they were starving," he said.

"School was boring, and their lunches were too skimpy," Maggie said. "I heard a litany of woes on the way over here."

"I turned them loose in the kitchen." Hugh came down the stairs, holding out his hand to Grant. "Good to see you again, Grant. I didn't realize you were staying on."

"Just giving Maggie a hand," Grant said. "This is quite a place you've got. I can't believe how extensive the camp is. When it's in full swing the place must be pretty busy. Doesn't that get in the way of your business?"

"When the camp's in session, we come and go through the other side of the parking lot. This entrance is gated. That discourages most of the intruders." Hugh smiled, his teeth flashing in his tanned face. "Occasionally we find some idiot wandering through the nursery or the greenhouses, but they're usually lost. They're grateful to be led back to the camp."

"Do you live here?" Grant asked.

"I used to have a place in town, but eventually I was spending all my time here anyway, so I couldn't see any sense in driving back and forth."

"It probably gives you more time with your son, too," Grant said. "How much land have you got?"

"Just twenty acres. Most of it's uphill, but the college rents us some tillable fields as a part of an agriculture internship they run. It's a win-win situation. They train future farmers and agrochemists, and we grow plants and trees for the nursery business. Would you like a tour?"

"If you've got the time," Grant said.

Maggie couldn't believe how talkative Hugh was. Usually he answered her questions with a series of grunts or nods of the head. It must be a guy thing, she thought with some resentment. As if Hugh sensed her annoyance, he turned to her.

"Want to come too?" he asked, putting an arm around her shoulders and leading her up the stairs.

"No. I'll keep an eye on the boys," she said, flushing when she saw Grant's sharpened interest at Hugh's familiarity. "I have a feeling they're up to something."

"Crap! Don't tell me we're in for another suspension from school."

"Last time," Maggie explained to Grant, "they smuggled a snake into school and let it loose during lunch hour. The boys explained to Mrs. Micheff, the principal, that it was just a baby and wasn't even poisonous, but she didn't see a lot of humor in the prank."

Grant laughed. "Remind me to give you both my card. I have the distinct feeling these boys will need a good defense lawyer in their later years."

Inside, the room on the left, originally the dining room, held a large counter across the open archway, behind which three women were working. Computers, phones, fax machines and copiers were part of the equipment that covered the desks. On the right, the living room had been turned into Hugh's office and was enclosed by a set of oak French doors that opened off the foyer. Along with a desk and credenza, there was a round conference table covered with landscape drawings and plant catalogs.

Hugh led the way down the hall toward the back of the house and pushed open the door to the kitchen to the accompanying sound of breaking glass. Kenny and Jake were staring down at the jar of mayonnaise that had shattered on the tile floor.

"Sorry for the mess, Dad," Kenny said in his whispery voice. "We were making sandwiches."

"So I see." Hugh's voice boomed around the walls. "Well, don't just stand there. Get this mess cleaned up."

"Yes, sir," Jake said, pulling Kenny by the sleeve of his shirt toward the sink. "You get the paper towels, Kenny. I'll get the wastebasket."

"Why don't you show Grant around, and I'll give the boys a hand?" Maggie suggested.

Hugh reached up to the pegboard beside the refrigerator and took down a ring of keys attached to a round plastic disk. Inside the disk there was a picture of a hawk, wings spread wide in flight.

With one more sharp glance at the two boys, Hugh led the way back outside.

Grant was surprised at Hugh's strong reaction to the mishap. Spills and kids generally went hand in hand. A single father should be used to it. More worrisome for Grant was the flash of fear he'd seen cross Kenny's face as the boy stared up at his father.

"I'll take you over to the mews," Hugh said.

"That'd be great. Jake was telling me a little about the hawks," Grant said. "I never realized there were falconry clubs around. How'd you get interested in it?"

Obviously Grant had hit the right subject. Hugh's tight-lipped frown was replaced by a lighter expression.

"My dad had a friend, Patrick O'Shea, who had learned falconry in Ireland. I used to spend a lot of time at his place. O'Shea saw I was willing to give the time to the sport, so he took me on as his apprentice. It's a highly regulated sport."

"Does it take a long time to get proficient?" Grant asked.

"Two-year apprenticeship with an experienced falconer. You can't get a hawk before you take an exam and have the required housing for the bird."

"Why so tough?"

"For the bird's protection. Falconry is a major commitment. Anything less is detrimental to the bird's health and well-being." Hugh paused. "Don't get me started. I'm pretty obsessive about the subject. I'll take you up to the mews, and you can see for yourself. That's better than a lecture any day."

Hugh led the way around the side of the house to a mulched trail that led off the service road toward two red-sided structures in a clearing. The first building was a large equipment storage and repair shed. The double doors stood open, and Grant could see a submerged pit for oil changes on the left. Around the sides and along the back there were enough used parts for garden, hardware and automotive equipment to rival any repair superstore.

"We use a lot of machines," Hugh said. "Give them hard use. I had this equipment garage built about ten years ago and hired a full-time mechanic. April through October, when we're busiest, we usually take on one or two additional guys."

Grant liked the fact that the equipment garage had been built to match the older structure on the other side of the clearing. Dating back at least seventy years, the red-sided building was oval with a steeply slanted, green shingled roof that rose to a netted center opening.

"This is the mews," Hugh said, pulling out the ring of keys on the plastic disk.

He unlocked the dead bolt on the door and led Grant into the building, closing and locking the door behind them. Walking through the tunnel, they entered the inner circle of the mews.

The center yard, a hard-packed dirt surface, was open to the sky, and the late afternoon sun illuminated a row of three-sided roofed structures. Plastic netting was fastened securely to close off the fourth side on the front of each cage. Some sort of blind was pulled down on the outside of the netting in three of the cages, but Grant had an unobstructed view into the fourth. He had been expecting to feel sorry for the birds in confinement and was pleasantly surprised at how spacious their living quarters were. Each cage was twelve foot square with a ceiling height of nine feet.

"In England this is called a weathering. The birds require a place to shelter from the elements that's safe from predators and easy to keep clean. With this arrangement I can power hose inside the cage and spray the place with disinfectant. I like to keep things pretty simple. The floor is uncrushed pea gravel. It's rounded stone so if a bird picks up a piece to aid in digestion, it won't do her any damage when she regurgitates it."

"One bird to a cage?"

"Yes. We've got plenty of room here."

As he approached the cage, Hugh let out three short whistles followed by soft squeaking sounds as he drew air in through his closed lips.

"This is Morgana. She's a female goshawk. A shortwing. I've had her for three years. Keep your voice low and your movements to a minimum," Hugh cautioned. "She's a solitary bird and fairly shy, especially around strangers."

"A female?"

"The females are bigger and stronger than the males, so they can strike down larger prey."

Grant eyed the bird that was standing on the shelf, high on the back wall of the chamber. He had to admit she was impressive. She stood about fifteen inches tall. Her chest was gray with thin horizontal stripes in black, black wings and a black-and-gray-striped tail. A slash of white feathers, like eyebrows, gave her a haughty look and added to the piercing quality of her red eyes.

"What does she hunt?" Grant asked, keeping his voice low.

"A wide variety of prey. She'll fly at squirrels, rabbits and even pheasants."

"How long does it take to train a bird?"

"Ten to twelve weeks initially," Hugh said. "The process is called manning. Basically the hawk has to lose its natural fear of man. I chose a bird that will imprint. During the training period, I'm the one who provides food, shelter and entertainment. She depends on me for everything."

"A parent and child relationship," Grant said.

He stared hard at the beautiful bird in the cage, all too aware that part of his objective was to find out if somewhere else in the building there wasn't another caged animal. Not a bird this time, but a child.

"I saw a documentary once that showed a falcon hunt," he said. "Even on film it's exciting, so I can imagine the thrill when it's real. Don't you have to worry the first time you release the bird that she won't come back?"

"Not if you've trained her right." Hugh's gaze was intense as he watched the hawk and scanned the inside of the cage. "Before she's entered, she's been flown on a creance, which is a braided field leash, and she's become familiar with a swing lure."

He turned his head and grinned, and this time the smile was genuine.

"I know much of this is gibberish to you," Hugh said, "but it's hard for me to break it down into really simple terms. That's why I don't do many of the show-and-tell programs at the schools. Connie is good at those, but I'm not patient enough. I always get some smart-mouthed kid who asks a stupid question to see if he can get a laugh from his peers."

"I'll keep that in mind," Grant said.

Hugh let out a sharp bark of laughter, cutting it off immediately when the hawk spread her wings and hopped along the shelf. Grant was curious to learn more about the exotic sport. He could see why someone could get hooked on it.

"Do you bring the hawks inside during the winter?" he asked.

"No. Because of the way the building's constructed, we don't have to worry about the wind, only falling temperatures. If you look, up above the perch there's a heat bulb that I can turn on when the weather is really nasty. The shade on the outside of the netting rolls down to keep the drafts out and hold in the heat."

"How many birds do you have here?" Grant asked, looking along the line of cages.

"Connie keeps two birds here." Hugh pointed to the cages at the end of the line. "They're both gyrfalcons. She prefers them because they're the largest and fastest of all the falcons. They're also willful, refusing to do anything they don't see any point in doing. Sort of like Connie herself."

"I've only just met her," Grant said, "but she has the same elegant poise as your hawk and gives the impression she's only waiting for a moment of freedom so she can spread her wings and soar."

"Not a bad assessment, Grant," Hugh said. "I'm sorry you can't see her hawks now, but they're in the last stage of the molt. That's why the blinds are drawn. If a hawk gets upset, the new feathers could grow in with fret marks, sort of a fault bar which weakens the feather."

Hugh pointed to the closed cage beside Morgana's.

"My second bird is a peregrine falcon. She's a longwing in her fifth season, almost at her full potential. She's got a case of bumblefoot from a trauma to her ankle. I'm treating her with an antibiotic and trying to keep her quiet for a couple days. As the master falconer I can have three birds, but with my business I don't have the time for another one."

"From what I've seen, it's an enormous time commitment," Grant said. "Where do you get the birds?"

"Connie bought her two from a breeder. Paid big tickets for them." Hugh snorted in disapproval. "Thirteen thousand for Rowena and a whopping fifteen thou for Isolde."

"Judas! Not only a time-consuming sport," Grant said, "but a costly one as well. Just this building is a major investment."

"I've only had this arrangement for the last ten years. When I decided to build the equipment barn, Connie suggested I renovate this building into a mews. Brent designed the plans and worked with the construction people to get it right. Connie and I split the expenses, and we've hired someone to do most of the cleaning and some of the day-to-day checking on the birds."

"Who watches the birds when you're on vacation?" Grant asked.

"Most falconers don't vacation without their birds."

Grant thought Hugh might be kidding, but he could hear no hint of amusement in his voice. He had noticed that when Hugh smiled, it rarely touched his eyes. Probably his business sense had taught him to be gracious and charming, but in actual fact, he appeared to have little sense of humor.

Aware of Grant's surprise, Hugh continued.

"That's not totally true. Connie's going to Europe next month for four weeks, so I'll be taking care of her birds. It coincides with some renovation work being done on the mews, so I'll probably move all of them to a temporary site so they aren't upset by the noise and confusion."

"Do you breed the birds?" Grant asked as he followed Hugh around the complex.

"No. I leave that to the experts. The bald eagle is a great example of a successful breeding program. It brought them back from the brink of extinction. In 1963 there were only four hundred seventeen pairs in the lower forty-eight states. Now there are more than five thousand pairs."

"So many things to learn," Grant said.

Hugh shrugged. "Sorry. I tend to run on."

"To be perfectly honest, I'd like to hear more. Does anyone in your club hunt with an eagle?"

"No. Because of their size and weight, the logistics are complicated," Hugh said. "You need a much larger cage to accommodate the wingspan, and all your equipment needs to be heavy-duty. Even the glove. An eagle could crush your hand in an ordinary falconer's glove. They're aggressive, and combined with the fact they're so fiercely territorial, a falconer has to be aware of the presence of danger whenever he works with them."

"Sounds more like drudgery than fun."

"If you want fun, you ought to see the peregrine in flight. You can see why she merits such high esteem from falconers. She's built for speed chases and steep plunging dives, called stoops."

For the first time, Grant could see that Hugh was answering on an emotional level rather than an intellectual plane. He had wondered how the man could devote so much time and energy to the sport, but as he talked about the falcon, his face lit up and his words were almost poetic.

"Silhouetted against the sky she appears to be filled with joy as she circles and waits on the prey," Hugh continued. "At times it's like she's playing. She'll harass other birds by stooping at them without striking, tapping them with a closed foot. Just one touch and the falcon soars back up into the sky. Ultimate power. The choice of life over death."

CHAPTER
FIFTEEN

"CAN I GO UP in the treehouse, Mom?" Jake asked as they pulled into the parking lot behind George's house.

Maggie couldn't help the sinking feeling that she got in the pit of her stomach. She never would have believed a time would come that she'd be nervous about leaving Jake alone outside George's house, but each day her fear for his safety grew stronger and made it more difficult for her to let him out of her sight.

"Mom? Can I?"

"Sorry, Jake. I was daydreaming," Maggie said. "Yes. You can play out here for a bit, but not long. It's five o'clock, and I'm already starving."

"You can stay here for dinner," Grant said. "Ham and I are going to order chicken."

"I like chicken," Jake said, getting out of the car and pulling on his backpack.

"Not tonight," Maggie said. "It's a school night, and you've got homework."

She waited below while Jake climbed the ladder. He looked unbalanced with the bulky backpack, but he moved steadily up the rungs and opened the trapdoor in the bottom of the treehouse. She held her breath as he teetered on the top step, pulled off the backpack and shoved it through the opening, then disappeared inside.

"What a great place for a kid to play," Grant said as he followed Maggie to the back door of the house. "I went up there yesterday and I was impressed. I tried not to think of insurance claims and viewed it from the perspective of a child, and I had to admit, it's a winner."

"It took me a while before I was comfortable with him playing up there. George and my husband convinced me that a boy needed independence and that I had to let him go. It's not easy being a mom," Maggie said with a final glance at the treehouse.

"You must have heard me opening the refrigerator," Ham said as they entered the kitchen. "I was getting a beer. How about you?"

"Draw two," Maggie said.

"Make it three," Grant added.

Ham pulled the cold bottles out of the refrigerator, opened them and handed them around. Maggie sat down at the kitchen table.

"How'd it go over at the camp?" Ham asked. "Did you get in to see the birds?"

"Yes," Grant said. "It's quite a setup. Hugh showed me all around the mews. As far as I can tell, we saw every part of the place, including storerooms and the clinic. I tried to consider the outer dimensions of the building, and there were no spaces unaccounted for. No secret rooms. No locked doors."

"Don't sound so discouraged," Ham said. "It's early days yet. You didn't really think you'd hit the jackpot first time out."

Grant shrugged. "I'm the optimistic type. Then Hugh took me through the greenhouses and chemical sheds. No hesitation that I could pick up about looking through any of the buildings. He was very hospitable for a man who's got a business to attend to. By the time we'd covered the lot, Maggie and the boys were waiting by the car. I never did ask what you and the boys did."

"It took a while for Kenny and Jake to finish cleaning up the mess from the broken mayonnaise jar. They suggested we take a march up into the woods. The boys took their backpacks and enough supplies to last us if we got lost. We went up past the mews and then crossed over into the campground. They dragged me through the outdoor theater and a couple other buildings. They were all empty."

She took a sip of the cold beer, sighing at the bite in the back of her throat as she swallowed. She understood how Grant felt. Each time she and the boys had approached a building, she was disappointed when she found it vacant.

"By the way," Ham said. "I got hold of Dave Gerbitz. He's making copies of some aerial pictures of the golf course and the camp, and I added Connie and Brent's place on the south side of the lake."

"It's a pretty substantial piece of property," Maggie explained to Grant. "It was her grandfather's estate, and Connie inherited it when her father died."

"Any chance of finding out what killed her father?" Grant asked. "I gather there's some mystery there."

Ham tilted his head back and scratched under his chin. "Connie and Brent have been married seventeen years. Her father died about a year after the wedding. I was already in Chicago when I heard about the fire, but I don't remember any of the details. I'll ask Nell. If she doesn't know, she'll know whom to ask."

"Nell may have an idea of the layout of Connie and Brent's place. We'll need to check it out," Grant said. "Once you get the pictures of the camp and the country club, we'll mark off each of the buildings as we inspect them. That way we'll have less chance of missing one."

"Look, Grant, we're never going to find Tyler working this way," Maggie said, verbalizing her frustration at the enormity of the project. "At least when you're looking for a needle, there's only one haystack."

"Don't get discouraged, kiddo," Ham said. "Crimes are never solved without one hellava lot of footwork."

"When I was walking with the boys over at the camp today, I realized that if whoever is holding Tyler gets wind of the fact we're searching for him, all he has to do is move him to one of the places we've already ruled out."

"You're right, but we have to make a try at finding him," Ham said, looking to Grant for support.

"I've had similar misgivings, although my real fear is that the kidnapper will decide that Tyler is a risk." The scar rippled as Grant clenched his jaw. "The clock is ticking. The longer we investigate, the more chance there is that the kidnapper will become aware of our activities."

"Today is Wednesday," Ham said. "George died on Saturday. How long do we have?"

"By Sunday my continued presence in Delbrook will be hard to justify," Grant said.

Damn, Maggie thought. He was an annoyance she could do without, but she had to admit she'd hate to see him go back to Chicago. Despite his uptight attitude, he had a solid reliability that she appreciated since her entire world seemed to be shifting and changing.

"What can we do to improve the odds?" she asked.

"Using the facts we have, we've got to narrow down the list of suspects," Grant said. "The only real hope we have of finding Tyler is to figure out who killed George. Once we know that, we'll be able to pinpoint where to search."

"So we investigate the people, not the places?" Maggie asked.

"We do both." Grant grinned. "Even if I'm a hard-assed lawyer, I was raised on Perry Mason and those last-minute miracle endings. Who knows? We could find Tyler."

"Why not?" Ham said. "I drove over to Milwaukee today to look up an old girlfriend of mine. Paula Craig is on the police force there. Paula used to be with animal control but now works homicide. She told me if I came back tomorrow, she'd get me a look at the police reports on the little girl found at the zoo."

"Great work, Ham," Grant said, saluting him with his beer bottle. "I've been talking to Michelle Hoppe, the principal at Eddie Harland's school. She tried to convince Eddie's parents to talk to me after Tyler disappeared. She was devastated when they refused. She's always been convinced that the boy will eventually self-destruct if he doesn't talk about his experiences."

"Poor little bugger," Ham said. "I've investigated a lot of child abuse cases. Bottling up traumas only increases the pressure, and these kids eventually explode."

"Mrs. Hoppe called me about a month ago," Grant said. "She wanted to know if Tyler had been found. Apparently she's established a solid relationship with Mrs. Harland and has been talking to her about getting psychiatric help for Eddie. Eddie's nine, and according to Mrs. Hoppe, he's depressed. Failing in school and generally withdrawing."

"It's so hard being a parent," Maggie said. "All you want is what's best for your child, but there are no hard and fast rules to guide you. I'm sure Eddie's parents thought they were doing the right thing by letting him bury the experience. First they have to deal with their guilt over the kidnapping, and now a double whammy if he's coming apart."

"That's exactly the situation. Mrs. Harland won't let anyone talk *to* Eddie, but she may be willing to talk *about* him."

"That would at least be something," Ham said.

Grant looked across the table at Maggie. The muscles across her shoulders began to tighten with the intensity of his gaze.

"I talked to the principal earlier today, and she thought Mrs. Harland might talk to you," Grant said.

"Me?" Her stomach fluttered at his words, and her hand tightened around the beer bottle. "I'm not qualified. I don't know enough about the case."

"It doesn't matter," Grant said. His gaze held hers, refusing to let her back away. "You're a mother of a boy Eddie's age. You'll be able to understand her fears more easily than I can. In my opinion, she'll speak to you more freely than she will to me."

Maggie's gaze traveled back and forth between the two men, seeing the appeal in their eyes. The whole idea terrified her. The responsibility was too much.

"Not a chance. You're the lawyer. You've had training on how to interrogate a witness. I'd screw it up," she said, verbalizing her fear.

"We'll be no worse off than we are at this point. Besides, you owe me one," he said, wincing as he touched the cut on the side of his head.

"Really, Holbrook, you can't throw that in my face at every turn. The damn thing's nearly healed, so give it a rest."

A boyish grin stretched his mouth, and his eyes flashed.

"I'm not too proud to beg," he said. "If the principal can get Mrs. Harland to talk, will you do it?"

It was strange, Maggie thought. Although she had agreed to help Grant with the investigation, she had never really believed that she would have anything of importance to contribute. As much as the prospect frightened her, here was at least a chance for her to do something concrete.

"Yes," she said. "I'll talk to her."

As she looked at the two men, it seemed to her as if she'd passed some test. That thought didn't offer a great deal of comfort when she compared it to the possibility that she might fail to learn anything of consequence. She'd just have to wait and see.

"I'm supposed to call Mrs. Hoppe back tonight," Grant said. "If it's possible, I'd like to set it up for tomorrow."

"So soon? Where does Eddie live?" she asked.

"Detroit. We can fly up in the morning and be back before Jake gets out of school," Grant said.

"I can't just take off for Detroit at a moment's notice," Maggie said.

"Why not?" Ham asked.

"Because," she said. Seeing Ham's grin, she wanted to smack him. "Does it have to be tomorrow?"

"Mrs. Harland is very ambivalent. We have to act quickly, before she gets cold feet and backs out," Grant said. "I know it's asking a lot of you, but could you go tomorrow?"

Maggie threw up her hands in defeat. "Yes, I can go. Let me know if the interview is on and what time the flights are so I can make some arrangements for Jake."

"I'll call you as soon as I know," Grant said.

"I'd like to make a suggestion," Ham said. "I think you should say you're going into Milwaukee for a day of shopping."

"What?" Maggie said.

"For you to fly off to Detroit for a day trip is out of the ordinary for you," Ham said. "It will raise more questions than you want to answer. Someone in Delbrook is watching for any strange behavior and might put two and two together and come up with Eddie Harland."

"I hadn't thought it through," Grant said, "but I think you're right."

"Do you know how many lies I've told since I met you?" Maggie set her beer bottle down on the table with a thump and glared at Grant. "I'll have to lie to Jake. I hate lying. I'm not good at it."

"Actually, kiddo," Ham said with a smirk, "you're getting better at it every day."

"Oh stuff it," she snapped.

"I'll take care of everything," Grant said.

He pulled open one of the kitchen drawers and reached in for the yellow lined pad he'd used the day before. He seemed perfectly at home in his surroundings, she noted with annoyance.

"Shouldn't you be going back to Chicago? What about your job?" she asked.

"Technically, I'm on vacation," he said. "I managed to shuffle a few cases around and got a continuance on an upcoming trial, which gives me a bit of breathing space."

"Does your firm know why you're in Delbrook?" Ham asked.

"Only one of the partners. I talked to him Sunday morning before I drove up here."

Maggie couldn't resist asking the question that had been nagging at her ever since she'd heard Grant's story. "Did you tell your sister that you might have a lead to Tyler?"

"No." Grant bit off the single word.

"If it were my child," Maggie said, "I'd want to know, no matter how slim the possibility was that it would amount to anything."

Grant didn't answer immediately. The muscles along his jawline rippled, and she could see the scar clearly.

"When Tyler disappeared, Barbara had just discovered she was pregnant. With the trauma of the kidnapping, she had a miscarriage."

"Oh, God. I'm so sorry," Maggie said.

"She's pregnant again. Seven months along," Grant said. "I can't risk doing anything that might upset her. It would kill her if she lost this baby, too."

Grant propped his feet up on the railing of the redwood deck, watching the play of lightning over the lake. Since his arrival at George's house four days ago, he'd made a point of sitting outside as much as he could. The early evenings had been perfect deck weather. No bugs, mid-seventies with a breeze off the lake. When he returned to Chicago, he'd miss this pleasant interlude.

It had been so long since he'd permitted himself any moments of quiet solitude. His every waking breath was taken up with surviving another day with the twin demons of guilt and regret riding herd on any attempts at self-analysis.

Neither Barbara nor Ken had ever blamed him for Tyler's kidnapping by as much as a glance or a sharp word. Perhaps if they had, he would have been able to deal with his own sense of responsibility. If he'd stayed in Cleveland one more day, Barbara wouldn't have taken Tyler shopping.

So much had changed since Tyler's disappearance.

He'd put his law practice on hold while he lived in Cleveland, helping his sister and her husband during the first weeks after the kidnapping.

Before the kidnapping, Grant had been a celebrated criminal defense attorney, representing any client who had the money to pay for his high-priced services. The guilt or innocence of a client had no bearing on his performance or dedication. Like most lawyers, he had a good idea of culpability after building the case and listening to the presentation by the prosecution.

If the price was right, it didn't matter what kind of a scumbag he returned to the streets. He had an occasional twinge of guilt when the crime was particularly brutal and he won the case, but he'd soothed his conscience with the adage that he was only an instrument of justice.

During the investigation into Tyler's disappearance, he'd learned more than he wanted to know about the perverts who preyed on children. He'd listened to the horror stories of repeat offenders in child molestation and pedophilia cases and no longer had the stomach to defend some of the clients who wanted his services.

When his engagement to Veronica ended, he'd left the law firm where her father was a partner and moved to a small firm, taking only clients whom he unconditionally believed were innocent. Most who wanted his services didn't fall into that category, so he had plenty of time to devote to his investigation of Tyler's disappearance.

And that had brought him to the redwood deck overlooking Falcon Lake. His mind was drifting, lulled by the beauty of the reds and purples of the sunset, when he heard footsteps coming along the side of the house. He was surprised that Ham had returned so quickly with the fried chicken.

"How close is that chicken place?" he asked. He turned to see Connie Prentice standing at the bottom of the steps to the redwood deck. "Oh, sorry. I thought you were Ham."

"I hope that's not some sort of pork reference or I'll be insulted," she said.

"Here, let me help you," he said. He crossed the deck to stand above her, holding out his hand to take the bag she was holding. "Bearing gifts?"

"Actually, it's dinner. I thought I'd better bring it over before the rain hits. I can't believe Hamilton is much of a cook, and I didn't know if you were. It's a chicken casserole, but I gather a chicken is already on the way."

"It is, but this will be a welcome addition to our bachelor stocked refrigerator." He took the bag and waited while she climbed the stairs. "I think we have twelve beers, two bags of chips and assorted dips. And of course, since it's Wisconsin, we have a couple sticks of spicy venison jerky and a bag of cheese curds."

"I hate curds," she said. "They squeak when you bite into them. I'd take one of those beers, if you're offering."

"Coming up. Make yourself at home."

Grant opened the screen door and took the bag to the kitchen. He unpacked it, putting everything in the refrigerator except for the brownies, which he set on the counter for later consumption. He opened two bottles of beer, found a beer glass in the cupboard and headed back to the deck. Connie was in the living room, looking at the pictures over George's desk.

Several of the drawers were partially open, as if she'd been searching for something.

"Shall we go back outside?" he said, holding the screen door open for her. "Ham should be back momentarily, and I'm sure we'll have enough chicken if you'd like to share."

"Thanks, no. The beer will be fine. Brent and I ate earlier."

He poured part of the beer into the glass and handed it to her. She took it and walked across to stare out over the trees at the lake, then turned around and hitched a hip up onto the railing. She saluted him with the glass, and he raised his beer bottle in response.

"To George. Damn, but I miss him." She sipped her beer, one eyebrow raised in amusement as his eyes roamed over her.

He had to admit, yellow enhanced her bronzed skin and blond hair, adding depth to her green eyes. She was a beautiful woman and she knew it. Definitely high maintenance with her diamond earrings, diamond and emerald rings and the wide gold bracelet on her wrist. He'd known enough women like Connie in Veronica's circle to recognize that her appearance was the tool she'd use for manipulation and barter.

Maggie's face flashed into his mind, and he was surprised at the feeling of warmth that invaded his body as he contrasted the two women. He preferred Maggie's softness to the brittle quality of Connie's overt sensuality.

"Do you always wear yellow?" he asked as he noted the expensive lemony silk shorts and matching blouse.

"How clever of you," she said. "You've only seen me a few times and yet you figured it out. It took Brent almost six months. Of course, he's my husband, so he doesn't have to notice."

"Lawyers are paid to be observant."

"You look like you're enjoying your visit to Delbrook," Connie said, looking at him over the rim of her glass.

"I feel downright decadent in blue jeans. I spend the better part of my life in button-down shirts and suits. My casual wear is a blazer. I'm enjoying the change."

"My mother always thought that a woman who was not wearing a dress, nylons, a slip and a girdle had gone 'native.' I can't imagine what she would think of this outfit."

She held her arms out wide to give him the whole effect.

"I'm sure she'd be jealous of the tan," he said. "I don't mean to be offensive, but may I ask you a question?"

Her eyes held his for a moment, speculation in their depth. "Go ahead. I can always refuse to answer."

"What were you looking for in George's desk?"

Aside from an archly raised eyebrow, his straightforward question didn't appear to ruffle her. She didn't answer immediately, and he sensed that she was deciding whether to give him the truth or make something up. She took a long swallow, finished the beer, and set the glass on the top of the railing.

"Thanks to my mother's obsession with golf and the fact there was a swimming pool there, I grew up at the country club. Mark Collier, Maggie's husband, was just a couple years younger than I was. We spent a lot of time together when George was playing cards."

Grant wondered where Connie's discourse was heading. She seemed content to talk, and he pulled up a chair, propped up his feet and watched the play of emotions across her face.

"Mark was your first love?"

"Lover, yes. Love, no." She gave him a quick smile, teeth a flash of white in the tanned face. "The story in Delbrook is that Mark Collier was the model son, loving husband and all-around great father. The truth is, he was a real bastard. The original roving eye. I doubt if he had it in him to be faithful. The only person he loved was Mark Collier."

"Did Maggie know about the other women?"

"Yes."

The revelation surprised Grant. He mentally apologized to Maggie for assuming she had led a storybook life up until Mark's death. He should have known most fairy tales have a villain.

"So that's why you're hanging around Delbrook," she said.

Grant wanted to deny his interest in Maggie but knew she would see through his bluff. Besides, it was safer if people speculated that he was staying in town because of his attraction to her.

"I'll admit she intrigues me," he said.

"Just like Mark. At first I couldn't understand why he married Maggie. It's the eyes." Connie's mouth pulled into a twist of bitterness. "Blue eyes full of truth and goodness and honesty. Beneath that soft, sweet exterior, there's a banked fire that's a real challenge."

"She strikes me as a person with a strong moral compass. Why didn't she divorce her husband?"

"She would have stuck out the marriage for Jake's sake, but eventually Mark wanted out. When he asked her for a divorce, she agreed. I may be the only one to know that except Maggie."

"Mark told you?"

"Yes. We used to call each other a lot. I'm sure I knew more about his love life than Maggie. He liked to tell me about his other women. He told me once he loved the chase, not the conquest," Connie said, twisting the wide bracelet on her wrist. "Once he bedded them it was over. Most of the women let him go without too much of a fuss. Until he met Joy Edwards."

"Ah, I like the name," Grant said. "She gave him more joy than he'd expected?"

"You might say a whole bundle of joy." She laughed, the sound a sharp bark that held little amusement. "Joy Edwards was young, practical and determined to marry Mark when she discovered she was pregnant. She wanted the child to have a name."

"Just an old-fashioned girl."

"The last time I talked to Mark was the day of his accident. He and Joy were coming up to Wisconsin the next morning to tell George about his decision to divorce Maggie and remarry. Joy had insisted that he get George's approval. She was the traditional sort; she wanted to be part of a family, not an interloper."

"Was Mark pleased with the prospect of a new child?" Grant asked.

"No. He didn't like change. He didn't want to give up his established lifestyle. He did his best to hide his infidelities. He wanted everyone's approval, especially Jake's and his father's. He was worried that they would be angry when he told them about the divorce." She sighed, staring across at Grant for a moment before she continued. "The irony is that he and Joy and the baby were killed before he could tell anyone except Maggie and me."

"He went to the grave with his secrets intact," Grant said. "Hard on Maggie. Hard to live with that knowledge."

The chirp of crickets was the only sound to break the silence on the deck. Connie was relaxed, her legs crossed at the ankles as she leaned against the railing. Grant waited, wondering how they'd come so far afield from his original question.

"You're a good listener. Just like George," she said as if she had read his mind. "As I told you, I spent a lot of time at the country club. When it rained, I used to watch the card games. George was always kind to me. He never shooed me away from the table. That's how I learned to play poker."

"At George's knee?"

"Exactly. It wasn't until I was married that I was permitted into the weekly games. Things were fine until Mark died. Then George took up drinking as a serious endeavor. That and poker were his only interests. Sometimes he was so drunk that I'd drag him outside and walk him around the golf course until he was sober enough to play. All the time we walked, he would talk. Ranting mostly about the unfairness of life."

She must have seen the questioning expression on his face, because she grinned suddenly.

"You're probably wondering if there's a point to all this. I've been enjoying myself. I don't have that many people I can confide in. Do you suppose this conversation is covered under the lawyer-client privilege?"

"I think we could stretch it for that," he said. He returned her smile, liking her much more than he thought he would when she first arrived.

"All right, I'll get to it. During one of our walks, I told George that I thought Frank Woodman would make a good mayor and that I was encouraging him to run. I was worried that Charley Blessington would make a try for it. George said not to worry, that he had the one piece of evidence that would stop Charley in his tracks."

Grant dropped his feet to the deck and leaned forward in his chair. "And that was?"

Connie shook her head. "I don't know. He said he'd stumbled across something in Charley's background that would take him out of the running. When I asked what it was, he snapped his mouth shut and refused to tell me. All he'd say was that if Charley announced he was running, George would show him the report and that would be the end of that."

"So George had some kind of report," Grant said.

"Yes. That's what I was looking for in the desk. It was stupid, because I can't imagine he'd have left it right out in plain sight if it was something explosive. George said Charley would do anything to keep the information from getting out."

CHAPTER
SIXTEEN

MAGGIE WAS HALFWAY DOWN the staircase to the bookstore, carrying a laundry basket of dirty clothes, when a crash of thunder exploded over the house. Below her, lightning flashes illuminated the steps. Knowing the fragility of the electrical connections in the old house, she remained where she was.

The lights flickered and went out.

"Oh damn!" she muttered as she inched her way across the step until her hip touched the banister.

"Mom?" Jake yelled.

"Give it a minute," she called back.

She held her breath and waited. The lights blinked once, then popped back on. Overhead, the thunder grumbled as the storm closed in.

She retraced her steps, set the laundry basket down at the top of the stairs and headed along the hallway to the kitchen. The phone rang, and Jake tore out of his room, skidding past her.

"I'll get it," he yelled as he raced for the phone in the kitchen.

By the time Maggie arrived, Jake was talking into the phone.

"Just do it, Kenny," he said.

He turned his back to Maggie and spoke under his breath so that she didn't catch any more of the conversation. She opened the junk drawer, pulled out a flashlight and pressed the switch. A minuscule circle of light beamed out, slowly faded and died. No amount of tapping or pressing could rejuvenate it. Tossing it back in the drawer, she opened the cabinet over the stove and took out three votive candles in glass holders. Behind her, Jake hung up the phone.

"Can I have a candle in my room?" he asked, flinching at the boom of thunder outside.

The lights flickered, but this time they didn't go out.

"I'm not too keen on that," she said. "I'm going to light a couple candles before I go back down to finish the laundry, so if the lights go out you won't be in the dark."

She lit one and placed it on the counter. Carrying the other two, she went into the living room and lit another one and set it on the coffee table in front of the loveseat.

"What if the lights go out during the night?"

"I'll put one in my room and leave the door open so you can see the light. OK?"

"I guess so," Jake said.

"It's eight o'clock, so if you've finished your homework you can watch a half hour of television in here."

"I'm all done. I was just reading some stuff," he said, flopping down on the loveseat and reaching for the remote control.

"Keep the volume down," she said as the sound of the television followed her into the hall.

Maggie took the last candle and set it in the laundry basket just as the telephone rang. Rats! She'd never get finished at this rate. Once more Jake raced out to the kitchen and she stood at the top of the stairs waiting.

"It's for you, Mom. It's Aunt Nell."

Maggie went into her bedroom and picked up the portable phone. "I've got it, Jake."

"I'm sorry to be such a disappointment," Nell said after Jake hung up. "Obviously he was expecting someone more exciting. He's not at the age when the girls call all the time, is he?"

"No. Thank goodness. I'm not sure what's up. He's been jumping for the phone every time it rings," Maggie said. "I think Kenny's involved as well, so I'm expecting a call from school in the next day or so telling me that they've both been suspended again."

"Can you see why I was so thrilled to have girl children? They're wonderful to shop with and talk to, and hopefully they might even take care of me in my old age." Nell chuckled. "Although Jean Frances says the moment I look a bit shaky, it's bam, right into the rest home."

"First you've got to find a place that will take all your art supplies. How's the painting going?"

"Slow. I was planning on working late tonight, but with the light show outside it's hard to concentrate."

Maggie shivered as rain pelted the bedroom window. Wind whipped against the trees, and in the streetlights along the boardwalk she could see it roughening the surface of the lake. The temperature had dropped earlier in the evening, so it looked to be a cold, nasty night ahead.

"It's the same here. I'm doing laundry." Maggie jumped at the sound of the door buzzer. "Damn it, now someone's at the door."

"I'll get it," Jake yelled.

"Go ahead and see who it is," Nell said. "I didn't have anything of importance. I just wanted to make sure you were all right. Talk to you tomorrow."

Maggie hung up and walked along the hall as she heard the rumble of voices coming up the back stairs. To her surprise she found a very wet Brent Prentice standing in the middle of the kitchen, breathing heavily from the stair climbing.

"Sorry for not calling first, Maggie," he said, looking awkward as he stood holding a ceramic bowl covered in aluminum foil in one hand and a bag in the other. "I'm getting your floor all wet."

"Don't worry about the floor," she said, reaching out to take the foil-wrapped dish.

"I can take the bag," Jake said, earning a smile of approval from Maggie.

Even after his hands were free, Brent seemed unsure of what to do about the water that dripped off the edge of his raincoat, so he just remained where he was.

"Connie was taking something over to Ham and that cousin of Edna's and wanted me to bring this casserole over, but I suspect you've already had dinner. I had some errands to run and didn't realize it was getting so late."

"What's in the casserole?" Jake asked, prying up a corner of the aluminum foil.

"Jake," Maggie said, swatting his hands away from the dish.

"It's a chicken-and–water chestnut thing." Brent chuckled at Jake's less than enthusiastic expression. "Don't worry. There are chocolate brownies in the bag along with some rice and a salad."

"Thanks, Mr. Prentice. Brownies are my favorite," Jake said. He set the bag on the counter and disappeared into the living room.

"It'll be a real treat not to have to think about cooking a meal. Please tell Connie how much I appreciate her thoughtfulness," Maggie said.

She suspected that the gesture had been prompted by Brent. The old-fashioned tradition of providing food after a death seemed more in keeping with his character than Connie's.

"I'll tell her," he said. With the tips of his fingers, he smoothed the damp white hair at his temples.

"What a boob I am to let you stand around when you're soaked," Maggie said. "Would you like a drink before you head back out into the storm?"

Brent shook his head. "No. Thanks for the offer, but it's getting late."

"Well the least I can do is lend you an umbrella."

She flipped on the light in the stairwell and reached for the umbrella she kept with her raincoat on one of the clothes hooks on the wall. The hook was empty.

"Jake? Have you seen my umbrella?" When there was no immediate answer, she called again. "Jake? The umbrella?"

"Isn't on the stairs?" came the drowsy answer from the living room.

"No. It's not." Maggie frowned, trying to remember when she'd last seen it. She was too tired for guessing games. If she could remember where she'd left her raincoat, she'd probably find her umbrella.

"Please don't fuss," Brent said. "I'm parked right out in back and I'm heading home. Just thought I'd stop by and make sure you were both all right. What with the storm and all."

"A couple of those thunderclaps were right overhead," Maggie said, walking back to the counter to put the casserole in the refrigerator. She smiled when she opened the bag and found a new flashlight. "You must be psychic, Brent. The lights went out a little while ago, and my flashlight died in my hand."

"I had to stop at Mackie's Hardware Store to get one for myself, and knowing how precarious the electricity is in these old houses, I thought you might need an extra."

"You're very thoughtful," she said.

For some reason Brent's kindness brought tears to her eyes. When he realized she was upset, he looked positively stricken.

"Please don't worry," she said. "I was thinking of George. He used to fuss at me about things like flashlights, squeaky hinges and oil for my car. Sometimes I'd get so impatient with him, but it's silly things like that that remind me of him."

"I know just what you mean. I remember when Connie's father died, I didn't realize how much I'd miss the little everyday things."

Now that he was talking, Brent seemed more at ease. He crossed to the sink and unrolled several sheets of paper towels. When Maggie tried to take them, he waved her away.

"Did you know Edmund Falcone, Connie's father?" he asked as he knelt down to wipe the floor.

"No. He was gone before my mother moved back to Delbrook."

Resting his forearm on his knee, he looked up at her, a thoughtful expression on his face. "He wasn't a big man in size, but he had the kind of power that made you think he was taller. He bustled when he walked. It's an old word, but it describes how he moved. He gave the impression that there were not enough minutes in the day to get things done unless he hurried through each task."

"I've known people like that," Maggie said, leaning against the counter. "They usually end up having a heart attack or a stroke."

"That's what happened to Edmund." Brent gave the floor a final sweep of the towels and rose to his feet. "He had a stroke the night Connie and I were married."

"How dreadful," Maggie said, reaching out to take the paper towels and throw them in the wastebasket.

"He must have had the attack right after the wedding guests left. He had a housekeeper in those days. Cait Darlington. She had fantastic managing skills but was a bit too sharp-tongued for my taste. Mrs. Darlington found Edmund the morning after the wedding. Connie and I were on our honeymoon when we got the call that her father had been taken to the hospital."

"How serious was the stroke?"

"The worst. Although his mind still functioned, he was almost totally paralyzed and had lost his capacity for speech."

Maggie shuddered. How would it feel to be imprisoned inside your own body? As Brent had said, worse than death. "How long did he survive?"

"He died just short of our first anniversary."

"Dear God. A year."

"It wasn't quite as bad as you'd imagine. Connie was devastated. She couldn't bear to look at the man she had adored in such a weakened condition. We agreed that she would go to work and I would stay home to care for him. Don't look so astonished," he said. "Men can be excellent caregivers."

"My look wasn't meant to be disparaging," she said. "I've never known much about you, and it was a side of you I hadn't seen before. I've always thought you were very kind, so I'm not surprised that you would opt to take on Edmund's care."

Brent's shoulders rounded and a blush rose to his cheeks.

"I'd hate for you to think I selflessly sacrificed my life for my father-in-law. I'm practical by nature, and it seemed the most logical solution. Edmund would have hated being dependent on nurses."

"Yes, I can imagine if he was the bustling sort, he would prefer to keep his infirmities a private matter."

Brent nodded. "I had the help of nurses and therapists, but I was the one who was responsible for his day-to-day care. Knowing his mind was still intact, I read to him as much as I could. Newspapers, magazines, books. Anything I thought might be of interest."

"That must have been a godsend for him."

"I hope so." A shadow crossed his face. "One never knows."

"It must have been hard on both you and Connie, especially since you were newlyweds."

"Not really," Brent said. "I was comfortable with Edmund. I'd lived in the house on and off over the years since I was sixteen. One of my teachers brought it to Edmund's attention that, although I was a bright child, my mother couldn't afford to send me to a private school, let alone college. Connie's father sponsored me all the way through school and, after my mother died, gave me a room in the house where I spent vacations and holidays."

"How good for all of you," Maggie said. "It must have been good for Connie and her mother to have someone else in the house if it was so big."

"Actually, Edmund's wife left when Connie was ten. My addition to the household took the pressure off Connie to be the son that Edmund never had."

Brent laughed, but the sound was harsh rather than lighthearted. He

paced across the floor to look out the window at the rain, his face thoughtful as he turned back to Maggie.

"It was a case of poor little rich girl," he said. "Connie was totally different then. Looking at her now you'd never guess that she was quite a
tomboy in those days. She never wore anything feminine. Her hair was
cut short, and she had a swearing vocabulary that would rival any long-
shoreman's speech."

Maggie couldn't picture the elegant Connie as Brent described her.
"She's definitely changed for the better."

"I think so," he said, his voice soft and admiring. "She had always
been desperate for her father's approval, and when her mother left she
tried even harder to please her father. If he wanted a son, she would be
one."

"Was Edmund blind to the fact?" Maggie asked.

"I don't know. Maybe that's why he chose to mentor me. He transferred his expectations to me, and eventually Connie learned to enjoy her
role as a female."

Brent's comments made Maggie feel some guilt over not liking Connie more. She'd automatically stereotyped her as a spoiled only child but
should have known there was more to the story.

"I understand there was a fire in the house. Is that how Edmund
died?"

"Yes and no. When Edmund discovered the house was on fire, he had
another stroke. This one was fatal. I carried him outside, and Connie and
I stood beside his body and watched the house burn to the ground."

"Dear God, how tragic," Maggie said, hearing the remembered horror in his voice.

"I designed the new house," he said. "It's lovely, even though it can't
compare in size to the original. Old Delbrook Falcone, Connie's grandfather, had hopes of housing a dynasty on the shores of Falcon Lake. It was
a huge rambling affair. Next time you're at the library, ask to see the pictures of the place. It was called Falcon's Nest."

Falcon's Nest. An aerie. The name sent a shiver through Maggie's
body. Feathers, birds, eagles, falcons. The continual references frightened her, as if the words held some special warning. Like a bird of prey,
fear hovered over her, threatening to swoop down at any moment and
carry away everything she held dear.

• • •

Mouse Ears and Shorty were still alive.

The mice were shivering in a corner of the cage. There was blood on the shavings at the other end. Tyler pushed his finger in between the wires to touch his friend's fur. He could feel the warm body beneath the scratchy coat.

Tyler sorry. Tyler help.

The man would be angry. He might bring the bird and let it bite Tyler. He jerked his hand back away from the cage. Mouse Ears scrabbled in a circle as if he were searching for his friend.

Tyler reached out and pulled the cage toward the edge of the table. Picking it up, he set it on the floor. He sat down cross-legged in front of it. His fingers touched the latch. The hinges squeaked as he opened the little door.

Tyler made clicking sounds with his tongue. Come Mouse Ears.

Shorty ran toward him, but his friend crawled under the cedar shavings. The end of his nose twitching, Shorty stuck his head out the cage door. Before Tyler could grab him, he jumped onto the mud floor and raced toward the back of the room until he was lost in the shadows.

Tyler snapped his fingers.

The shavings rustled and Mouse Ears raised his head. Tyler snapped them again. The mouse crawled across the cage to the door. Tyler reached out and grabbed the mouse in his hand. He sucked in air at the feel of the wriggling body. Standing up, he carried his trophy across to the shelf bed. He held on to the tail as he set the mouse in the nest of blankets.

With the tip of one finger, he stroked the top of Mouse Ears' head. The mouse went still, no longer pulling at his tail. Tyler sang the ABC song and then with a sigh released his friend.

Mouse Ears remained motionless. Tyler touched the rounded back. The mouse turned and jabbed his pointed nose against his fingers.

Tyler cupped both his hands. Inching along in a circle, Mouse Ears brushed his palms, nuzzling against them. He could feel the tickle all the way up his arms.

Beyond the door, he heard a sound. His heart hammered in his chest as his hands closed protectively around the mouse. With a shudder he opened his fingers.

Run Mouse Ears.

Tyler snapped his fingers. The mouse raised his head, then with a bouncing run, he jumped off the bed and disappeared in the darkness beneath the shelf.

Maggie finished folding the last of Jake's shirts and set it on top of the pile of clean clothes. Rain was still falling outside, and she was grateful that she'd been able to spend the evening at home. After Brent left, she'd come downstairs to do the laundry. While she waited, she'd tried to read, but her mind had been filled with all the things that he'd told her.

It struck her that one could socialize with people and yet know very little about their lives. Most people had secrets, either things they preferred to keep private or things no one ever asked them about.

She was pleased that Brent had volunteered the information about Edmund Falcone. She'd sensed a kindness in him, and his care of Connie's father added another layer to his personality that she might never have suspected.

It made her all the more curious about Brent's relationship with Connie.

Maggie'd only seen the couple in social situations, but even then she'd been aware of a tension between the two. Although Connie was the demonstrative type, Maggie had never seen her give Brent the kind of loving touch that most couples exchanged. Never a caress in passing or even the sort of visual cue that was tantamount to an embrace.

Nell had told her that Connie had had an affair with Hugh Rossiter several years ago. It was after Hugh's wife left. The gossip ran rampant, and neither one had been particularly discreet. If Brent knew about it, he apparently had forgiven Connie. In conversation, his voice was either conciliatory or self-deprecating. It was Connie's tone that held the sharp edge.

No matter what Brent said about his closeness to Edmund, it was strange that Connie hadn't been the one to take care of her father. Brent said that she adored her father, and yet she preferred to put his welfare in her husband's hands. Although it didn't reflect well on Connie, Maggie tried not to condemn her. Many people couldn't handle acting as a nurse for a loved one.

She wondered why they'd never had children. It was hardly a question she could ask. Perhaps they couldn't have them. In any case it was a shame. Brent would have made a loving father, and perhaps a child would have softened the brittle edge that Connie showed to the world.

Life had been simpler before George's death. Now she wondered if anything was ever what it seemed to be. Was Grant? So much depended on whether she could trust him.

He had called earlier, and she had to admit she'd enjoyed the conversation. Even through the phone he'd been able to sense her uneasiness. He talked for a while as the storm crashed overhead, and she'd been so involved the majority of the thunder and lightning had passed unnoticed.

It was only then that he told Maggie that Eddie Harland's mother had agreed to speak to her. He gave her the flight information and told her he'd pick her up at nine in the morning for the drive to the airport. Despite her apprehension, she said she'd be ready.

Please, God, let it go well, she thought.

Maggie placed her hands at the small of her back and stretched backward to ease her stiffness. One glance at the clock and she sighed. Ten o'clock. "Never enough time," she muttered. Balancing the laundry basket on her hip, she switched off the light in the laundry room and walked through the kitchen into the darkened bookstore.

The upstairs hall light streamed through the open door. The phone rang as she started up the staircase, and she cursed the fact that she'd forgotten to bring the portable. She quickened her steps, but before she could get to the top, Jake's door opened and he ran across the hall to her bedroom and the ringing phone. She could hear him talking as she closed and locked the door to the bookstore. When she entered the bedroom, he was whispering into the phone, one hand curled around his mouth so she couldn't hear his words.

"Who is it, Jake?" she said, her voice sharp with worry.

"It's for you," he said.

She set the laundry basket on the bed and held out her hand for the receiver. After a momentary hesitation, he placed the portable phone in her hand.

"I didn't think you'd get upstairs in time to answer the phone," he said.

"I appreciate your concern," she said. "Now get back to bed."

"Night, Mom."

He hurried past her and into his own room, closing the door with a solid click of the latch. Maggie raised the receiver.

"Hello?" she said.

For a moment all Maggie could hear was the sound of rain. It took her a moment to realize that whoever was on the other end was calling from a phone that was outside. Either a cell phone or a pay phone. She pressed the receiver to her ear as she heard the rasping voice on the line.

"Missus Jake?"

Her fingers tightened on the telephone at the unfamiliar greeting. "Who's calling? Who is this?"

"It's Tully, missus."

"Tully! Are you all right?"

"Yes, missus. I had to get away because I was afraid of what would happen."

"That's what I thought, Tully. But you need to come back. It's not good for you to be hiding and frightened. No one means you any harm."

Even as Maggie said the words she wondered if they were true. Someone might want to keep Tully from talking.

"I can't come back yet. Blessington has been looking for a reason to put me in jail. I'd die in jail. I've got some thinking to do. Need to find out who's against me. Soon's I know, I'll come talk to you."

She could hear the withdrawal in his voice. She didn't know what to do for the best. The sound of the rain decided her.

"Do you want to come here, Tully? You need a place to stay and you'd be safe here. Jake and I would be glad to have the company."

"He's a good boy. And you too, missus. It's risky to come there. People will be watching. No time to be reckless."

Frustrated at her inability to convince Tully that he might be in danger, she felt like crying. "Do you need anything?"

"I wanted to tell you I didn't hurt George," he said, ignoring her question.

"Jake told me you wouldn't, and I believed him. Do you know who did?"

"I didn't see. I don't know why he was killed." His voice sounded baffled, as if he were trying to work out some puzzle. "Maybe I can find out."

"Please, Tully, it's dangerous to be out there on your own. You have friends here in Delbrook who can help you. Will you come and talk to me?"

"Not yet, missus. Don't worry about Tully. I'm good at hiding. Just wanted to tell you I wouldn't never hurt George any more than I would hurt you or Jake."

Tully's voice faded away. For a moment Maggie heard the sound of rain, then a click and the line went dead.

CHAPTER SEVENTEEN

DENNIS NYLAND STROKED HIS FINGERS along the row of silver rings lining the edge of his ear. The soft tinkling sound was soothing. He'd gotten in the habit of doing it whenever he talked to his mother. It made it easier to ignore the whine in her voice as she cataloged his sins of commission and omission.

He was twenty-five. Too old to live at home. If he didn't get out soon he'd be trapped forever.

Dead as old Collier.

Dennis shivered as he remembered touching the dead man. Even though George Collier's body had still been warm, he had felt as if the heat were being sucked out of his fingers wherever he touched the man's flesh.

Getting up from his desk, he walked across to the far side of the garage to the beat-up refrigerator and opened the door. It was stuffy in the garage, and he breathed in the cool air before leaning over to take out a beer. He shut the refrigerator with the heel of his shoe and opened the entry door beside it.

He stood in the open doorway, looking out at the dark night. The sky was clear, but the air was heavy after the fury of the rain that passed through earlier. He enjoyed working in the garage during a thunderstorm. He'd turn up the volume on his CD player and blast the music. It was what he imagined it would be like inside the eye of a tornado.

It was midnight, and the neighborhood was quiet. Everyone was in bed. Wednesday night. A workday tomorrow. He stuck his head out until he could see around the corner of the garage to the back of the house. Just one light in the kitchen so he'd be able to see his way when he came inside.

Ma'd gone upstairs. He could see the faint blue light from the TV in her bedroom window. Every night when he came upstairs, she'd be sound asleep, the TV blaring in the silent house. Some nights he wanted to smash the screen.

He had to get out of Delbrook.

Leaving the door open, he made a circuit of the garage, making sure that everything was ready in case his visitor wanted the tattoo immediately. He checked to see that the autoclave was plugged in. Everyone was paranoid about catching AIDS. New clients always checked to see that the sterilizer was functional.

Back at his desk, he flipped through the pages of flash, pleased with the new designs he'd created for his display book of tattoos. He was driving to Madison on Saturday to see about a full-time job and had been working for the past week setting up sample books of photographs so he could show the owner the kind of tattoos he'd done.

A month earlier he'd gone over to Madison to a body modification convention and met Tony DeVita, the owner of Tony's Tattoo Parlor. They'd hit it off immediately. The parlor was two blocks from the University of Wisconsin, and when he had stopped by to check it out, the place had been loaded with students.

Tony had an opening, and Dennis wanted the job. Although several tattoo artists worked there, no one could do custom work. Dennis could draw anything freehand anywhere on the client's body. He was convinced that once Tony saw the kind of work he could do, the job was his.

Nobody'd hassle him in Madison. The cops weren't as provincial as Charley Blessington.

Blessington had been on his case for years. Giving him the hard eye whenever he saw him at the country club. Just like Sunday when the cops had picked him up at his girlfriend's place. You'd have thought he was the one who offed Collier.

Thank God he'd told the chief that Collier was already dead when he found him. It made him panicky to think that someone else might have been there and overheard Collier.

"Tattoo."

That's what Collier had said. Just the one word. Dennis had been in his shirtsleeves, and in the bright moonlight the dying man must have seen the tattoos on his arms. If Blessington heard about that, he'd take it as a deathbed accusation and slap the cuffs on him, despite the fact he'd already told the chief that he'd seen Tully Jackson running away.

Dennis heard a car pull up outside the garage. He touched the drawing on his desk for good luck. He hoped he'd gotten it right. He'd only gotten a quick look at the original tattoo.

He grinned, remembering his surprise to find someone coming out of the shower tonight at the country club when he thought the locker room was empty. He'd started to clean earlier than usual, but it was no big whoop.

And then to be accused of staring like some kind of pervert!

Shit! All he cared about was the tattoo. He'd just gotten a quick look before the towel covered it.

He couldn't resist asking who'd done the drawing. It wasn't anyone local. Dennis knew the few artists in the area.

Despite the glare and his own feeling of discomfort, Dennis refused to retreat with his tail between his legs. He pulled out one of the new business cards he'd printed up. The colors were vivid and the design was original. With a flourish, he flipped it on the bench between the lockers. He mentioned he did custom work and offered a discount on a tattoo before he left the room.

Dennis stroked his hand across the stencil paper on his desk. He was pleased with the colors he'd chosen. The original must have been an old tattoo, because the colors weren't as vibrant as the ones he'd placed.

An eye-catching gold for the arrow and a bright cherry red for the bleeding heart.

"Why do I have to go to Aunt Nell's after school?"

Jake stood at the bottom of the back stairs of the bookstore, his body rigid, elbows out and his fists jammed against his waist. Maggie wondered why she hadn't told him about her trip at breakfast to avoid this last-minute confrontation. Probably because she knew he'd put up a fuss, she thought.

"Let's not get into an argument," she said. "I've already arranged for Nell to pick you up after school."

"Why can't I go to Kenny's?"

"Because I said so." She hated falling back on the motherly defense, but she had to admit it came in handy in cases like this. "We're not going to discuss this further. I'll try to get back in time to pick you up, but in any case, we'll go out for dinner when I get home."

"I won't be hungry."

If it hadn't been so frustrating, Maggie would have smiled at the hangdog expression that accompanied his words. He'd been sullen and uncooperative since she'd told him that she was going to Milwaukee for the day. She couldn't imagine how he'd react if he knew she was going to Detroit.

"I'd like to think that by the time I get back you'll be in a better frame of mind."

"I won't be," he said. "I still don't see why you have to go to Milwaukee with him."

Jake's oblique reference to Grant gave Maggie a clue as to the reason for his antagonism. It wasn't the trip he was angry about; it was the fact she was going with Grant. What on earth did he have against Grant? Oh rats! Why did a crisis always occur when she had no time to deal with it?

"Look, Jake," she said, "I know you're unhappy about this, but give me a break. I have to go to Milwaukee today, and since Grant is going there too, it only makes good sense that we go together. When I get back, you and I need to sit down and have a little chat."

"I don't want to talk about him. Why doesn't he go back to Chicago? Every time we go someplace, he has to come too. I don't like him."

He'd apparently bottled up his resentment against Grant, and the words spilled out in a whiny litany of complaints. Seeing Hugh Rossiter's car coming down the street, Maggie sighed. At least she knew the source of Jake's latest round of hostility, and when she returned she'd have to deal with it.

"Enough," she said, her voice sharper than she'd intended. "We'll talk about this tonight. Give me a hug and don't give your teacher any grief today."

Hugh pulled up beside her, and she opened the back door of the car. She gave Jake a squeeze, but he hung limp in her arms, not responding in any way except for a mumbled goodbye. Hugh looked at her quizzically, and she rolled her eyes.

"Thanks for picking up Jake," she said, leaning in the open passenger window. "I've got to go over to the police station and make a report about George's car."

Hugh turned off the motor and stepped out, walking with her over to George's dark green Malibu. "I see they broke the side window to get in. They take anything?"

"Not that I can tell. Whoever it was looked through the glove compartment, under the seats and in the trunk. I doubt if there was anything to take. The police already went over the car, so they have an inventory of what was there. When I called to report it, they told me to come in and take a look at the list. They didn't seem too concerned about finger-prints."

"Only idiots leave prints nowadays," Hugh said. "Did it happen last night or this morning?"

"It must have been after the storm came through, because the inside of the car is dry."

He walked around the car, peering at the maps and papers littering the inside. "You didn't hear anything?"

"No. It was still raining when I went to bed. Nell called me to tell me about it. She needed a sugar fix this morning and went out to get choco-late éclairs." Maggie shuddered at the thought. "She walked over to Corky's Bakery and didn't see the window until she was coming back."

"You better call George's insurance company," Hugh said.

"Damn. I didn't think about that."

He put his arm around her shoulders as they walked back to the car. She could feel the strength of his body as he pulled her close against his side. Normally she tried to be self-reliant, but she was just tired enough that she appreciated the protective feeling that radiated from him.

"I'll call a friend of mine and have him repair the window," he said. "He can do it here without your bringing the car into the shop."

"That would be great. Are you sure you've got time to call him?"

"For you, I've got time," he said, getting back into the car. "I'd like to do more. How about dinner when you get back from your shopping spree in Milwaukee?"

Maggie blushed at the thought of the number of lies she'd told since George's death. The worst of it was that she was finding it easier to do and she felt less guilty when she did it.

"I think I'll pass on that, Hugh. Some other time."

"I'll give you a call tonight. I didn't get a chance to talk to you yesterday."

"Thanks for showing Grant the birds," she said. "He was really impressed."

"He certainly asked a lot of questions. For a while I thought he was planning to give up the law and open his own falconry club."

"He's the curious type. I suppose that's what comes from being a lawyer. Always building a case," she said.

"You driving in to Milwaukee?"

"No. Grant has some business there, so I thought I'd tag along."

Hugh's brows bunched over his eyes, and he gave her a comprehensive glance. "How long is he staying over at George's?"

"I don't know," she said, awkward with the question.

"Delbrook's an interesting change of pace for him. Eventually he'll get his fill and return to his life in Chicago."

Uncomfortable under the intensity of his gaze, Maggie stepped away from the window. "I better let you go or you'll be late. Have a good day, boys."

She waved as the car started up. Kenny was the only one who returned the wave. So, along with Jake being angry about her spending the day with Grant, Hugh was ticked. She didn't see that he had any reason to be. She hadn't given him any reason to believe that he had the inside track to any relationship with her.

At least she didn't think she had.

Did Hugh? He'd acted unusually territorial when she brought Grant over to look at Camp Delbrook and the birds, touching her in a more intimate manner than he usually did. Did the mere fact that another male was around bring out that sort of competition?

"Oh, damn!" she said aloud.

Thank goodness she had plenty to do to keep her from thinking about the irrationality of men. She drove over to the police station and completed the paperwork on the car break-in, then returned to the bookstore to help Beth shelve the new stock and pack up returns until it was time to get ready for her trip to Detroit. She couldn't decide what to wear, and when she found herself considering a frilly sundress she hadn't worn in five years, she was so annoyed at herself she grabbed an old denim skirt and plain white blouse.

Why was she acting so weird? She didn't usually obsess over her appearance. The thought that it was Grant who was making her crazy irritated her, and she was crabby when he picked her up for the drive to the airport.

"I'd offer a penny for your thoughts," he said as she climbed in and buckled her seat belt, "but by the look on your face, I'm not sure I want to know."

"Jake hates you," she said, blurting out the first thing that came to her mind.

"Ah," he said. "I wouldn't worry about it. He'll get over it."

She turned at the cheerful comment and caught the almost puckish grin on his face.

"What's so funny?"

"It's a guy thing. He's protecting his territory."

"You're kidding!"

"Look at it from Jake's viewpoint. He's been the main man in your life since his father died. With his grandfather gone, he's once again the man in charge. He's not going to welcome anyone into your life, let alone a stranger."

"He's never reacted this way to Hugh," she said, deciding not to tell him about Hugh's display of jealousy.

"I wondered if you were dating him."

"We've gone out a few times. A movie. A dinner. If it's any of your business."

"I see."

Grant's voice was noncommittal, and Maggie kept her eyes focused beyond the windshield, unwilling to look for any reaction to her comments.

"So why isn't Jake hostile about Hugh?"

"Probably because he doesn't see Hugh as a threat."

"What's that supposed to mean?" she said, turning to glare at him.

"For starters, Hugh is the father of his best friend. Jake's used to seeing you two together. He probably doesn't see Hugh as someone who might want to have an intimate relationship with you. Besides, I suspect Jake senses you're not head over heels in love with Hugh."

Maggie took a breath, prepared to defend her position, then thought better of it. Just because Grant was easy to talk to didn't mean that she needed to blab out her life story.

"So I can expect Jake to react this way to every man that comes into my life?"

"Not every man," Grant said. "Just certain ones."

At the husky note in his voice, Maggie was disgusted at the blush that she could feel flooding her cheeks. She refused to rise to the bait, staring out the window as if she were fascinated by the scenery. What on earth was the matter with her? It wasn't as though she was interested in Grant Holbrook. He had come to Wisconsin by chance, and he would be leaving to return to his life in Chicago.

She had given up her life in the city to raise Jake in the small-town atmosphere of Delbrook. She had been happy here, and when Grant left, she would be contented with the life she'd chosen for herself and Jake. Maybe she'd discover she could love Hugh. Anything was possible. In the meantime she needed to remember that her relationship with Grant was one born out of necessity not shared interests or mutual attraction.

As they drove she told him about George's car being broken into. He didn't look surprised. It was almost as if he'd expected it.

"Nothing was taken?" he asked.

"Not as far as I could tell. At the police station I looked over the list that they made when they checked the car. Everything seemed to be intact. I guess I was hoping I'd find something missing that would explain the break-in."

"Whatever it is that someone is looking for," Grant said, "must not be very obvious."

"Why?"

"The thief must have known that the police had already been over the car. If there was anything incriminating, they would have found it."

"What could it be?"

"I haven't a clue, but the search has come full circle. Whoever it is searched George's house, your purse, the hospital bag and now his car. Maybe they'll conclude there's nothing to find, but in the meantime you'll have to be very cautious. Your apartment and the bookstore might be the next on the list."

Maggie closed her eyes and breathed deeply. She'd worried about that right after George was killed, but in the last few days she'd thought the danger had passed. She'd have to remind Jake to be careful about locking the doors.

So much had happened since Sunday morning. Just five days. It seemed like a lifetime.

"Oh, I forgot to tell you," she said. "Tully called last night."

Grant's hands jerked on the steering wheel, and the passenger-side wheels skidded in the gravel along the shoulder until he got the car under control again.

"You might give me some warning that you're planning to drop a bomb like that when I'm driving eighty," he said.

"You shouldn't be speeding," she said.

He glared at her, then returned his eyes to the road. "Are you purposely trying to annoy me?"

Although it was a rhetorical question, she gave it some thought.

"I think I might be. It's a bad habit I have when I'm nervous. My husband never figured that out," she said, surprised that Grant had caught it. "I've been worried about Jake and I'm taking it out on you. All last night he was as nervy as a cat with his tail in a light socket. Every time the phone rang, he ran to get it as if he were waiting to get the news he'd won the lottery."

"That's interesting. He didn't say anything about it?"

"No." She sighed. "And I didn't ask. He's growing up, and I'm trying to respect his privacy. Being a single parent really bites sometimes."

She stared out the window, aware that part of her ill humor and apprehension was just a holdover from her own lack of confidence in her mothering skills.

"At any rate, Tully called," she said. "He wouldn't tell me where he was, and I couldn't convince him to come talk to me."

"What did he say?"

"He wanted to tell me that he hadn't killed George."

After a moment of silence, Grant asked, "Did you believe him?"

"Yes." Maggie gave the one-word answer without hesitation. "I'm frightened for him. He said he was going to think about who might have killed George. That could be dangerous."

"You're right about that. No clue as to where he might be?"

"No. He was calling from a pay phone or at least someplace outside."

"Any chance that Jake was waiting for Tully's call?"

"Whoof." Maggie hadn't thought about that. She'd just assumed that he and Kenny were up to something outrageous. "If he was, he only had time to say a few words to Tully before I got upstairs."

"It was just a thought. You might ask Jake if he's had any contact with Tully since George died."

"Yesterday I ran into Charley, and he asked me to talk to Jake too. Do you think he really knows anything?"

"He might. It's worth asking him," Grant said.

Maggie was silent the rest of the way to the airport. The flight to Detroit left on schedule, and before she knew it, they were in a rented car on their way to her appointment with Eddie Harland's mother.

"Where are we meeting Mrs. Harland?" she asked.

"At Gifford Elementary. It's on the north side of Detroit. Small private school with a good reputation for working with kids on an individual basis. Eddie and his family live right in the neighborhood, and the community has been helping out financially since he was returned."

"I don't need to tell you that I'm really apprehensive about this," Maggie said. "Are you sure you shouldn't be the one talking to Eddie's mother?"

"To be honest, I wanted to be the one to interview her, but Mrs. Hoppe, the principal, said no. The mother's name is Katrina, she's from Russia, and her husband is from Germany. They've been in the United States for ten years, but according to Mrs. Hoppe, she's still afraid of any kind of authority figures. Men especially."

"How did Mrs. Hoppe convince her to talk to me?"

"Katrina Harland is beginning to realize that Eddie needs psychological help. Except for some counseling through the school, her husband won't consider it. Mrs. Hoppe told Katrina that if she spoke to you about Eddie, it might help locate Tyler, and if that happened, I'd arrange to get the help Eddie needs."

"And you would?"

"Without question," Grant said.

"What should I ask?"

"Try to get any information you can about what Eddie told his parents after he started talking again. Things like what the kidnapper looked like, whether the place he was held was urban or rural, if there were other people involved. Visual clues would be crucial. Anything specific could help us to pinpoint Tyler's location."

"I feel totally inadequate," Maggie said.

"Have a little faith. Take your time and feel your way through it. Go with your heart. You're a mother. Ask whatever you feel is appropriate. If she gets upset, back off a little and maybe just listen."

Maggie clasped her hands in her lap and tried not to think of all the things that could go wrong.

It didn't take long for them to reach Gifford Elementary, a neat brick building in a residential area. The school yard and the parking lot were surrounded by a wrought-iron fence that looked more decorative than functional. Grant pulled up in front of the school and handed her a paper with a phone number where he could be reached when she was finished. With a two-fingered salute, he drove away. Maggie swallowed hard as she headed up the stairs.

A hall monitor met her just inside the door and pointed out the principal's office. Heels clicking on the highly polished linoleum floor, she walked along the silent hall.

"Thank you for coming such a distance for this meeting. The flight must have been right on time," Mrs. Hoppe said. The tall, slender woman rose from her desk and came around to shake hands. "I've been looking forward to meeting you since talking to Mr. Holbrook. He told me about your father-in-law. May I offer my condolences?"

"Thank you," Maggie said. "It's still hard to believe that it happened only five days ago. In many respects it seems like it was much longer than that."

"I've always found it interesting that in stressful situations time is either compressed or elongated." She took Maggie's arm and led her back out into the hall. "I'm sure you're anxious to meet Mrs. Harland, so I won't keep you waiting. Katrina arrived just a few moments ago, and I've put her down the hall in a conference room. One of the teachers is keeping her company because she's a bit skittish. Her husband doesn't know that she's here and would disapprove strongly if he did."

"I appreciate the warning. I'll try not to upset her any more than I have to."

Mrs. Hoppe's mouth tightened. "Don't let her tears deter you. She cries easily because she's afraid. Afraid of her husband. Afraid for her son."

With that caution, the principal opened a door leading into a small lounge. The deeply cushioned couch and chairs were upholstered in a bright chintz pattern that looked warm and inviting. Mrs. Hoppe introduced Maggie to Eddie's mother, and then she and the other teacher left the room. Mrs. Harland's eyes flickered owlishly as the door clicked shut.

"Is that coffee?" Maggie asked, pointing to the tray on the table against the wall.

"Yes. It's very strong."

A trace of an accent gave Mrs. Harland's voice a soft, buttery sound. Without makeup and with her limp brown hair pulled back behind her neck, the woman looked to be in her late thirties, but her skin texture indicated she could be ten years younger. She was wearing a formless black skirt, a faded print blouse and sensible shoes.

Katrina clasped her hands together just beneath her breasts and stood uncertainly in front of the couch while Maggie poured herself a cup of coffee and brought it over to the table.

"I can't tell you how much I appreciate your seeing me today," Maggie said. "It must have been a very difficult decision."

"I don't know if this is a good thing. My husband, Lothar, would not approve," Mrs. Harland said. "If only I could be sure it would help Eddie."

She looked as if she might make a bolt for the door, and Maggie tensed, wondering how to get the woman to relax. She should never have let Grant talk her into this. She tried to think of something to say, but the exhaustion of the last week made it difficult for her to concentrate.

"Would you mind if we sat down?" Maggie said. "I think I need a little of that coffee."

The request startled Mrs. Harland, and she peered closely at Maggie.

"You are very pale. You are not well?" she asked.

"I'm just tired. My father-in-law died this week, and my legs are still aching from standing so much during the wake."

Mrs. Harland crossed herself and reached out to pat Maggie's arm. "It was sudden?"

"Yes." Maggie could see no point in explaining the situation.

"How sad for you and your husband. Was he close to his father?"

"My husband died two years ago. It's just myself and my son, Jake."

"Oh, my dear, please do sit down. The coffee is very good, and it's strong enough to revive you."

Although Maggie would have never thought to use her own circumstances to gain the other woman's confidence, she realized the revelations had given them a sense of bonding. In the ancient tradition of women sharing and mourning their losses together, they drank coffee and talked about their children. Katrina was pleased to know that Jake was so close in age to Eddie.

"The principal mentioned that Eddie was having problems in school?" Maggie asked to ease into the subject that had brought her to Detroit. "I remember that Jake had a hard time after his father's death. His teacher called me on several occasions to talk to me about it."

Katrina's shoulders sagged, and she nodded.

"When Eddie first came here to school four years ago, he was normal. Like the other children. Each year he has had a little more difficulty. Now he is failing all his classes. He is not making trouble in the classes. He seems to have lost interest in school. And he doesn't play with the other boys."

"When he's home, does Eddie play with his brothers?"

"No. He doesn't go outside and play ball with the boys, and he didn't go to the pool this summer. He stays in his room. When I ask him what's wrong, he tells me nothing."

Katrina's voice was thick with tears of frustration.

"Does he listen to music or play computer games?"

"Music, yes. Loud and hard on the ears. All the time, the music. And he ties knots."

"Ties knots?" Maggie asked.

"Yes. Every day. He ties knots in everything. Everywhere I look there are knots."

Maggie felt out of her depth. She didn't know anything about obsessive behavior. She wondered if the psychiatrist at the school knew about this.

"What kind of knots?" she asked.

Katrina jerked to her feet, and for a moment Maggie thought she was distraught and was ending the interview. Instead she went across to one of the chairs and picked up a bulky black fabric handbag. She brought it back to the couch and sat down. Opening the top, she reached inside and withdrew a metal key ring. A short black string, the thickness of a shoelace, was tied to the ring with a fancy knot, and beneath it was a second knot.

"I brought this to show you," Katrina said, handing the ring to Maggie. "I used to keep my house keys on this ring, until one day Eddie tied this on it. I couldn't bear to untie it, and yet I didn't want my keys touching it. It would be bad luck, I think."

Maggie held the ring and the knotted cord in the palm of her hand. The knot was unusual, but she didn't know enough to be able to recognize it.

"May I keep this?" she asked.

"Yes. I don't want it back. I have knots everywhere to remind me. This was the first one, and it still troubles me."

Maggie didn't want to jam it into her purse for fear she'd change the position of the knot. She folded the key ring inside several tissues and placed it carefully in the zippered compartment of her purse for added safety.

Once the knot was out of sight, Katrina appeared less agitated, as if she'd made the commitment to talk about Eddie. Maggie didn't push, but eventually she asked about the kidnapping, the investigation and the awful year that followed Eddie's disappearance. The joy in his return was tempered by the realization that as time passed, the boy appeared to be failing physically, mentally and socially.

"You said that according to the doctors, Eddie was not injured in any way while he was gone."

There was a slight hesitation before Katrina answered. "No. He was very healthy." She shuddered. "My husband was frantic when Eddie came back. He was so afraid that he had been hurt in a sexual way. He kept asking, and the doctors all told him that Eddie was 'untouched.' I'm not sure that Lothar believed them."

"I think my husband would have worried about the same thing," Maggie said. "Mothers are different. Our first priority is to have our children returned home and safe again."

Tears overflowed Katrina's eyes. "You understand what I feel."

Maggie waited as the woman blew her nose and wiped her eyes.

"I know that Eddie didn't speak when he first returned home," she said. "That must have been awful for you."

"It was. It confirmed for Lothar that something dreadful had happened to Eddie. I don't think my husband wanted to know what it was that had gone on in that year. Maybe if he knew, he would not be able to love Eddie again." Katrina hunched her shoulders, pulling her body in on itself. "For me, not knowing is worse. I've pictured every unspeakable horror. If I knew, I could accept it."

"Did you ever ask Eddie?"

"Once," she said, her voice just above a whisper. "Lothar heard me. He flew into a rage, screaming at me to let the boy forget. I could see that Eddie was terrified by his father's fury, so I did not cry out when Lothar hit me. I smiled at Eddie and told him I was sorry."

Maggie could have wept listening to Katrina. What a terrible situation. All three of them torn apart by the aftermath of the kidnapping. No wonder Eddie was self-destructing.

She felt as if she ought to have been able to learn more in the interview. She knew that Grant was hoping for actual information about Eddie's year of captivity. Any clue that might give the police a lead as to the whereabouts of Tyler. She had learned nothing of value.

A question came to her mind, and she wondered if she was reading more into Katrina's answers than was there. Maybe she was grasping for straws. Deciding not to second-guess herself, Maggie asked, "You said Eddie wasn't hurt, but there was something different about him when he returned, wasn't there?"

Katrina caught her breath and looked so frightened that Maggie was afraid the woman might faint. She remained motionless, knowing that her stab in the dark had hit a nerve.

"It was the tattoo," Katrina whispered.

Her voice was so low that Maggie wasn't sure she'd heard correctly. "Tattoo?"

Katrina reached out and took Maggie's hand and placed it on her own chest. Beneath her fingertips Maggie felt the woman's frantic heartbeat.

"A tattoo. On his skin. Right here."

Maggie blew out her breath at the shock of Katrina's revelation. "It wasn't there before?"

Katrina shook her head. "Lothar told the police it was. He didn't understand what the tattoo meant. He thought it marked the boy. Like the evil eye. Lothar was ashamed."

"Oh, Katrina, how hard this has been for you."

Maggie put her arms around the woman and hugged her. For so long Katrina must have bottled up her fears and anger, because she burst into tears, sobbing uncontrollably for several minutes. Maggie held her, ignoring the tears that slid down her own cheeks as she thought about Jake and how she would feel if anything happened to him.

Please, God, keep him safe, she prayed.

When the shaking of the other woman's body eased, Maggie gave her a reassuring hug. Katrina pushed away, her eyes swollen and her cheeks red with embarrassment. Maggie rose and poured more coffee. The caffeine helped.

"What does the tattoo look like?" she asked.

"A heart. Drawn on his skin," Katrina said. Her voice shook with revulsion. "And there is an arrow, too."

"Could you draw it for me?"

Maggie searched her purse for a piece of paper, eventually settling for a deposit slip that she tore out of the back of her checkbook. She handed that and a pen to Katrina. The woman set it on the table. With angry strokes, she drew the picture of a heart with a short, stubby arrow running through it from right to left. Beneath it, she drew several dots.

"This is how I see it on his body," she said. "It is in color. The arrow is gold. The heart is red. And also the circles are red. Red tears of blood. Like the heart is crying."

"No words?"

Katrina looked confused.

"Sometimes there are dates or names or several words along with the picture," Maggie explained.

"No." Katrina shook her head. "No words. Just the arrow and the heart that bleeds."

CHAPTER
EIGHTEEN

"WHY CAN'T I PLAY up in the treehouse until you get back?" Jake said, taking off his backpack and setting it on the ground beside the tree.

"Oh, Jake, give it a rest," she said. He'd been whining since she'd picked him up at Nell's and told him she was bringing him over to George's house. "While I'm gone you can give Grant a hand making dinner."

"You're just dumping me here?" Jake's voice grew shrill. "Aren't you going to eat with us?"

"Yes, but first I have to go see Chief Blessington."

She had just gotten back from the airport and was on her way to pick up Jake at school when Charley called asking her to come to the police station. Grant had offered to make dinner, so she phoned to say she and Jake would be late. He suggested she leave Jake with him while she talked to Charley.

"Why can't I come with you?"

Maggie threw up her hands in exasperation and walked down the path to the back porch.

"Because Chief Blessington wants to see just me," she said, speaking over her shoulder.

"You told me this morning we were going out to dinner as a treat," Jake said. He stomped along the path behind her.

"This is out," she said. "And any time I'm not cooking is a treat."

"Who's cooking? Is he?"

"His name is Grant," she snapped, realizing with a start that she was now calling him that instead of "Holbrook." Somewhere during the trip to Detroit, they had become friends. "I'd appreciate it if you'd start using his name."

Jake's eyes widened, and she turned to see Grant standing in the open doorway.

" 'Master Chef' to those who have tasted his exotic cuisine," Grant said.

Maggie flushed, aware he had overhead their conversation. "Are you sure about this?" she said with a nod of her head toward the sulking boy.

"Positive," Grant said. "We'll rattle along here while you're gone."

"I won't be long." She thrust a salad bowl into his hands. "Connie sent this over yesterday. I froze the casserole, but this will spoil if we don't use it."

"It must have been her day for good works. She brought some for us bachelors, too. Run along. We'll have dinner ready when you get back."

Maggie didn't know if she was doing the right thing, leaving the two of them alone together, but with a shrug of resignation, she leaned over and kissed Jake on the forehead before he could duck away. Refusing to look back, she hurried down the path and headed for town.

She had assumed the chief wanted to see her about George's car, but when she spotted several mobile news vans parked in front of the station and a crowd of reporters milling around outside, she could feel a zing of excitement at the possibility there'd been some break in the case. Her stomach lurched at the sight of the activity, and she was grateful that Charley had told her to park in the back and she wouldn't have to run the gauntlet of reporters. She parked close to the building and hurried up the back steps and was buzzed inside.

The police station had been recently renovated. Outside it retained its small-town charm, but inside it had the look of a modern organization with the latest in technology and manpower. A quiet efficiency pervaded the atmosphere, which she found somewhat intimidating.

"Come on in, Maggie." Charley Blessington came to his feet as Maggie was shown into his office. "Why don't you sit right here? Would you like some coffee or some soda?"

"No thanks. I'm fine." She sat down in the battered leather-and-steel chair in front of his desk, crossed her legs and smoothed the skirt over her knee. "I saw the news people out front. Has something happened?"

"I just had a press conference to bring them up to speed on the status of the case." Charley returned to the chair behind his desk. "The dispatcher told me about George's car. Nothing was taken?"

"No. And I don't even know if the insurance will pay for the repair of the window," she muttered. "You know I almost left the car unlocked yesterday when Wayne drove it over. Just picture trying to explain to Marty Karac that I'd left it unlocked if the car had been stolen instead of burglarized."

Charley let out a bark of laughter. "Marty's my insurance agent, too. Years ago I was transporting a horse to my dad's farm when I stopped to have lunch. While I was eating, someone stole the horse, and I had to tell Marty I hadn't locked the trailer. He groused about how much it was going to cost the insurance company, and I got mad and told him the damn premiums were high enough to cover a singing eunuch and a dancing horse."

His humor eased a little of the tension that had been building since she saw the reporters out in front of the station. She sat back in her chair, trying to relax.

"By the way, Maggie," he said, "did you manage to ask Jake if he knew where Tully might be holed up?"

"Yes, I did," she said. "He said Tully used to have a lean-to in the woods behind the Pat Jackson War Memorial over at Camp Delbrook. Tully told Jake that he was related to the Jackson family and felt most at home near the memorial. Jake says it's kind of hidden and Tully doesn't like for anyone to know where it is."

Charley made a couple of notes, his big hand dwarfing the pen. "I'll send one of the uniforms over there to snoop around. Has Jake been in touch with Tully since we talked last?"

"I saw you Wednesday. Was that only yesterday?" Maggie said, nervous under his steady gaze. "As far as I know, Jake hasn't seen or talked to Tully."

She didn't know whether to be appalled at the fact she hadn't told Charley that she had talked to Tully or to be shocked that she felt no guilt for omitting that information. She had decided in her own mind that Tully was innocent, and she couldn't bring herself to do anything that might lead to his arrest.

Almost as if he sensed that something wasn't right, Charley looked up from his notes and stared at her, his eyes hard and challenging.

"I have the feeling, Maggie, that you're holding something back. I don't know why that would be, since you surely want to get to the bottom of this case as much as I do," he said. "But if you are, it's a dangerous game you're playing."

Maggie clasped her hands in her lap. She had so much information that might or might not have to do with George's murder, but she didn't know where the danger lay. Without knowing if Charley was to be trusted, what could she tell him? After some thought she made a decision.

"I know this sounds stupid, Charley, but I think George's death has something to do with the pictures from Jake's party."

Charley drew his head back so that his chins doubled as he looked down his nose at her. "You mentioned those pictures before. What do they have to do with anything?"

"I don't know, Charley. Maybe I'm grasping at straws, but at least hear me out."

She opened her hands, brushed them together, then placed them flat on her lap. She leaned forward in her chair, trying to organize her thoughts so that he would understand what she had worked out.

"I talked to George before he went to the poker game. He was perfectly normal, teasing Jake and talking easily about Mark. As far as I could tell there was nothing on his mind other than a slight guilt that he wouldn't be taking Jake to the movies. He said he'd pick up the pictures from Jake's party and bring them to our place for dinner the next day. Are you with me so far?"

Charley was tilted back in his chair, looking relaxed, but she could see by the intensity of his gaze that he was taking in every word. "I'm following you," he said.

"George gets to the club, and during dinner he passes the photos around the table. Now, according to Frank, who was sitting across from him, George suddenly focused on one of the pictures. He seemed troubled and he gave the pictures another look. Frank didn't know which photo had caught his attention. The game ends, and George goes out for a cigar and is attacked. His wallet and his watch are stolen. Something else is taken. The photographs."

Charley's chair tilted upright, and his feet hit the floor with a hard smack.

"What do you mean the pictures were taken?"

"Frank said that George put the photos in the pocket of his sport coat. They were not there when his body was found."

"Why would anyone take the pictures?"

"I don't know," Maggie said. "I can't believe if it was an actual robbery that anyone would take them. George never carried a lot of money, and the watch was worthless. It seems to me the real purpose of the robbery was to take the photographs."

"That's just plain crazy," Charley said. "George coulda left them in the club or in the car or just lost them."

"No," she said, shaking her head. "I'm not being stubborn, but I've checked everywhere and talked to as many people as I could. The pictures are gone. My question is why?"

"Damn it, Maggie, what kind of question is that?" He glared across the desk at her. "How would I know why or where the pictures are? I looked at them, and they were just a lot of silly shots of the kids at the Renaissance Faire. Nothing exceptional or newsworthy."

"Then why did the person who killed George take them?" She could see by Charley's expression that she had done little to convince him. "I guess my problem is that I can't believe Tully killed George. Somebody could have put the watch in his car, and Dennis Nyland could have been mistaken about seeing him on the green."

Charley ran the thick fingers of one hand through his hair, the strands standing up like blond spikes. His eyes were hooded as he stared across the desk.

"You haven't heard about Nyland?" he asked.

"Heard what?" Maggie could feel her heartbeat speed up.

"Dennis had a graphic arts business that he ran out of his garage. His mother called a little while ago. She said Dennis generally works late at night and she didn't see him when she left for work this morning. She's a bookkeeper for Rouse Accounting over on Fairview. When she came home today, she discovered his bed hadn't been slept in. She went out to the garage and he was there. Dead."

"How awful." Maggie had a panicky feeling in the pit of her stomach as she thought about Dennis's death. "How did he die?"

"He was stabbed. Just like George." Charley's mouth pulled tight in a grim line. "A direct hit to the heart."

. . .

Maggie sat in the car outside the police station. She gripped the steering wheel to keep her hands from shaking. Poor Dennis. What had he known that made him a risk to the murderer? Had he seen something or heard something as he bent over George's body that jeopardized the security of the killer?

She started the car and drove slowly back to the Estates, where Jake was waiting. She would have to be careful that he got no hint of this latest murder until she'd had a chance to talk about it with Grant. As she pulled into the parking area behind George's house, she felt a bit like Scarlett O'Hara. She'd think about all of this tomorrow.

"What took you so long, Mom?" Jake had heard her drive up and stood on the back porch, hopping from one foot to another. "We're starving."

"Sorry, guys," she said as she came down the walk. "I must have talked to Chief Blessington longer than I thought."

"Just wait until you see what I—what we made," Jake said. "It's way cool."

"I can't wait," she said, hugging him.

Jake raced into the house, and Maggie looked at Grant with new-found respect as he stood back to let her into the house.

"What happened to the crabby son I left with you?" she whispered as she passed him.

"You have such little faith in me, Maggie. He's a great kid. Once we had a chance to talk he decided I wasn't so bad. Besides, I showed him how to make something he really likes. I'm not allowed to tell you. He wants it to be a surprise."

"Sounds like bribery to me," she said. "I hope it's chocolate chip cookies. He considers that one of the food groups. And so do I."

"Can I get you a drink?" Grant narrowed his eyes as he pulled out a chair at the kitchen table for her. "You look done in."

"It's been a long day," she said with a flickering glance at Jake. "Something cold, wet and nonalcoholic would be a godsend."

"I can make lemonade, Mom," Jake offered.

"Do you think Grampa has any?" she asked.

"Sure, and I know right where it is."

He pulled a chair over to the counter and climbed up to reach the cabinet door.

"I found it," Jake said, holding out a packet of premixed pink lemonade. "It's the same kind we use."

"Do you know how to mix it?" Grant asked, setting a plastic pitcher beside the sink.

"Cinch-o," he crowed.

"What can I do?" Maggie asked.

"Nothing," Grant said. "We thought you'd be home pretty soon, so we have dinner already in the oven. You just relax."

Maggie was amazed at how well the two worked together. Grant showed no hint of annoyance when Jake spilled the lemonade as he poured it into glasses, tossing the boy a towel without missing a beat. Grant put ice in the glasses but let Jake bring the drink to his mother.

"Boy, that's just what I needed," she said after taking several swallows. "So what are we having for dinner? I didn't smell anything when I came in, but I'm starting to get a very nice aroma from the oven."

"Grant showed me how to make it. Guess what it is?"

Maggie was pleased that Jake was actually referring to Grant by name. She considered that a fair indication of how far they'd progressed during the short time they'd been together.

"Tuna noodle casserole?" she asked.

"Oh gross, Mom. You know I hate that."

She sniffed. "Smells Italian. How about spaghetti?"

"You're getting warmer."

"Meatballs?"

"You'll never guess," Jake said, too impatient to wait. "Grant showed me how to make pizza."

"No way," she said.

"Way," he said. "You should have seen the kitchen when we were done. There was flour all over everything."

"I can imagine. How soon do we eat?"

"Soon?" Jake said, turning to Grant.

"Couple more minutes. Just enough time to set the table and serve the salad."

Without any argument, Jake helped find silverware and dishes. They worked with a minimum of conversation, but the silence was an easy one. They'd come a long way in a short time, Grant thought.

Earlier, while they worked on the pizza, Jake had talked a lot about his life in Chicago, and it had become apparent that although the boy hadn't seen that much of his father, Mark had done a good job of parenting. According to what Connie had told him, Mark might have been a disaster as a husband, but he had been a strong and stable influence in Jake's life.

The bell on the oven dinged, and Jake leaped to his feet. He crouched in front of the oven door, peering in through the lighted window.

"Just wait'll you see it, Mom. It's got pepperoni and onions and olives and tomatoes. You're going to love it."

He opened the oven door and watched with wide eyes as Grant pulled out the first of two baking sheets and carried it across for Maggie's inspection.

"Did you really make this, Jake? It smells terrific and it looks very professional."

"It's a bit lumpy on that end." Jake, his face flushed with pride, was quick to point out a slight flaw.

"I think it will eat just fine," she said.

"A very impressive first effort, Jake," Grant said. He grinned at the boy, who responded with a wide smile of his own.

"I'm beginning to drool," Maggie said. "Let's eat."

"Apparently George didn't make a lot of pizza," Grant said as he set the baking sheet on the counter. "We couldn't find either pizza pans or a pizza cutter. Your son has great imagination and decided that scissors would work just fine."

He cut the pizza and set it down in the center of the table. Jake was practically vibrating with impatience, and Grant was impressed that he waited for his mother to take the first bite, his face apprehensive as he waited for her verdict.

"Mmmm," she said. "This is really good, Jake. And I'm not just saying it because you made it. It's excellent."

"Dig in, Chef Jake," Grant said.

Grant kept the conversation general during dinner. He could see that it was an effort for Maggie to keep up the cheerful banter. Something must have happened at the police station to upset her. To keep Jake occupied, he asked about his classes and told him an anecdote about his own school days.

"I can't eat another bite," Maggie said, pushing her plate toward the center of the table.

"An exceptional dinner, Jake." Grant got up and poured a cup of coffee. "Normally I'd let you off from doing dishes, but your mom looks tired. Let me get her settled on the deck with this coffee, then I'll come back and we'll get this place cleaned up."

"You're spoiling me," Maggie said, rising to her feet. "And I love every minute of it."

Carrying the coffee, Grant followed Maggie out to the deck. She walked over to the edge, placed her hands flat on the top of the railing and stood quietly, staring into the night.

"What happened at the police station?" Grant said, setting the mug of coffee on the picnic table. "I assumed Charley wanted to see you about George's car, but it's clear that you've been upset all evening. Do you want to talk about it?"

She turned, and he moved closer so that she could speak quietly.

"You're right. It wasn't the car." She took a deep breath and, lowering her voice to a whisper, said, "Dennis Nyland, the man who found George's body, has been murdered."

"What?!" Grant shot a glance over his shoulder to make sure Jake wasn't within earshot. "Murdered?"

"Yes, he was stabbed," Maggie said. "Just like George."

"God Almighty! What did Charley say?"

"Only that Dennis's mother found his body this afternoon when she got home from work. According to Charley, Dennis was working last night in his garage, where sometime after midnight, someone attacked and killed him. Why would anyone kill Dennis?"

Grant didn't immediately answer her question. He knew what he had to tell her would upset her further, but she had to know, and the sooner he told her, the sooner she'd be able to come to terms with the implications.

"What is it?" Maggie asked.

She seemed to sense he had something unpleasant to tell her. She placed the palms of her hands on his chest, and he could feel the slight tremor of her body.

"Dennis was into graphics," Grant said, "but he also had a hobby. He was a tattoo artist."

"Oh dear Lord! Eddie's tattoo?"

Maggie raised her head, and he could see a frightened bewilderment reflected in the darkness of her blue eyes.

"I don't know," Grant said. "But if Dennis knew about the bleeding heart tattoo, the knowledge killed him."

"Yes, I heard about Dennis," Maggie said, cradling the phone against her shoulder. "It's really frightening, Hugh."

"I thought you might be upset," he said. "I've been out most of the day and just picked up my messages. Connie left me a voice mail about Nyland's murder."

"Charley called me in to the station when I got back this afternoon. He didn't tell me much other than that Dennis was stabbed. Do they know any more?"

"Not much according to Connie. Might be another robbery. Nyland's mother says someone took his tattoo design pictures."

"What?" Her knees gave out, and she dropped down onto the foot of Jake's bed.

"She's says he kept books of all the tattoos he drew. The books are missing. Strange, huh?"

Knowing about Eddie Harland's tattoo made this new information even more damning than before. Her mouth was dry, and she was afraid to comment. Hugh would hear in her voice that she was holding something back.

"Are you still there?" he asked when she didn't respond.

"I'm here. It's just the whole thing is so scary."

"You should consider it a warning."

"A warning?" Maggie said. "What do you mean?"

"First George was killed and now Nyland. That guy must have known more than he told the police. He might have seen who did it."

"He told Charley he just saw Tully."

"Maybe yes, maybe no." Hugh pronounced each syllable slowly and precisely. "He must have known something, or why would he be murdered?"

To Maggie it was unimaginable that they were discussing murder as if it were a normal topic of conversation.

"What are you suggesting?" she asked.

"I think Nyland tried to make some money and got caught in his own trap. Meddling in murder is a dangerous business. It got Nyland killed.

Hugh's voice was angry, almost threatening. She shivered.

"Don't tell me any more. It's frightening me."

"Do you want me to come over?"

"No." She cleared her throat to cover the sharpness of her reply. "I appreciate the offer, but it's late, and I want to get Jake into bed. I still haven't decided whether to tell him about Dennis tonight or wait until tomorrow."

"News like that can wait until morning," Hugh said.

"You're right," she said, speaking quietly so that her voice wouldn't carry down the hall to where Jake was just finishing his shower. "There's no school tomorrow because of teacher conferences. I'll have more time in the morning, and I won't have to worry that it'll give him nightmares."

Just talking about it made her feel less apprehensive. Standing up, she pulled back Jake's bedspread and stared at the sheet-covered bed, wondering where the blanket had disappeared to. It had been warm the last several nights, but usually Jake just kicked off the covers. She looked under the bed but couldn't find it.

"What time is your teacher conference?" he asked.

"I drew the evening shift. Eight o'clock."

Too tired to look for the blanket, she turned on the table lamp, switched off the ceiling light and walked across the hall to her own bedroom, sitting down in the chair beside the window.

"Then I won't see you there. I'm going after lunch, then I'm taking Kenny up to Door County to see my mother. I'm coming back Saturday morning, and she'll bring him back Sunday late. Oh, before I forget, could you check to see if Jake has Kenny's windbreaker? We've got Jake's. Kenny says they got mixed up yesterday when you brought him home."

"Does he need it before you go to your mother's?"

"No. He's got a spare."

"It's probably in Jake's backpack. If I find it, I'll drop it off sometime tomorrow," Maggie said.

"That's great. If I'm not there, it'll be in the mudroom closet."

"I'm done, Mom," Jake yelled from the open door of the bathroom. "Can I have some cookies?"

"Just a minute, Jake. I'm on the phone," she said. "Sorry, Hugh. Jake's just getting out of the shower."

"Kenny's still in the tub. He spends more time in the bathroom than the bedroom. He's content for hours with that flotilla of boats he's got. Not much room left for water, let alone soap."

It was out of character for Hugh to chitchat. Get to the point, she thought, holding back a sigh.

"Jake's just as bad," she said. "I would have thought they'd give that up now that they're getting so grown up."

"Kenny's starting to lengthen out. All of sudden he's eating more. I suppose a sign his body's changing. He and Jake polished off a loaf of bread and a package of ham the other day when you were here."

"It's funny you should mention that. Jake's been taking apples and oranges to school and still complains that he's hungry. Times are changing, Hugh," she said. "By the way, thanks for getting the window of the car fixed. I called the insurance company, and it's covered. Let me know how much I owe you."

"We'll call it a deposit on dinner," he said. "I'd like to get together. Just the two of us."

Maggie grimaced at the tone of his voice. She wondered why he was suddenly pressing her. It couldn't just be the fact that he was jealous of Grant. It seemed as if there was a new urgency in his voice.

"Since George died there's been no time," she said, knowing it was a weak excuse.

"Time enough for shopping in Milwaukee."

She might have been more sympathetic if Hugh had sounded like he felt neglected. Instead his tone was angry, as if she were purposely avoiding him. Oh rats! I don't have time for this.

The awareness of how supportive Hugh had been over the past year and how many secrets she was keeping from him combined to make her feel guilty. Perhaps he sensed that she was shutting him out. Although unfounded, he clearly saw Grant as a threat to their developing relationship.

"It would be good to get together, Hugh," she said, leaning her head against the back of the chair, too tired to argue. "Since Sunday it's been hectic, but now things are loosening up. Today's Thursday, and you get back from Door County on Saturday. Would Sunday about six o'clock work for you?"

"Absolutely. Kenny won't be back until nine. How about Hills' Haufbrau Haus?"

"Sounds great," she said. "Now I better get Jake off to bed. Thanks for calling, Hugh. I'll see you on Sunday."

Maggie could hear the relief in his voice as he said goodnight. She'd have to give some serious thought to their relationship before Sunday. It would be unfair to string him along if there was no interest on her part.

"Now can I have some cookies, Mom?"

Jake was waiting in the kitchen, his hair standing up in damp spikes and his cheeks pink from his vigorous towel drying. He was wearing pajama shorts, and the fresh scent of soap rose from his skin to fill her senses. She leaned over and kissed the top of his head.

"Since you don't smell like an old tennis shoe anymore, you can have a treat," she said.

She put some chocolate chip cookies on a plate and poured him a glass of milk. He carried them to the kitchen table and sat down, pulling his bare feet up onto the seat of the chair. He picked up a cookie and then set it back down on the plate and looked over at Maggie.

"Mom, I'm sorry I was mean about Grant this morning. I think he's a good guy."

"I'm glad you like him. I do too," she said, "but I have a confession to make. I didn't like him when I first met him."

"You didn't?"

"Next time you're with him, ask him to tell you about the canoe paddle."

"The canoe paddle?" Jake asked.

"Yes. I know you want to know now, but I'm not going to spoil the fun. I think you'll really get a laugh out of hearing the story from Grant."

"OK."

He raised the cookie again, stopping just short of his mouth, then returned it to the plate. Apprehension was clear in his expression.

"Mom, I had a talk with Grant and told him some stuff, and he's going to tell you about it. Promise you won't get mad?"

She felt a momentary stab of jealousy that Jake had talked to Grant about something that was clearly troubling him. Part of the problem with being a single parent was that she tried to be all things to Jake. Mother, father, friend, playmate, teacher. The list was interminable. Any time he turned to someone else, she felt a twinge as if she were inadequate to fill her roles.

"You know how I hate when you want me to promise I won't get mad. Best I can do is promise to listen and try to understand." She worried when his expression didn't lighten. "I hope it's not too bad. You didn't rob a bank, did you?"

He shook his head. "Grant will tell you."

As if Grant's involvement relieved him of all responsibility, he went back to eating his cookies with a look of contentment.

"After you're in bed," she said, "I'm going down to the bookstore. Grant's coming over shortly. I'll leave the door open, so if you wake up all you have to do is call."

"Uncle Ham and Aunt Nell are coming too?" Jake said, wiping the milk mustache off his lip with the back of his hand. His eyes crinkled at her start of surprise. "I heard you guys talking."

"Don't you know it's not polite to eavesdrop?" She rubbed her knuckles on the top of his head.

"If I didn't, I'd never know anything." He looked up at her, eyes wide and serious. "You know, Mom. I'm not a baby anymore."

Maggie sighed. "I know, Jake. Sometimes I forget that. Moms have a tough time when their boys grow up."

For an instant she could hear Katrina Harland saying much the same thing. It was hard to believe that she'd been in Detroit earlier in the day. No wonder she was tired. Thinking about Eddie's mother triggered another memory, and she let out a small gasp.

"What's the matter, Mom?" Jake asked.

"I just thought of something I forgot to show Grant," she said.

She picked up her purse from the kitchen counter where she'd dropped it when they came home. She carried it across to the table and set it on the edge.

"Do you know anything about knots, Jake?"

"Some. Kenny showed me how to do some fancy ones. He's a wizard at them."

She opened the zipper compartment of her purse and withdrew the tissue-wrapped package she'd put inside for safe keeping.

"Somebody gave me this today, and I forgot all about it."

She unwrapped the tissue, setting the key ring with the knotted cord in the center of the table. Jake crammed the last cookie in his mouth.

"I don't recognize the knot," she said. "Do you?"

"Sure," he said, chewing and swallowing before he continued. "Kenny showed me how to tie one just like that. It's called a falconer's knot."

CHAPTER
NINETEEN

"A FALCONER'S KNOT?" Ham said, staring down at the key ring with the knotted cord attached. "Jake's sure?"

"Yes. He tied some knots for us, and they were identical to this one," Grant said. "Kenny Rossiter showed Jake how to tie the knot, and he thought it was really cool because you only use one hand to do it."

"You tie the knot with one hand?" Nell asked.

"Yes. Picture this. The hawk is sitting on your gloved left hand, and you need to secure his leash. You only have your right hand." Grant demonstrated, using a piece of string. "Jake showed me the basics, but it takes me a couple tries before I get it looking right. You should see him. He can do it at lightning speed."

"What's the second knot for?" Ham said, touching the original knotted cord.

"It's sort of a safety knot so you don't release the first one unintentionally," Grant said. "The knot's designed to be untied quickly. You just take out this free end and pull sharply."

Maggie could feel the tension rising as Grant tried to bring Ham and Nell up to speed on what they'd learned about the knot. She sat back, letting Grant do the talking.

Trying to appear normal during the dinner with Jake and Grant had taken a toll on her energy. They had just finished when Ham called to tell Grant that he and Nell had just come back from dinner and heard about Dennis Hyland's death. After a low-voiced conversation, Grant asked if they could all meet later at the bookstore.

Maggie had been grateful that she could get Jake safely tucked into bed while Grant told the other two about her meeting with Katrina Harland. She'd brought a pot of coffee and a bottle of brandy when she came downstairs.

Ham leaned across the table, speaking directly to Maggie. "Grant called me after you had your meeting with Katrina Harland. He knew I was going to Milwaukee. Noreen Flood, the second child kidnapped, died at the zoo there. My friend Paula Craig was going to let me look at the files."

"Did you learn anything?" Maggie asked.

"Grant told me to check if there were any identifying marks on Noreen's body," Ham said. "There was. She had a tattoo."

"Oh God!" Maggie cried, thoughts of Eddie Harland and Dennis Nyland fresh in her mind.

He took out a Xerox sheet, unfolded it and passed it across to Maggie. Her hands shook as she smoothed the paper. It was a copy of a close-up photograph of the dead child's chest. Above the left nipple was a red heart with a golden arrow through it. Beneath the heart were several droplets of blood.

"It's just like the drawing Eddie's mother made," Maggie said.

She swallowed hard as she stared down at the tattoo. Grant handed Ham the drawing of the bleeding heart that Katrina Harland had given Maggie.

"Hearing about it was bad enough," Maggie said. "Seeing the actual picture is even worse."

Her eyes filled with tears, and she covered her shaking lips with her hand. Grant placed a comforting hand on her arm. She could feel the warmth of his touch, but it didn't diminish the chill of fear that invaded her body.

"I asked Paula if they had ever come across any other tattoos. She's tracked several similar in Wisconsin and Minnesota," Ham said. "Over the last ten years four bodies have turned up with tattoos that were similar to the one on Noreen's chest. Paula said there could be more in other states, but she's only been able to find these four."

"Four? God in Heaven!" Maggie said. "Were they children?"

"No, thank God," Nell said. "That was my first question too. They were young men. Two of them were runaways in their late teens. The other two were in their twenties. Homeless and heavily into drugs."

"Two in Wisconsin. Trego and Green Bay. Two in Minnesota. Minneapolis and Grand Rapids," Ham said. "They'd been stabbed. A single wound from a thin-bladed knife. The tattoos were done after death. They were similar but not as refined or as professional looking as the one that Noreen had. Paula thought the killer might be a tattoo artist in training."

Even though Ham spoke in an impersonal tone, Maggie could not hold back the sense of horror that surrounded her. It was like Pandora's box. Once the investigation was opened, there was no holding back the ripples that spread out to include even more shocking details. Suddenly a new thought jolted her.

"Do you think Dennis Nyland was killed because he did the tattoos on Eddie and Noreen?" she asked.

"I don't think so," Grant said. "The kidnapper is intelligent. He's made few mistakes. It would be too dangerous to have someone local do the tattooing. Besides, he isn't aware that we know anything about the tattoos. I think it's more likely that Dennis was killed because he found George's body."

"I agree," Ham said. "He must have known something that represented a threat to the killer. It's possible he could have recognized him."

"Not Tully," Maggie said.

"No," Grant said. "Dennis had already told Blessington about Tully. Maybe he saw someone else, too, and for some reason didn't mention it. Dennis might have approached that person later. If so, the killer would have no choice but to eliminate him."

"If only we could talk to Tully," Maggie said. "Dennis Nyland's death proves that Tully is in danger."

"The killer is getting rattled," Ham added. "Nyland's death suggests he's cleaning up loose ends."

"We've been looking for something to narrow down the suspect list, and it's my opinion that the falconer's knot tips the scales toward the falconry club," Grant said.

"I'd have to agree," Maggie said. "At least we should put them at the top of the list of suspects. Ham?"

"I can see where you're heading, but I still think we can't leave anyone who was at the poker game off the list."

"OK. Let's combine the two and see what we end up with." Referring back to several pages of the yellow pad, Grant wrote down two lists of names. After he'd completed it, he stared down at what he'd written, then passed it to Maggie. "We have eight names."

"I can help you eliminate one of the names," Maggie said after scanning the list and handing it to Nell. "Mike Offenlach is in the falconry club, but he and his wife were in Illinois visiting her mother last weekend. I talked to Mike at the memorial service, and the night George was killed he was at an antique auction."

Nell drew a line through Mike's name.

"While I'm at it, I can take out another member of the falconry club. When I was at the bakery this morning, Donna Harper was telling the owner that her husband was rushed to the hospital Wednesday evening with an appendicitis attack. So that lets Brian Harper out."

"We're making some progress," Nell continued. "I've got one more name I think we should take off the list. Walter Kondrat."

"Is that a sentimental choice?" Ham asked, his mouth drawn tight in disapproval. "He was at the dinner and the poker game. He might not be into falconry, but hanging around with that bunch, enough of it could have rubbed off so that he'd be familiar with a falconer's knot."

Nell glared across the table at Ham.

"I'm not making a sentimental decision, you dunce," she said. "Walter is not the brightest bulb in the chandelier when it comes to anything outside of the insurance business. He doesn't have enough intelligence to pull off a murder, let alone a kidnapping."

"It doesn't take intelligence to stab someone. Unrestrained anger would do it," Ham said. "It's entirely possible that George was killed not only because he had seen the pictures but for another reason altogether. We know that Walter had an explosive fight with George that night over money. More people are killed over money than over fear of exposure."

"Walter didn't kill George," Nell said. "I know what they were arguing about. George called me that night from the club and told me."

"What?" Ham yelped.

If Nell had dropped a bomb in the center of the bookstore, she couldn't have gotten a more shocked reaction. Maggie stared at the older woman, who tried to appear unconcerned at the consternation she'd created. She smoothed one hand across her salmon-colored hair, then reached out to the bottle of brandy, pouring a substantial dollop into her coffee.

"Why didn't you tell us?" Maggie said.

"Because it had nothing to do with the investigation. All George and I talked about was his argument with Walter, and I didn't think it had any bearing on his death."

"Judas Priest!" Ham said. "You're a very exasperating woman. Don't you know that in a murder case everything has relevance? Each detail fills the holes in the puzzle and eventually helps the investigators find a solution."

He threw himself back in his chair, spreading his arms and raising his palms to the sky in resignation. He looked at Grant, who had been silently watching the byplay but now leaned forward to speak.

"I'm sure you had cogent reasons for not telling us about George's call," Grant said, "but it would be constructive to hear what you talked about."

Nell took another sip of her coffee and set the mug back on the table. She picked at a spot of paint on her denim blouse and then looked up and began to speak.

"My husband, Hal, and Walter were partners in the insurance company. After his wife died, Walter spent a lot of time at our house, and the three of us became good friends. When Hal died, people assumed that after a suitable mourning period Walter and I would marry. Even my children pushed for it. They only saw that he would be a solution to their worries about my being alone."

Nell stared down at the table, running one hand along the edge, her face thoughtful.

"About ten years ago, Walter asked me to marry him. I wasn't in love with him, but I was going through a lonely period and I strongly considered it. One night I ran into George at an election rally and we got talking, and I asked him if he thought Walter was ready to marry. George misunderstood and said Walter had told him he had no plans to marry Jeanne Vadnais but was content with their long-term affair."

"The randy old bastard," Ham muttered.

"Naturally it was a bit of a blow to my pride, since I'd had no idea. Jeanne and I were friends. She was sort of a psycho bitch in her younger days but eventually mellowed into a very nice woman. Always wears great shoes."

"Oh for God's sake, Nell. What do her shoes have to do with anything?" Ham asked.

"It was just an observation. No need to foam at the mouth," she said.

"George realized that I didn't know about Walter's affair, and I made him promise he wouldn't tell him that I knew. I gather that for ten years George kept his word. Until Saturday night."

"So George was fighting with Walter about his ongoing affair?" Grant asked.

"Yes. When he called me he was very upset for breaking his silence. It seems that Walter was drinking and made some disparaging remark about my refusing to marry him. George lost his temper and said I'd never marry a man who I knew was having an affair with another woman. Then the you-know-what hit the fan."

"All the more reason to keep Walter on the list," Ham said, his eyes flinty.

"According to Doris Blessington, Walter spent the night at Jeanne's house after the poker game," Nell said. "Jeanne lives next door to the Blessingtons. Doris said she thought it was Charley coming home, and when she looked out the window, she saw Walter driving into the garage. It was about twelve-thirty, and if George was killed right after the game, Walter wouldn't have been able to get to Jeanne's by that time."

"The time of death isn't all that accurate," Ham said.

"Give it up, Ham," Nell said. "Walter is not a man of action. He'd have sued George, not killed him. I appreciate your championing my cause, but just because you don't like Walter, you can't nail him for murder."

Maggie caught the smile that passed from Nell to Ham, and her eyes opened wide. Why hadn't she noticed that the two of them had established some kind of relationship in the last few days? She shot a glance at Grant, who had obviously come to the same conclusion.

"Since we're trying to narrow down the list," Grant said, "I think I'd agree with Nell. Walter looks like a poor suspect. But something you said makes me wonder about Charley Blessington. You said Doris thought it might be Charley coming home. Where was Charley?"

"He's in the falconry club and he was at the dinner," Maggie said. "I know he's the police chief, but it worries me that he keeps asking about Tully. It's like he has a personal reason to get hold of him. Do we have any evidence against Charley?"

"Yes," Ham said. "I would have mentioned it, but I only confirmed it today."

Maggie wondered if this was the information that Connie had been looking for. Grant had told her about his conversation with Connie and had asked Ham to look through George's papers to see if he could find any report that would sabotage Blessington's chances to be elected mayor.

"You have to go back twelve years ago," Ham said, "when Amelia Fowler was the mayor. She'd been a movie actress and had been elected not for any governing qualifications but rather because it was rumored she'd slept with some big-name stars. Turned out to be a good, tough mayor. She was running for reelection and she'd just fired the chief of police for sexual harassment of his female personnel."

"It was the best scandal in Delbrook history," Nell said. "The chief's wife caught him spanking a bare-assed beat cop—if you'll pardon the expression—in his office and screeched so loudly there was no way of covering it up. It was such a hot topic of conversation that the chief, his wife and the rosy-bottomed cop all left town."

"So Amelia was desperate for someone who could restore dignity and discipline to the office of chief of police," Ham said. "One of the names mentioned for the job was Charley Blessington, and the newspaper did a story on him. It turned out that Charley was a genuine hero. He'd saved the life of a young girl during a bank robbery down in Florida. The robber panicked when the alarm went off and started shooting. Charley shielded a little girl with his body and took the bullet that might have killed her."

"Way to go, Charley," Grant said.

"When Charley was questioned he tried to downplay his role, but they had a picture from the newspaper showing him strapped to a gurney with his bandaged arm around the little girl trying to comfort her. I've seen the picture, and it's a real heart tugger."

"How come I never heard that story?" Maggie asked.

"It happened twenty-three years ago," Ham said. "Charley was twenty-one or two."

"During the election campaign, the newspaper gave the story plenty of space," Nell said.

"Amelia thought Charley was the perfect candidate. He'd been an assistant chief of police in a mid-sized town in Ohio, had an excellent reputation and was an all-American hero to boot. So Amelia appointed him chief." Ham paused, poured some brandy into his coffee and took a sip. "Charley's done a good job as chief. There's no question of that. The only problem is that the story that got him the job wasn't true."

"The picture was a hoax?" Maggie asked.

"No, the picture was real. The report I found among the papers in George's desk was a letter from Brandon Terrell, who's the photo editor of the *Park Ridge Advocate* newspaper. When he was starting out as a photographer in Florida, he took the picture that appeared on the front page of the paper after the shooting. I don't know how George got onto this whole thing, but the letter Terrell sent confirmed that the name beneath the photo had been misidentified. It was not Charles Blessington but Charles Lester who had saved the child's life."

"Poor Doris," Nell said. "She really loves Charley. Gossip's always been her thing, but this would be tough to deal with. He'd either end up as a laughingstock or get labeled as an opportunistic liar. In her eyes, I don't know which would be worse."

"How did the mix-up happen?" Maggie asked.

"Charley had been at the bank, but he wasn't the one on the stretcher who saved the girl. Brandon Terrell, the man who wrote the letter to George, shot a bunch of pictures at the scene of the shooting, including one of Charley being interviewed as one of the witnesses. The man on the stretcher was also named Charles, and Terrell identified him as Blessington instead of Lester."

"If Charley runs for mayor, the lie is bound to surface," Nell added. "Connie knows there's something in Charley's background that could hurt him politically. She has the money and the resources to do a thorough check."

"These days I don't know if something like that would be enough to cause a scandal. Look at what goes on in Washington," Grant said. "Charley could always say that once the story was in the paper, there wasn't anything he could do about it. The more he denied it, the more people would believe it."

"That might be true, except when I went back to the newspaper archives, I came up with at least five instances where Charley talked about the story as if it were true," Ham said.

"Would Charley kill to keep this information from getting out?" Maggie asked.

"I don't know him well enough to say," Grant said. "One thing to consider is that, if he was the one who searched George's house, he would have found that letter and destroyed it."

"Maybe that's what he was looking for and just didn't see it," Ham said. "Charley was at the poker game, he saw the photographs and he's a falconer, so he'd know the knot." Ham didn't want to take anyone off the list. "He could have had two reasons for killing George."

"All right. Blessington is still a suspect," Grant said. He took the list back from Ham and put a check mark in front of Charley's name. "Next is Hugh Rossiter."

Maggie was aware they were waiting for her to speak. She felt awkward, since they all knew that she'd dated Hugh.

"I hate this, you know," she said. "I've never had to look at everyone I know and wonder if they have the capacity to do evil things. Shouldn't it be apparent?"

"My mother always said, when you touch pitch, it sticks to your fingers," Nell said. "I wish there were a litmus test for killers."

"The thing is," Maggie continued, "I'm so paranoid, I'm afraid to leave Jake with anyone. I realized this morning when Hugh drove Jake to school that there was a part of me that wondered if I could trust him with my son. How can I suspect a man who's been so good to both of us?"

"It's natural," Grant said. "It would be naive, knowing what you know, not to question everyone in Delbrook. Jake's safety is most important. The thing to remember is that, unless George's killer is unmasked, you will never be able to trust anyone again and you will never feel that Jake is really safe."

Maggie stared down at her hands, letting his words sink in. She didn't know if he'd said what he'd said to reassure her, but it hadn't worked. Examining her friends made her sick to her stomach. It took all of her resolve to think about Hugh in an objective way.

"Facts against Hugh? He's the master falconer, so of all people, he would know the falconer's knot. He was at the Renaissance Faire, at the dinner and poker game and saw the photographs. On the pro side, he's a caring father, a hard worker and appears reasonably normal," she said. "You know what's sad? When I started to think about Hugh, I realized how little I really knew about him. I know dumb things like what kind of movies he likes and that he prefers Italian food over Mexican, but I don't know anything about his past or even his present life."

"If you had wanted to know, you would have asked," Grant said.

"I guess what I'm saying," she continued, ignoring his comment, "is that I don't know anything negative about Hugh, unless it's that at times he's a bit tough on Kenny."

Grant shifted in his chair, suspecting that Maggie would feel a general sense of betrayal with what he was about to say. He wanted to tell her that it was not personal, just a part of the investigation process, but he didn't think she'd believe him.

"While you were meeting with Katrina Harland, I went to see Hugh Rossiter's sister-in-law, who lives in Detroit."

Maggie's eyes widened, and the glow that had been reflected in the blue depths faded. Grant swallowed to get the dryness out of his throat before he continued.

"According to the rumor mill here in town, Julie Rossiter left Hugh three years ago for another man. No one seems to know who this man was, but he wasn't local. It seemed to me unusual that she wouldn't still be in contact with her son, but apparently that's the case. More than once I heard the phrase 'she disappeared off the face of the earth,' and I decided to find out where she was."

"Why the hell didn't you tell me this before?" Maggie asked.

"I didn't think you'd like it," Grant admitted. "I called Amy Caldwell, Julie's sister, and asked if I could talk to her about Julie. She agreed because she was curious to know why I was looking for her."

"I knew Amy," Nell said. "Married a lazy good-for-nothing who used to spend his days watching game shows and the Home Shopping Network. She must have taken back her maiden name after her divorce."

"She did. She's got two kids, five and six, and has a good job with a computer repair company in Detroit. She doesn't know where Julie is. According to her, Julie has never contacted her since the day she left three years ago."

"Did she know why her sister left?" Ham asked.

"According to Amy, Julie ran off because Hugh beat her."

"What a rotten thing to say," Maggie said.

"I'm telling you Amy's story, not mine," Grant said.

"I can't believe it," Maggie said. "No one has ever hinted at anything like that."

"If it was true, probably no one was aware of it," Nell said. "Women keep it a secret because of misplaced shame. They give a million excuses why they have a bruise or a cut. Sometimes members of a family suspect what's going on but are afraid to say anything or purposely ignore it."

Grant could see Maggie withdraw at Nell's comments. He suspected she was equating it to her own life and the fact she had kept Mark's infidelities a secret. Everyone had something they would rather not talk about.

"Amy said that she'd seen evidence of Hugh's abuse," Grant said, "and when she confronted Julie, she admitted that he'd beaten her. She said he was sorry and had sworn it would never happen again. The abuse must have continued. Amy said that Hugh was very jealous, and she thinks the reason that Julie has never contacted anyone is that she's afraid of Hugh finding out where she is."

Grant glanced at Maggie, who was staring down at the tabletop, her mouth drawn into a tight line.

"I don't know if Amy's story is true," he said. "All I can tell you is what I heard. It will take further investigation to prove any of this."

"Even if it's true, that doesn't make Hugh a murderer or a kidnapper," Maggie said.

"That's right," he said. "Everything we're learning about the people on the list is just information. We haven't come up with anything that makes us point to one person and say that's the killer. Our only hope is that by a process of elimination we can come up with one person who had the opportunity and the motive to commit murder."

Grant placed a check mark in front of Hugh's name. He could feel Maggie's resistance to the idea as if it were a physical thing. Knowing that each day he was drawn more strongly to her, he wondered if any relationship would survive the soul-searching that was required in this investigation.

"Frank Woodman?" Ham asked, eager to change the subject.

"I don't know of anything that would put him on the list except for the fact he was at the club," Nell said. "The strongest reason to assume he's innocent is that I don't think he would have mentioned anything about George looking at the photographs if he had killed him in order to keep them a secret."

"That's a good point," Grant said. He started to cross off Frank's name but instead put a question mark in front of it. "We'll keep him on the list until we do a bit more checking into his background. We know he was at the country club when George's body was discovered, so he had the opportunity. Dennis Nyland was killed around midnight. If Frank is normally at the country club at that time, someone may have seen him and be able to give him an alibi."

"The killer appears to have picked times and places to attack George and Dennis where he is unlikely to be seen," Grant said. "He either arranged for George to meet him on the fairway or he waited outside until he could approach him through the trees. He went to Nyland's place after midnight, and once again no one saw him."

"I keep meaning to bring this up," Nell said. "I object to the use of 'he' for the killer. Nothing suggests that the killer is male. It wouldn't take only a man's strength to stab someone. I don't think you can rule Connie out."

"I agree," Maggie said. "She's a falconer, and she was at the dinner and the poker game."

"My use of the male pronoun was strictly for ease of speaking. Connie's name is on the list. I'm not sure I consciously discounted her," Grant said.

Maggie wasn't so sure about that. She could see in both the men's faces that they could not picture Connie Prentice as either a murderer or a kidnapper.

"All right, let's talk about Brent and Connie," Maggie said. "Do we have any evidence against either of them?"

"They were both at the Renaissance Faire, and neither one has an alibi for the time George was killed," Nell said.

"Maybe they didn't leave together, but as a couple it would be hard to be gone long without the other person knowing about it," Ham said. "Doris knew that Charley wasn't home."

"Charley could always tell Doris he was on police business, and that would be enough of an explanation," Grant said. "But what excuse could Brent and Connie make to each other?"

"None would be necessary," Nell said. "Connie and Brent live in separate wings of the house. They don't live as a married couple and haven't for many years. I doubt if either one would be aware of the other's comings and goings."

"That might explain why Brent has that air of sadness about him when he looks at Connie," Maggie said. "He told me once he'd fallen in love with Connie the first time he saw her and there's never been anyone since."

Grant shrugged. "Things change. Connie sounds caustic and bitter around him. Like something's happened that she doesn't understand."

"Does everyone lead a secret life?" Maggie asked. "God, this is awful."

"Doris did drop a piece of information that might have some bearing," Nell said. "Connie and Brent wanted children. Connie was pregnant when Falcon's Nest caught fire. She went into labor, and the child lived only a few hours after it was born. It was a boy."

"You're suggesting that they might kidnap children in order to replace the child they lost?" Grant asked.

"I'm not suggesting a thing," Nell said. "I'm reporting what Doris told me."

"Brent missed the dinner, so he wasn't there when the photographs were passed around," Ham said. "Does anyone know if he saw them?"

"No. I think we need to make an assumption here. If he didn't see the actual pictures, he would have heard them discussed and known they were taken at the Renaissance Faire," Grant said. "He also could have overheard George's phone call. Even though he's not in the falconry club, Connie is, so he would be familiar with the falconer's knot."

"Are we making any progress?" Maggie asked.

"We've got a list of prime suspects." Grant held up a finger as he ticked them off. "Hugh Rossiter, Charley Blessington, Brent Prentice and Connie Prentice."

"I can't believe any of them could commit a murder," Maggie said. "We have nothing but bits and pieces. Nothing that points to a killer."

"That's how police work is done, kiddo," Ham said. "You compile as much info as you can, and then eventually a pattern begins to emerge. It's hard work. Killing's fast. Catching a killer takes time."

"We don't have a lot of time." Maggie splayed out her fingers and pressed them on the table in front of her. "First George is killed and now Dennis. I have this sick feeling that Tully will be next. He may have a key piece of information, and therefore he's in terrible danger."

"Isn't there any way to contact him?" Nell asked. "Doesn't anyone know where he is?"

"Yes, someone knows where he is," Grant said. "Someone's been hiding him for the last couple of days."

"No shit, Sherlock," Ham said. "Who?"

"The one person Tully trusts," Grant said. "Jake."

CHAPTER
TWENTY

"JAKE IS HIDING TULLY?" Maggie sagged in her chair, expelling a slow stream of air. "That's why he's been acting so strange. I suppose Kenny was involved, too."

"Yes. Reluctantly, I gather," Grant said.

"God in heaven! How am I ever going to explain this to Hugh?" Maggie muttered.

"Very enterprising boys," Ham said.

"Aren't they cute, the little darlings?" Nell said, salmon curls quivering as she shook her head.

"You'll have to give Jake points for confessing before I got out the thumbscrews," Grant said. "I've been trying to piece together where Tully could be, and I decided if he was still in Delbrook, someone was helping him. Once I got suspicious of Jake, everything fell into place."

"I can't believe Tully put Jake in danger by contacting him," Ham said.

"He didn't," Grant said. "Jake made the contact. He was afraid Charley Blessington was going to arrest Tully."

"No wonder Jake wanted me to promise I wouldn't get mad when you told me something tonight," Maggie said. "I forgot about it when I came downstairs because I didn't know it had anything to do with the investigation. You better give me chapter and verse so I know how much trouble he's in."

"Tully lives in a lean-to in the woods over in Camp Delbrook. When Jake goes over to Kenny's, he usually brings some Snickers bars, along with anything else he thinks Tully would like. He leaves everything in a hollowed-out tree in the woods beyond the mews that the boys refer to as the mailbox."

"I think the military could use these kids," Ham said.

"The first couple days after George died, Tully stuck to the woods. Jake was worried that he wouldn't be able to buy groceries, so he got Kenny to make a drop at the mailbox. Kenny supplied sandwiches, and Jake added fruit and a couple bottles of juice. Do you remember when Kenny broke the mayonnaise jar?" Grant asked. "I wondered why he looked so frightened. It seems they'd just made a bunch of sandwiches for Tully, and he was sure we'd discover them."

Maggie groaned. "Hugh and I were just discussing how the boys' appetites have increased. And of course that's why they took their backpacks on the hike. They were taking the food to Tully. I can't believe I didn't pick up on any of this."

"Well, dear," Nell said, "you've had a few things on your mind. The trouble with children is that they're born provocateurs. Their minds cope much better with conspiracies than adults' do."

"Everything was going all right until yesterday," Grant said, "when the volunteer cleanup began over at Camp Delbrook. With the additional people around, the chances that someone would spot Tully increased. Besides, rain was predicted."

"This just gets worse and worse," Maggie said. "All right, Grant, how the hell did you figure it out?"

"The tip-off was Tully's call. You said Jake had been jumping to answer the phone, so I wondered if he was waiting to hear from him. That was it. On Wednesday, the boys left a note along with the food for Tully and told him where to go to get out of the rain."

"I'm too old to play guessing games," Nell said.

"Tonight when Maggie left Jake with me at George's house, I noticed that he'd left his backpack beside the ladder to the treehouse. I realized the treehouse was the perfect place for Tully to hide." Grant shrugged. "I asked Jake straight out, and he confessed the whole thing."

Maggie remembered yesterday when they'd returned to George's house. She had a mental picture of Jake climbing up to the treehouse with the bulging backpack. It was so clear now, but then it had meant nothing.

"What did Jake have in the backpack yesterday?" she asked.

"A blanket, your raincoat and an umbrella." He grinned at Maggie's start of surprise. "Missed those, did you? Don't worry, they're still up there. Jake and I checked it out tonight before you got back from the police station. From what I could tell, Tully had been there during the storm."

"Where is he now?" Ham asked.

"I don't know," Grant said. "Jake wrote Tully a note, asking him to come and talk to me. He left it in the treehouse along with the sandwiches that Kenny passed him at school today. After you and Jake left tonight, I took up some leftover pizza and a thermos of coffee, but there was no sign of Tully. All we can do is wait and see if he comes back and if he's willing to talk."

"He's got to," Maggie said. "There's a killer running loose here in Delbrook. I can't let Jake continue to shield Tully. It's too dangerous."

"I agree," Grant said. "George might have been killed on the spur of the moment out of fear of discovery, but Dennis Nyland's death is different. He was deliberately murdered. For some reason Nyland was a danger that had to be eliminated. The murderer won't think twice about killing the boys if they get in his way."

The sleep of the innocent, Maggie thought as she stared down at Jake. He lay on his back, his arms spread wide, his little boy's chest achingly vulnerable in its nakedness. Since Mark's death, she had stood many nights beside Jake's bed, aware of the fragility of life and terrified of losing Jake.

She leaned over to kiss his cheek, inhaling the soapy smell that clung to his hair after his shower. Please, God, keep him safe.

Picking up the dirty sneakers beside the bed, she took them out to the kitchen, where she sprayed them with disinfectant. They were only a few weeks old, yet they looked and smelled as if Jake had been wearing them for years. He hated socks. He said his feet couldn't breathe. In the winter it wasn't too bad, but when it was hot, the sweat combined with the materials in the sneakers to create an odor that brought tears to the eyes.

She set the shoes on the floor by the stairs and picked up his backpack. She unzipped the bag, finding Kenny's windbreaker jammed on top. She shook it out and hung it over the back of a kitchen chair.

The backpack needed airing, too. She made a mental note to wash it on the weekend. She pulled out several schoolbooks and set them on the counter along with a plastic pencil case, two dog-earred Batman comic books, old brown paper sandwich bags and a collection of rocks, bottle caps and intriguing metal parts.

When the bag was empty, she inverted it over the sink and shook it. Crumbs, scraps of paper and miscellaneous grit showered down on the metal surface of the sink. She gave the backpack one final shake, and out floated a feather.

The feather was pure white with a little clouding near the shaft. She recognized it immediately. It was the tail feather of a bald eagle.

Her fingers tightened on the backpack, and her heart pounded in her ears. The feather was perfect, with no gaps or crimping along the edges. The flawless condition of the feather indicated it had not been scrunched in the bottom of Jake's backpack for days on end.

Hands shaking, she picked up the receiver of the phone and dialed George's telephone number. Grant answered.

"I just found an eagle feather in Jake's backpack," she said, swallowing to loosen the dryness in her throat.

"I'll be right there," he said.

Maggie blinked several times as she heard the dial tone droning in her ear. She hadn't expected such an immediate reaction, but she felt instant relief at Grant's response. Hanging up the phone, she unbolted the door to the stairwell and walked down the stairs. She unlocked the outer door and opened it, standing in the darkness, looking out into the night.

The air was cool, the crisp chill hinting at the winter ahead. Her face was warm, and she rested her head against the frame of the door, sighing as a puff of wind fluttered across her skin. She tried to shut her mind off, floating above her emotions until she heard the sound of an approaching car. Footsteps crossed the wooden floor of the porch.

Grant closed the door as he entered, enclosing them in the darkened stairwell. He put his arms around her, and she clung to him, transferring her fear to him as naturally as if she had known him for a long time instead of only a week. They stood together, pressed into a single unit, and she drew the strength she needed from his presence. He seemed to sense when she had recovered her equilibrium. His arms dropped, and he released her.

"Show me," he said.

She led the way back up to the kitchen. She pointed to the feather that still lay in the bottom of the sink. He seemed as reluctant as she to touch it, leaning over to look at it more closely.

"It's definitely an eagle feather," he said. "It was in Jake's backpack?"

"Yes. But not long."

"Agreed." He paced across to the living room archway. "Do you think Jake could have found it?"

"It doesn't look as if it's been outside in the elements," Maggie said. "I didn't want to wake him up, but I'll ask him in the morning. Usually when he finds a feather of any kind, he sticks it in a buttonhole or tucks it behind his ear. This one was down in the bottom of the backpack."

Grant frowned, walking back to stand in front of the sink.

"Jake left his backpack outside beneath the treehouse when you dropped him off, and we didn't bring it inside until just before you came back from the police station. Anyone could have put the feather inside."

"Why?" Maggie clasped her hands to keep them from shaking. "Why would someone do that?"

"A joke? A warning?" Grant shrugged. "I wish I knew."

"Jake's in danger. I know he is," Maggie said, unable to keep the quiver out of her voice.

"It could be intended as a warning to all of us, but we can't ignore the fact that the feather was left in Jake's backpack. I think for the next several days we should keep him in sight."

"We've unleashed a monster," Maggie said.

"Wrong. The monster was always there. Just think of the situation if we didn't know he existed."

"Could it be Tully?"

"I don't think so. Ham and I checked the treehouse after we left here. Nothing has been touched. Tully hasn't been there. Ham's keeping watch for him while I'm over here." Grant picked up the feather. "What do you want me to do with this?"

"Get it out of my sight." Maggie shuddered.

Grant slipped the feather into the inside pocket of his jacket.

"What have you got planned for tomorrow?" he asked.

"Nothing much. I was hoping Kenny could come over, but Hugh's taking him up to Door County to stay with his grandmother. Jake can help Beth and me downstairs in the bookstore for most of the day. Then after dinner, I've got a conference with Jake's teacher, and I'll take him with me."

"Why don't I pick Jake up in the afternoon, and he can knock around with Ham and me? We'll fast food it for dinner and go to a movie while you're at the conference."

"That would be great, but are you sure you're up to all of that?"

"I had a good time with Jake yesterday. Besides, I suspect you could use a bit of time when you don't have to worry about him," Grant said.

"It would be bliss," she admitted. "Jake could use some time away from me, too."

"Would you like me to stay here tonight?" Grant asked.

His sudden question came as a surprise. She didn't know if he was asking in order to soothe her anxiety or for more personal reasons. She didn't know which she would prefer.

"When do you go home?" she asked, answering his question with one of her own.

"I'm not sure. If it looks like I'm not getting anywhere, I'll have to leave."

"That's a safe lawyerly response," she said. She opened the door at the top of the stairs. "I appreciate your coming over. Just having someone to talk to has calmed my initial panic. Thanks for the offer to stay, but I'm turning you down. It's a small town, Holbrook. By morning everyone would know."

"Can't handle being thought of as a fallen woman?" he asked.

She started down the stairs, aware of his presence behind her. At the bottom, she opened the door to the side porch and turned to face him.

"It was your reputation I was worrying about," she said.

As he passed her, he leaned forward and kissed her on the mouth. "Next time I'll walk over and no one will know I'm here."

"There won't be a next time," she said, grinning despite a heaviness in her heart. "Carpetbaggers aren't welcome in Wisconsin."

"You won't have to suspend Jake again," Maggie said half-jokingly as she faced Rachel Velasco across the teacher's desk. "We had a nice talk today, and he said to tell you he wouldn't talk so much during class."

"Generally he's not disruptive," Rachel said, "but this week I've had to reprimand him several times."

"Kenny Rossiter?" she guessed.

"Yes. The two of them are trouble with a capital T. Thank heavens, they're mischievous not naughty."

"I think you'll have a quieter week from both of the boys. They had a scheme in progress, but it's been curtailed."

Maggie's morning talk with Jake had been difficult. To alleviate some of her own fear, she would have loved to scream and rant at his actions, but if she had any hope that he would confide in her again, she needed to keep things in perspective. After she extracted a promise from him that he would not have anything to do with Tully without letting either her or Grant know, she felt considerably calmer.

She had not slept well. Finding the feather in Jake's backpack had brought home with explosive force the danger that surrounded them. She had left her door open when she went to bed, getting up several times in the night to check on Jake and to pace the halls, testing doors and listening to the creaks and groans of the old house.

In the morning, when she asked Jake, he knew nothing about the feather, confirming that someone had placed it in the backpack deliberately.

Most of the day she had kept him busy helping shelve books and doing general cleanup chores in the bookstore. Jake could hardly contain his delight when Grant arrived with an offer of fishing and a movie. After she'd agreed to meet them on George's deck for drinks and a summary of their day, Grant and Jake sauntered out of the bookstore, looking very pleased with themselves.

Freed of her immediate worry over Jake, she'd had a peaceful day, and after a dinner of salad and fruit, she drove to St. Bernard's and her conference with Jake's teacher. As she looked through Jake's papers and drawings, she could feel the tension easing across her back. She handed the folder back to the teacher with a smile.

"These look good," Maggie said.

"Yes. The purpose of today's conference is to look at the first couple weeks of work and identify any problem areas. Jake's doing fine academically," Rachel said, consulting her notes. "His spelling's a bit weak, so it would help if you could work with him on it. Math is good. Reading excellent. Your owning a bookstore gives him validation and a strong motivation to do well."

"How do you think he's doing emotionally?" Maggie smoothed the cotton wrap skirt across her knees. "He tries to hide his feelings from me so he won't add to my own grief."

"I've talked to Alice O'Neill, the school psychiatrist, and we both agree that he's handling his grandfather's death appropriately. Dr. O'Neill and I were worried that the violent nature of the crime might be too strong a reminder of his father's death and precipitate a regression in his attitude."

"Poor kid's really under a microscope," Maggie said. "Both here at school and with me at home."

"It's only natural that you'd be concerned. From the school perspective, he seems to be moving through the mourning process properly."

"That was what I thought too. We had an excellent therapist after my husband died, so it's not as if Jake hasn't had to work through this before."

"He's a very mature child," Rachel said.

"Necessity, I'm afraid."

"After your father-in-law died, the teachers planned several sessions of the school day so that the children could discuss violence and their feelings about death," Rachel said. "Dr. O'Neill has helped us prepare lesson plans for just this sort of situation. Unfortunately violence has become a national problem, and we need to deal with it in the schools as well as the home."

"Sometimes when I'm watching the news I wonder if anyone can really be safe," Maggie said. "How do you prepare for random violence?"

"You can't. Here at school we're learning to deal with the aftermath of violence. What we need are programs that will identify and prevent problems that can escalate into some sort of incident."

"Amen to that," Maggie said.

After the conference was over, Maggie stood on the steps of the school, looking at the lake. Only a few boats skimmed across the surface, heading for home as the evening began to close in. It was eight-thirty, and Grant and Jake wouldn't be out of the movie until nine. With the temperature in the seventies and a light breeze, she was looking forward to a peaceful interlude on George's deck until they returned.

She walked down the stairs, stopping at the bottom, trying to recall where she'd left her car. Lately her brain had been on automatic pilot. She took several steps to the right, then remembered she was parked closer to the shopping area and abruptly turned around. She didn't see Connie Prentice until she collided with her.

"Oh, sorry!" Maggie cried.

Connie staggered, dropping her purse and the paper bag she was carrying. Maggie made a lunge for the bag. The corner ripped and spilled the contents onto the sidewalk.

"Really, Maggie," Connie snapped. "Can't you look where you're going?"

"I'm so sorry. I wasn't paying attention," Maggie said. "Here, let me help you."

"Oh, don't fuss. Nothing's breakable. It's just plates and napkins for the Ladies Golf Luncheon at the country club," Connie said.

Maggie stuffed everything back in the bag, then with the torn edges held together with one hand, she clasped the bundle in her arms and stood up.

"My car's over there," Connie said, pointing to the light blue BMW convertible beside an expired parking meter.

Connie scooped her purse off the sidewalk and reached inside for her keys. She unlocked the car and opened the passenger-side door.

"Just put it on the seat."

Maggie set the bag down. The tear promptly opened again, and the contents tumbled onto the floor of the car. Connie sighed in exasperation.

"Leave it," she said. "I'll take care of it when I get home."

"This is my day to be inept," Maggie said, closing the car door. "Next time I'll watch where I'm going. Actually, though, I'm glad I bumped into you. Thanks for sending over the dinner the other night. Even Jake's getting tired of fast food."

Connie waved her hand in dismissal. "Don't thank me. It was Brent's idea. He's Wisconsin's answer to Ms. Manners."

Maggie laughed. "Even so. I appreciate the thought and the deed."

"It forced me to cook a meal. We seem to be eating out more these days. Brent's gone so much I may end up living the life of a recluse, raising cats and talking to myself. Thank God the food is good at the country club. Poker nights lure me out of the house a couple times a week."

"Speaking of poker, do you remember the pictures George was passing around at the country club?"

"Yes. And between you and me, Maggie, I don't think Jake will ever earn a living as a photographer."

Maggie was so used to the bite in Connie's voice that until she saw the smile she didn't realize the woman was joking.

"I agree," Maggie said. "By any chance, did you see what happened to the photos?"

"Don't you have them?"

"No. No one seems to know where they are. I know Brent came late. Do you suppose George might have given him the pictures?"

"Why all the interest in these photos?" Connie asked.

"They were from Jake's party. It would be nice to have them."

Connie passed her car keys back and forth between her hands, eyeing Maggie with sharpened interest.

"I don't know if Brent even saw the pictures. He missed dinner."

"Maybe George showed him the pictures when they took a break," Maggie said.

"Trust me, Maggie. The boys don't go to the bathroom in pairs like us girls do." Connie snorted in amusement. "I think you're beating a dead horse. The only time Brent left the table was when I got ticked at his snide remarks and quit. He came chasing after me to apologize."

"Did you leave the club right away or did you hang around?"

Connie's fingers stopped twisting the wide gold bracelet on her wrist. "And this would be your business how?"

"I was curious about something that you said when you stopped by George's house," Maggie said, all too aware of the other woman's annoyance. "You said George was still at the club when you and Brent left. I assumed you'd driven together, but now I realize that you left at separate times."

"Yes. I left early," Connie said. "I was furious with Brent and I went home early. What does it matter anyway?"

"I don't know if it does," Maggie said. "I just wanted to know what had happened the night that George died."

"What did you think? That I had come back for a secret tryst with him and then, in a fit of passion or rage, killed him?" Connie laughed. "By your expression I'd say that was exactly what you thought."

"That's not what I was thinking," Maggie said, suspecting that she was blushing in her embarrassment.

"Oh, don't mind me. I've got a headache."

"Want to walk in the park for a bit?" Maggie asked. "The fresh air might help."

Connie looked surprised by the invitation but nodded her head. "I'd like that."

They crossed the street to Wolfram Park, angling down to the lakeshore and the lighted boardwalk. Maggie raised her face, sighing as the breeze cooled her cheeks. Connie stood beside her, eyes closed, drawing in deep breaths of the moist air.

"I should have thought of this earlier," she said. "Brent's in Milwaukee. I'm going to meet him there for the weekend. With this headache, I was dreading the drive, but I'm already beginning to feel better. Thanks for the suggestion."

"Lake air always rejuvenates me," Maggie said.

"If you had lived here in Delbrook after you married Mark, do you think we would have been friends?"

The question came out of the blue. Looking at Connie, Maggie could see a genuine curiosity in her expression. She thought about it for a moment before she answered.

"With Mark as our connection we might have been. I could have used a friend," Maggie said.

"Yes, I know."

Maggie had always assumed that no one knew about her situation with Mark. Connie's knowledge came as a surprise.

"Mark told you?"

"Yes. We were always close. Perhaps I should have married him, and things might have turned out differently for all of us."

Maggie wasn't offended by the comment. Mark had told her they had been lovers when they were younger and that after it was over they had gone back to being friends.

"Were you in love with Mark?"

"Good heavens, no." Connie sounded shocked by the question. "I understood him. And he understood me."

"Didn't either of you consider it?"

"Mark might have, but for me it was out of the question. Very early in life, my father explained that I would be making an advantageous marriage and he would choose my life's partner. A bit archaic, but I didn't question it. Mark was two years younger and not what my father would have considered the kind of man to father a dynasty."

Maggie walked along the boardwalk, wondering if she'd misjudged Connie. Listening to Brent Wednesday night, she had automatically taken his side. She had always felt he was unfairly the target of Connie's sharp words. But looking at Connie's pale face and nervous gestures, Maggie saw a vulnerability she'd never noticed before.

"And your father chose Brent?" she asked.

"Brent was born here in Delbrook. You probably know that my father sponsored him," Connie said. "My father was the controlling sort who loved playing Lord Bountiful to the starving masses. He never spent money unless he got a good return. He thought Brent was the answer to his prayers. Father groomed him to take over as the head of the Falcone dynasty."

According to Brent, Connie had tried to be the son her father never had, suppressing her own femininity to please Edmund. It was difficult to picture her as anything but a beautifully poised young woman. Had she been grateful or resentful when her father turned his attention to Brent?

"How old were you when you married?" Maggie asked.

"Twenty. Brent was fourteen years older. Father thought he would be a steadying influence on me," Connie said, an acid tone creeping into her voice. "Brent idolized Edmund. He saw himself as a mirror image of my father. He was convinced that our children would be exceptional. He, like my father, wanted a large family. Unfortunately, when I miscarried, we discovered there would be no other children."

"I'm sorry," Maggie said. "Sometimes life conspires to take away our choices."

"Don't mind me," Connie said. "I don't usually bare my soul. I used to talk to George a lot. It's been a crappy week, and I miss having him around."

Under the park lights, she didn't look well. Her makeup didn't hide the dark circles under her eyes, and the blush stood out starkly against the pallor of her cheeks. She looked as if she were living on her nerves. Her manicured fingers flashed in constant movement, touching her earrings, her bracelet and then reaching down to pick at a loose thread on her yellow pleated skirt.

"Is everything all right?" Maggie asked.

Connie looked startled. "Well of course it is," she said. "What makes you think it wouldn't be?"

She flipped her hair back away from her face and brushed her hands across the material of her skirt. The safety chain of her gold bracelet caught on a loose thread. The movement of her arm was so quick that the clasp snapped open and the bracelet dropped to the boardwalk and rolled into the grass.

"Damn it all," Connie muttered.

"I see it," Maggie said, leaning over to pick up the bracelet. "The chain's broken, but the clasp looks OK."

Connie rubbed her wrist as Maggie handed her the wide gold band.

"Are you hurt?" she asked.

"It's just a scratch," Connie said.

Seeing a trace of blood, Maggie reached in the pocket of her skirt for a tissue.

"Here. Don't get blood on your clothes."

Maggie reached out to dab the cut when she spotted the drawing on Connie's wrist.

"You have a tattoo," she blurted out before she could help herself.

"Don't sound so horrified," Connie said. She snatched the Kleenex and wiped the blood away, then covered the mark with the gold bracelet. "I got it a long time ago. Brent hates it. He doesn't like being around the birds, and I don't think he likes my obsession with them. That's why I always wear a bracelet to cover it."

"I wasn't being critical," Maggie said. "It was seeing the tattoo that made me think about Dennis Nyland. I assume you heard about him."

"Yes," Connie said. "It's frightening."

"Did you know that Dennis was a tattoo artist?"

"Yes. We talked about it a couple of times when I saw him at the country club," Connie said. "It's sad. He was very talented. He created some beautiful designs. And, if you're wondering, Dennis didn't draw my tattoo."

Maggie was stunned at the coincidence of Connie, Dennis Nyland and the two children all having tattoos. Were they all connected?

"When did you get it?" she asked.

"It was right after Brent and I were married. I'd just gotten involved in falconry. Growing up, I always felt like an outsider. Poor little rich girl angst. I knew my father had wanted a boy, so my gender made me feel inadequate. In falconry, there was little bias. I could do the same things the men could do. I had found my niche and I excelled in it. Training the birds came naturally to me, and my gyrfalcons were first-rate hunters."

"I saw your program at the Renaissance Faire, and I was impressed," Maggie said.

"Thanks. As you can see I love the sport. It's a wonderful obsession. The tattoo was to celebrate my hawk's first kill. It's on the inside of my left wrist. A falconer carries the hawk on his left hand. That's the gloved hand. Every time I put on my glove I see the tattoo. For me it's a constant reminder of my success."

"Is it a picture of a hawk?"

"No. That was more of a commitment than I wanted to make. I'm not really into pain. I didn't have a lot of designs to choose from."

Connie unsnapped the bracelet and held out her arm. The sight of the tattoo raised goose bumps on Maggie's arms. It was a line drawing, the black ink sharp against the light skin tone of Connie's wrist.

"I wanted the tattoo to have some connection to falconry," Connie said. "This seemed the right choice. Instead of a hawk, I chose an eagle feather."

CHAPTER
TWENTY-ONE

"HOW COME UNCLE HAM didn't want to go to see *Tarzan*?" Jake asked as he bounded along the pavement to keep up with Grant.

"He's not into animated films, I guess."

"Oh."

After a few more steps the boy stopped, and when Grant looked down, his face was scrunched up in thought.

"What's up?"

"Did you like the movie?" Jake asked.

"Actually, I did. I have a fondness for dancing animals." Grant ruffled Jake's hair. "You worked that out just fine. You may have a career ahead as a lawyer."

"Mom says that lawyers—"

Grant held up his hand. "I can just imagine what your mother has to say about lawyers. I don't think she likes me very much."

"Yes, she does," Jake said, starting to walk again. "If she didn't like you, she just wouldn't talk to you."

"Not a bad system. I may have to try that."

They walked along the sidewalk toward Grant's car in companionable silence.

"I was impressed last night when you told me about helping Tully," Grant said. "I know you were feeling bad·about keeping the secret from your mom."

"Uh-huh. It wasn't *ezactly* a lie, but I knew she wouldn't like it."

"Well I've been feeling bad about something I told you. And in my case it was a lie."

Jake tilted his head, looking up at Grant out of the corner of his eyes. "Is it about bein' Dad's cousin?"

Grant came to a halt, staring down at Jake as a grin crept across the boy's face.

"You knew?"

"Dad told me he didn't have any cousins."

"Oh. How come you didn't say anything?"

"I was scared at first that you were a bad guy."

Grant put his hand on Jake's shoulder, squeezing it for reassurance. "I'm very sorry I frightened you. Even for a second."

"That's OK. I told Kenny about it when his dad took you to see the hawks. He said to wait and see."

"And?"

"The pizza we made was good."

Grant bent his knees until his face was on the same level with Jake's. He held the boy's shoulders between his hands and looked him straight in the eye.

"You're a fine boy, Jake. I promise I will never lie to you again. Friends?"

"Friends," Jake said. They walked a short distance in silence, then he asked, "Do you have lots of money?"

Grant was surprised by the sudden question. "Do you need a loan?"

"Uh-uh. I just thought it would be really cool if you could buy Grampa's house. Then Kenny and I could still play in the treehouse."

"I see. Do you think your mom would like that?"

Jake thought for a minute, then shrugged his shoulders. "Maybe. You better ask her though."

"Speaking of your mother, we better get moving. She's going to think we've gotten lost."

"Can I have something to drink when we get to Grampa's?" Jake asked. "I'm really thirsty."

"Next time don't put so much salt on the popcorn. Did you finish the whole box?" Grant asked.

"Yep. I'm stuffed." He pulled his knit shirt down tight to show off his rounded belly. "Dinner was good too. I don't think I ever ate three whole tacos before. Wait'll I tell Kenny."

"Speaking of Kenny, your mom is going to talk to Mr. Rossiter about Tully."

"That's what she told me. I hope he won't be too mad. It was my fault. I made Kenny help out."

Grant heard the anxiety in his voice. "Mr. Rossiter has a temper, huh?"

Jake's gaze flashed up to meet his. "Sometimes he's pretty mean to Kenny. Even when it's not Kenny's fault."

"I used to feel bad when I was your age because I'd get my sister to do something really dumb and then she'd get in trouble."

"That happens all the time." There was guilt in the rounded shoulders as Jake said, "Taking the snake to school was my idea."

"I had a feeling it was." Grant laughed. "Remember this, Jake. People choose what they want to do. You might come up with the plan, but each person has to decide if they want to go along with it. Do you understand what I'm saying?"

"Maybe. I still have to watch out for Kenny though."

Grant opened the door of the car. "Hop in. We've got one more stop before we head home."

"Did Tully come to the treehouse last night?" Jake asked as he buckled his seat belt.

"No. Ham and I took turns watching for him, but he didn't show up."

"You don't think something's happened to him, do you? Mom told me about Dennis Nyland." His voice shook slightly.

"My guess is that Tully heard about Dennis too and he's laying low. I put fresh coffee and some fried chicken up in the treehouse in case he comes back tonight."

"Thanks, Grant. Tully might be getting tired of the sandwiches." Jake stretched his neck to see out the window. "Where are we going?"

"Kruckmeyer's Pharmacy. I stopped by earlier to see the owner, but she doesn't come to work until after nine. I wanted to talk to her."

"Mrs. Kruckmeyer talks to everyone. Except kids. She can be real grouchy when they're in the store."

"I'll keep that in mind," Grant said as he parked the car and led the way into the store.

"Can I get some gum?" Jake asked.

"As long as it's sugar free," Grant said.

"That's just what Mom always says."

Jake rolled his eyes and wandered down the candy aisle as Grant walked over to the heavyset older woman behind the checkout counter.

"Mrs. Kruckmeyer? My name's Grant Holbrook."

"Ah," she said. "Edna's nephew. The lawyer from Chicago."

"Guilty as charged," he said, grinning at the familiar designation.

"Just call me Ann." She held out her hand and gave his a hearty shake. "What can I do you for?"

"I wondered if I could ask you some questions."

"Shoot."

"It's about the disposable camera Maggie brought in the other day for developing."

"The one from Jake's birthday party?" At his nod, she drew herself up, frowning across at him. "I'm real sorry the photos are lost, but we don't keep copies. We develop everyone's pictures in town. Can you imagine if we tried to keep copies of every roll of film?"

"You'd need a bigger store." Grant smiled at her, and her expression lightened. "Actually, what I wanted to ask you about was George. I understand he picked up the pictures on Saturday."

"Yes, he did. I waited on him myself. Imagine how I felt when I heard about his death. It's just a shame that something like that could happen in our town. A lot of riffraff hangs out around the lake. They get to thinking we're easy pickings."

"Crime always goes up in lake communities during the summer," he said.

"You got that right. I'm always bending Charley Blessington's ear that he ought to do more to curb that element." She waved a hand at the theft detectors in front of the doors. "I had to install those damn things because I was losing my underdrawers to shoplifters. Little pissants no bigger than Jake here."

Arriving at the counter just then, Jake jerked his hand up and dropped a package of gum on the counter as if she were accusing him.

"That'll be eighty cents," she said, passing it across the antitheft strip.

Grant handed her the money. "So George picked up the photographs?" he asked, hoping to get her back on track.

"Yeah. And four cigars." Ann rested one ample hip on the stool behind the counter. "You know, Mr. Holbrook, this is a small town and everyone knows everyone else's business. George's doctor told him to give up cigars about six months ago. I knew he shouldn't be buying them, but hell, I ain't his mother."

"I can understand that," he said.

"I sold him some nicotine patches a couple months back, so I asked him if he'd given up on the patches. He said they didn't help." She tipped her head forward and looked down her nose at Jake. "I hope you won't ever take up that filthy habit."

"No, ma'am," Jake said, his eyes wide. "My mom told me she'd be really cross with me if I did."

"Good boy. You mind your mother and you'll grow up just fine." She shifted her gaze back up to Grant. "So I told George he ought to give the patches another try. I'd been a pretty heavy smoker, and it took me three times before it took, I told him. Three times is the charm, I said."

"Did he buy them?"

"Naw. He paid for the cigars and the pictures. He tucked one of the cigars in his inside jacket pocket and winked. He said he'd just take one to smoke after the poker game."

"What happened to the others?" Grant asked.

"I put them in a bag. There wasn't anyone else in line, so he opened up the package of pictures and took them out to show me." Once more she looked down at Jake. "Your granddad was real proud of you, Jake. He got quite a laugh over the picture of Kenny Rossiter tossing his cookies. When you get a bit older you better take a photography class. You wasted a lot of film. Some of those pictures woulda looked better if you hadn't cut the heads off."

"Mom says I have to remember to hold the camera still."

"That'd be good for starters," she said. "So then George sticks the pictures in the folder and puts them into the pocket of his jacket. After promising to buy a box of the patches next week, he puts the negatives in with the cigars and leaves."

It took a moment for Ann's words to sink in, and when they did, Grant thought he'd taken a shot to the stomach.

"What did you say about the negatives?" he asked.

"George put them in the bag with the cigars."

"Judas. Why didn't I think of that?"

"Think of what?" She looked totally confused.

"Nothing," Grant said. "What did he do with the bag?"

"How would I know?" she said.

"Thanks so much for your help," Grant said, anxious to be away from the woman in order to have time to think. "I've got to be getting Jake home, but I appreciate all you've told me."

He pushed Jake out the automatic doors, unlocked the car and got inside while his mind was busy reviewing everything the woman had told him.

The negatives. The killer had taken the photographs from George, but he didn't get the negatives. That's got to be what he's been searching for. If only the negatives were still in the bag with the cigars.

"All I have to do is find the bag of cigars," he muttered aloud, smacking his hand on the top of the steering wheel.

"I know where it is."

Grant jerked around to stare at Jake.

"You know where the bag with your grandfather's cigars is?"

"Sure. It's up in the treehouse."

The matter-of-fact response left Grant speechless. He shook his head to clear it and tried to keep the strain from showing in his voice when he asked, "What's it doing up there?"

"Grampa didn't want Mom to find the cigars. He always hid them up there." Jake sounded surprised at Grant's question. Apparently his grandfather's deception was well accepted.

"Is the bag still there?"

"I guess. I just put it in the coffee can like Grampa showed me. That's so the cigars don't get soggy."

"How about we go see if we can find them?" Grant said as he flipped on the headlights and put the car into gear.

His fingers cramped on the steering wheel as he drove through the dark streets on the way to the Estates. He had to make a conscious effort not to speed when his first inclination was to press the gas pedal to the floor. Jake sat quietly beside him, unaware of the explosion he had set off with his comments.

Adults tended to ignore the presence of children, speaking freely, forgetting the small ears that sucked in everything for later processing. Kids knew far more than adults realized. Once Grant had determined the existence of the negatives, he'd have to consider what other information Jake might have.

He pulled into the parking spot beside Ham's car. Jake scampered out the door and climbed the ladder and disappeared inside the tree-house. In a flash he was back, his face framed by the open trapdoor.

"I got it," he said. "I'll drop it to you."

Grant caught the coffee can and waited for Jake to return to the ground. He held out the can and nudged the boy.

"Let's take it inside," he said.

"I heard the car," Ham said, handing Grant an open bottle of beer as they entered the kitchen. "Coke, Jake?"

"Super," Jake said, setting the metal can on the kitchen table.

Ham reached into the refrigerator for a bottle of pop, opened it and handed it to the boy. "What's that?"

"The jackpot, I hope," Grant said, waiting as Jake took a long swallow of the soda. "OK. Let's see what you've got."

Jake pried off the plastic lid of the coffee can and pulled out the white bag with the red letters of Kruckmeyer's Pharmacy. He opened the top and turned the bag on its side. The contents slid out onto the oak surface of the table. Three cigars and a transparent plastic envelope containing narrow strips of film.

Grant opened the envelope and slid out one of the strips, holding it up toward the ceiling light. He was barely able to control his elation as he stared at the film.

"What have you got?" Ham asked.

"The film from Jake's party pictures," Grant said. "The negatives from the Renaissance Faire."

The security guard at Camp Delbrook was gone for the day when Maggie drove in through the entrance. Lights flickered through the trees in the dining hall, and she could see people moving around beyond the windows. Music and laughter floated across to her as she passed. Apparently the volunteers weren't too exhausted from the fall cleanup.

She parked the car in front of Hugh's place, anxiously checking the clock on the dashboard. Nine o'clock. Grant and Jake should be getting out of the movie now. If she hurried, she'd arrive at George's about the same time as they did. She felt a sense of urgency to talk to Grant. Time was running out.

With Kenny's jacket slung over the strap of her purse, she got out of the car and climbed the stairs to the front porch. She lifted up a corner of the mat, picked up the key Hugh had left for her and unlocked the front door.

A lamp was on in Hugh's office, spilling light across the foyer. Her footsteps sounded loud in the empty house, and she hurried along the hall to the kitchen. She pushed the door open and felt along the right-hand wall for the light switch. She pressed it, and the overhead light flashed on, the illumination so bright that Maggie couldn't hold back a gasp of surprise.

Her heart pounded as if she'd been running, and she could feel an uneasiness creep through her as she scanned the room. Don't be so jumpy, she muttered to herself as she crossed the tile floor to the open door of the mudroom.

She pressed the light switch, prepared this time as the lights popped on to reveal a washer and dryer on one side and a long closet on the other side. Jake's jacket was on a hanger inside the louvered doors of the closet. She exchanged the jackets and closed the doors, turning off the lights as she returned to the kitchen.

She took the key to the front door out of her skirt pocket. Hugh had told her to hang it on the pegboard beside the refrigerator, since the front door would lock automatically when she closed it. She hooked the key on one of the empty pegs. As she released it, her fingers brushed against the round plastic disk attached to the ring of keys for the mews. The disk swung back and forth, and the hawk inside looked as if it were in flight.

Birds. Feathers. Tattoos.

Maggie had to admit that the sight of Connie's feather tattoo had shocked her. Despite her attempt to downplay her reaction, Connie had seen it and become defensive. Minutes later she announced that she needed to leave or she'd be late meeting Brent in Milwaukee. Maggie was left staring after the blue BMW and wondering what conclusions she could draw from their conversation.

Now, as she stared at the ring of keys hanging on the pegboard, she thought about everything she knew about Connie.

Connie had been at the Renaissance Faire. She'd been at the poker game and had seen the photographs. She was a falconer with knowledge of the falconer's knot and access to feathers.

Everyone had assumed that George had been killed by a man, but as Nell had pointed out, there was no reason that a woman couldn't have done it. Connie was used to talking to George, so it would be perfectly natural for her to walk along with him as he smoked his cigar after the poker game. Without raising his suspicions, she could have gotten close enough to him to stab him.

"It can't be Connie."

Maggie winced at the sound of the spoken words. She crossed her arms over her chest. Pacing over to the sink and back she moaned softly as if she were in pain. It can't be any of them. She didn't want it to be any of them. Charley, Brent, Connie and Hugh. Especially Hugh. She knew these people. She loved them.

They were all George's friends. They had mourned his death. She could see that they missed him. None of them could have killed him.

Charley was the chief of police. No secret in his past would be worth murder. And Hugh. Even if it turned out he had beaten his wife, it didn't mean that he would commit murder. Just the thought of it felt like a betrayal of her friendship. He had been nothing but kind to her and Jake. What reason would either of these men have to kill George?

The same reason as anyone else. George had recognized Tyler's picture.

Full circle and no closer to the truth.

She looked at the key board and thought again about Connie.

A kidnapper? What had Connie said about her marriage to Brent? Maggie closed her eyes and tried to bring back the exact words. She said after the miscarriage, she couldn't have any more children.

Maggie swallowed hard, her throat suddenly dry. She had read about women who were so desperate to have children they went to hospitals and stole babies out of the nurseries. Surely if Connie was that emotionally disturbed, someone would have noticed.

Maggie stared up at the hawk swinging from the ring of keys. Connie kept her birds in the mews. Hugh had taken Grant through the building, and he had found nothing suspicious. Could Grant have missed something?

She'd never have a better chance to find out. Hugh was in Door County, and Connie and Brent were in Milwaukee. She didn't know where Charley was, but if she was going to search the mews, this was the perfect opportunity.

It was the flashlight lying on the counter beneath the pegboard that decided her. Knowing that if she thought about it she would chicken out,

Maggie grabbed the flashlight, the ring of keys and at the last moment re-membered to take the key to the front door.

Outside she walked quickly, her footsteps muffled on the mulched path that led up toward the mews. She came to the clearing, and the equipment garage loomed ahead of her. Bushes crowded close against the sides of the building, leaving much of the area in deep shadow. She walked around to the side, looking for a good place to leave her purse and the windbreaker. Tucking the front-door key into the pocket of Jake's jacket, she folded it and shoved it under the edge of a small shrub and an-chored it with her purse.

Flashlight in one hand and the ring of keys in the other, she contin-ued along the path to the mews. Shielding the beam of the flashlight with her body, she found the key and unlocked the door.

Standing inside the tunnel, she waited for the pounding of her heart to slow enough for her to breathe without gasping. The air was still, musty smelling. Taking a last fortifying breath, she pushed away from the door and walked out into the open yard.

Not wanting to startle the birds, she flashed the light into each of the cages, keeping the beam low. The slight rustling of the hawks was the only sound to break the stillness of the night. She made a full circuit of the cages, then started on the infirmary and the storage areas. By the time she was finished she was sweating.

The search had been a waste of time.

Frustrated by her failure to discover anything and anxious to get away, she hurried out through the tunnel, locked the door and started back along the path.

Had Grant seen the inside of the equipment garage the day he'd gone to the mews with Hugh?

She stared down at the keys in her hand, wondering if one of them would open the door into the building. She should be getting back, but she hated to lose the opportunity to search.

"If the key fits, I'll check it."

The whispered words sounded loud in the silence of the night. Forc-ing her feet to move, she approached the door and switched on the flash-light, shining the beam of light on the lock. The second key slid in easily. She turned it and heard a click.

Her hands shook as she pulled the key out. The plastic disk hit the doorknob, and the ring of keys flew out of her hand. They hit the ground with a soft thud. She was afraid to take the time to search for them. She'd look for them on her way out.

Taking a deep shuddering breath, she pulled the door open and stepped inside. The door closed silently behind her on well-oiled hinges. She kept the beam of light close to the floor as she walked farther into the building. She played the light slowly, sliding it over and around the boxes piled along the walls and jutting out into the room, searching for a storage closet or a door to another room. Anything that might be worth investigating.

The darkness beyond the beam of light closed in around her, increasing her fear. Every muscle was tense as she strained to see the slightest movement or hear any sound to indicate her presence had been discovered.

Hurry! Get out!

Her nerves screamed at the passage of time, but she knew she'd never get another chance to search the garage. Steadying her hand on the flashlight, she worked her way around the perimeter of the room. The light flickered across the stacks of equipment and shelves of parts, up and down, probing every shadowed crevice.

Nothing.

She clenched her teeth in disappointment, breathing loudly through her nose as she completed the sweep of the room. The garage was empty. Nothing even slightly suspicious.

The floor was a vast array of concrete, littered with parts, hand tools and electrical equipment. Toward the far side of the room was a long pit where the mechanics could work on the underside of the vehicles without having to rely on a pneumatic lift. She walked over to the edge, shining the flashlight down into the opening.

She didn't hear anything, only felt the presence of someone behind her. Before she could move, fingers dug into the hair at the back of her head and dragged her away from the pit.

She let out a small cry as her head was yanked backward. Instinctively she raised her hands, lashing out with the flashlight. It connected with a hard body, but the impact jerked it out of her hand. There was the sound of breaking glass, then darkness.

"Why couldn't you leave it alone?"

Words shrilled in her ear, accompanied by wrenching shakes of her head. She struggled to tear the hand away from her hair, scratching at the flesh in a frenzy of pain. In the darkness she fought blindly, twisting her body to face her attacker.

A fist crashed into her face, glancing off her cheekbone. She cried out and raised her arms for protection. Another blow caught her on her forearm, and as she pulled away, she was rocked by a punch to the side of her head, next to her ear.

Her knees buckled. The hand in her hair was the only thing holding her up. The darkness closed in around her, and her head fell forward as her attacker released her. She collapsed, her hands breaking her fall, so that when her head hit the concrete, there was an instant of pain before she lost consciousness.

CHAPTER
TWENTY-TWO

"KRUCKMEYER'S DOESN'T HAVE ANYONE THERE who can develop the film," Grant said, hanging up the phone. "What's open at this hour on a Friday night?"

"Nothing," Ham said. "Besides, we need the pictures now. Not in three days. Let me call Alexis Beckwith. She's a retired photographer who lives here in the Estates."

Ham grabbed the phone book and flipped through the pages until he found the number he wanted. Grant looked at his watch, then stepped outside where Jake was sitting on the top step of the porch.

"Where's Mom?" Jake asked without taking his eyes from the parking space behind the house.

For the last fifteen minutes, Grant had been wondering the same thing. Maggie knew the show was over at nine, and he was surprised that she hadn't called or left a message to say she'd be late. He'd already called both the bookstore and the second-floor apartment, but there'd been no answer either place.

"I don't know, Jake. I thought she'd be waiting for us on the deck. She said she had errands to run and the conference with your teacher. Maybe she stopped to get something to eat."

The kitchen door opened, and Ham came out holding the plastic envelope of negatives.

"We're in luck. Alexis has a darkroom. She told me to bring the negatives and she'll print them right now."

"Dynamite. Jake and I will stay here and wait for Maggie," Grant said.

He'd already voiced his concerns to Ham. They'd agreed to give Maggie another half hour in case she had car trouble or was just running late. Grant didn't like it. He knew Maggie wouldn't be away from Jake this long unless she'd run into an emergency.

"Want something to drink, Jake?"

"Nuh-uh," he said.

His elbows rested on his knees and his chin was cupped in the palms of his hands as he watched Ham disappear down the street. Grant leaned against the kitchen door. The silence lengthened and the small night sounds returned, slowing his pulse even though his anxiety level remained high at Maggie's continued absence. Ten minutes later, Jake leaped to his feet.

"Hey, Tully," he said, racing down the path toward the treehouse.

Grant picked out the dark shadow standing close to the trunk of the tree. He remained on the porch, afraid that any movement on his part might spook the man into bolting. He had to trust that Tully had come in answer to Jake's note and let the boy make the initial contact. His muscles cramped as he tried to appear at ease, listening to the soft murmur of voices beneath the treehouse.

Tully paced away from the tree, stepping into a thin patch of light. Grant's first impression wasn't encouraging. Although at a distance he couldn't distinguish Tully's features, he could see the long hair and scraggly beard topped by what appeared to be a white top hat. He wore shapeless khaki pants and a short-sleeved undershirt, the front of which had been torn in a jagged cut from neck to the middle of his chest. The plastic raincoat he had on over his clothes completed the bizarre look of the man.

Grant heard the pleading note in Jake's voice and inhaled sharply as Tully turned to face the porch. He released his breath in a slow stream of relief as Jake came down the path holding the hand of the enigmatic Tully.

"This is my friend," Jake said.

Grant smiled, wondering which one of them the boy meant. In the light from the kitchen he could see a reflection of his own amusement in the other man's eyes.

"Grant Holbrook," he said, holding out his hand.

Removing his hat, Tully brushed his free hand against the side of his pants and gave Grant a surprisingly firm handshake.

"Tully Jackson." His voice was raspy, as if he weren't used to speaking. "Jake says you need Tully's help."

"We'd appreciate whatever you can tell us," Grant said, intrigued by the third-person reference. "It'll be safer to talk inside."

He led the way into the kitchen, but Tully hesitated at the threshold. "Don't be a baby. It'll be OK," Jake said, pushing the man inside.

Tully looked around, settled the top hat back on his head and chose the chair farthest from the door. The plastic raincoat crackling with each movement, he sat down facing Grant. Jake walked over to stand beside him. The boy didn't crowd him, just stood close enough so that Tully could feel his presence.

"Did you kill George Collier?" Grant asked without preamble.

"No."

"Did you see who did kill him?"

"No."

Jake cleared his throat, and Tully looked over at the boy. His closed expression softened. His eyes, shadowed by the brim of his hat in the overhead light, crinkled at the corners.

"Tell what you saw," Jake prompted.

"Tully saw someone kneeling beside George. He was too far away to tell who it was. Better?" Tully asked.

"Some," the boy said.

"How did you happen to be on the golf course?" Grant asked, leaning against the sink counter.

"Tully was dozing in the chair at the boat ramp when something woke him. He started packing stuff away when he heard someone yelling. Outta control kind of yelling."

Tully looked at Grant to see if he understood. Getting a nod, he continued.

"It came from the golf course. He climbed the fence. Tully don't like to get involved in other people's business. Too easy to end up in the crosshairs."

"Then what happened?" Grant asked.

"Tully came out about halfway between the clubhouse and where he heard the shouting. There's a raised part where the golfers stand to hit the ball. It's all dark like with trees and bushes behind." Tully's tongue shot out and licked his lips in a circular motion, the skin glistening in the nest of hair. "Tully looked up there and saw someone. Light cloth reflecting in the dark night. Tully didn't like what he saw, so he let out a shout. Whoever was there got up, all crouched over, and scuttled like a crab into the bushes at the back. Running to beat all."

"Away from you?"

"Toward the fence by the boat ramp. Tully loped along to the tee and found George." Tully turned to Jake in apology. "Your grandfather didn't have any truck with Tully, but Tully wouldn't hurt him."

"That's OK," Jake said. "I knew it wasn't your fault."

"Tully couldn't help him," he said. "Tully turned him over and saw the blood and the wound and knew it was too late. Then someone called out, and Tully knew he couldn't stay. Next would be the police, and Blessington would be there to say Tully did it. It was better for Tully to go to the other side of the lake."

"Why didn't you take your car?" Grant asked.

"When Blessington left the country club, he drove through the parking lot of the boat ramp. He always does that. He slowed his car when he drove past Tully dozing in the chair. If someone saw Tully leaving after George died, Blessington would be down on him like a ton a bricks. Better to leave the car there. Safer to walk."

"Do you have any idea who killed George?"

"No. Tully's been listening and watching, but he can't get a clear idea. No reason that Tully can see for anyone to hurt George."

Depression clamped around Grant. He'd hoped for more. Some clue that might point to the killer. Nothing. He tried not to show his disappointment, but as he looked at Tully, he realized the man knew exactly what he was feeling.

"Tully's sorry."

The kitchen door opened. Tully shot to his feet as Ham Rice came into the room. Jake stepped in front of Tully, his arms out, palms facing the startled man.

"He's Grampa's friend."

Ham stood still, head up as he faced Tully, blinking owlishly in the sharp illumination of the overhead light. Slowly a smile spread across his face.

"Hi ya, Tully. It's Ham Rice."

Tully flopped down in his chair, exhaling like a deflating balloon. A sheepish grin lightened the impression of a cornered animal. He raised a shaking hand to touch the corner of his head in a jaunty salute.

Grant spotted the folder in Ham's hand.

"Did you get them?" he asked.

"Have a look," Ham said as he started to spread the newly printed photographs on the kitchen table.

"My party pictures," Jake cried. "Way cool."

Grant, Jake and Tully gathered around, leaning over to inspect each picture. Ham began the second row. He snapped down the third picture, and Grant sucked in his breath, staring at the boy in the background. His hand shook as he picked up the photo, holding it by the corner. His eyes swept back and forth across the half-turned face of the boy.

Tyler.

The lump in his throat threatened to choke him. He closed his eyes, counted to three and opened them again. He stared at the boy, seeing the cowlick of blond hair shooting up at the front of his head. No amount of gel could keep that spray of hair in place. Despite the fact that it was twenty months since he had seen him, there was no doubt in Grant's mind that he was looking at his nephew.

"There's another one," Ham said. His voice was tinged with emotion, and he coughed to cover it.

Grant searched the rows of pictures, finding the second one. In the center of the picture was a knight in full armor, astride a horse, his gauntleted hand holding a long striped pole. At the side, closer to the camera, Tyler stood with his back to the fence that circled the jousting arena.

"That's him," Grant said, touching the edge of the print.

"I know him," Jake said.

"You know him?" Grant asked in disbelief.

"I mean I saw him at the fair. It's the deaf kid."

"What do you mean?"

"We were all jumping around except for this kid who was sitting at the end of the bench," Jake said. "We were making faces and trying to get him to move, because Kenny wanted to sit there. The kid just sat like a statue and didn't look at us. Not even when Kenny threw up."

"So why did you think he was deaf?" Grant asked.

"Right after Mom hauled Kenny away to clean him up, the trumpets blew for the start of the jousting. The boy stood up, and he was shaping out words with his hands just like the deaf kid we have at St. Bernard's. I felt real bad that we'd been laughing at him."

"Then what?"

Jake shrugged. "I don't know. The horses came out and the fighting started. He wasn't there when it was over."

"Was he sitting with anyone?" Ham asked.

"Nope. He was sitting by hisself."

"There's your proof," Ham said, his voice quiet but firm. "Two weeks ago Tyler was at the Renaissance Faire."

"Who's Tyler?" Jake asked.

"The boy you call the deaf kid is my nephew, Tyler McKenzie," Grant said. "He's been missing for a long time. I came to Delbrook to find him."

"Oh wow," Jake said. "He lives here?"

"Someplace around here. I don't know where. That's what we're trying to figure out."

Tully picked up the picture of Tyler. He held it close to his eyes, his body hunched over in concentration. "Tully saw him with the birds."

"You saw this boy?" Grant asked.

Tully recoiled at the intensity of Grant's question. With the tip of his index finger, he tapped on the chest of the boy in the picture. "Tully saw him in the birdhouse."

"The birdhouse over by Camp Delbrook?"

Tully set the photo back on the table and nodded, his head bobbing up and down several times. "Tully goes at night to see the birds."

"How do you get inside?" Grant asked. "The place is all locked up."

"Tully goes over the roof to the open spot and climbs down. He doesn't hurt the birds or scare them. Tully whistles, and they know he's there."

"When did you see the boy?" Grant said, pointing to the picture.

"Tully's seen him lots of times. Sometimes in the woods. Sometimes in the bird place. Always at night."

"Is he alone?"

"No. He's with the trainer."

"The trainer?" Grant asked. This time he kept his tone quiet so he wouldn't spook the man. "Do you know who it is?"

"No. When they're with the birds, Tully's too far away. When they're in the woods, Tully has to hide. You can see someone's face real clear against the trees and bushes. The trainer wears blackface, but his eyes glow like beacons in the night."

Ham gathered up the photos, leaving the two of Tyler on the table. "What do they do in the woods?" he asked.

"He makes the boy run and jump. Sometimes he marches him just like the army. Other times he takes him up to the high place."

"What's the high place?" Grant asked.

Before Tully could answer, Jake chimed in.

"I think it's the rock cliff Grampa took me to a couple times. In the woods by Camp Delbrook. It's way up on the top, and you can sit on the rocks and see all the way to Chicago. At least that's what I used to think when I was a little kid."

"Before the peregrines died out," Tully said, "they had a nesting spot on the ledge. The falcon would scratch around with her claws to form a bare hollow and then lay her eggs. It's called an aerie."

"An aerie is a nest. Falcon's Nest," Ham said. "That was the name of Edmund Falcone's house. Connie and Brent's old house. The one that burned."

For Grant, the pieces of the puzzle were beginning to fall into place. He couldn't see the whole picture, but he knew they were getting closer. If only they had enough time.

Time! He glanced at his watch. Eleven. How could he have forgotten about Maggie? Where was she? She had to be in trouble to be this late.

"Jake, do you know what your mom was going to do today besides go to the conference at school?"

Jake's eyes widened as he was reminded of his mother's absence. "Where is she? Why isn't she here?"

"I don't know," Grant said. "That's what we have to figure out. What was she going to do today?"

"Work downstairs in the bookstore. Then she was going to clean the house and go grocery shopping." Eyes squinched tight, he rocked back and forth, thinking.

"Was she going anywhere? Did she have any appointments?" Grant asked, hoping to coax some memory out of the boy.

"She was going to the library. I had a book overdue. And Kenny's jacket."

"What about Kenny's jacket?" Grant asked.

"We got 'em mixed up. She had to take Kenny's to the Rossiters' and pick up mine."

"Why don't we call over there and see if she's still there?" Grant said, grasping at any explanation for Maggie's lateness.

Jake shook his head. "Kenny's not home. Him and his dad went to see Kenny's grandmother."

"Damn, I forgot," Grant said. "I think we better give Charley Blessington a call."

"Are you sure?" Ham asked.

"I don't think we can wait," Grant said. He nodded at Tully. "Something you said makes me think Charley's no longer a suspect. You said that he drove through the parking lot of the boat ramp after he left the poker game. Just like he always did. If that's the case, he couldn't have been walking along the fairway with George."

"Damn straight," Ham said.

"It's time to lay all the cards on the table," Grant said. "Can you call Charley and tell him everything, Ham?"

"Me?" Ham asked. "Where are you going to be?"

"I'm going over to Camp Delbrook to look for Maggie."

Maggie woke to pain. Her entire body hurt, and there was something wrong with her eyesight. She blinked to bring things into focus. Her head was tipped forward. Her hair hung loosely in front of her eyes, blocking her vision.

Memory of the attack in the equipment garage flooded back.

She cringed as she remembered the fists beating her and the final blow that had dropped her to the concrete floor. Even as she lay helpless, her attacker continued to scream and rant, and she curled into a ball, trying to protect her body as he kicked her.

Her cheek throbbed where she had taken the first blow. When she looked down, she could see that the left side of her face was swollen. She licked her lips and tasted blood. Her bottom lip was split, dried blood caked at the corner of her mouth. Her entire body felt bruised, but aside from an intense pain that might indicate a broken rib, she didn't think any of her injuries were serious.

Breathing shallowly through her partially open mouth, she strained to hear any sound that would indicate she wasn't alone. She counted to twenty. Even though she heard nothing, she kept her movements to a minimum as she lifted her head. A sharp stab of pain lanced through her at the motion. The veil of hair parted, giving her a frightening view of her situation.

She was seated in a chair inside a narrow rectangular room. A string of lights hung around the perimeter, sending fingers of illumination across the white acoustic ceiling tiles. A door was set in the short wall on her left, and across from her was a shelflike cot piled with blankets. A small chest of drawers, another wooden chair and an old Formica kitchen table were the only other pieces of furniture in the room. On the floor beside the table was an animal cage, door open and apparently empty.

In the dim light, she stared around the room trying to figure out where she was. The floor was hard-packed earth. She breathed in the chill air. It smelled musty and had a metallic taste. She tried to move, only to discover that her wrists were tied with black nylon cord to the arms of the old wooden desk chair. Although she couldn't see them, she could feel the ropes binding her feet to the legs of the chair. She strained at the rope, twisting and turning to free her hands. The cord cut into her skin, but it didn't loosen.

She sagged against the back of the chair, clenching her teeth against the panic that threatened to overwhelm her. To have any hope of survival, she had to stay in control.

Who had attacked her? She had been so busy defending herself, she had only an impression of a black-clad figure before the flashlight broke and she passed out.

"Why couldn't you leave it alone?"

Maggie remembered the words screeching in her ear. Voice high-pitched and shrill. Oh God! Connie! She ground her teeth together to keep from screaming aloud.

Connie must have seen her suspicion, and instead of driving off to Milwaukee, she had followed her to Hugh's place. When she snuck into the mews and the garage, Maggie would have confirmed the fact that she was searching for answers.

How long had she been unconscious?

Her watch was broken. The crystal was smashed and one of the hands was missing. She wondered when Grant would begin to worry. If only she'd left a message, telling him where she'd gone. Jake would be frantic.

Jake. Oh God, help me.

If she thought about Jake, she would go insane. She needed to stay focused in order to find some way to escape. She might be alone now, but she knew with a certainty that Connie would return to kill her.

She strained at the nylon cord. She twisted on the seat and felt a slight give in the joints of the chair. She pressed her feet against the ground, shoving her body against the back of the chair. Her head hit the wall with a jarring blow, and for an instant she thought she would pass out again. She opened her mouth and pulled in a slow, steady breath, holding it for an instant, then blowing it out through her dry lips.

She rocked the chair from side to side, hoping to loosen the cord. When the ropes remained tight, she gave it up. She was afraid to continue, for fear the chair would tip over. She'd be worse than helpless if that happened.

Closing her eyes, she swallowed the lump in her throat.

A slight rustle on the far side of the room sent her heart racing. She clenched her teeth to keep from screaming as the blankets on the cot moved. She scanned the far side of the room until she spotted the figure wedged into the corner of the shelf, partially covered by the blankets.

She squinted, and as her eyes focused she saw the child.

It was a boy. Four or five years old. A cowlick of blond hair fanning out over his forehead. Wide, staring blue eyes.

"Tyler. Tyler McKenzie." Maggie breathed the name in a soft whisper.

No flicker of recognition in the eyes of the child.

"Tyler," she said, speaking louder this time. "Tyler? Are you Tyler?"

The boy's eyes remained fixed on her. Aside from a slow owlish blink, he showed no reaction to her presence.

"Can you hear me?"

She scratched her fingernails against the arms of the chair. The child jumped at the unexpected sound.

"So you can hear. Thank God."

After all the searching she had come face-to-face with the missing child. Part of her was filled with elation that he was alive, but the other part acknowledged the fact that the discovery had come too late.

"Tyler. My name is Maggie. Maggie Collier."

Maggie didn't know why she continued to speak, because he either would not or could not respond to her. She remembered the pain in Katrina Harland's voice as she spoke of her frustration with Eddie's inability to speak. It didn't matter. She needed to hear a voice, even if it was her own, to remind her she was not alone.

"Do you remember your uncle? Uncle Grant. He's come here to find you."

Maggie wondered if the boy was drugged. He didn't respond to her in any way. It was almost as if he were in a trance. Even though he hadn't acknowledged her presence, she knew he was aware of her. Hoping to break through his silence, she kept talking.

"Your uncle told me you have a dog, Tyler. His name is Barney. Barney Google."

Maggie began to hum the tune to the song.

"I have a son named Jake," she said, catching her breath in a hiccup as she struggled to keep her emotions at bay. "His grandfather used to sing him that song too. 'Barney Google with his goo goo googly eyes.' "

She repeated the refrain but couldn't remember any of the words to the verse. She sang it again, then hummed it. Still no reaction from Tyler. She thought about all the songs she'd sung to Jake over the years, and one by one she sang them, hoping for some sign of recognition from the child on the cot.

She announced the name of each song, and after she sang it she repeated the title to the boy, finishing up with another rousing chorus of "Barney Google." She talked to him between times, telling him the little she knew about his mother and father and talking about Grant and the dog and anything else she could think of. Nothing penetrated the mask of detachment.

Eventually he relaxed, sliding down until he was lying stretched out on the cot. His eyes were open, and he stared at her blankly, as if she wasn't really there.

"That's all right, Tyler. You can go to sleep. I'll be right here."

Maggie hummed quietly. He stared at her for a while, then he closed his eyes, and she could hear the rhythm of his breathing change as he fell asleep. She continued to hum, resting her head against the wall behind her chair. She needed to conserve her energy if she hoped to make one last bid for freedom. Closing her eyes, she let her mind drift.

She came awake with a racing heart as she heard the lock click and the door of the room opened. She swallowed down the knot of fear as she faced the doorway. The dark figure stepped forward, and she let out a gasp of surprise.

"Oh, thank God, Brent!" she cried. "You've found us."

CHAPTER
TWENTY-THREE

"FOUND YOU?" Brent asked. "I didn't know you were lost."

Brent's conversational tone and expression of amusement sent a chill through Maggie. In a heartbeat she realized her mistake.

"Oh, God, Brent. Not you."

"Why not me? Were you expecting someone else?"

Maggie squeezed her eyes shut, wanting to block him from sight. All the bumps and bruises her body had sustained could not compare in pain to the knowledge of Brent's duplicity. He had been George's best friend, and she and Jake had been fond of him. How could they have missed the fact that, beneath the mask of civility, he was a monster?

"Connie said you were in Milwaukee. What are you doing here?" Maggie asked, blurting out her first thoughts.

"So that's why you look so surprised," Brent said. "No need to worry about Connie. When she gets to the Pfister Hotel, she'll find a note saying I'm delayed on business."

He glanced over to the shelf bed and smiled when he saw the two blue eyes staring at him from the mound of blankets.

"I gather you've met the boy," he said.

The focus of attention, Tyler scrambled into the corner, pulling the covers close around his neck. His face was expressionless, eyes wide and alert.

Brent's foot brushed the side of the wire cage. He stared down, his head extended forward on his neck. Bending over, he picked up the cage and turned toward the boy on the bed. Maggie could see the blanket shake as Tyler drew his body into a tighter unit.

Holding the cage at eye level, Brent peered inside. The door swung back and forth as if to emphasize that the cage was empty. Eyes focused on the child, Brent released his hold on the cage, and it fell to the floor. It bounced once, then came to rest against the wall beside the bed.

Brent turned his back to the boy and walked across the room until he stood directly in front of Maggie. He towered over her, and she had to tip her head back to stare up at him. She gripped the arms of the chair to keep herself from shaking.

She could only wonder at the transformation in the man. Externally he was the same. He was dressed more casually than usual in black slacks and a black turtleneck, but he looked as distinguished as ever. With the white wings of hair at his temples, he looked more like an elder statesman than a killer or a kidnapper.

The way he carried his body and the change in his voice tone were a reflection of the internal changes that had taken place. She had the distinct impression that he had become another person entirely. A new person she didn't know.

"I'm sorry about the bruise on your face," he said.

"Why did you attack me?"

"Ah, such an innocent."

He reached out to touch her face. Unable to bear his touch, she pulled her head back, knowing it was a mistake when she saw the flash of anger in his eyes.

He drew his hand back, then he slapped her.

The blow wasn't hard, but it was devastating, pointing up her helplessness. The total detachment on Brent's face as he watched her reaction was a sharp reminder that she was not dealing with a rational human being. The aftermath of murder and kidnapping had taken a toll on the man she had once known. Whoever he had become was evil, impervious to arguments or pleadings.

She had two options. She could cringe and whine in hopes that Brent would not hurt her any more before he killed her, or she could forget about her own pain and try to figure out a way to save herself and Tyler.

There was only one way. She would have to kill Brent.

A spurt of adrenaline shot through her. Frightened he would read the new resolution in her eyes, she dropped her head, hiding behind the curtain of hair that swung in front of her face. She'd play the whining coward he expected and look for her chance.

She'd only get one chance to defeat him. She'd have to make it count.

Slowly she raised her head. She didn't have to pretend to be cowed by Brent's presence. His closeness was stifling as he waited for her full attention. He continued speaking as if there had been no break in the conversation.

"I've been worrying about you, Maggie. You've been prying into things that don't concern you. If you'd left them alone, you wouldn't be in this predicament. So for the last few days I've been keeping a close eye on you. I still haven't figured out where you went with Grant Holbrook, but I suspect it wasn't Milwaukee."

Maggie pressed her lips together, trying to keep her expression from giving away any of her thoughts. Brent stood in front of her, rocking from foot to foot as he talked.

"Today I got worried when you ran into Connie. I saw her showing you the tattoo. I wondered if that would set you thinking. Did you come to the conclusion that Dennis Nyland drew it and that she had killed him?" He chuckled, and his mouth twisted into a smug smile. "I can see you did. Well, I'll tell you a secret. Dennis didn't do the tattoo. I did."

"You drew Connie's tattoo?" Maggie didn't have to fake astonishment at this piece of information.

"Everyone underestimates my talents," Brent said, voice tinged with anger. "I was eighteen when I got a tattoo. The whole process intrigued me. I've always been drawn to a mixture of pain and pleasure. Watching my own blood bubbling up around the pen aroused me. I wish I had time to initiate you into the art. I think you'd see what I mean."

He placed his open palm against her throat, pressing her chin upward with his thumb.

"I'm sorry I had to hurt you," he said. With his free hand he touched the bruise on her cheek. Even though he didn't press against the bone, she winced at the pain. "I followed you to Rossiter's. I had to park my car farther up in the woods so no one would spot it. When I got back you were gone. I waited for a while beside the car, but when you didn't come I got worried. Then I realized you'd gone up to look around the mews. I walked along the trail, and just as I came to the clearing, I saw you entering the garage."

He brushed the hair away from her face with a brisk sweeping motion of his fingers.

"Snooping again," he said. "When I found you standing beside the pit, I was so angry that I couldn't help but strike out at you."

His hand moved up and down on the column of her throat, his touch light and caressing at first, then slowly his fingers began to tighten. Maggie pressed against the back of her chair, trying to pull away from the hand that was choking her. She thrashed from side to side, gasping for air as Brent watched her, his eyes glowing with excitement.

Oh, God, don't let me die yet! Her strength ebbed, and she sagged in her chair, sinking into the darkness.

Suddenly he released her.

"Such a shame I can't keep you here for a while," he said. "I could teach you pleasures you've never known."

Brent's voice came from a distance as she fought to pull air into her lungs. Tears blinded her, and frightened sobs welled up inside her. It was one thing to know she was going to die, but it was quite another thing to fight the fear. For an instant she wanted to beg and plead for her freedom. His indifference to her pain reminded her that he was beyond compassion, beyond rational thought.

Brent reached into the pocket of his shirt and brought out a thin sheet of parchment paper. He unfolded it and held it up toward the light so that Maggie could see it. It was a drawing of the bleeding heart tattoo.

"Dennis Nyland was very talented. He drew this to show me, the night I visited him. It's beautiful, isn't it? He was kind enough to sign it before I killed him."

Maggie closed her eyes, wanting to block out the picture of the bleeding heart and the triumphant smile on Brent's face.

"I had planned to draw it on your body," he said.

Her eyes flew open as he placed his open hand on her chest, sliding it inside the neck of her blouse. His fingers pushed beneath her bra strap, pressing lightly over her racing heart.

Terrified of provoking him, she kept her eyes down, her body submissive. She screamed inside her head with the effort to remain still.

Brent sighed and withdrew his hand.

Maggie shook with the aftermath of fear. She tightened her muscles, trying to convert her terror into anger. She wanted to beg God for the chance to kill Brent, but she didn't know if He would grant such a request.

"No time for pleasure," he said, folding up the parchment paper and returning it to his pocket. "They'll begin searching for you soon. They'll never think to look at Camp Delbrook until tomorrow though."

"We're still at the campground?" Maggie's voice was raspy, and her throat was raw from the choking.

"You haven't figured it out yet?" Brent leaned over and pulled at the black cord around her wrists, checking to make sure it was still tight. "We're actually in a room underneath the equipment garage."

"Underneath?"

"Ingenious, isn't it?" Brent smiled. "I read about a man who kept a child in a room he'd built under his garage. No one found it even though they searched the place several times looking for the girl. So when Hugh began talking about a mews, I suggested that he build a storage and maintenance garage. Since Connie was going to pay for half of the mews project, I offered to draw up plans and oversee the construction of both buildings."

He checked the cords on her ankles, satisfied that she was secure in her chair. Then he walked across to the shelf bed.

"There are definite advantages to being the architect and construction supervisor. Hugh was busy and only saw the completed garage. He had no idea of the additions I'd made to the original blueprints. Two rooms marked for underground storage. Also a tunnel leading from the equipment garage to the mews and another one leading outside into the woods."

He pulled the covers back and motioned to the child. Without hesitation, Tyler swung his feet over the side of the shelf and stood up.

"This is my apprentice," Brent said, placing a hand on Tyler's shoulder. "He has been training to be a warrior. He's learned the discipline of silence and communicates through sign language. He is very proficient."

Tyler stood motionless, staring at Maggie. Despite her singing and talk of his past life, there was nothing in his expression that acknowledged her presence or indicated he had made any connection with her. Brent released him, signing to him to sit on the edge of the cot.

It dawned on Maggie that Brent had no idea she knew who Tyler was. She would have to be careful that she gave none of her knowledge away, or the life of the boy could be in jeopardy.

"Where did you get the boy?" she asked.

"It doesn't matter," Brent said. "He belongs to me."

"Do you keep him here in this room?"

He caught the edge of horror in her question and glared at her.

"He is well cared for," he snapped. "There is a kitchen area and a play area in the other room. This one is for sleeping. He gets fresh air and good food and a system of education that suits us both. You can see how fit he is. I have been training him."

"Why are you training him? Why is he here?"

"This is not like in the movies where you keep me talking until the cavalry arrives," Brent said. "There will be no rescue for you, Maggie."

"I know that, but I'd still like to know why."

"It's simple," he said. "Connie couldn't have any more children."

"If you wanted children so badly, couldn't you have adopted some?"

Brent's face darkened, and he glared at Maggie. "I wanted Connie's children. That was why I married her. She was Edmund's daughter. Together we would carry Edmund's genes into a new generation. We would create the dynasty that he had envisioned."

"Did Edmund know that was your plan?" Maggie asked.

"I told him the night we were married." Brent paced back and forth in front of Maggie. His rising agitation frightened her. "I thought he would be thrilled when I explained it all to him, but he threatened to have the marriage annulled."

"On what grounds?"

"Edmund Falcone was my father. Connie is my half sister."

Brent's words left Maggie speechless. It was obvious he was pleased by her shock.

"Didn't guess, did you? Nobody knew but Edmund. And he had forgotten."

Brent's momentary smirk changed back to narrow-eyed fury.

"He didn't have the slightest remembrance of the fact he'd impregnated my mother. He'd given her some money, but that was long gone. My mother told me who my father was, but she refused to beg him for anything more. We lived in soul-crushing poverty, and I swore that eventually he'd accept me as his true son."

"Why didn't you tell him when he began sponsoring you?"

"I was angry that he could have forgotten my birth. I decided that I would present him with an accomplished fact once I was married to Connie. I expected him to be delighted. Instead he was appalled. He ranted and raved at what he called an unnatural act. As his fury increased, his body betrayed him and he had a stroke."

"I thought you were on your honeymoon when that happened."

"That's what everyone thought. He fell down on the floor of his bedroom. He was paralyzed and couldn't speak. I thought he would be dead by morning. I told Connie that he was tired and was going to bed. We left, and it wasn't until the next morning that the housekeeper found him. Unfortunately he was still alive."

Maggie couldn't even imagine what that long night must have been like for Edmund. And the year that followed. Dependent on Brent for everything.

"Edmund must have prayed for death," Maggie said.

"I think he did."

Brent chuckled, and the sound sent a shiver down Maggie's spine. He switched back and forth between anger and amusement, triggered by a single word or action. He was losing control, and his unpredictability would make him more dangerous to deal with.

Opening the top drawer of the dresser, Brent took out a pair of blue jeans and a dark blue knit shirt. Even in the dim light, Maggie could see that they had never been worn and was reminded of the new clothes worn by the two other children Brent had kidnapped.

"Put these on," Brent said, placing them on the cot.

Without a change in expression, Tyler removed the loose-fitting shirt and sweatpants he was wearing and put on the jeans and pulled the shirt over his head. When he picked up the new sneakers that Brent set on the floor, Maggie's mind was filled with images of Jake, and she had to bite her lip to hold back a cry of despair. She turned her head away, concentrating on Brent.

He stood facing her, holding a gun in his hand. When he saw he had her full attention, he tucked it into the belt at his waist.

"You will not be tied up when we leave here. You will walk ahead of the boy. If you try anything, I will shoot him. Do you understand me?"

Her mouth was too dry for her to speak, so she nodded.

"Good," he said.

Maggie swallowed, forcing herself to make one plea for Tyler. "Do what you have to do with me, Brent, but don't involve the boy. If you release him, I won't give you any trouble."

"You have no say in this," he said. "If you'd learned to mind your own business, you wouldn't be here. Just like George. Do you think I wanted to kill him?"

"George was your friend, Brent. He would have given his life for you. That's the kind of man he was. And you killed him."

"I had to kill him. He recognized the boy."

"George was your friend. You could have explained about the boy. He would have tried to help you. It was a cowardly thing to do. You killed George because you were afraid," Maggie said.

"Don't say that," Brent shouted.

As he charged across the room, Maggie glimpsed Tyler frozen in place, back pressed against the wall and eyes so wide they were ringed with white. She had no time to react before Brent was on her. He grabbed her by the hair and jerked her head backward until she was staring up into his enraged face. For Tyler's sake, she tried not to whimper.

"Don't be stupid, Brent," she said through gritted teeth. "You'll gain nothing by killing me. Don't you see that everything is falling apart? The police are already searching for the person who killed George and Dennis. If you kill me, the investigation will intensify. You know Charley. He'll keep hunting until he finds the murderer."

"You're the one who's stupid," Brent said.

He threw his hand up, releasing her hair, and her head snapped back, hitting the wall. When she cried out, his anger was replaced by satisfaction at her pain.

He paced back and forth between Maggie and Tyler. She could see Tyler watching him, his eyes following every movement. Obviously months of captivity had taught him to be wary of Brent's anger.

"Once you're gone," Brent continued, "the investigation will end for lack of interest and lack of evidence. I've been very clever to cover my tracks. There's no connection between me and either of the murders. No reason for me to kill George, and no reason that I would even know Dennis Nyland. No motive. No evidence. No case."

"I don't think Charley will give up."

"Of course he will. Just think about it, Maggie," he said. "Everything is working out perfectly."

She looked at Tyler standing motionless beside the cot.

"And the boy?" she asked.

"I think he will accompany you on your journey," Brent said. "Connie and I are going away on vacation. Time enough when I return to look for another child."

Brent's voice had taken on a singsong cadence, and his face had the intensity of a fanatic. Maggie bit her lip to keep from crying out as she realized Tyler's fate.

"Can't you let the boy go? Please?"

"He has not worked out as well as I hoped. I thought about bringing you here to help me train the boy. I've been impressed with how well you've raised Jake. If you hadn't poked and pried, such a plan might have been possible. Look how you've spoiled everything."

Maggie closed her eyes so that he wouldn't see the fear in her eyes at the mention of Jake. The thought of her son, alone without her protection, terrified her. It was the one thing that could weaken her resolve. She wanted so badly to live.

"Enough talk," Brent said, words sharp in returning anger. "I have made my decision. It's time."

Brent stopped his pacing and stood directly in front of Maggie. He raised his shirt and turned sideways so she could see the knife bound to his side in the leather sheath.

"It's called a *misericorde*," he said. "In medieval times, it was worn every day. Close to the body so it was ready to use against an enemy. Or a friend."

As he spoke, he unfastened the straps, holding the sheath in his hand so that she could see the hilt of the knife. The braided silver wire on the handle gleamed in the dimly lit room. He slid the knife out of the sheath, turning it so that the light reflected off the thin blade.

He held the knife by the steel blade, between his thumb and index finger. Reverently he placed the *misericorde* across the palm of his left hand. Walking to Tyler, he held the knife out.

"As my apprentice," Brent said, "you will make the first cut."

Grant drove the last hundred feet without lights, easing into the parking spot next to Maggie's car. Knowing sound would carry on such a quiet night, he kept his voice low as he spoke to Tully.

"I'll check the house."

He got out of the car, touching the hood of Maggie's car. It was cold.

He went up the stairs to the front door of Rossiter's house. The door was locked. He looked through the windows but could see nothing to indicate anyone was inside.

When Grant returned, Tully was waiting several yards along the trail that led up into the woods. He looked almost reassuring. Once he had volunteered his help, he had left behind his plastic raincoat and traded his top hat for Jake's baseball cap. At Grant's approach, he pointed down at a footprint, clearly visible in the soft mulch at the edge of the trail. The small size and shape indicated it was Maggie's.

"Up that way is the mews," Tully said.

There was enough moonlight to make it easy to walk on the path. Tully, used to the woods, moved soundlessly. Grant let him take the lead, his eyes moving from side to side as he searched for any other signs of Maggie's passage. They reached the clearing and the equipment garage, and Tully angled off toward the mews. Grant had only gone a few feet when he spotted something at the side of the garage and whistled softly.

Tully loped back, joining Grant. Grant's mouth went dry as he recognized the windbreaker on the ground beneath one of the bushes.

"It's Jake's," Tully said.

"Maggie's purse, too. Looks like she left them here."

He flashed the beam of light along the ground, searching for tracks, and caught a metallic flash in the grass beside the door. Leaning over he picked up the ring of keys attached to the plastic disk with the hawk inside. The keys were the ones that Hugh Rossiter had used when he gave him a tour of the mews. Maggie had either dropped or thrown the keys on the ground. Either way it wasn't a good sign.

Grant found the right key, and when the door of the equipment garage was unlocked, he pulled it open. He stepped over the threshold, Tully crowding in behind him. The door swung closed, leaving them in darkness.

Both flashlights clicked on at the same time, sending a V of light across the concrete floor. The garage appeared empty, but Grant was taking no chances. He flashed his light around the walls, then swung it back and forth across the floor as he moved deeper into the building. Something sparkled in the beam.

The flashlight lay at the edge of the pit, the glass face shattered. Grant knelt down to pick it up, moving the switch back and forth. The flashlight had been on when it broke. Grant could feel a tightening in his stomach as he pictured Maggie dropping the flashlight as she struggled with an attacker.

Shining his own flashlight around, he saw the drops of blood.

"Missus Jake is hurt," Tully said.

Heart pounding, Grant got to his feet and walked over to the edge of the pit. He gritted his teeth as he shined the light down into the pit, half expecting to see Maggie's body. His relief was enormous when he found it empty.

Tully scrambled down the ladder, flashing his light along the floor of the pit. At his low whistle, Grant joined him, leaning over to stare at the blood spot in the circle of light.

"Tully thinks he brought her down here."

Grant agreed. They worked their way along the side, checking each of the shelf units attached to the wall. Midway they found what they were looking for. The metal shelf unit was more securely attached than the others had been. Running the lights underneath each shelf, they found a latch against the wall under the third shelf.

Grant turned it, but it didn't give. There was a lock beneath the latch, and he pulled the ring of keys out, trying each one. The door was locked, and they didn't have a key.

"He's got Maggie and probably my nephew in there," Grant said. "We've got to get help, Tully."

They climbed up the ladder and hurried across the floor to the door. Grant cursed the fact he didn't have his cell phone. Their best bet would be to break into Rossiter's house and call from there. He doused the flashlight and opened the door, waiting to let his eyes adjust to the night.

As he stepped outside, Tully grabbed his arm in a grip of iron, pointing up toward the mews. Grant froze, straining to hear above the beat of his heart. Silence, then a muffled cry and the sound of a slap, a sharp crack of hand against flesh. After a pause he could hear the low murmur of voices, then the noise of people continuing up the trail faded into the distance.

"He's taking her to the high place," Tully said. "He'll kill her there."

CHAPTER
TWENTY-FOUR

"I COULDN'T HELP IT," Maggie whispered. "I tripped."

She cried out as Brent hit her on the shoulder with the barrel of the gun to urge her to her feet. She'd have to be careful not to overplay her hand. Each time she stumbled or lagged behind he lost more of his control. If she pushed him too far, he might injure her so badly she would be incapable of making a bid for freedom.

She looked beyond Brent's menacing figure to Tyler, waiting patiently beside the trail. When she fell to her knees, Brent had pushed forward, shoving the boy to the side of the trail. She'd have to wait until Tyler was close enough for her to reach before she made her move. She couldn't escape without him, and she wasn't convinced he would come with her if she ran.

"Get up," Brent hissed.

He reached out with his free hand and pulled her to her feet. The motion ripped at the already bruised muscles in her shoulder, and she let out a low moan.

"Shut up."

He raised his hand to slap her again, and she threw up her arm in front of her face.

"Don't hit me," she said. "I'm doing the best I can."

"It's not good enough. If the boy can do it, so can you."

"He's been in training," she argued. "And he hasn't been beaten like I have."

"Get moving, damn you."

In the moonlight Maggie could see his clenched teeth and knew he was close to the breaking point. Knowing that he was rattled was enough, and she turned away and started walking again.

As the trail got steeper, she had more trouble catching her breath. She held her left arm against her side to try to steady her rib cage, but each step jarred her and she had to continually bite her lip to keep from crying out. The effort to keep moving was tiring her, and the shallow breaths of air didn't give her enough oxygen to restore her energy.

She tried not to think of anything except the placement of one foot in front of the other. She was grateful to be outside. She had been afraid she was going to die in the underground room.

When Brent had given the knife to Tyler, Maggie thought he was going to force the boy to stab her. Her heart raced as the boy approached. Tyler raised the knife, and she closed her eyes, praying silently. The sawing motion as he cut the ropes made her giddy with relief. As circulation flooded back into her arms, she grabbed the arms of the chair, fighting against the waves of painful sensation.

Brent slid the knife back into the sheath and strapped it around Tyler's chest. How incredible to watch the interchange between the psychotic killer and the small boy. Brent spoke firmly but with great patience as he explained to the child the importance of the night mission.

"We will take her to the Aerie," Brent said.

Maggie had no clue where that was, but thought it might be another name for the mews. She focused on her breathing, knowing that the time for action would be soon. When Brent dragged her out of the chair, she walked haltingly, trying to overcome her pain and stiffness. She had little awareness of her surroundings as Brent took them through a tunnel that eventually led outside. She'd fallen to her knees, sucking in the fresh air, stalling to regain some strength.

Now as Maggie struggled along the trail, her energy dissipated with each step. Brent was right behind her. He shoved the gun against her back.

"Keep moving."

"How much farther?" she asked.

Suddenly the leather sole of her shoe slipped on the mulch, and she sprawled full-length on the trail. Her fall was unintentional, and the mistake was costly. Pain lanced through her rib cage, and she pulled her knees up to her chest to relieve the strain. Tyler came to stand beside her, moving off the trail as he waited for Brent.

"Get up," Brent snarled in her ear.

"Please," she whispered. "I think my ribs are broken. I can't catch my breath. Just let me rest a minute."

He bent over to stare at her. He must have seen the pain reflected in her face.

"I'll count to thirty," he said.

"Where are we going?" she asked between gasps for air.

"You'll know soon enough."

He was staring up the trail, paying little attention to her. For a moment, she debated attacking him. She knew she'd only have one chance, and she couldn't squander it unless she was sure of success.

"It's time," Brent said, nudging her with the muzzle of the gun.

He stepped back, putting some distance between them as she rose to her feet. He jerked his head in the direction of the trail, and they began the ascent again. The wind had picked up. The woods were noisy with the scrape of branches. She had the feeling they were approaching the top of the bluff, because the trail was growing steeper.

She was tiring, and her steps slowed. Tyler came up alongside her, and she wanted to reach out and take his hand. She had tried so hard not to think about Jake, but as time ran out, he was in her mind and heart, and she could barely hold back the agony that cut through her.

What would happen to him? How would he survive if he lost her too?

Oh, God, please help me.

Knowing she couldn't afford to break down, she tried to concentrate on her breathing. She adapted each breath to her steps. Right foot, breathe in. Left foot, breathe out. It helped her establish a rhythm.

She glanced sideways at Tyler. He climbed the steep trail without effort. His mouth was moving as he walked. Knowing Brent had forbidden him to speak, she strained to hear, and a thin whispery sound came to her ears.

Tyler was humming. She picked up the tune, and tears began to roll down her cheeks. Tyler was humming "Barney Google."

Knowing she had broken through the barrier to remind him of his past gave her a jolt of energy. They were walking nearly side by side. It was time.

Her eyes searched the trail ahead until she spotted a slim branch that crossed the path at shoulder height. She slowed her steps, letting Tyler pull ahead slightly. It was the steepest part of the path, and she had to reach out to the surrounding bushes for handholds to pull herself forward.

Ten more feet.

Five.

One foot in front of the other. She kept her breathing even, drawing in the oxygen to give herself additional energy.

Tyler was three feet ahead of her. He walked beneath the branch, and as Maggie approached, she raised her arms to grab hold of it.

Her fingers clutched the rough bark, and as soon as she sensed she had a solid grasp, she turned her body until she was facing downhill. Brent looked up. He started to raise the gun. Maggie gripped the tree branch as she pushed off the ground, and her body swung out over the trail. Pain ripped through her rib cage, but she held on to the branch.

Her feet slammed into Brent's chest.

The impact tore the breath from his body. His arms windmilled as he fought for balance. His hand smacked against the trunk of a slender tree, and the gun dropped into the underbrush. With a guttural shout, Brent toppled over and rolled backward down the trail. Maggie didn't wait. She released the branch and clawed her way up the trail.

As she passed Tyler, she grabbed his hand and scrambled up the trail. She could hear Brent thrashing around in the woods, and it gave added incentive to her race for freedom.

Tyler clung to her hand, neither helping her nor struggling for release. Her ribs burned, and she knew she couldn't climb much farther. She was afraid to leave the trail for fear of getting lost. Her only hope was to reach the top and then follow the path down the other side and pray she had enough of a head start on Brent.

Ahead, she could see the trail branching off to the left and sobbed in relief. Her ribs were in agony, pain tearing at her with each step. She had to make it to the top.

Five more steps.

Two more.

Oh God, she'd made it.

As her muscles collapsed, she let go of Tyler and slid to the ground. He stood beside her, his eyes questioning.

"Go down the path, Tyler." She gasped out the words. "Go for help."

The boy didn't move. He turned his head, looking back down the way they'd come. She could hear nothing above the sound of the wind in the trees, but she knew it was only a matter of time before Brent would be on them. She searched the woods on either side of the trail for anything she could use as a weapon.

"Go find Grant, Tyler. He's down there," she said, nodding to the path where it turned downhill.

She spotted a dead tree branch and pulled until a piece broke off in her hand. It was futile against the gun, but at least it gave her a sense of control. Then she remembered the *misericorde*. She pulled Tyler toward her, until she was face-to-face with him.

"I need this," she said, unfastening the straps on the leather sheath around his chest. Just as it came free she heard the sounds of pursuit and struggled to her feet, jamming the sheath into the waistband of her skirt. "He's coming."

Tyler's eyes widened, and he took her hand again. He opened his mouth, but no sound came out. With his free hand, he pointed into the woods, his finger jabbing in silent agitation. A game trail cut through the underbrush, and she could see on her left the top of a rock ledge.

She didn't want to leave the path, but Tyler was insistent. Knowing it was useless to argue, she followed him. The path was narrow, and he released her hand. He led the way along the top of the bluff just below the rock ledge. She walked behind him, and when the wind died down, she could hear Tyler humming.

"Barney Google." The bouncy tune was incongruous with the tension of their flight.

Maggie used the stick and her forearm to push her way through the bushes. Tyler walked with ease and soon was well ahead of her. She stopped for a moment to listen, but the wind had picked up again and she couldn't hear anything over the whipping branches and her own breathing and the beat of her heart.

Ahead she could see moonlight as the underbrush thinned out. She quickened her pace, afraid of losing sight of Tyler. She came through the opening and froze when she saw him.

He was standing on the top of a flat rock bluff, the toes of his shoes touching the very edge. The moonlight illuminated the scene, picking out the details of trees and boulders and far below the shimmering surface of Falcon Lake.

Hearing her approach, Tyler turned to face her. He extended his arms, moving them up and down as if he were a bird landing on a rock ledge.

"Aerie," she said. "Falcon's nest."

The words were a whisper on the wind. With a sinking heart, she realized Tyler had brought her to the one place where Brent would find them.

Tyler stood on the edge of the precipice, and she was afraid if she spoke again she would frighten him. She beckoned to him, and without hesitation he came to her side. She looked around the flat top to see if there was some way to escape. The ground fell away on one side, and straight ahead was the rock ledge she had seen from the trail. It jutted out in a series of flat planes that rose about three feet over the place where they stood. She wished they had gone farther up the trail, since she would have felt safer on the ledge than in this cul-de-sac.

The only way off the top of the aerie was back along the game trail.

"Come," she said.

She used the stick to steady herself as she walked across the rock surface. Tyler kept pace with her, and when she arrived at the rock ledge, she searched along the edge until she found a narrow cleft in the rock.

"Sit here," she said, pointing at the crevasse with the stick.

He looked at the crack, then back at her. When he didn't move, she opened her mouth to repeat the command.

"I know where you are, Maggie," Brent shouted.

Although she couldn't see him, she knew Brent was coming up the game trail toward the opening.

"Go and sit down," she said. Her voice was firm, and with only a momentary hesitation, Tyler obeyed.

"Stay where you are, boy," Brent shouted. "I'm coming."

Maggie could see his outline as he trotted along the game trail. She dropped the stick and grabbed the sheath stuck in her waistband. One of the leather straps caught on her hand. She jerked her arm up, and the sheath along with the knife flew out of her hand, falling over the edge of the rock ledge.

Maggie let out a cry of despair as her only hope to save either Tyler or herself disappeared into the night. She bowed her head in defeat.

"Welcome to the Aerie, Maggie," Brent said.

He stood in the opening, the moonlight lighting his face as he stared across at her. A long gash ran on an angle from the end of his eyebrow to the middle of his cheek. Blood ran from the end of the wound in a crimson line to his jawbone. As he stepped out in the open, she could see he was limping.

"Where is the child?"

"I don't know."

Brent limped toward her.

"I would have been here sooner, except I had to look for this."

He raised his hand, and she could see the dark shape of the gun.

"Where is he, Maggie? What have you done with him? Stalling will make it worse for you. Where are you, boy?" Brent shouted. "Come to the Warrior."

Hearing the sounds of movement behind her, Maggie turned. Tyler stood up and moved into the open where Brent could see him. She should have known that months of captivity would supersede any commands that she might give him. Brent had trained him too well.

"Come to me, boy," Brent said.

Suddenly there was a rush of movement behind Brent, and Grant appeared in the opening to the game trail. Brent whirled, aiming the gun at the new threat.

"Don't shoot," Maggie shouted.

When she took a step forward, he swung the gun back in her direction.

"It won't do any good to kill us, Brent," Grant said, his voice calmly reasonable. "It's all over. The police are on the way."

"You're lying," Brent shrieked. "Why would they come? No one suspects me. There's no way they can connect me to George's murder."

"Charley Blessington knows everything. He knows about the boy found in the movie theater, and he knows about the girl who died at the zoo. And he knows about this child," Grant said, pointing at Tyler.

"That's not possible." Brent's voice had dropped to a hoarse whisper, as if he couldn't believe what he was hearing. "No one knows about this boy."

"I know," Grant said. "He is Tyler McKenzie. He is my nephew."

Grant took a step forward, and Brent pointed the gun at Tyler.

"Stay away from the boy," he shouted. "Get back or I'll shoot him."

A scream of anger tore through the night, the sound ricocheting off the rock face. Brent staggered backward as a dark figure rose above him on the rock ledge. Tully tore off the baseball cap he was wearing and threw it like a Frisbee. It sailed through the air, landing with a soft plop inches away from Brent's feet.

With another shriek Tully leaped off the ledge, arms spread as if he were flying. Brent raised the gun and fired.

The shot was muffled as Tully crashed into Brent, knocking him to the ground. Bodies locked together, the two men rolled across the rock surface and disappeared over the edge of the cliff. There was a single thud, followed by a high-pitched scream that was cut off abruptly as something bounced and tumbled down the side of the hill.

Then silence.

Tyler, his face blank, eyes wide and staring, started toward the edge.

"Hold him," Grant said, shoving him into Maggie's arms.

The child struggled against her. He was in shock, and Maggie was afraid of what he would do now that his master was gone. She sank to the ground, dragging the child with her. Wrapping her arms around him, she pulled him against her chest. She held the shaking child in an iron grip, rocking back and forth and humming under her breath as she stared across at Grant.

He lay down on the rocks, inching his upper body out over the edge. He turned on the flashlight and played the beam down the side of the hill. Fifteen feet below there was a narrow ledge. The light was diffused, and at first he could only see the slashes of white where branches had been broken.

Then he saw Tully.

His body was wedged between the face of the hill and a small sapling that clung to the very edge of the ledge. He was lying on his back, one leg doubled under him, his face turned toward the rock face. Grant flashed the light around but couldn't see any sign of Brent.

"Tully!" Grant yelled.

"Oh, God, you found him," Maggie cried. "Is he alive?"

"I don't know. He's not moving."

Grant shone the light on Tully's face, but the beam was too weak for him to tell if the man's eyes were open or closed. He could see a blood-stain on the right side of his shirt. Even if the fall hadn't killed him, Brent's gunshot might have.

"Tully! Can you hear me? It's Grant!"

Down below, Grant heard a wail of sirens. Beams of light slashed through the leaves of the trees. Car doors opened and slammed shut, and the crackle of police radios cut into the night's silence.

"Damn it, Tully. Answer me."

"Tully hurt."

The words were only a whisper, but Grant heard them.

"Oh, thank God, Tully!" he shouted. "Don't move. Help is coming."

He flashed his light down toward the police cars, waving it back and forth as he shouted.

"Up here. We're up here."

For a moment he wasn't sure that anyone had heard him. Then a spotlight shot up through the trees, and he could hear voices shouting back at him.

"Just stay very still, Tully," Grant said, hanging over the edge so that Tully could hear him clearly. "We'll have you out of there in no time."

"Missus Jake?"

"She's safe, thanks to you. And the boy, too," he said. "I'm going to tell them about you, and when the police get up here, they'll have rope to bring you up. Just stay still."

Grant pushed away from the edge, rose to his feet and walked across to where Maggie sat holding Tyler.

"I think Tully will make it," he said.

"And Brent?"

"No sign of him. I think he's at the bottom."

Maggie nodded, and he knelt down beside her. Tyler's face was pressed into the curve of her neck, his body slack against her chest. Grant couldn't believe the child was safe. There would be years of therapy ahead, but it didn't matter as long as the boy was alive. He ignored the tears that slipped down his cheeks as he stroked the soft blond head of his nephew.

Tyler froze at his touch. Maggie continued to rock him, humming softly. Slowly Tyler turned his head until Grant could see his face. The boy's eyes were wide and unblinking. Moonlight lit the child's features, and Grant could see the mouth pulled tight in fear.

"Don't be afraid, Tyler. I've come to take you home." Grant swallowed the painful lump in his throat. "Do you remember me? I'm your uncle Grant."

Tyler stared unblinking, then turned his head back into the hollow beside Maggie's throat. He sighed, his breath a thin flutter of air in the stillness of the night.

"Uncle," he said.

Grant closed his eyes and offered thanks. He wiped at the dampness on his face, smiling across at Maggie. She was crying too, and he raised his hand to wipe away her tears.

She looked at him, her face white in the moonlight. He could see the bruises on her cheek and the cut and swollen lip. He had come close to losing her, and he hadn't known until it happened how much she'd become a part of him.

"It's over, Maggie. You and Jake have nothing more to fear."

"I can't take it all in." She looked down at the boy in her arms. "Will we ever know the whole story?"

"I don't know. Perhaps Eddie Harland will be able to help. Together he and Tyler could find a healthy bond in their ordeal."

"Will you take Tyler to your sister's in Cleveland?"

"Yes. Then I'll come back," Grant said. "Jake wants me to buy George's house."

"If you lived here in Delbrook, you wouldn't be a carpetbagger."

He squeezed her hand, and they sat quietly as the rescue party approached. Lights and voices cut through the sound of the wind. Maggie let out a soft cry as one voice rose above the rest.

"Don't worry, Mom," Jake called. "We're coming to get you."